D1037754

Introduction to
LITERATURE

pearson custom library *Poetry*

Prof. Michele L. Wallace-Ixim
Union County College - Cranford
English Composition II
English 102

Pearson Learning Solutions

New York   Boston   San Francisco
London   Toronto   Sydney   Tokyo   Singapore   Madrid
Mexico City   Munich   Paris   Cape Town   Hong Kong   Montreal

Senior Vice President, Editorial and Marketing: Patrick F. Boles
Senior Sponsoring Editor: Natalie Danner
Development Editor: Mary Kate Paris
Assistant Editor: Jill Johnson
Operations Manager: Eric M. Kenney
Production Manager: Jennifer Berry
Rights Manager: Jillian Santos
Art Director and Cover Designer: Renée Sartell

Cover Art: Photography by Chris Beaudoin.

Copyright © 2011 by Pearson Learning Solutions

All rights reserved.

This copyright covers material written expressly for this volume by the editor/s
as well as the compilation itself. It does not cover the individual selections herein that
first appeared elsewhere. Permission to reprint these has been obtained by Pearson
Learning Solutions for this edition only. Further reproduction by any means, electronic
or mechanical, including photocopying and recording, or by any information storage
or retrieval system, must be arranged with the individual copyright holders noted.

Printed in the United States of America.

Please visit our website at *www.pearsoncustom.com.*

Attention bookstores: For permission to return any unsold stock, contact
us at *pe-uscustomreturns@pearson.com.*

Pearson Learning Solutions, 501 Boylston Street, Suite 900, Boston, MA 02116
A Pearson Education Company
www.pearsoned.com

ISBN 10: 0-558-04380-1
ISBN 13: 978-0-558-04380-3

Introduction to
LITERATURE

pearson custom library *Poetry*

Editorial Board

Kathleen Shine Cain, Merrimack College

Kathleen Fitzpatrick, Pomona College

Janice Neuleib, Illinois State University

Stanley Orr, University of Hawai'i

Paige Reynolds, College of the Holy Cross

Stephen Ruffuss, Salt Lake City Community College

Acknowledgements

A project as broad, far-reaching, challenging, and path-breaking as *The Pearson Custom Library: Introduction to Literature* could not be undertaken or accomplished without the support and participation of many colleagues. For their contributions, research, ideas, and suggestions, the editors particularly wish to thank David L.G. Arnold, University of Wisconsin, Stevens Point; Lydia M. Barovero, Providence College; Lisa Bickmore, Salt Lake City Community College; Claire Connolly, University of Wales–Cardiff; Allison Fernley, Salt Lake City Community College; Lisa Fluet, Boston College; Clint Gardner, Salt Lake City Community College; Curtis Gruenler, Hope College; Hilary Justice, Illinois State University; Martin Kevorkian, University of Texas, Austin; Lynn Kilpatrick, University of Utah; Susanne Liaw; Mark Lovely, Merrimack College; James J. Lu, California Baptist University; Sarah McKibben, University of Notre Dame; Cristanne Miller, University of Buffalo, The State University of New York; Jim Miracky, College of the Holy Cross; Bill Morgan, Illinois State University; Mark Morrison, Pennsylvania State University; John Mulrooney, College of the Holy Cross; Jamil Mustafa, Lewis University; Lisa Perdigao, Florida Institute of Technology; Jason Pickavance, Salt Lake City Community College; Robin Schulze, Pennsylvania State University; Mary Trotter, University of Wisconsin–Madison; Steve Vineberg, College of the Holy Cross; Helen Whall, College of the Holy Cross; Mario Pereira, Brown University; and Janice Wiggins.

Your *Introduction to Literature* purchase includes access to online resources designed to complement your readings. This Companion Website is located at the following URL:

http://www.pearsoncustom.com/dbintrolit/introlit/student

When prompted, enter the User Name: **ilstudent** and Password: **illearn**

(*Note:* The User Name and Password are case-sensitive, so be sure to use upper and lower case characters exactly as shown above.)

Once logged in, you will have access to the following resources:

Link Library. A collection of vetted web links organized by key terms and literary figures which offer you background and context for many of the selections you'll be reading.

The Writing Process. Advice that can aid you during the writing process. Included are guidelines and suggestions for each phase of writing, from start to finish.

Plagiarism. Suggestions to help you maintain academic honesty, with illustrative examples.

Grammar Guide. Spells out some of the rules and conventions of standard written English.

MLA Style. A brief guide to help you follow MLA style in citing your sources. The Modern Language Association style is widely used for papers in English composition, literature, and foreign languages.

We invite you to explore!

Contents

MLA Documentation

DOCUMENTATION IS LIKE TRAFFIC SIGNS AND SIGNALS. Everyone in a culture agrees to use them in a certain way. Everyone in a community of readers and writers agrees that they will identify their sources according to agreed upon rules. Sometimes the rules are logical and have written cues, like stop signs, and sometimes the rules are more like dinner manners: We begin with the salad fork because everyone has agreed to do it that way. There are several forms of documentation for particular areas of study and specific journals. The MLA format is used for English and American literature and foreign language literature in the United States.

MLA Manuscript Format

The Modern Language Association (MLA)
- Cites sources in the text, not in footnotes or endnotes.
- Lists sources alphabetically by author's last name in a Works Cited section.
- Uses hanging indention (first line flush against the margin, second and subsequent lines indented) in the list of sources.
- Uses no punctuation when designating a page number.
- Separates items with periods.

Place name, date, and course information in the upper left-hand corner of the first page, and double space between lines, and before the centered title. Leave at least one inch margins, indent the first line of each paragraph five spaces, and double space. Quotations longer than four typed lines should be indented five more spaces. Place page numbers in upper right-hand corner, one half inch from the top of the paper. Use last name or short title before the number for identification. Leave one space after all punctuation: MLA allows either single or double space after periods or question and exclamation marks. Form a dash with two hyphens, using no spaces. The works-cited page begins with the centered words "Works Cited" and is alphabetized by author's last name unless there is no author; then works are alphabetized by book or essay title. For second and subsequent uses of the same author's name in the list, use three hyphens.

MLA in text citation

1. AUTHOR NAMED IN THE PAPER:
    If the author is named in the text, only page numbers are given.

    > Barri J. Gold discusses the influence of poetry on science (449).

2. AUTHOR NOT NAMED IN TEXT:
    When the author is not named in the text, the name appears in the notation.

    > The argument of the 1800s ran that evolution was an optimistic idea (Gold 451).

3. TWO OR THREE AUTHORS:
    When two or three authors appear as one, they are cited as follows.

    > Linkon, Peckham, and Lanier-Nabors claim that working-class interests are influencing literature (149).

4. FOUR OR MORE AUTHORS:
    All four authors may be named in the text; or first author named, followed by "et al." (Latin for "et alia," which means "and others") may be referenced in parentheses.

    > Mentors with much teaching experience will give more help than mentors who have taught little (Duin, Lammers, Mason, and Graves 143).

    > Or, the reference can be written as: (Duin et al.).

5. UNKNOWN AUTHOR:
    The title substitutes for the author's name in the text or in parentheses.

    > "The Twin Corbies" is a poem about two crows (119).

6. CORPORATE AUTHOR:
    A corporate author can be named in either the text or in the parentheses.

    > Illinois State University has 264 professors (1).

7. TWO OR MORE WORKS BY ONE AUTHOR:
    When two or more works by one author appear on the works-cited page, either name the work in the text, or include a short form of the title in the parentheses.

    > In "Unto My Books—So Good to Turn," Dickinson praises books as her friends (296).

    If author and shortened form both appear in parentheses, use the form as follows: (Dickinson, "Unto My Books" 296)

8. A SOURCE QUOTED IN ANOTHER SOURCE:
    To show that one author is quoting another, use the abbreviation "qtd." in.

Orr's "All Morning," illustrates a poetic introduction with "All morning the dream lingers" (qtd. in McCormick, Waller, and Flower 54).

9. NOVEL, PLAY, OR POEM:

Give the title if not mentioned in text when the work is first referred to, then follow with specific information.

NOVEL: part or chapter.

Ged said, "I fear what follows behind me" (<u>A Wizard of Earthsea</u> 117: ch. 6).

PLAY: act and scene and line numbers in Arabic numerals.

"He who tells too much truth is sure to be hanged," cries Joan (<u>St. Joan</u> 1.6).

POEM: refer to the part (if applicable) and line numbers.

"Surely some revelation is at hand," muses Yeats' "The Second Coming" (10).

10. WORK IN AN ANTHOLOGY:

Cite the author's name, not the editor's name.

In his essay "On Stories," Lewis observes that "No book is really worth reading at the age of ten that is not equally worth reading at the age of fifty." (100).

11. ENTIRE WORK:

Name the author in the text or note in parentheses.

Freire was introduced to North American scholars in <u>Freire for the Classroom</u> (Shor).

Works Cited

<u>Books</u>

1. ONE AUTHOR:

   LeGuin, Ursula K. <u>A Wizard of Earthsea.</u> New York: Ace, 1968.

2. TWO OR THREE AUTHORS:

   Jensen, George H., and John K. Ditiberio. <u>Personality and the Teaching of Composition.</u> Norwood: Ablex, 1999.

3. MORE THAN TWO AUTHORS OR EDITORS:

   Lawson, Bruce, et al., eds. <u>Encountering Student Texts.</u> Urbana: NCTE, 1989.

4. EDITOR:

   Hooper, Walter, ed. <u>The Letters of C. S. Lewis.</u> New York: Macmillan, 1979.

5. AUTHOR WITH EDITOR:

> Tolkien, J.R.R. <u>The Tolkien Reader.</u> Christopher Tolkien, ed. New York: Ballantine, 1966.

6. UNKNOWN AUTHOR:

> <u>Pearl.</u> Boston: Houghton Mifflin, 1975.

7. CORPORATE AUTHOR:

> Illinois State University. <u>Facts 1998–9.</u> Normal, IL: ISUP, 1999.

8. TWO OR MORE WORKS BY THE SAME AUTHOR:

> Lewis, C. S. <u>The Lion, The Witch, and The Wardrobe.</u> New York: Macmillan, 1950.
> —-. <u>The Magician's Nephew.</u> New York: Macmillan, 1955.

9. TRANSLATION

> Tolstoy, L. N. <u>Anna Karenina.</u> Trans. Rosemary Edmunds. New York: Viking, 1954.

10. WORK IN AN ANTHOLOGY

> Walsh, Chad. "The Reeducation of the Fearful Pilgrim." <u>The Longing for a Form.</u> Ed. Peter J. Schakel. Kent, OH: Kent State UP, 1977. 64–72.

Periodicals

1. NEWSPAPER ARTICLE
(Signed)

> Flick, Bill. "This Year in History," <u>The Daily Pantagraph</u> 31 December 1998: A 14.

(Unsigned)

> "Teachers Take Nashville" <u>The Council Chronicle</u> September 1998: 7.

2. MAGAZINE ARTICLES
(signed)

> Gould, Stephen Jay. "Capturing the Center." <u>Natural History</u> December 1998: 14, 1–18, 20–24.

(unsigned)

> "College Can Give You Grief." <u>Psychology Today</u> Oct. 1998: 20.

3. PERIODICAL ARTICLES
(with continuous page numbering from issue to issue within a year)

> Barri J. Gold. "The Consolation of Physics: Tennyson's Thermodynamic Solution." <u>PMLA</u> 117 (May 2002): 449–464.

(with each issue paged separately)

> Boyd, Ian. "In Search of the Essential Chesterton." <u>VII</u> 1:1 (March 1980): 28–45.

(1:1 meaning vol. 1, issue 1)

Other Sources

1. THE BIBLE

   > <u>The New International Bible.</u> Colorado Springs: International Bible Society, 1972.

   (Note. The King James Bible need not be named or underlined. You need only note chapter and verse in parentheses in the text (Matt. 12.1–3). Translations of the Bible other than King James should be identified and underlined.)

2. LETTER TO THE EDITOR

   > White, Curt. Letter. The Vidette. February 18, 1999: 6.

3. PERSONAL OR TELEPHONE INTERVIEW

   > Kay, Martha. Personal interview. Danville, Illinois, 10 March 1999.

4. RECORD, TAPE, OR CD

   > Kingston Trio. *Greatest Hits.* Curb Records. D2–77385, 1991.

Electronic Sources

These sources include a variety of types of communication: personal e-mails between persons or among private group members; list servs among several individuals with common work or interests; or news groups that serve associations or subscribers. The World Wide Web connects the individual to a wider community, including businesses and other commercial groups. For all these sources, a writer should include the author's name (if known), the e-mail address in brackets, the date of publication or communication, the URL in angle brackets, and the date of access in parentheses.

1. E-MAIL

   (include name of sender, e-mail address in angle brackets, title, date of transmission, type of correspondence, and date of access in parentheses.)

   > Scharton, Maurice. <scharton@mail.ilstu.edu> "Editing Information." 3 Mar 1999. Personal email. (11 March 1999).

2. LISTSERVS AND NEWS GROUPS

   (include information for e-mail but add the address of the group cite in angle brackets before the date of access.)

Larkin, Gregory. <Gregory.Larkin@NAU.EDU> "The Problem with Listserves." 24 April 1997. <river97-l@NAUVAX.UCC.NAU.EDU> (10 March 1999).

3. CD-ROM

1998 Compton's Interactive Encyclypedia. CD-ROM. Cambridge: The Learning Company, 1998.

4. WORLD WIDE WEB
National Resource:

Mengisteab, Kidane. Globalization and autocentricity in Africa's Development in the 21st Century. Africa World Press, 1996. <http://www.ilstu/ressub/subject/business/maynewkk.html> (11 March 1999).

Library Resource:

Hatfield, Edward, and Susan Sprecher. Men's and Women's Preferences in Marital Partners in the United States, Russia, and Japan. Journal of Cross-Cultural Psychology. 26(6):728–750, Nov. 1995. <http://www.milner.ilstu.edu> (22 January 1999).

Note that the second date is always the date this site was accessed while the first date is the time of publication.

Professional Site

NCTE Home Page. 6 January 2004. National Council of Teachers of English. 4 March 2004 <http://www.ncte.org>.

A Personal Site

Neuleib, Janice Witherspoon. Home page. Illinois State University. 26 February 2004 <http://www.ilstu.edu/~jneuleib>.

A Book

Crane, Stephen. The Red Badge of Courage. Gutenberg Project. University of California Berkeley Archives. 4 September 1996. Sunsite Berkeley. 4 March 2004 <http://sunsite.berkeley.edu/Literature/Crane/RedBadge/>.

A Poem

Dickinson, Emily. "A Narrow Fellow in the Grass," *Poetry Archive*. <http://www.emule.com/poetry>.

An Article in a Reference Database

"On 'Behave.' " Oxford English Dictionary Online. Second Edition. 1989. Oxford English Dictionary. 5 March 2004 <http://dictionary.oed.com/cgi/entry/00019662>.

An Article in a Journal

Applebee, Arthur N., and Judith A. Langer. "Discussion-based Approaches to Student Understanding: Classroom Instruction in the Middle School Classroom." <u>American Education Research Journal</u> 40:3 (2003). 2 March 2004. <<u>http://www.ncte.org/about/research/ articles/115102.htm</u>>.

An Article in a Magazine

Perkins, Sid. "Avalanche." <u>Science News On Line 2</u> March 2002. 16 February 2004 <http://www.sciencenews.org/articles/20020302/ bob14.asp>.

Formal Writing Assignments in Literature Classes

IN A LITERATURE CLASS you can expect to spend a good deal of time discussing various features of literary works; you may also be asked to write informal responses to the works in order to help you interpret their meaning. Almost certainly, however, you will be evaluated on your ability to compose formal essays that explore some feature of a literary work. Such essays are normally divided into two categories: *explication* and *analysis*. *Explication* refers to explaining how the meaning of the literary work emerges; *analysis* refers to examining how different parts of the work contribute to its meaning. Those parts include *character, setting, symbols, point of view (narrative perspective), language,* and *theme*. Whether you are asked to explicate or to analyze, it is essential that you make specific reference to the literary work in order to support your interpretation. This chapter provides a brief overview of formal writing assignments, with examples of explication and analysis of Robert Frost's poem "Mending Wall" and Kate Chopin's short story "The Story of an Hour." (The complete poem and story can be found at the end of the chapter.)

Explication

When you *explicate*, you demonstrate how the pieces of a literary work come together to make meaning of the whole. Explication is more than mere summary: The emphasis in explication is not on what happens in the work but rather on how each piece contributes to your sense of the work as a whole. Because of this emphasis, explication requires careful, close reading of the literary work. Although it can be helpful to explicate fiction and drama, explication is most often associated with writing about poetry. Consider the following explication of the first eleven lines of Robert Frost's poem "Mending Wall":

> The speaker in this poem feels rebellious toward the tradition of maintaining walls between neighbors. The very first line of the poem, "Something there is that doesn't love a wall," suggests that some force greater than humans or nature is at work in damaging the wall each winter. The speaker recognizes the gaps resulting from nature's "frozen-ground-swell" and from hunters who "have left not one stone on a stone." But he is at a loss to explain all of the damage: "The gaps I mean,/ No one has seen them made or heard them made,/ But at spring mending-time we find them there." The speaker implies that this "something," this mysterious force, conspires each winter to undo what he and his neighbor accomplish each spring when they mend the wall.

Notice how the explication goes beyond simply summarizing the passage to explore its relationship to the overall meaning of the poem.

Analysis of Character

One of the most common writing assignments for fiction and drama (as well as for some forms of narrative poetry) is analysis of *character*, largely because it is through identification with or recognition of characters that readers come to understand a literary work. Just as you observe and draw conclusions about people whom you meet in real life, you observe and draw conclusions about fictional characters as well; however, unlike real people, fictional characters exist in a world carefully constructed by the writer, and thus understanding those characters helps readers to make meaning of that world. In constructing a character analysis, you may focus on personality traits, on behavior, on development, on motivation, or on interactions with other characters. Your analysis will also be informed by the character's physical description and his or her language.

Kate Chopin's "The Story of an Hour" provides only brief glimpses of Mrs. Mallard, but those glimpses provide a powerful characterization of the woman who has just been informed that her husband is dead. Here is a paragraph in which Mrs. Mallard's character is analyzed:

> *Through the course of this hour, Mrs. Mallard undergoes a transformation from a typical subservient housewife into a powerful independent woman. Chopin presents these changes in physical terms, describing Mrs. Mallard first as a woman "afflicted with a heart trouble" who is "pressed down by a physical exhaustion" when she retires to her room after hearing the news of her husband's death. But gradually, as she stares out her window, a metamorphosis begins: "There was something coming to her and she was waiting for it, fearfully." She attempts to fight off the feeling, but her will is "as powerless as her two white slender hands would have been." When Mrs. Mallard finally succumbs to the feeling and utters the words "free, free, free," the image of fragile woman "afflicted with a heart trouble" is replaced by one of a strong woman whose eyes are "keen and bright" and whose "pulses beat fast" with "coursing blood." When she finally leaves her room, it is with "a feverish triumph in her eyes." These physical descriptions reflect a far more substantial transformation within Mrs. Mallard, one that reaches into her soul.*

Notice how this analysis focuses on the physical descriptions of Mrs. Mallard and her reaction to her husband's death in order to underscore the profound change that her character undergoes in the story.

Analysis of Setting

The fictional world inhabited by these characters constitutes *setting*, which includes not just place (e.g., geographical location, nature, buildings, and weather), but also time (e.g., era, season, and time of day) and cultural environment (e.g., social, political, and religious contexts). When analyzing setting, you may focus on its influence on the behavior of characters, its impact on the action, or its contribution to the tone of the work.

In "The Story of an Hour," setting contributes significantly to the transformation of Mrs. Mallard, as the following analysis demonstrates:

> *The contrast between the house and the world outside illustrates the emergence of Mrs. Mallard from the conformity of nineteenth-century views of women into the freedom of the wider world. The house is a place of confinement, with doors to keep the world outside at bay. Within that house Mrs. Mallard is subject to her husband's will, as was considered appropriate for a middle-class housewife of that period. But her room also has a window through which she can see "the tops of trees that were aquiver with the new spring of life" and smell the "delicious breath of rain . . . in the air"; through the window she can hear the "notes of a distant song which some one was singing" and the "twittering" of "countless sparrows." It is through that window that the "something" comes to Mrs. Mallard, causing her to embrace the freedom represented by the sights, smells, and sounds of the natural world outside.*

Notice that the analysis makes note not only of the house and nature, but also of the time period in which the story is set, with particular focus on the expectations for married women during that era.

Analysis of Symbol

In poetry as well as fiction and drama, *symbols* contribute significantly to meaning. A symbol can be an object, a place, or a character whose meaning extends beyond the literal. The concrete nature of symbols makes them readily visible to readers in much the same way that characters are visible. Analysis of symbols leads to a richer understanding of the meaning of the literary work.

In "The Story of an Hour," nature performs a symbolic role, representing the freedom that beckons to Mrs. Mallard. Consider the following analysis of the symbolic role played by nature in the story:

> *If the house in this story represents the restrictions placed upon women in the late nineteenth century, then the scene outside Mrs. Mallard's window represents freedom. It is springtime, a time of rebirth, and Mrs. Mallard looks out to "the tops of trees" reaching toward the sky. While Mrs. Mallard is still in the grip of her conventional life, she can only see "patches of blue sky." The thing that reaches out to her, however, comes "creeping out of the sky, reaching toward her through the sounds, the scents, and color that filled the air." Those sounds, scents, and colors of nature come together to symbolize the freedom that she feels once she realizes how confining her marriage has been.*

Notice that the same material used in the previous analysis of setting is used here to analyze symbols. The same feature can serve many different purposes in a literary work; indeed, this richness is what makes a literary work so memorable.

Analysis of Point of View (Narrative Perspective)

In fiction and narrative poetry, the *point of view* (or *narrative perspective*) from which the story is told has a significant impact on the reader's perception of the story. Analysis of point of view may focus on the credibility of the narrator, the narrator's prejudices or beliefs, or other relevant features of the narrator's character.

The speaker in "Mending Wall" exhibits not only specific personality traits, but also a firmly held belief in the wrong-ness of building and maintaining walls. The following paragraph analyzes the narrative perspective of the poem:

> The speaker in Frost's "Mending Wall" approaches his subject from a whimsical perspective at first, speculating on what that "something" is "that doesn't love a wall." He muses over whether nature actually "sends the frozen-ground-swell" up to tumble the rocks, and envisions hunters who "would have the rabbit out of hiding,/ To please the yelping dogs." The speaker also teases his neighbor, asking why they need the wall: "He is all pine and I am all apple orchard/ My apple trees will never get across/ And eat the cones under his pines, I tell him." This whimsy, however, leads to a more serious objection to the notion of walls, when the speaker says, "Before I built a wall I'd ask to know/ What I was walling in or walling out,/ And to whom I was like to give offense." By the end of the poem he describes his neighbor, who insists on rebuilding the wall each year, as "an old-stone savage armed" who "moves in darkness," this final image establishing firmly the speaker's heartfelt belief that "Something there is that doesn't love a wall."

Notice that analysis of point of view often overlaps with character analysis. Again, this overlap is evidence of the richness of the literary work itself.

Analysis of Language

The effect of a literary work on readers is influenced heavily by the language a writer uses. The writer's *tone*, or attitude toward characters and subject, can affect how readers make meaning of the work. *Style*—sentence or line length, relative complexity of sentences, relative formality of diction, and use of figurative language—also affects readers' perceptions. More often than not, assignments focusing on analysis of language refer to the writer's use of figurative language: *metaphors* (implied comparisons) and *similes* (stated comparisons). A writer's use of figurative language reflects his or her perspective on the subject or character.

An analysis of figurative language in "Mending Wall" reveals the subtle shift in tone as the poem progresses, as seen in the following paragraph:

The language of "Mending Wall" reflects the change in the speaker's attitude toward the annual ritual of repairing the wall. Early in the poem he refers to the boulders that have fallen from the wall as "loaves" and "nearly balls" that play games with him and his neighbor, who "have to use a spell to make them balance." The game image is made explicit when he refers to mending the wall as "just another kind of outdoor game,/ One on a side." As the speaker becomes more serious, however, the images change. His neighbor is no longer a participant in a game, but rather an enemy, "Bringing a stone grasped firmly by the top/ In each hand, like an old-stone savage armed." This savage, far removed from the speaker who identifies with the "mischief" of spring, "moves in darkness . . ./ Not of woods only and the shade of trees." The images at the end of the poem are themselves dark, illustrating the shift in tone from playfulness to sorrow, even fear.

Notice that in this paragraph the writer refers to a number of features, including tone, metaphor, and simile in examining the language of the poem.

Analysis of Theme

A *theme* is a central unifying idea of a story, a play, or a narrative poem. Although similar to the moral of a fairy tale or a parable, theme is more complex, reflecting an understanding of what it means to be human. Character, setting, symbol, point of view, and language all contribute to theme in a literary work.

Readers of "The Story of an Hour" have articulated a number of themes related to love, marriage, freedom, and gender roles. The following analysis examines the story as a commentary on women's experience of marriage in the late nineteenth century:

"The Story of an Hour" can be read as Kate Chopin's commentary on the oppressive nature of marriage in the late nineteenth century. As Mrs. Mallard slowly becomes aware that the "something coming to her" through her bedroom window is freedom, she first resists it, "striving to beat it back with her will." The reader recognizes at this point that Mrs. Mallard has been unaware of how oppressive her marriage has been; she has never before sought freedom from her husband. In fact, she knows that "she would weep again when she saw the kind, tender hands folded in death; the face that had never looked save with love upon her, fixed and gray and dead." Her husband was never abusive; it is the institution itself that has abused her. In surrendering herself to that freedom "creeping out of the sky" she revels in the thought that she will no longer be subject to her husband's "powerful will bending hers," and instead can look forward to "a long procession of years to come that would belong to her absolutely." She realizes that it does not matter whether she has loved her husband or not; what matters is the "self-assertion which she suddenly recognized as the strongest impulse of her being." So powerful is

Mrs. Mallard's embrace of liberation that when her husband appears alive at the end of the story, she drops dead. According to Chopin, death is preferable to a continuing life of oppression.

Notice that the writer does not simply claim that the story is about oppression within marriage, but instead articulates the statement that the story makes about that oppression. The analysis also demonstrates how different features of the story contribute to the theme.

Supporting Evidence for Analysis

Each of the paragraphs above explores literary works in different ways, but all share one common feature: *supporting evidence.* If an explication or an analysis is to be credible, the writer must do more than simply assert his or her opinion. For opinion to become legitimate interpretation, reference to the literary work must be offered in support of that interpretation. The characterization of Mrs. Mallard above, for example, focuses on the contrast between the descriptions of her as "pressed down by a physical exhaustion" and as exultant, with "keen and bright" eyes and "pulses [that] beat fast" with "coursing blood." Similarly, the analysis of point of view in "Mending Wall" contrasts lines such as the playful "My apple trees will never get across/ And eat the cones under his pines" with the more serious "Before I built a wall I'd ask to know/ What I was walling in or walling out,/ And to whom I was like to give offense." In each case, specific reference to the story and the poem lend credibility to the writer's interpretation of the works.

There is no such thing as a single correct interpretation of a literary work. However, no interpretation can be considered valid without supporting evidence from the work itself. When responding to writing assignments in literature classes, it is essential to demonstrate that you have read the work closely and that there is ample evidence within the work to support your interpretation.

Mending Wall

ROBERT FROST

Something there is that doesn't love a wall,
That sends the frozen-ground-swell under it,
And spills the upper boulders in the sun;
And makes gaps even two can pass abreast.
The work of hunters is another thing: 5
I have come after them and made repair
Where they have left not one stone on a stone,
But they would have the rabbit out of hiding,
To please the yelping dogs. The gaps I mean,
No one has seen them made or heard them made,   10
But at spring mending-time we find them there.
I let my neighbor know beyond the hill;
And on a day we meet to walk the line.
And set the wall between us once again.
We keep the wall between us as we go.   15
To each the boulders that have fallen to each.
And some are loaves and some so nearly balls
We have to use a spell to make them balance:
"Stay where you are until our backs are turned!"
We wear our fingers rough with handling them.   20
Oh, just another kind of outdoor game,
One on a side. It comes to little more:
There where it is we do not need the wall:
He is all pine and I am apple orchard.
My apple trees will never get across   25
And eat the cones under his pines, I tell him.
He only says, "Good fences make good neighbors."
Spring is the mischief in me, and I wonder
If I could put a notion in his head:
"*Why* do they make good neighbors? Isn't it   30
Where there are cows? But here there are no cows.

First appeared in Frost's second book of poems, *North of Boston,* in 1914.

Before I built a wall I'd ask to know
What I was walling in or walling out,
And to whom I was like to give offense.
Something there is that doesn't love a wall,   35
That wants it down," I could say "Elves" to him,
But it's not elves exactly, and I'd rather
He said it for himself. I see him there
Bringing a stone grasped firmly by the top
In each hand, like an old-stone savage armed.   40
He moves in darkness as it seems to me,
Not of woods only and the shade of trees.
He will not go behind his father's saying,
And he likes having thought of it so well
He says again, "Good fences make good neighbors."   45

[1914]

The Story of an Hour

KATE CHOPIN

KNOWING THAT MRS. MALLARD was afflicted with a heart trouble, great care was taken to break to her as gently as possible the news of her husband's death.

It was her sister Josephine who told her, in broken sentences, veiled hints that revealed in half concealing. Her husband's friend Richards was there, too, near her. It was he who had been in the newspaper office when intelligence of the railroad disaster was received, with Brently Mallard's name leading the list of "killed." He had only taken the time to assure himself of its truth by a second telegram, and had hastened to forestall any less careful, less tender friend in bearing the sad message.

She did not hear the story as many women have heard the same, with a paralyzed inability to accept its significance. She wept at once, with sudden, wild abandonment, in her sister's arms. When the storm of grief had spent itself she went away to her room alone. She would have no one follow her.

There stood, facing the open window, a comfortable, roomy armchair. Into this she sank, pressed down by a physical exhaustion that haunted her body and seemed to reach into her soul.

She could see in the open square before her house the tops of trees that were all aquiver with the new spring life. The delicious breath of rain was in the air. In the street below a peddler was crying his wares. The notes of a distant song which someone was singing reached her faintly, and countless sparrows were twittering in the eaves.

There were patches of blue sky showing here and there through the clouds that had met and piled above the other in the west facing her window.

She sat with her head thrown back upon the cushion of the chair, quite motionless, except when a sob came up into her throat and shook her, as a child who has cried itself to sleep continues to sob in its dreams.

She was young, with a fair, calm face, whose lines bespoke repression and even a certain strength. But now there was a dull stare in her eyes, whose gaze was fixed away off yonder on one of those patches of blue sky. It was not a glance of reflection, but rather indicated a suspension of intelligent thought.

First published in 1894.

There was something coming to her and she was waiting for it, fearfully. What was it? She did not know; it was too subtle and elusive to name. But she felt it, creeping out of the sky, reaching toward her through the sounds, the scents, the color that filled the air.

Now her bosom rose and fell tumultuously. She was beginning to recognize this thing that was approaching to possess her, and she was striving to beat it back with her will—as powerless as her two white slender hands would have been.

When she abandoned herself a little whispered word escaped her slightly parted lips. She said it over and over under her breath: "Free, free, free!" The vacant stare and the look of terror that had followed it went from her eyes. They stayed keen and bright. Her pulses beat fast, and the coursing blood warmed and relaxed every inch of her body.

She did not stop to ask if it were or were not a monstrous joy that held her. A clear and exalted perception enabled her to dismiss the suggestion as trivial.

She knew that she would weep again when she saw the kind, tender hands folded in death; the face that had never looked save with love upon her, fixed and gray and dead. But she saw beyond that bitter moment a long procession of years to come that would belong to her absolutely. And she opened and spread her arms out to them in welcome.

There would be no one to live for her during those coming years; she would live for herself. There would be no powerful will bending her in that blind persistence with which men and women believe they have a right to impose a private will upon a fellow-creature. A kind intention or a cruel intention made the act seem no less a crime as she looked upon it in that brief moment of illumination.

And yet she had loved him—sometimes. Often she had not. What did it matter! What could love, the unsolved mystery, count for in face of this possession of self-assertion which she suddenly recognized as the strongest impulse of her being!

"Free! Body and soul free!" she kept whispering.

Josephine was kneeling before the closed door with her lips to the keyhole, imploring for admission. "Louise, open the door! I beg; open the door—you will make yourself ill. What are you doing, Louise? For heaven's sake open the door."

"Go away. I am not making myself ill." No; she was drinking in a very elixir of life through that open window.

Her fancy was running riot along those days ahead of her. Spring days, and summer days, and all sorts of days that would be her own. She breathed a quick prayer that life might be long. It was only yesterday she had thought with a shudder that life might be long.

She arose at length and opened the door to her sister's importunities. There was a feverish triumph in her eyes, and she carried herself unwittingly like a goddess of Victory. She clasped her sister's waist, and together they descended the stairs. Richards stood waiting for them at the bottom.

Someone was opening the front door with a latchkey. It was Brently Mallard who entered, a little travel-stained, composedly carrying his grip-sack and umbrella. He had been far from the scene of accident, and did not even know there had been one. He stood amazed at Josephine's piercing cry; at Richards' quick motion to screen him from the view of his wife.

But Richards was too late.

When the doctors came they said she had died of heart disease—of joy that kills.

[1894]

Glossary of Literary Terms

ACCENT. The emphasis placed on syllables in the rhythm of a line of poetry.

ACCENTUAL METER. Accentual meter measures the rhythms in poetic verse based on the number of speech stresses per line. Different accents create different meanings, e.g., "government *by* the people, *for* the people, as opposed to government by the *people*, for the *people* . . . ."

ACT. The major division in the action of a play. Smaller divisions within acts are called *scenes*.

AFTERWORD. A final passage or scene following the conclusion of a story or play, also called an *epilogue*. The afterword often presents the narrator's assessment of the overall meaning of the story.

ALIENATION EFFECT. An effect, such as a mask or a surreal setting, designed to prevent audiences from becoming emotionally involved in a play. This technique was used by the German dramatist Bertolt Brecht to move audiences to political action.

ALLEGORY. A narrative in which the characters, action, and dialogue work to represent an abstract concept. The fable of the ant and the grasshopper, for example, is an allegory advocating industriousness.

ALLITERATION. The repetition of a sound, usually the initial sound, in a sequence of words, such as "Full many a flower is born to blush unseen" (Thomas Gray, "Elegy Written in a Country Churchyard").

ALLUSION. A reference, often to a historical figure, myth, or artwork, that exists outside the literary work. Allusions to the *Bible* are common in Western literature.

AMBIGUITY. A deliberate use of language to suggest multiple meanings. For example, Young Goodman Brown's adventure in Nathaniel Hawthorne's story of the same name may have been a dream, or may have actually occurred.

AMPITHEATER. Originating in classical Greece, a theater designed with a stage surrounded by tiers of seats arranged in a semicircle.

ANALOGY. A comparison between two apparently unlike things that share some common features; a reference to the familiar in order to help readers understand the unfamiliar.

ANAPEST. A metrical foot comprised two short syllables and one long syllable, e.g., like a child, like a ghost.

ANECDOTE. A brief episode within a longer work, designed to make a point or illustrate an idea.

ANTAGONIST. The character who opposes the lead character, or protagonist. Occasionally, when the conflict is internal, the antagonist is actually another side of the protagonist's own personality.

ANTICLIMAX. A failure to achieve the anticipated high point in a narrative, usually resulting in disappointed expectations.

ANTIHERO. A main character who does not possess the normal positive qualities of a hero; antiheroes appear primarily in modern works.

ANTISTROPHE. With *strophe* and *epode*, a stanza in a Greek Ode. The antistrophe represents the reverse of the strophe.

ANTITHESIS. The balancing of one word or expression against a contrasting word or expression, as in "It was the best of times, it was the worst of times" (Charles Dickens, *A Tale of Two Cities*).

APOSTROPHE. An address either to a person who is dead or not present, to an inanimate object, or to an abstract concept, designed in part to provide insight into a character's thoughts.

APPROXIMATE RHYME. Also referred to as slant or near rhyme, these rhymes share sound qualities or sounds within words. An example of such a rhyme is the feminine or half rhyme. Approximate rhymes are often repeated strategically within a perfect rhyme scheme in order to achieve a particular affect, e.g., told, woe.

APRON STAGE. Popularized by Elizabethan theater, a stage that extends toward the audience, beyond the arch of the stage.

ARCHETYPE. A character, place, or event that represents a universal truth, often of mythic proportions. The archetype appeals to what psychologist Carl Jung referred to as the "collective unconscious," or the sublimated memories of an entire race.

ARENA STAGE. A stage that is surrounded on every side by the audience, with actors entering and exiting through the aisles.

ARGUMENT. An introductory statement to a longer work of prose or poetry that summarizes the main point of the work.

ASIDE. In drama, a monologue spoken by an actor directly to the audience, outside the hearing of other characters onstage. The aside was relatively common in Elizabethan drama, used to express a character's inner thoughts; in modern drama, it is sometimes used for humorous effect.

ASSONANCE. A pattern of identical or similar vowel sounds, usually in stressed syllables of words with different end sounds. For example, the "o" sound is repeated five times in this line from George Gordon, Lord Byron's "Childe Harold": "Roll on, thou deep and dark-blue ocean, roll!"

ATMOSPHERE. The general feeling evoked through setting or dialogue. In Charlotte Perkins Gilman's "The Yellow Wall-Paper," for example, the early description of the narrator's house creates as sense of foreboding and unease in the reader.

AUBADE. A lyric poem in which two lovers express their regret over the coming of the dawn.

AUDITORY IMAGE. A mental perception that recalls a particular sound, specifically a word or words that refer to something heard.

AUGUSTAN AGE. The period of English literature encompassing the first half of the eighteenth century, featuring such writers as Jonathan Swift and Alexander Pope, who emulated the work of figures in ancient Rome such as Virgil and Horace.

AUTHORIAL VOICE. An idealized projection of the author, or someone to whom the reader must give approval, that is the beliefs, attitude, and tone of the author, as opposed to the narrator or any other character in a work.

AVANT GARDE. Any form of writing that deliberately rejects tradition, instead employing thoroughly innovative style or subject matter.

BACCHIC. In classical Latin poetry, a foot consisting of a short syllable followed by two longs or a weak syllable followed by two strong syllables.

BALLAD. A song or poem that tells a story and often features a repeated refrain. Because the ballad was originally an oral rather than written form, a single ballad may appear in a number of different versions.

BEAST FABLE. A short tale illustrating a moral truth, featuring animals as the main characters. Aesop's tales, such as the tortoise and the hare or the fox and the grapes, are the most widely known beast fables.

BEAT. The pattern of stress in a poem.

BEGINNING RHYME. The rhyme located in the first syllables of a poem, e.g., Why should I have returned?

BILDUNGSROMAN. A novel, often autobiographical, that recounts the development of a character from childhood to maturity, for example, Ralph Ellison's *Invisible Man*.

BIOGRAPHY. A full account of a person's life written by another. Biography moves beyond mere facts to create a portrait of the subject. *Autobiography* refers to such an account of the writer's own life.

BLANK VERSE. Unrhymed verse written in iambic pentameter. Considered to be the poetic form closest to normal speech patterns, blank verse is featured in Shakespeare's plays and in narrative poems such as John Milton's *Paradise Lost*.

BLOCKING. The positioning of actors on a stage, including their movements and physical interaction. The director is responsible for blocking.

BOX SET. A stage designed to represent a room realistically, with three walls and an invisible fourth wall facing the audience.

BROADSIDE BALLADS. Popular in sixteenth-century England, cheaply printed ballads, speeches, and diatribes.

BURLESQUE. A comedy presented in the style of a lofty, serious work but featuring gross exaggeration and distortion.

CACOPHONY. A series of discordant or harsh sounds used to jar the senses of the audience, as in Thomas Hardy's antiwar poem "The Man He Killed": "You shoot a fellow down / You'd treat if met where any bar is."

CAESURA. Any pause in a line of poetry, often in the middle of a line, sometimes used to create rhythmic effect, e.g., "Had we but world enough, and time."

CANON. Originally referring to the authenticated books of the Bible, now used to indicate those works considered by scholars to represent the best writing in a literary tradition, the masterpieces. Since the 1960s, many scholars have questioned more traditional interpretations of the canon because of the absence of works by women and writers from other marginalized groups. Canon may also refer to a comprehensive list of works by a specific author (e.g., the canon of Shakespeare).

CARPE DIEM. Latin for "Seize the day," a common theme in lyric poetry emphasizing the need to pursue sensual pleasure because life is short. The theme was prevalent in English love poems written during the sixteenth and seventeenth centuries.

CASTING. The selection of actors to play specific roles in drama.

CATASTROPHE. The conclusion of a tragic drama, in which the protagonist often dies. Based on Gustav Freytag's analysis of typical five-act plays, catastrophe follows introduction, rising action, climax, and falling action.

CATHARSIS. According to Aristotle, the purging of emotions at the end of a tragedy. During the play, audiences experience pity and fear as they identify with the tragic hero; a successful tragedy ends by reaffirming traditional human values, allowing the audience to experience catharsis.

CHARACTER. A person presented in either fiction or drama, whose behavior contributes to the plot and whose personality lends meaning to the narrative.

CHARACTERIZATION. The methods by which a writer brings a character to life, usually through the character's own words and actions, the responses of other characters, and the narrator's commentary.

CHORUS. In classical Greek drama, a group of actors set apart from the main action of the play, who commented regularly on the implications of the action. The chorus often wore masks and performed ritualized dance movements as they chanted.

CHRONOLOGY. The arrangement of time in a work. Some works follow a *linear* chronology, relating a story from beginning to end, while some begin *in medias res*, or in the middle, and move back and forth in time.

CLASSICISM. A value system based on the culture of ancient Greece and Rome, focusing on such features as balance, simplicity, clarity, order, and reason.

CLICHÉ. A figurative expression that has become trite from overuse, such as "raging inferno" or "ship of state." In drama and fiction, a character or setting can be a cliché, such as the prostitute with a heart of gold or the dark and stormy night.

CLIMAX. The high point, or point of greatest tension, in the plot. Climax is sometimes referred to as the turning point.

CLOSED COUPLET. A couplet consisting of two rhymed lines of poetry expressing a complete thought, e.g.,

> A dog starved at his Master's Gate
> Predicts the ruin of the State

CLOSED FORM. Closed form refers to any poem that conforms to established conventions for rhyme, meter, or stanza form, such as a sonnet or haiku.

CLOSET DRAMA. A play written primarily to be read rather than performed onstage.

COLLOQUIAL DICTION. Language representative of ordinary people speaking informally, often using slang, such as the language in Bobbie Ann Mason's "Shiloh."

COMEDY. Drama featuring a happy ending, designed to amuse the audience.

COMEDY OF MANNERS. Popular in late seventeenth-century England, drama that satirizes the behavior of sophisticated, high-society characters.

COMEDY OF THE ABSURD. A type of twentieth-century drama rooted in existentialism, portraying humans as isolated creatures living a meaningless existence. Such plays dismiss conventional plot, setting, and characterization.

COMIC RELIEF. A humorous character or scene, usually introduced in a serious play, whose jokes and buffoonery are intended as a brief break from the tension created by the main narrative. A character introduced for comic relief will often comment directly upon the absurdity of the protagonist's dilemma. Examples of such characters include the drunken porter in Shakespeare's *Macbeth*.

COMING-OF-AGE STORY. A narrative which takes as its subject the central character's emergence from childhood into some form of maturity; this emergence is often produced by a traumatic experience of the adult world. Examples of the coming-of-age story include Sharon Olds' "Rites of Passage" and Julia Alvarez' "Trespass."

COMMEDIA DELL'ARTE. A form of improvised drama that developed in Italy during the fourteenth century, and that flourished in the sixteenth and seventeenth centuries. Commedia dell'arte (or "comedy of the profession," pointing to its creation by professional performers) used stock characters and scenarios, usually farcical in nature, but required actors to embellish and develop their roles in order to maintain the attention of the audience.

COMPLICATION. In the Aristotelian model of a narrative's action, a complication occurs after the onset of the narrative's problem, interfering with the protagonist's attempts to restore the status quo or a state of equilibrium. Complications generally function to push the plot along and to heighten the audience's tension.

CONCEIT. An extended metaphor, often using an unusual image to show the resemblances between otherwise unlike things. Common conceits in Elizabethan poetry include the frequent comparison of the beloved to a flower or a garden. The "metaphysical" poets extended the conceit in ways that were often startling and provocative, such as John Donne's comparison between a flea bite and a sexual encounter in "The Flea."

CONCRETE DICTION. Language that describes qualities that can be perceived with the five senses. Concrete diction is defined in opposition to abstract language, which cannot be so perceived; an adjective such as "good" is thus abstract, while "sweet" is concrete.

CONCRETE POETRY. Poetry that is shaped on the page, often to resemble the object it describes. For example, George Herbert's "Easter Wings" creates those wings both typographically and through its imagery.

CONFESSIONAL POEM. A poem which focuses on its narrator's state of mind, often describing that state of mind in less-than-flattering terms. The chaos or trauma of the narrator's internal life is often intended as a metaphor for the world at large. Confessional poets include Anne Sexton, Sylvia Plath, and Robert Lowell.

CONFLICT. A struggle between two forces that drives a narrative's plot. The two forces in conflict can be two characters, a character and his or her environment or society, or two large social groups. Conflict can also be wholly internal to a character, as in narratives in which a character struggles with his or her psychological issues or conflicting desires.

CONNOTATION. The implied or figurative meaning that a word or image carries, as distinct from its literal or explicit meaning. Connotation often includes contextual or culturally specific overtones. For instance, "home" literally means the place one lives, but it often carries the connotations of safety and security. See denotation.

CONSONANCE. A pleasant combination of sounds; also, the repetition of consonants or groups of consonants, particularly at the ends of words. See also alliteration, assonance.

CONVENTIONS. Structures, devices, or other features that are traditional or expected within particular literary genres. For instance, an English sonnet's rhyme scheme is a convention; similarly, the *femme fatale* is a convention of hardboiled detective novels.

COSMIC IRONY. Irony related to a deterministic or fatalistic view of the world, usually implying that fate or some other cosmic force is toying with human lives.

COUPLET. Two successive lines of poetry of the same metrical length, usually rhyming, that form a complete unit.

COZY. A light English mystery novel, filled with suspense but typically avoiding gruesome bloodshed or terror. The detective in a cozy is generally an amateur sleuth, and often a sweet elderly lady likely not to seem a threat to a criminal. Agatha Christie's Miss Marple novels are typical of the genre.

CRISIS. The peak of a narrative's tension; the critical turning point of a narrative's action that usually leads to or produces its climax.

CRITICISM. The interpretive or analytical work performed by a serious reader of a text, in which the reader evaluates the textual evidence in order to more fully comprehend a text's meaning. Criticism is so named not because it is of necessity "negative," but rather because the critic asks difficult questions in performing such analysis.

CYBERPUNK. A sub-genre of science fiction, growing out of the work of writers including William Gibson and Bruce Sterling, often focused on a dystopian, heavily computerized near-future world. Cyberpunk combines the nihilism of the punk movement with an interest in the ways new technologies shape the future of human societies.

DACTYL. A three-syllable metrical foot composed of one stressed and two unstressed syllables. Examples include "strawberry" and "horrible."

DECORUM. Literary and dramatic appropriateness, particularly in terms of the use of appropriate language and form. Decorum is a key principle of classical rhetoric.

DENOTATION. The literal or explicit meaning that a word or image carries, as distinct from its implied or figurative meaning. Denotation usually disregards the cultural or contextual overtones of a term. Dictionary definitions are generally denotative. See connotation.

DENOUEMENT. The outcome or resolution of a narrative's action. "Denouement" derives from a French term meaning "unknotting" or "unwinding," and thus refers to the period after a narrative's climax, during which the status quo or equilibrium is restored.

DETECTIVE STORY. A branch of mystery stories focusing on the investigation of a crime. The genre of the detective story was established in Sir Arthur Conan Doyle's tales of Sherlock Holmes, and was later revolutionized by the work of Dashiell Hammett and Raymond Chandler. The detective story frequently focuses as much on the psychology of the detective him- or herself as on the puzzle he or she is charged with solving.

DEUS EX MACHINA. Literally, "god from the machine," the device often used to resolve Greek drama, whereby a god would be lowered onto the stage in order to bring a divine end to the play's conflict. The term has come to be used to describe any improbable or unrealistic solution to a narrative's plot.

DIALECT. The language of a particular class, ethnic group, or region, as represented in literature. Dialect is a method of characterization that uses spelling, grammar, and word choice to represent the sounds of that character's speech, often with the intent of distinguishing the character from others in the narrative. A famous example of the use of dialect can be found in Mark Twain's *The Adventures of Huckleberry Finn*.

DIALOGUE. The lines spoken by a character in a work of fiction or drama, and particularly a conversation between two characters.

DICTION. The particular word choices made by an author. Diction may be formal or informal, concrete or abstract; diction is a major contributor to an author's style.

DIDACTIC POETRY. Poetry that is instructive in aim, seeking to teach its reader a lesson, or otherwise convince its reader of a particular argument.

DIMETER. A poetic line consisting of two metrical feet.

DISCOURSE. Traditionally, a formal verbal expression or exchange, taking place in either speech or writing. "Discourse" has been adopted as a key term in recent critical theory to describe the ways in which meaning, and particularly ideology, is disseminated within a culture through its uses of language.

DOCUMENTARY THEATER. A recent mode of theatrical production that brings together ethnographic research with performance, creating a play which is both factual and dramatic. The term usually implies that the dialogue has been taken verbatim from interviews. Documentary theater has roots in the Depression-era Federal Theater Project and the German "theater of fact" of the 1960s. Examples of documentary theater include Anna Deveare Smith's *Fires in the Mirror* and the Tectonic Theater Project's *The Laramie Project*.

DOGGEREL. Comic verse composed in a loose, irregular measure. "Doggerel" is today most often used in a derogatory fashion, to refer to crudely written or otherwise bad poetry.

DOUBLE ENTENDRE. A French term for "double meaning." A double entendre is a deliberately ambiguous phrase, usually conveying a secondary meaning of a humorously sexual nature.

26

DOUBLE PLOT. Two interwoven plots contained in one narrative. Often one plot is treated more centrally than the other, producing a main plot and a subplot. An example of such a double plot is contained in Shakespeare's *King Lear*, one with Lear at its center and the other revolving around Gloucester.

DRAMA. A genre of literary work, written in either prose or verse, in which characters enact a narrative through dialogue and pantomime. Most drama is written to be performed on the stage, though "closet" drama is intended to be read rather than performed.

DRAMATIC IRONY. A dramatic device in which the reader or spectator knows something about a situation that a character does not, with the result that the character either behaves inappropriately or expects an outcome that is opposed to that which the reader knows is forthcoming. Dramatic irony runs rampant in Sophocles's *Oedipus Rex*, as Oedipus repeatedly curses the murderer of Laius, not knowing that he is in fact that murderer.

DRAMATIC MONOLOGUE. A poem narrated by an individual speaker who addresses either the reader or an implied listener. The poetry of Robert Browning includes many dramatic monologues, including "My Last Duchess."

DRAMATIC POETRY. Drama written in verse. Also, poetry that presents a character speaking directly to the reader or audience without additional authorial devices.

DYNAMIC CHARACTER. Also known as a round character; a complex character depicted as having psychological depth, particularly one who develops and changes over the course of a narrative. See flat character.

DYSTOPIA. Literally, "bad place." As opposed to a utopia (a good place, an idealized imaginary world), a dystopia is a nightmarish fictional future world, in which characters lead dehumanized, fear-filled lives. Dystopian narratives often focus on totalitarian regimes, and are often satiric commentaries on our own society. Examples of dystopian narratives include George Orwell's *1984* and Margaret Atwood's *The Handmaid's Tale*.

ECHO VERSE. A kind of literary resonance, in which a sound, or word, or image in a text recalls a similar effect in another text. As a poetic form dating back to late classical Greek poetry, the final syllables of the lines repeat in reply or commentary.

ELEGY. In classical literature, "elegy" referred only to poems written in strict elegiac meter, with alternating lines of hexameter and pentameter. Since the Renaissance, however, "elegy" has been used to describe any poem that conducts a sustained and formal lamentation, usually over the death of a particular person. The poem, usually longer than a lyric but not so long as an epic, generally contains a speaker and is delivered in the first person, often uses classical allusions and motifs, and frequently traces the speaker's path from grief through acceptance to joy.

ELISION. The omission of a letter or syllable, often combining two words into one, for metrical effect.

END RHYME. Rhyme occurring in the final words or syllables of two or more lines of poetry, as opposed to internal rhyme, which occurs within a line.

END-STOPPED LINE. One of two major types of line breaks in poetry. End-stopped lines generally end in conjunction with the end of a phrase or a sentence. Contrast with enjambment.

ENGLISH SONNET. Also known as a Shakespearean sonnet. The English sonnet typically contains three quatrains and a couplet, with an abab/cdcd/efef/gg rhyme scheme.

ENJAMBMENT. One of two major types of line breaks in poetry. Enjambed lines break in mid-phrase, and thus do not contain a sustained pause at the end of a line. Contrast with end-stopped line.

ENVIRONMENTAL THEATER. A form of political theater, related to performance art, in which the performance moves out of the restricted space of the theater and into the public arenas of streets or parks, intentionally blurring the lines between performance and audience, and between reality and illusion.

ENVOY. Also spelled "envoi," a brief postscript to a poem or a piece of prose writing, which often dedicates the poem to its patron or sends it on its way into the world. "Envoy" is also a term for the short concluding stanza of a ballad or sestina.

EPIC THEATER. Commonly associated with Bertolt Brecht, a form of theater in which the style of acting, the inclusion of multimedia effects such as film and electronic sounds, and the presentation of rational argument are used to create a shock of realization in the audience. Epic theater operates through what Brecht called the "alienation effect," which works to distance the viewer from the play's characters, maintaining a constant awareness of the spectacle's unreality. By preventing the audience from identifying with the play's characters, Brecht hoped to engage them intellectually in thinking about the play's issues.

EPIGRAM. Originally, an inscription in verse on a building, monument, or coin. "Epigram" is now used to refer to short, often witty verse, usually with a surprising turn at the end.

EPIGRAPH. A quotation or verse taken from another poem, used to introduce a literary text.

EPIPHANY. The sudden revelation or dawning insight that a character frequently reaches at the climax of a short story, usually sparked by ordinary circumstances but of such power that it is understood to be life-changing.

The term was most notably used by James Joyce to describe the experiences of characters such as Gabriel, the young central figure in "The Dead."

EPISTLE. A poem that imitates the form of a personal letter. An example is Alexander Pope's "Epistle to Dr. Arbuthnot."

EPITAPH. Literally, an inscription on a gravestone. "Epitaph" is also used to describe a brief poem in memory of a dead person, as well as the final words spoken by a character before his or her death.

ESSAY. An interpretive or analytical piece of literary writing. Essays can be personal or critical in focus; the essay nearly always treats its subject from the limited point of view of the author.

EUPHEMISM. The substitution of a more pleasant or agreeable word or phrase for one that might be considered rude or offensive. For example, "passed away" is a euphemism for "dead."

EUPHONY. A grouping of words that produces a pleasant, soothing sound, as opposed to the harsh sounds of cacophony.

EXACT RHYME. Also known as "perfect rhyme," a rhyme in which the final vowel and consonant sounds are the same, as in "rhyme" and "crime." Homophones (such as "die" and "dye") are sometimes included in discussions of exact rhyme. Contrast with inexact or imperfect rhyme, eye rhyme, half rhyme, or slant rhyme.

EXODUS. The last piece of a Greek tragedy, including or following the final choral ode.

EXPLICATION. A detailed analysis of a piece of prose or poetry, one which attempts to account for the meaning and function of all of the elements of the text.

EXPOSITION. The early portion of a play or story's narrative structure in which the characters and situations are introduced. Exposition is also used to refer to any parts of a narrative that provide background information necessary to understanding the story.

EXPRESSIONISM. A style of art or literature, particularly associated with early twentieth-century Europe, in which the artist or writer focuses upon the expression of his or her internal feelings and emotions. Expressionist literature emphasizes the psychological and emotional aspects of the text.

EXTENDED METAPHOR. A sustained metaphor that is elaborated over the course of an entire stanza or poem.

EXTENDED SIMILE. A sustained comparison between two things, using "like" or "as" to draw the connection.

EYE RHYME. Words that give the appearance of rhyming when in print, but that are pronounced slightly differently, as in "bury" and "fury." Contrast with exact rhyme.

FABLE. A legendary tale usually including animals as characters, who display and represent human foibles, and often having a moral or instructional aspect to the telling. Fables are often humorous, and the animals often take on stylized traits—the tricky fox and the clever rabbit.

FAIRY TALE. A tale that constructs a world of the imagination often with ancient settings and/or characters of either royal or peasant background interacting. Many of the old fairy tales were transmitted orally before they were collected and written down. These stories usually contain magical elements, including supernatural creatures, and suggest a world where anything but the ordinary is likely to happen.

FALLING ACTION. In the plot of a narrative the action rises to a particular point (a climax) and then begins to fall to the inevitable conclusion. (Also referred to as the fourth part of plot structure.)

FALLING METER. Poetry includes regular beats that are divided into feet which include accented and unaccented syllables. Falling meter occurs in trochaic and dactylic meters when a foot ends with an unaccented syllable or two unaccented syllables. Trochaic: fearsome. Dactylic: tragedy.

FANTASY. A fantasy must have magic and magical characters, and these characters must find themselves in amazing and imaginative situations. The stories often unfold in worlds far away or long ago, and the characters often find themselves doing and experiencing things quite impossible in the ordinary world.

FARCE. A play that includes the boisterous and even crude types of action that happen when characters indulge in horseplay and sexual humor. Characters usually speak in colloquial terms and may even knock one another about and tumble down with and upon one another.

FEMININE RHYME. In poetic metrical feet, a foot that ends in an unaccented syllable is said to have feminine meter. Feminine rhyme occurs when two lines with feminine meter rhyme: Today comedy, tonight tragedy.

FICTION. A narrative shaped or made (from the Latin *ficio*, to shape or make) from the author's imagination. Parts of a fictional story, novel, or drama may refer to factual reality, but the story and characters arise from the musings of the creator.

FIGURATIVE. Referring to the use of figures of speech, that is, language that explains through metaphors or similes, comparing one thing to another in order to enhance or underscore the meaning.

FIGURES OF SPEECH. An image that relies on the comparative imagination of the reader or listener, e.g., cold as ice, mad as a hornet.

FIRST PERSON NARRATIVE. Literary works appear in a variety of voices. The speaker may be a master narrator who tells the story from outside of the characters' worlds, or the speaker may know about the characters' thoughts but still not be in the story him or herself. Finally, the first person narrative speaks from the point of view of one character in the narrative. That person has complete control of the line of the narrative. Readers are dependent on the point of view of that narrator and must either trust or suspect the speaker throughout the narrative.

FIXED FORM. Poetic form may be either open or fixed. Fixed forms are those in which the poet decides to follow a particular form both for the effect on the reader and for the challenge of expressing the meaning through a controlled rhythm and rhyme scheme.

FLASHBACK. An interruption in the line of the narrative which occurs when a character suddenly remembers a past event so vividly that it takes over the line of action for a time. Flashbacks are used in both novels and film to enhance the story line or to add information that is necessary to the plot of the work. Often in stories of war or conflict, the character will suddenly find him or herself out of time and into an episode of memory. This memory may explain something in the current action or something in the motivation of the character.

FLAT CHARACTER. A character who usually carries the action of a narrative without adding emotional insight or plot development. E. M. Forster coined the term to describe a character with few traits. The parlor maid in a play or the sheriff in a cowboy movie may be a flat character if she or he is there merely to facilitate the scene.

FLEXIBLE THEATER. Also called experimental theater and sometimes referred to as a black box. The theater is small, often with space for 100–200 persons in the audience, often providing flexible seating and space, allowing for theater in the round, a proscenium arch or fourth wall, thrust staging, or other innovative designs.

FLY-ON-THE-WALL NARRATOR. A narrator who does not enjoy knowledge of the thoughts or feelings of the characters but tells what is seen from a distance. The narrator does not intrude in the action but also does not give emotional insight into the characters except through observation of action. This form of narration demands that the reader follow the narrator in the inferences that are made from the observations, though perhaps the reader may also be encouraged to guess at more than the narrator is revealing.

FOIL. A character that sets off or contrasts with another character maybe serving as a foil or opposite.

FOLK BALLADS. Ballads that were sung by minstrels for hundreds of years before being written down. They are usually in a set ballad form with set rhyme and often with a repeated chorus that begins to draw and hold the listener in the story. Often, ballads exist in several forms since they changed as they were sung and passed on from minstrel to minstrel.

FOLK EPIC. An oral tradition that tells the story of a nation's heroes, the folk epic may have a variety of versions, as do the great Norse and Celtic legends, or the epic may have been recorded so long ago that one author claims the tale as in Homer's *Iliad* and *Odyssey*.

FOLKTALE. A tale that has been passed down by oral tradition, usually not having found a set form in the manner of a fairy tale.

FOOT. In poetry, the means of measuring meter. A foot has either two or three syllables with varying accents.

FORESHADOWING. In a narrative work, events are constructed so that early events will suggest later events in the development of the plot; thus a gun in the first act of a play suggests that someone will be shot in a later act. Without foreshadowing, the reader or audience might not be prepared for the outcome of the narrative.

FORM. Humans want to see order in the world, and authors and their readers or viewers are no exception. Thus a work of art will have some kind of form, whether that be a traditional plot or a more experimental shape. Poetry especially can be constructed in prescribed forms or can take more inventive shapes, but finally the form must be there as an essential part of the telling and understanding.

FORMULA LITERATURE. Literary works fall into genres that have more or less predictable forms. When the form controls the literary work to the extent that the outcome may be predictable or even obvious, the narrative work is considered to be formulaic, e.g., romance novels or westerns or action movies. The formula does not necessarily mean that the work is of less value, but when the formula so dominates the work that the creative element bends to the expected form or shape, then the work may not please the reader.

FOUND POEM. The poet may notice words in an ad or in a conversation, write them down, and then rearrange them into a pleasing and meaningful pattern, thus, a found poem.

FOURTH WALL. A proscenium "wall" located between the curtain and the orchestra used in modern experimental theater to create space outside the stage itself for movement and action.

FRAME NARRATIVE. In a story within a story, the outside story is the frame narrative or the story that enfolds the second narrative. Shakespeare's *Midsummer Night's Dream* tells the story of a group of characters, some of whom in turn are working on their own story, the acting out of the old tale of star-crossed lovers who meet at a wall. In this play the frame is the main narrative, and the internal narrative is entertaining and also linked to the main plot. In other narratives, such as *Heart of Darkness*, the narrator tells his own story and then that of another trip to the same dark place, the second tale being the main narrative of the story.

FREE VERSE. Free verse has no prescribed form or meter, but free verse does have form, often a form found by the poet while composing. Meter and rhythm vary according to the needs and demands of the poem itself.

FREYTAG'S PYRAMID. In 1863 Gustav Freytag (Technique of the Drama) suggested that the five parts of classical drama suggest a pyramid, the rising action peaking at the climax and leading to the falling action; the five are exposition, complication (conflicting elements), climax, catastrophe, and resolution.

GENRE. The literary form that an author chooses to follow, assuming that the reader or viewer will enter into the agreed upon pattern. Thus if a work begins with a rhymed couplet and continues with more couplets, the reader quickly knows that the genre is poetry and reads accordingly. If a playgoer sees a very silly master of ceremonies appear before the curtain, the viewer will assume that the genre is dramatic comedy.

GOTHIC FICTION. The genre of fiction suggesting terror and suspense, often with the use of heavy medieval architecture (also referred to as Gothic). Horace Walpole is credited with the first Gothic novel, *The Castle of Otranto*, in 1764, but the Bronte's and Poe have given the form is true shape.

HAIKU. An unrhymed form derived from Japan, requiring seventeen syllables in a set five, seven, five form and using imagery from nature; the poem often resolves into an observation about nature and meaning in the last line.

HALF-RHYME. In poetic form, the middle of the line and the end of the line rhyme.

HAMARTIA. The Greek word for error, but in drama the word has come to mean something more drastic. For example, Hamlet is too hesitant to think clearly about the political situation in which he finds himself. His hesitance is his fatal error that will lead to his death. This error is not one that the character intends to make but is rather a part of the personality that cannot be evaded or avoided but that will inevitably lead to disaster for all involved.

HARD-BOILED FICTION. The hard-boiled detective of either gender works in a dangerous world where criminals are vicious, deaths are violent, and only a tough character can survive and solve the crime. This world of fiction has evolved in the twentieth century as detective fiction moved from the polite mysteries of the drawing room and the tea parlor to the mysteries of the streets where everyone carries a weapon, and the criminals are most certainly not gentlemen or gentlewomen.

HEAVY-STRESS RHYME. A poetic rhyme involving a spondee (two accented syllables together) or a free-verse form that uses internal emphatic rhyme.

HEPTAMETER. A line of poetry that has seven feet, including seven primary stresses.

HERMENEUTICS. Originally meaning the close study and interpretation of the *Bible*, but in modern criticism it means the principles and systems used to interpret meaning in any text.

HERO/HEROINE. In Greek epics, the leading warriors were called by the term from which hero is derived (heros). The term came to mean the lead character in a narrative or drama, the character who saves the day or who triumphs over adversity. Heroine was used as a feminine term, but current usage applies hero to both genders.

HEROIC COUPLET. A couplet written in iambic pentameter, that is five feet per line, each foot being an iamb, or two beat syllable with the stress on the second syllable. The heroic couplet is a closed couplet, a form that sums up an idea in two lines, but the heroic couplet must follow the metric form as well. Heroic couplets often appear at the end of scenes in Shakespeare's plays to sum up the action of the scene and to send the actor off stage with an exact and effective closing line.

HEURISTIC. From the Greek word for the modern word *eureka* (*heureka*, meaning "I found it"), any method or technique that helps a writer or speaker come up with ideas for a topic or for developing a topic.

HEXAMTER. Poetic lines with six rhythmic feet are said to be written in hexameter.

HIGH COMEDY/VERBAL COMEDY. Comedy that derives its humor from witty and satirical conversations on the parts of the players. The comic wit is often at the expense of human foibles, especially in the Restoration form known as the comedy of manners in which romantic alliances among upper-class partners are played out through witty exchanges between the characters.

HUBRIS. From Greek drama, the term used to describe a character who is laid low by his pride and arrogance, inasmuch as these qualities make anyone unable to see his or her own weaknesses.

HUMOR. Occurs in literature in at least two distinct ways, one being the farcical action where actors or characters buffet one another about and speak in crude and colloquial language. The other form of humor occurs when more observant and reflective characters satirize the foibles of human nature.

HYMN. A song of praise, best shown by the psalms in the Judeo-Christian scriptures or by other poetic songs written in praise.

HYPERBOLE. An overstatement used to stress a point.

IAMB. A poetic foot consisting of at least two syllables. An iamb is a foot with one accented and one unaccented set of syllables: beside or demand are words which demonstrate an iamb. This meter is common in English poetry, for it reflects the form of many English words.

IDENTICAL RHYME. Occurs when the same word is used for a rhyme in a poem.

IDEOLOGY. A a system of beliefs and values belonging to an individual or to a group.

IDIOM. A particular means of expression used in a particular language. In American English one stands "in line," but in British English one stands "on line."

IMAGE/IMAGERY. In poetic writing the stress may be expressly on the image that is being described or envisioned. Imagery is also used in fiction to create a particular mood or impression. It is important to keep in mind that these images appeal to the senses, giving an evocative picture of that which is being described.

IMAGISM. This movement in American twentieth century poetry stressed the image above all, leaving behind the poetic forms that emphasized meter and rhyme. The imagists such as Ezra Pound owed much to the Japanese haiku form that stresses one vivid picture.

IMPERFECT FOOT. In poetic meter, a foot is usually one stressed and one unstressed syllable, or one unstressed and one stressed, two unstressed and one stressed, one stressed and two unstressed, or two stressed syllables. Any variation from these five patterns is considered an imperfect foot.

IMPERFECT RHYME. Imperfect rhyme, including slant rhyme, presents a rhyme that is almost a rhyme but not quite so: love/leave.

IMPRESSIONISM. In fiction, impressionism stresses the impact of the external world on the internal world of a character. Flannery O'Connor's intellectual characters often muse over the possible meanings of the various incidents that happen in rural southern Georgia.

IN MEDIAS RES. Literally translated from Latin to mean "in the middle of the circle." It is used to refer to an epic tale that begins in the middle of the story and then reveals the previous incidents. *Star Wars* was a movie series that began in medias res.

INCREMENTAL REPETITION. This poetic term refers to phrases or lines that occur regularly at particular points in a poem as do the choruses in ballads or the repeated lines in some set poetic forms such as a villanelle which repeats lines from the first stanza in set form throughout the poem.

INEXACT RHYME. Like imperfect rhyme, inexact rhyme refers to a poetic variation on the expected rhyme: heart/hearth; laugh/wrath.

INITIATION STORY. A story that provides the first experience of a person, usually young, who faces a great life experience for the first time, especially death, sex, or religious doubt and faith. James Joyce's collection of stories, *Dubliners*, includes these three types of initiation stories.

INTERIOR MONOLOGUE. In fiction, the place where a character muses over a problem or issue internally. This musing is written out in the voice of the character but is not spoken to another character.

INTERNAL ALLITERATION. Within the lines of a poem, vowels or consonants will be repeated so that the internal alliteration will strike the reader's or listener's ear almost unaware: the slippery snake hissed softly.

INTERNAL RHYME. Within the line of a poem, words will rhyme, affecting the ear more than the rhythm, as does a rhyme at the end of a line: with laugh the gaff was gone.

INTERTEXTUALITY. Texts constantly refer back to other texts, even when one text does not quote another. Speech and writing are full of references to well known stories or to the Bible or Shakespeare. Writers like the poet T. S. Eliot use intertextuality purposefully to emphasize meaning; at the end of his poem "Little Gidding" he quotes Dame Julian of Norwitch, "And all shall be well/All manner of things shall be well," but he does not reference the quote, assuming that his intended reader will know and understand the reference. Cited references demonstrate intertextuality as well, showing the relationship between the text being written and earlier writers on the subject.

IRONY. Occurs in a literary work when the text operates on at least two levels of meaning. Dramatic or tragic irony occurs when the audience has information that the characters do not, as in *Romeo and Juliet* when the audience knows that Juliet is not dead but Romeo thinks she is. Situational irony occurs when the story turns out to be the opposite of the expected as in *The Open Window* in which the woman telling the story to the visitor has created a false story that will shock the visitor when the truth is known. Cosmic irony occurs when the character can do nothing to change the fate that is prepared, and verbal irony occurs when the words spoken are the opposite of the meaning intended.

ITALIAN SONNET. The Italian or Petrarchen sonnet consists of an octet (eight lines) of iambic pentameter (five feet of unaccented and accented syllables) which presents the argument or dilemma and a sextet (six lines) that answer the argument or sorts out the dilemma. The lines are rhymed aaba/aaba and cdecde or cdcdcd.

KINETIC IMAGERY. Imagery in motion; thus a poem or story will show a vivid image in action.

LIMERICK. A short form of poetry including five anapestic lines (two unaccented and one accented syllables) rhymed aabba. Lines one, two, and five have three feet, and lines three and four have two feet.

LINE. In drama, refers to words spoken by a particular character. In poetry, a line is one specific line of poetry that can be either metric or set off in free verse for emphasis.

LITERARY BALLAD. A narrative poem written in calculated imitation of the form and style of traditional, anonymous ballads. Unlike traditional ballads, a literary ballad is not sung; it is written for sophisticated readers.

LITERARY EPIC. A careful, conscious emulation in writing by an individual author of earlier oral folk epic. Literary epics, such as Virgil's *Aeneid* or Milton's *Paradise Lost*, frequently compare the present to the glorious past

LITOTES. An indirect affirmation, usually understated, made by the denial of its opposite, such as "I was not a little hungry" to mean "I was very hungry."

LOCAL COLOR. The use in fiction of distinctive though typically superficial regional material intended to provide realistic background. Regional particularities can be expressed in specific types of setting, dialect, dress, custom or habit.

LOW COMEDY/PHYSICAL COMEDY. Characterized by boisterous activity or clownish behavior without intellectual appeal. Low comedy attempts to incite laughter by employment of jokes, gags, or slapstick humor.

LYRIC. A short, emotionally expressive poem by a single speaker. Commonly written in the first person, lyric poetry is frequently emotional, highlighting personal moods, thoughts, feelings, perceptions, and states of mind. Lyric typically evokes a songlike or musical quality. In ancient Greece, "lyric" was sung to the accompaniment of a lyre.

MADRIGAL. Short, secular song, typically dedicated to love or pastoral themes, arranged in counterpoint for several voices without accompaniment. The madrigal originated in Italy during the fourteenth century and triumphed in England during the Elizabethan period.

MAGIC REALISM. Contemporary narrative that combines mundane events and descriptive details with fantastic and magical elements in a realistic framework. Though usually associated with Latin American fiction, magic realism has blossomed into an international trend.

MALAPROPISM. The mistaken, comic use of a word in place of another with which it shares a close resemblance. The inaccurate, inappropriate word choice derives from confusion between the two words. The term derives from the character Mrs. Malaprop in *The Rivals* (1775) by Richard Brinsley Sheridan.

MASCULINE RHYME. Rhyme consisting of single stressed syllables or of stressed final syllables in polysyllabic words.

MEDITATION. A contemplative essay or sermon.

MELODRAMA. A popular form of theater that features stereotyped characters, such as villains, heroes, and young lovers, engaged in sensational events, intrigue, and action. Melodrama presents suspenseful plots centered on exaggerated conflicts between good and evil. The term is often employed pejoratively to connote a lack of psychological depth and an excess of emotional excitement.

METAFICTION. A type of fiction that renounces the illusion of verisimilitude to explore or comment on, in a self-conscious and self-referential manner, its own fictional nature. Repudiating realism, metafiction concentrates on the role of author and reader in the creation and reception of fiction.

METAPHOR. A figure of speech, not meant to be factually true, in which one thing is compared or substituted for something else. Although the two things are not identical, they are associated in language to emphasize a similarity between them.

METER. A regular, recurring rhythm, or pattern of stresses and pauses, in lines of verse.

METONYMY. A figure of speech which substitutes the name of one thing with that of another with which it is closely associated in common experience. The use of the "White House" or "Oval Office" to refer to the United States presidency is a familiar example.

MIME. A non-literary performance that involves acting with movement and gesture, but without any words.

MIMESIS. Imitation or mimicry intended to represent or reproduce reality.

MINIMALISM. A form of contemporary fiction written in an austere style with a severe restriction of content and setting, such as the work of Raymond Carver.

MISE EN SCÈNE. French term referring to the elements of a dramatic production including costume, scenery, lighting, etc. In cinema, the term refers more specifically to the arrangement of action in front of the camera.

MONOLOGUE. A long speech by one person. In drama, the monologue provides the spoken thoughts of a single character. In fiction, an interior monologue can similarly represent the thoughts, not the actual spoken words, of a character.

MONOMETER. A verse line with one metrical foot.

MONOSYLLABIC FOOT. A unit of meter with a single syllable.

MOOD. The atmosphere or tone of a literary work, conveyed through diction, characterization, and setting.

MORALITY PLAY. A form of religious drama popular in Europe during the fifteenth and sixteenth centuries consisting of moralized allegories. Featuring a variety of personifications, morality plays showcase the struggle for the Christian soul and communicate simple messages of salvation.

MOTIF. Any element that is repeated and developed throughout a narrative. Motif also refers to an element that recurs in many different literary works. Motifs encompass a wide variety of possible elements such as image, idea, situation, action, incident, or theme.

MOTIVATION. The explicit or implicit reason provided for the actions of a character. In drama or fiction, motivation defines what a character desires.

MULTICULTURALISM. In literary studies, the attention to work produced by or about cultural "minorities."

MYSTERY PLAY. A popular, religious medieval play on biblical themes.

MYTH. Traditional, anonymous story derived from oral tradition usually involving supernatural or heroic figures. Adopting a cosmic perspective, myths offer accounts of origins of human, social, and natural phenomena in boldly imaginative terms. It is believed that the fictional narratives of myth embody the popular ideas, values, and belief systems of cultures that create them.

MYTHOPOEIC. A term employed to describe writing that uses myth as a source or that bears a strong resemblance to myth especially in subject matter.

NARRATIVE. The ordered account of a true or fictitious event, or of connected events. Narrative selects and arranges the recounting of these events in a particular sequence.

NARRATIVE BALLAD. A common form of narrative poetry.

NARRATIVE POEM. A class of poem that tells a story.

NARRATIVE STRUCTURE. See "plot."

NARRATOR. The voice or character who relates the story of the narrative. The narrator is different than the author. The degree of participation, perspective, and personality of the narrator varies greatly though the narrator generally provides information and commentary on other characters and events.

NATURALISM. An extreme, deliberate form of realism in fiction or drama in which human characters are inevitable products or passive victims of the natural or social environment or of a particular genetic inheritance. Writers promoting naturalism strove for precise, objective recording of reality capable of demonstrating laws of causality, and aspired to scientific status for their researched, detailed accounts of behavior.

NEAR RHYME. See "slant rhyme."

NEOCLASSICAL COUPLET. Due to its popularity during the Neoclassical Period (a.k.a. the Augustan Age), the neoclassical couplet is another name for a heroic couplet (two successive rhyming lines of iambic pentameter).

NEOCLASSICAL PERIOD. See "Augustan Age."

NEW COMEDY. In ancient Greece, a form of comedy developed between 400–300 B. C. E. New comedy, frequently associated with Menander, is witty and offers unexpected plot twists.

NOVEL. Extended fictional prose narrative of book length. As a genre, the novel is enormously open and flexible, admitting innumerable exceptions. The novel is distinguished from the short story by its greater number of characters, variety of scenes, and span of time covered.

NOVELLA. Novel or narrative story of intermediate length, longer than a short story but less complex than a novel.

OBJECTIVE CORRELATIVE. The external expression of an interior mood or feeling by the deliberate use of a specific object, scene, or event to evoke a particular emotion.

OBJECTIVE POINT OF VIEW. The dramatic third person point of view, when the narrator reports on events and speech, but does not comment on the thoughts of other characters.

OCCASIONAL POEM. A poem expressly written for or inspired by a specific, typically significant, event.

OCTAMETER. A verse line with eight metrical feet.

OCTAVE. An eight line stanza. Octave indicates the first eight verse line section of sonnets.

OCTOSYLLABIC COUPLET. A type of couplet with eight syllables per line.

ODE. A formal, elaborate lyric poem of exalted style and serious, elevated tone.

OEDIPUS COMPLEX. Term used to describe child's attraction to the parent of the opposite sex; applied most frequently to the attraction of male children to a mother figure, often including overtones of jealousy directed at the father.

OFF RHYME. See "Inexact rhyme."

ONE-ACT PLAY. A shorter dramatic work, most one-act plays take place in a single location, focus on a limited number of characters, and depict a single, powerful incident. Like a short story or a poem, the characterization, setting, and themes must be presented efficiently and, consequently, one-acts sometimes seem less subtle than longer plays.

ONOMATOPOEIA. The attempt to label a thing by forming a word from sounds associated with it.

OPEN FORM. Free verse without any formal scheme including meter, rhyme, or stanza pattern.

ORCHESTRA. In classical Greek drama, the orchestra was the space separating the audience and the players on the stage. The chorus would perform in this space.

ORGANIC FORM. A concept that equates literature to living organisms in so far as both, it is believed, are created by a natural growth process. Value is placed on the entire literary work itself, whereby the "whole" exceeds the "sum" of its parts.

ORGANIC UNITY. Belief in the indissoluble synthesis of form and content in a literary work.

OXYMORON. A condensed paradox combining two contradictory terms, such as bittersweet.

PANTOMIME. Dramatic entertainment employing gesture, posture, and facial expression without speech to convey meaning, mimic action, and express feeling.

PARABLE. Brief, usually allegorical, tale intended to teach a moral or lesson. Typically the moral is only implied and consequently open to different interpretations.

PARADOS. In classical Greek drama, the section of the play that allowed the chorus to enter and comment on the events described in the prologue.

PARADOX. A statement or expression playing on words that initially seems self-contradictory, but which provokes reflection on ways or contexts in which it might seem valid. Also called an "oxymoron."

PARALLELISM. Arrangement of words, phrases or similarly constructed clauses or sentences in sequence or in a similar grammatical or structural way that suggests a recognizable correspondence between them.

PARAPHRASE. Restatement of the meaning or sense of a passage in different words often with the intention of clarification.

PARODY. Mocking or exaggerated imitation of distinctive features of a literary work, author, or style for comic, humorous effect.

PARTICIPATORY DRAMA. A form of drama in which audience members are encouraged to join in the action taking place around them, such as the popular *Tony and Tina's Wedding*.

PASTORAL. Derived from the Latin word for "shepherd," the pastoral is a literary mode that celebrates the virtues of rural, agrarian life and love. Also called "idylls."

PATHOS. This Greek word for passions has come to designate any element of a text that evokes sympathetic feelings in the reader or audience.

PENTAMETER. A line of poetic verse that consists of five metrical feet.

PERFECT RHYME. A rhyme in which the rhymed sounds precisely correspond, as in cat/hat, master/plaster, or dedicate/medicate.

PERIPETEIA. As defined by Aristotle in *Poetics* (350 B.C.E.), perepeteia or "peripety" denotes a sudden, often tragic, reversal in the fortunes of a protagonist.

PERSONA. Derived from the Latin word for the mask, the term "persona" refers to any speaker or narrator of a literary text.

PERSONIFICATION. Also known as "anthropomorphism," personification is the attribution of human characteristics to an inanimate object or phenomenon.

PETRARCHAN SONNET. Named after the Italian poet Francesco Petrarca, also known as Petrarch (1304–1374), the Petrarchan or Italian sonnet is a poem that consists of fourteen lines divided into two sections—the eight line octave and the six line sestet. The octave rhymes abbaabba and presents some kind of problem or conflict that is conventionally resolved in the sestet (rhymed cdecde). Also see "Italian sonnet."

PHONETIC. This term applies to transcriptions of words or letters that reflect the sound of spoken language.

PICARESQUE. Originating in fifteenth-century Europe, this literary genre concerns the escapades and misadventures of a wandering rascal ("picaro" is the Spanish word for rogue). Picaresque narratives are generally satiric, episodic, and involve minimal character development. Prominent examples include Le Sage's Gil Blas (1715), Henry Fieldings's Tom Jones (1749), and Voltaire's Candide (1759).

PICTURE POEM. As its name implies, a poem with its lines arranged in the form of a visual image.

PIDGIN. Derived from a Chinese pronunciation of the English word "business," a pidgin is a language heuristically developed by speakers of mutually unintelligible languages for purposes such as commerce and trade.

PLAY. A literary text intended for dramatic performance.

PLOT. The series of events unfolded throughout the course of a narrative. A conventional plot is organized in terms of conflict, climax, resolution, and denouement.

POETIC DICTION. The highly elevated and formalized language that rejects everyday speech in favor of literary devices such as archaism (outmoded words and expressions), epithets (personalized adjectival phrases, as in Alexander the Great), and circumlocution (roundabout or indirect description).

POINT OF VIEW. The perspective from which a story is told. Third-person omniscient and first-person narration are the most common points of view.

PREFACE. A short introduction that explains the purpose or intent of a given literary text.

PROLOGUE. Originally applied to the introductory speech of a Greek tragedy, this term has come to signify the preface of any literary text.

PROPAGANDA. Any literature written with the intention of recruiting its readers to a given social, political, or religious cause.

PROPS. A shortened form of the word "properties," the physical objects used to create the setting or "mise en scène" of a stage drama.

PROSE POEM. A poetic text written in prose form.

PROSODY. The collective formal techniques of poetry, including rhythm and meter, versification, and diction.

PROTAGONIST. The main character—whether hero or anti-hero—of any given literary text.

PSALMS. Worship songs, most particularly the collection of 150 sacred songs of praise collected in the Biblical Book of Psalms.

PULP FICTION. The collective name for sensational crime, adventure, and science-fiction stories printed on cheap "pulp" paper and published in popular magazines of the 1920s, 30s, and 40s.

PUN. A kind of word-play that depends upon identical or similar sounds among words with different meanings.

PYRRHIC. Within the context of poetic technique, a metrical unit with two consecutive unstressed syllables.

QUANTITATIVE METER. A type of meter based on the interplay between "long" and "short" syllables rather than stressed and unstressed syllables. Common to Greek and Latin poetry, quantitative meter concerns the duration of the spoken word.

QUATRAIN. A verse paragraph that consists of four lines.

RAP. This sub-genre of Rhythm and Blues music involves heavily vernacular lyrics spoken with the accompaniment of music. Also known as hip-hop, rap music was developed by African-American artists throughout the 1970s, 80s, and 90s.

REALISM. Originating in eighteenth-century Europe, this literary mode promotes faithful representation of human life and experience. Realist texts reject idealistic and fantastic subject matter in favor of detailed, accurate description and frank treatment of pessimistic themes.

RED HERRING. A distraction meant to divert the reader from a central point or issue. This tactic is particularly relevant for mystery fiction, in which the writer often frustrates the reader's attempt to arrive at a solution.

REFRAIN. Sometimes called the chorus, the refrain is a recurring line or set of lines in a poem or song.

REGIONALISM. Attention to the ways in which geographical location influences or emerges from a given literary text or set of texts. Also see "Local color."

RESOLUTION. The outcome or conclusion of a narrative conflict. A literary work that withholds clear resolution may be termed an "open-ended" narrative.

RESTORATION PERIOD. The interval between 1660–1700, following restoration of the British monarchy. In 1649, Oliver Cromwell successfully led a revolution against King Charles I; these strict Puritan rebels banned theatrical performance, which they considered worldly and decadent. When the monarchy was restored in 1699, King Charles II reopened England's theaters, giving rise to the bawdy "Restoration Comedy."

REVENGE TRAGEDY. Originating in England during the Elizabethan and Jacobean periods, revenge tragedy is a dramatic genre that concerns the protagonist's self-destructive attempts to avenge the death of a loved one. Notable examples include Thomas Kyd's *The Spanish Tragedy*, William Shakespeare's *Hamlet*, and John Webster's *The Duchess of Malfi*.

REVERSAL. A radical change in the situation of a literary character. See also "peripeteia."

RHETORIC. A term used to describe the collective techniques of persuasive writing.

RHYME. Concurrence of similar or identical sounds within different words.

RHYME ROYALE. Invented by Chaucer in the fourteenth century, the rhyme or "rime" royale is a type of poetic stanza which adheres to iambic pentameter and a fixed rhyme scheme of ababccdd.

RHYME SCHEME. The pattern of repeated words-sounds throughout the course of an entire poem or stanza.

RHYTHM. With respect to any literary text, rhythm refers to the sound-patterns created by organization of stressed and unstressed or long and short syllables.

RISING ACTION. With respect to conventional narrative structure, the term rising action describes the series of events that build tension and lead to a climax.

RISING METER. A metrical foot—such as an iamb or anapest—that concludes with a stressed syllable.

RISING RHYME. Also known as a "masculine rhyme," a rising rhyme concludes with a stressed syllable.

ROMANCE. Originally applied to medieval narratives of courtly love, the term has come to designate any adventure story that concerns fantastic situations and exotic settings.

ROMANTICISM. A nineteenth-century European artistic movement that stresses individualism, personal spiritual development, and human interactions with nature. Often favoring lyric poetry, Romantic writers favor intimate autobiographical themes and radical formal innovations.

RONDEL. Related to the rondeau, a rondel is a fourteen line poem that holds only two rhyming sounds. In this type of poem, the same two lines are repeated at the beginning, middle, and end of the poem.

ROUND CHARACTERS. Realistic literary characters distinguished by depth, psychological complexity, and even self-contradiction.

RUN-ON LINE. A line of verse that concludes without a natural pause or "caesura." This disjunction between syntax and versification often creates a feeling of anxiety or discomfort.

SATIRE. A literary text that uses comedy toward the end of derision.

SCANSION. The process of determining a poem's rhythmic pattern through recognition of stressed and unstressed syllables.

SCENE. Either the physical set of a play or one of the discrete narrative units that comprises an act in a play.

SELECTIVE OMNISCIENCE. Applies to a narrator that reveals only the perspective of a single character.

SELF-REFLEXIVITY. Most pronounced in metafiction, the quality of self-awareness in a literary text. A self-reflexive text underscores and celebrates its own status as a work of fiction.

SENTIMENTALITY. A style of writing that appeals to human sympathy and emotion rather than reason. This literary mode originated in eighteenth-century England; notable examples include Oliver Goldsmith's *The Vicar of Wakefield*, Susanna Rowson's *Charlotte Temple*, and Harriet Beecher Stowe's *Uncle Tom's Cabin*.

SESTET. The last six lines of an Italian sonnet. This conclusive stanza conventionally offers a resolution or response to the problem posed by the poem's first eight lines, which are known as the octave.

SESTINA. A thirty-six line poem that consists of three stanzas: six sestets and a final three-line "envoy." The sestina form also requires that the six words found at the end of the first sestet's lines variously recur at the end of the following sestet's lines and in the envoy.

SET. The physical elements that represent the setting of a dramatic production.

SETTING. The time and place in which a narrative takes place.

SHAKESPEAREAN SONNET. The Shakespearean or English sonnet consists of three quatrains and a conclusive couplet; its most common rhyme scheme is abab/cdcd/efef/gg. In contrast to the octave/sestet structure of the Italian, the Shakespearean form posits a thematic break between the twelfth and thirteenth lines of the poem. Also see "English Sonnet."

SHAPED VERSE. A poem printed in such a way that its visual shape reflects its content.

SHORT STORY. A work of prose-fiction that consists of 15,000–20,000 words.

SIGNIFYIN'(G). Within various African-American communities, "signifyin'(g)" represents the practice of appropriating, parodying, and otherwise transforming cultural elements of the dominant or mainstream group. African-American slaves, in particular, found signifyin'(g) a valuable form of resistance culture.

SIMILE. In poetry, a figure of speech whereby two unlike objects are compared to each other with the word *like* or *as*, e.g., "My mistress' eyes are nothing like the sun."

SITUATIONAL IRONY. A type of irony in which an action differs markedly from audience expectations, resulting in surprise and sometimes discomfort. Herman Melville uses situational irony in *Benito Cereno*, for example, as readers discover at the end of the novella that the reality of the situation is the complete opposite of their (and the protagonist's) perceptions.

SKENE. A wooden structure used by actors in fifth century B.C.E. Greek dramas, it typically represented a palace or temple. The skene was located in the back of the stage, allowing the actors to switch costumes when changing roles.

SLANT RHYME. Also referred to as near rhyme, in slant rhyme the sound of the words is nearly alike. This is because such rhymes share the same vowel sound but have different consonant sounds, e.g., scored and word.

SOLILOQUY. A speech given by a character in a play revealing the character's state of mind or motivation.

SONNET. Meaning little sound or song, one of the most popular poetic forms, particularly for poems dealing with love. It is comprised of fourteen lines written in iambic pentameter. Also see "Italian Sonnet" and "English Sonnet."

SPEAKER. In poetry, the speaker refers to the voice of the poem, the self or persona created by the author.

SPECTACLE. In drama, a scene often included for its spectacular effect.

SPENSERIAN STANZA. A form created by Edmund Spenser for *The Faerie Queen*, comprised of nine lines, the first eight written in iambic pentameter, and the ninth written in iambic hexameter.

SPONDEE. The spondee in poetry is composed of a metric foot of two accented syllables, often created for emphasis, e.g., "oh joy!"

STAGE BUSINESS. In drama, refers to any nonverbal action intended to capture the audience's attention and reveal the feelings of a character.

STAGE DIRECTIONS. In the text of a play, the directions that represent the playwright's view of the positions of the actors on the stage and their physical expressions.

STANZA. The basic unit of a poem typically comprised of two or more lines. A stanza operates much as the paragraph does in prose.

STATIC CHARACTER. A character who does not grow or change throughout a narrative.

STEREOTYPE. An unrealistic character based on assumptions about common traits of a certain group (e.g., women, homosexuals, Asians). Tom in Harriet Beecher Stowe's *Uncle Tom's Cabin*, for example, is a stereotype of the long-suffering, docile African slave.

STOCK CHARACTER. A kind of character, usually one-dimensional, appearing regularly in certain types of literature: the wicked stepmother in fairy tales, for example.

STREAM-OF-CONSCIOUSNESS TECHNIQUE. A technique in modern fiction designed to approximate the uncensored, disorganized flow of thought running through the mind of a character. Two of the most notable examples of the technique are James Joyce's *Ulysses* and William Faulkner's *The Sound and the Fury*.

STRESS. In poetry, the emphasis given a syllable often for metrical, or musical, purposes, e.g., *pro*ject and pro*ject* are different words depending on the stress and part of speech.

STROPHE. In poetry, strophe often refers to a stanza that does not have a regular metrical or rhythmic pattern.

STRUCTURE. Pertaining to any genre, the structure of a work refers to the arrangement of its elements.

STYLE. The term used to capture an author's way of expressing. Style is conveyed through the author's use of language, such as diction, syntax, metaphor and other figurative language.

SUBJECT. Refers to what a literary work is about, as distinct from its meaning.

SUBPLOT. A secondary plot within a larger story, normally related to and often reflective of the main plot.

SUMMARY. The summary of a work captures its main idea and the subtopics that develop the idea. Summaries come in various forms and lengths.

SURREALISM. The movement in literature and art founded by the poet Andre Breton in the early twentieth century. This movement attempted to capture the deepest recesses of the unconscious and dream-life through imagery that explored, as described by Arthur Rimbaud, "the reasoned disorder of the senses." For example: "Chicago/The trams make a noise like doughnut batter/dropped in oil."

SUSPENSE. The tension and anticipation that develops in the audience with regard to the plot, usually focusing on what will happen to the main character.

SYLLABIC VERSE. Poetry in which an established number of syllables in a line is repeated in subsequent lines, e.g., "Do not go gentle into that good night . . . Though wise men at their end know dark is right."

SYMBOL. A symbol in a work of art is an element that stands for something beyond its literal meaning in the text. It embodies an idea, such as the way in which the white whale in *Moby-Dick* is invested with meaning.

SYMBOLIST MOVEMENT. A literary movement that began in France during the late nineteenth century with writers such as Charles Baudelaire and Paul Verlaine, focusing on the mysteriousness of life, and relying on suggestion and symbol rather than explicitness and description.

SYNECDOCHE. A synecdoche is a figure of speech in which a part signifies the whole or the whole signifies the part, e.g., in the phrase "All hands on deck," hands stand for people.

SYNESTHESIA. From the Greek, a term meaning "perceiving together." The experience of two or more senses stimulated simultaneously when only one of them is being addressed; for example, "seeing" a color while hearing an actual sound (visualizing the color blue while hearing the Blues played on instruments).

SYNESTHESIS. In literature, refers to the description of one kind of sense in terms of another, such as "sweet as moonlight."

SYNOPSIS. A summary of the main points of an artistic work. In a short story, novel, or play, it relates the main plot line.

SYNTAX. Syntax refers to the way words are put together in sentences. The syntax of a sentence can make significant contributions to an author's style, e.g., "Ask not what your country can do for you . . . ."

TERCET. In poetry, a three line stanza, each line ending in the same rhyme. For example:

> Whenas in silks my Julia goes,
> Then, then, methinks, how sweetly flows
> That liquefaction of her clothes.

TERMINAL REFRAIN. A terminal refrain is that which appears at the end of each stanza of a poem, such as the "Nevermore" refrain in Poe's "The Raven."

TERZA RIMA. A three-line stanza in which one rhyme is used in the first and third lines and the rhyme in the second line is used in the first and third lines of the next stanza. It is also referred to as an overlapping or interlocking rhyme scheme, e.g.,

> I have been one acquainted with the night.
> I have walked out in rain—and back in rain.
> I have outwalked the furthest city light.
> I have looked down the saddest city lane,
> I have passed by the watchman on his beat
> And dropped my eyes, unwilling to explain.

TETRAMETER. In poetry, a meter consisting of four metrical feet, e.g., "Had we but world enough, and time,/This coyness, lady, were no crime . . . ."

THEME. In poetry, fiction, or drama, the theme is the dominating idea in a work. For example, one might say that the theme of *Romeo and Juliet* is the problem of star-crossed love.

THESIS. Associated mainly with the essay, the thesis represents the writer's main idea or attitude toward the subject of the writing.

THRUST STAGE. In theatre, a thrust stage is a stage where the audience is seated on three sides of the acting area.

TONE. Tone signifies the mood of a work of literature. The mood may be ironic, sad, joyful, or pensive.

TRAGEDY. A drama in which the main characters suffer a catastrophic end for the purpose of arousing pity on the part of the audience. Often a tragedy involves the downfall of a person of great significance.

TRAGIC FLAW. In tragedies, the tragic flaw represents the defect in the hero that is the cause of his downfall.

TRAGIC IRONY. A tragic irony is that which conspires against the hero in spite of his best efforts to avoid his fate.

TRAGICOMEDY. A play that uses the elements of a tragedy, but ends happily, such as in Shakespeare's *The Merchant of Venice*.

TRILOGY. A trilogy is a long literary work in three parts, each part standing on its own. William Faulkner's *The Hamlet*, *The Town*, and *The Mansion* are referred to as The Snopes Trilogy.

TRIMETER. In poetry, a meter consisting of three metrical feet. For example:

> The idle life I lead
> Is like a pleasant sleep,
> Wherein I rest and heed
> The dreams that by me sweep.

TRIOLET. A French poetic form of eight lines and using only two rhymes. The first two lines are repeated as the last two lines. Here is a playful example of this lyric form:

> Easy is the triolet,
> If you really learn to make it!
> Once a neat refrain you get,
> Easy is the triolet.
> As you see!—I pay my debt
> With another rhyme. Deuce take it,
> Easy is the triolet,
> If you really learn to make it!

TRIPLE RHYME. A triple rhyme occurs when the rhyming stressed syllable is followed by two unstressed syllables, e.g., "meticulous" and "ridiculous."

TROCHEE. A foot comprised of a stressed syllable followed by an unstressed syllable. Here is an example of an unrhymed trochaic:

> There they are, my fifty men and women
> Naming me the fifty poems finished!
> Take them, Love, the book and me together:
> Where the heart lies, let the brain lie also.

UNDERSTATEMENT. A figure of speech making something appear less important or true than it really is. Understatement is used to intensify meaning of a statement, as well as for the purposes of irony, sarcasm, or humor. It is the opposite of hyperbole., e.g, "Nor are thy lips ungraceful, Sire of men, / Nor tongue ineloquent."

UNITIES. The unities refer to the qualities of good plots, which possess unity of action, time, and place. Unity of action adheres to a sense of cause and effect inevitability. Unity of time adheres to the natural cycle of twenty-four hours. Unity of place adheres to consistency of location.

UNIVERSAL SYMBOL. The notion that a literary work may have some organizing principle, by virtue of its symbolism, to which all parts are related.

UNRELIABLE NARRATOR. A narrator whose judgment cannot be trusted by the reader, either because of the narrator's naivete, prejudices, emotional state, or mental age. In Eudora Welty's "Why I Live at the P.O.," for example, Sister's emotional instability, coupled with her hatred of her family, makes her an unreliable narrator.

UTOPIA. From the Greek word meaning "no place," a type of fiction that describes an ideal—or utopian—world.

VERBAL IRONY. A figure of speech in which the implied meaning of something differs from the literal meaning, such as in a sarcastic remark.

VERISIMILITUDE. Pertains to the qualities that make a work of fiction true to life. A work achieves verisimilitude when events, characters, situations, and places are plausible to the reader.

VERS LIBRE. A Latin term meaning free verse, or poetry without any consistent, fixed form or pattern.

VERSE PARAGRAPH. A verse paragraph appears in a poem lacking stanzaic form, that is, the lines are not grouped together within a regular, recurring pattern.

VILLANELLE. A nineteen-line poetic form in six stanzas. It uses only two rhymes and repeats two of its lines according to a set pattern.

VOICE. Refers to the attitude of the author as conveyed through the style or tone of the speaker in a work of literature.

WELL-MADE PLAY. A term that applies to the logical inevitability within so-called problem plays, farces, or comedies of manners.

Louisa May Alcott
[1832–1888]

Born in Germantown, Pennsylvania in 1832, LOUISA MAY ALCOTT *grew up amid the transcendentalist ferment of Concord, and Boston, Massachusetts. Daughter of Abigail May and Amos Bronson Alcott, Lousia breathed early the experimental atmosphere of the short-lived Temple School, founded in 1834 by her father with the assistance of reformer Elizabeth Peabody. The school's idealistic practices as well as its financial hardships were contributing factors in young Louisa's turn to authorship. In 1854, she published* Flower Fables, *a collection of fantasy tales written for the daughter of Ralph Waldo Emerson. Her first adult novel,* Moods *(1865) was in fact based on Emerson himself. The book borrows its title and epigraph from Emerson: "Life is a train of moods like a string of beads; and as we pass through them they prove to be many colored lenses, which paint the world their own hue."*

Throughout her career, Alcott wrote for distinct moods, painting a multiplicity of worlds in hues ranging from the sweet to the "lurid" (Alcott's own word for the style her "natural ambition" sometimes sought). Alcott's accounts of the composition process itself tend towards the sensational: "Genius burned so fiercely that for four weeks I wrote all day and planned nearly all night, being quite possessed by my work." Moods, *the product of this particular feverish possession, introduces the moody heroine, Sylvia, who confronts "her chameleon self" and learns to benefit from a changeable identity; her mutability delivers her from sorrow. "You shall be a law to yourself, brave Sylvia," a friend promises her. She thus claims a kinship with "Hester Prynne," the strong heroine of* The Scarlet Letter, *but, determined to sing in a chorus apart from the "sad sisterhood called disappointed women," Sylvia "possessed a purpose that took her out of herself and proved her salvation." Another highly autobiographical book,* Work *(1873), again focuses on a heroine who sheds serial identities.* Little Women *(1868, part 1; 1869, part 2), arguably the most beloved book in all of American literature, contains within it a record of Alcott's ability to shift authorial selves: "She took to writing sensation stories, for in those dark ages, even all-perfect America read rubbish." The editor of the "Weekly Volcano" knowingly informs heroine Jo March that "People want to be amused, not preached at, you know. Morals don't sell nowadays." Alcott's even more knowing narrator judiciously adds, "Which was not quite a correct statement, by the way." This started her on a path to a prolific wasting which included her acclaim and financial security. She supplemented her income with Gothic, sensational short stories, printed in various periodicals between 1858 and 1869. Alcott enjoyed financial success with both the sensational and the wholesome (and in realistic accounts of healing, for that matter) in* Hospital Sketches *(1863),* which draws upon her experiences as a nurse to Union soldiers in 1862. For her sensational tales, mostly written between 1858 and 1869, Alcott relied on anonymity, and sometimes used the pseudonym A. M. Barnard. The energetic literary detective work of Madeleine Stern has, since the 1970s, made this "alternative Alcott" increasingly available—and appreciated. Alcott's wholesome vector extended through the best-selling Little Men (1871) to her final work, Jo's Boys (1886).

—Martin Kevorkian, *University of Texas, Austin*

Actress

LOUISA MAY ALCOTT

FEELING THAT SHE HAD all the world before her where to choose,[1] and that her next step ought to take her up at least one round higher on the ladder she was climbing, Christie decided not to try going out to service again. She knew very well that she would never live with Irish mates, and could not expect to find another Hepsey[2]. So she tried to get a place as companion to an invalid, but failed to secure the only situation of the sort that was offered her, because she mildly objected to waiting on a nervous cripple all day, and reading aloud half the night. The old lady called her an "impertinent baggage," and Christie retired in great disgust, resolving not to be a slave to anybody.

Things seldom turn out as we plan them, and after much waiting and hoping for other work Christie at last accepted about the only employment which had not entered her mind.

Among the boarders at Mrs. Flint's were an old lady and her pretty daughter, both actresses at a respectable theatre. Not stars by any means, but good second-rate players, doing their work creditably and earning an honest living. The mother had been kind to Christie in offering advice, and sympathizing with her disappointments. The daughter, a gay little lass, had taken Christie to the theatre several times, there to behold her in all the gauzy glories that surround the nymphs of spectacular romance.

To Christie this was a great delight, for, though she had pored over her father's Shakespeare till she knew many scenes by heart, she had never seen a play till Lucy led her into what seemed an enchanted world. Her interest and admiration pleased the little actress, and sundry lifts when she was hurried with her dresses made her grateful to Christie.

---

[1]See the final lines of John Milton's *Paradise Lost* (1667): "The World was all before them, where to choose / Their place of rest, and Providence their guide: / They hand in hand with wand'ring steps and slow, / Through Eden took their solitary way" (XII: 656-49).

[2]Hepsey is a character that appears in the previous chapter of *Work*, an African-American runaway slave who serves as a cook and befriends Christie.

First published in *Work: A Story of Experience*, Chapter 3 by the Roberts Brothers in 1873.

The girl's despondent face, as she came in day after day from her unsuccessful quest, told its own story, though she uttered no complaint, and these friendly souls laid their heads together, eager to help her in their own dramatic fashion.

"I've got it! I've got it! All hail to the queen!" was the cry that one day startled Christie as she sat thinking anxiously, while sewing mock-pearls on a crown for Mrs. Black.

Looking up she saw Lucy just home from rehearsal, going through a series of pantomimic evolutions suggestive of a warrior doing battle with incredible valor, and a very limited knowledge of the noble art of self-defence.

"What have you got? Who is the queen?" she asked, laughing, as the breathless hero lowered her umbrella, and laid her bonnet at Christie's feet.

"*You* are to be the Queen of the Amazons in our new spectacle, at half a dollar a night for six or eight weeks, if the piece goes well."

"No!" cried Christie, with a gasp.

"Yes!" cried Lucy, clapping her hands; and then she proceeded to tell her news with theatrical volubility. "Mr. Sharp, the manager, wants a lot of tallish girls, and I told him I knew of a perfect dear. He said: 'Bring her on, then,' and I flew home to tell you. Now, don't look wild, and say no. You've only got to sing in one chorus, march in the grand procession, and lead your band in the terrific battle-scene. The dress is splendid! Red tunic, tiger-skin over shoulder, helmet, shield, lance, fleshings, sandals, hair down, and as much cork to your eyebrows as you like."

Christie certainly did look wild, for Lucy had burst into the room like a small hurricane, and her rapid words rattled about the listeners' ears as if a hail-storm had followed the gust. While Christie still sat with her mouth open, too bewildered to reply, Mrs. Black said in her cosey voice:

"Try it, me dear, it's just what you'll enjoy, and a capital beginning I assure ye; for if you do well old Sharp will want you again, and then, when some one slips out of the company, you can slip in, and there you are quite comfortable. Try it, me dear, and if you don't like it drop it when the piece is over, and there's no harm done."

"It's much easier and jollier than any of the things you are after. We'll stand by you like bricks, and in a week you'll say it's the best lark you ever had in your life. Don't be prim, now, but say yes, like a trump, as you are," added Lucy, waving a pink satin train temptingly before her friend.

"I will try it!" said Christie, with sudden decision, feeling that something entirely new and absorbing was what she needed to expend the vigor, romance, and enthusiasm of her youth upon.

With a shriek of delight Lucy swept her off her chair, and twirled her about the room as excitable young ladies are fond of doing when their joyful emotions need a vent. When both were giddy they subsided into a corner and a breathless discussion of the important step.

Though she had consented, Christie had endless doubts and fears, but Lucy removed many of the former, and her own desire for pleasant employment conquered many of the latter. In her most despairing moods she had never thought of trying this. Uncle Enos considered "play-actin' " as the sum of all iniquity. What would he say if she went calmly to destruction by that road? Sad to relate, this recollection rather strengthened her purpose, for a delicious sense of freedom pervaded her soul, and the old defiant spirit seemed to rise up within her at the memory of her Uncle's grim prophecies and narrow views.

"Lucy is happy, virtuous, and independent, why can't I be so too if I have any talent? It isn't exactly what I should choose, but any thing honest is better than idleness. I'll try it any way, and get a little fun, even if I don't make much money or glory out of it."

So Christie held to her resolution in spite of many secret misgivings, and followed Mrs. Black's advice on all points with a docility which caused that sanguine lady to predict that she would be a star before she knew where she was.

"Is this the stage? How dusty and dull it is by daylight!" said Christie next day, as she stood by Lucy on the very spot where she had seen Hamlet die in great anguish two nights before.

"Bless you, child, it's in curl-papers now, as I am of a morning. Mr. Sharp, here's an Amazon for you."

As she spoke, Lucy hurried across the stage, followed by Christie, wearing any thing but an Amazonian expression just then.

"Ever on before?" abruptly asked a keen-faced, little man, glancing with an experienced eye at the young person who stood before him bathed in blushes.

"No, sir."

"Do you sing?"

"A little, sir."

"Dance, of course?"

"Yes, sir."

"Just take a turn across the stage, will you? Must walk well to lead a march."

As she went, Christie heard Mr. Sharp taking notes audibly:

"Good tread; capital figure; fine eye. She'll make up well, and behave herself, I fancy."

A strong desire to make off seized the girl; but, remembering that she had presented herself for inspection, she controlled the impulse, and returned to him with no demonstration of displeasure, but a little more fire in "the fine eye," and a more erect carriage of the "capital figure."

"All right, my dear. Give your name to Mr. Tripp, and your mind to the business, and consider yourself engaged,"—with which satisfactory remark the little man vanished like a ghost.

"Lucy, did you hear that impertinent 'my dear'?" asked Christie, whose sense of propriety had received its first shock.

"Lord, child, all managers do it. They don't mean any thing; so be resigned, and thank your stars he didn't say 'love' and 'darling,' and kiss you, as old Vining used to," was all the sympathy she got.

Having obeyed orders, Lucy initiated her into the mysteries of the place, and then put her in a corner to look over the scenes in which she was to appear. Christie soon caught the idea of her part,—not a difficult matter, as there were but few ideas in the whole piece, after which she sat watching the arrival of the troop she was to lead. A most forlorn band of warriors they seemed, huddled together, and looking as if afraid to speak, lest they should infringe some rule; or to move, lest they be swallowed up by some unsuspected trap-door.

Presently the ballet-master appeared, the orchestra struck up, and Christie found herself marching and counter-marching at word of command. At first, a most uncomfortable sense of the absurdity of her position oppressed and confused her; then the ludicrous contrast between the solemn anxiety of the troop and the fantastic evolutions they were performing amused her till the novelty wore off; the martial music excited her; the desire to please sharpened her wits; and natural grace made it easy for her to catch and copy the steps and poses given her to imitate. Soon she forgot herself, entered into the spirit of the thing, and exerted every sense to please, so successfully that Mr. Tripp praised her quickness at comprehension, Lucy applauded heartily from a fairy car, and Mr. Sharp popped his head out of a palace window to watch the Amazon's descent from the Mountains of the Moon.

When the regular company arrived, the troop was dismissed till the progress of the play demanded their reappearance. Much interested in the piece, Christie stood aside under a palm-tree, the foliage of which was strongly suggestive of a dilapidated green umbrella, enjoying the novel sights and sounds about her.

Yellow-faced gentlemen and sleepy-eyed ladies roamed languidly about with much incoherent jabbering of parts, and frequent explosions of laughter. Princes, with varnished boots and suppressed cigars, fought, bled, and died, without a change of countenance. Damsels of unparalleled beauty, according to the text, gaped in the faces of adoring lovers, and crocheted serenely on the brink of annihilation. Fairies, in rubber-boots and woollen head-gear, disported themselves on flowery barks of canvas, or were suspended aloft with hooks in their backs like young Hindoo devotees. Demons, guiltless of hoof or horn, clutched their victims with the inevitable "Ha! ha!" and vanished darkly, eating pea-nuts. The ubiquitous Mr. Sharp seemed to pervade the whole theatre; for his voice came shrilly from above or spectrally from below, and his active little figure darted to and fro like a critical will-o-the-wisp.

The grand march and chorus in the closing scene were easily accomplished; for, as Lucy bade her, Christie "sung with all her might," and kept step as she led her band with the dignity of a Boadicea.[3] No one spoke to her; few observed her; all were intent on their own affairs; and when the final shriek and bang died away without lifting the roof by its din, she could hardly believe that the dreaded first rehearsal was safely over.

A visit to the wardrobe-room to see her dress came next; and here Christie had a slight skirmish with the mistress of that department relative to the length of her classical garments. As studies from the nude had not yet become one of the amusements of the *élite* of Little Babel, Christie was not required to appear in the severe simplicity of a costume consisting of a necklace, sandals, and a bit of gold fringe about the waist, but was allowed an extra inch or two on her tunic, and departed, much comforted by the assurance that her dress would not be "a shock to modesty," as Lucy expressed it.

"Now, look at yourself, and, for my sake, prove an honor to your country and a terror to the foe," said Lucy, as she led her *protégée* before the greenroom mirror on the first night of "The Demon's Daughter, or The Castle of the Sun!! The most Magnificent Spectacle ever produced upon the American Stage!!!"

Christie looked, and saw a warlike figure with glittering helmet, shield and lance, streaming hair and savage cloak. She liked the picture, for there was much of the heroic spirit in the girl, and even this poor counterfeit pleased her eye and filled her fancy with martial memories of Joan of Arc, Zenobia, and Britomarte.[4]

"Go to!" cried Lucy, who affected theatrical modes of speech. "Don't admire yourself any longer, but tie up your sandals and come on. Be sure you rush down the instant I cry, 'Demon, I defy thee!' Don't break your neck, or pick your way like a cat in wet weather, but come *with effect*, for I want that scene to make a hit."

---

[3]British queen who led an unsuccessful rebellion against the Romans in 60 or 61 C.E.

[4]Claiming divine inspiration, Joan of Arc (1412–1431) led French forces against the British in the Hundred Years War. She was later captured, condemned, and executed by British sympathizers in France. Zenobia was a third century queen of Palmyra. Britomarte is a fictional character—a female knight in Edmund Spenser's *The Faerie Queen* (1590).

Princess Caremfil swept away, and the Amazonian queen climbed to her perch among the painted mountains, where her troop already sat like a flock of pigeons shining in the sun. The gilded breast-plate rose and fell with the quick beating of her heart, the spear shook with the trembling of her hand, her lips were dry, her head dizzy, and more than once, as she waited for her cue, she was sorely tempted to run away and take the consequences.

But the thought of Lucy's good-will and confidence kept her, and when the cry came she answered with a ringing shout, rushed down the ten-foot precipice, and charged upon the foe with an energy that inspired her followers, and quite satisfied the princess struggling in the demon's grasp.

With clashing of arms and shrill war-cries the rescuers of innocence assailed the sooty fiends who fell before their unscientific blows with a rapidity which inspired in the minds of beholders a suspicion that the goblins' own voluminous tails tripped them up and gallantry kept them prostrate. As the last groan expired, the last agonized squirm subsided, the conquerors performed the intricate dance with which it appears the Amazons were wont to celebrate their victories. Then the scene closed with a glare of red light and a "grand tableau" of the martial queen standing in a bower of lances, the rescued princess gracefully fainting in her arms, and the vanquished demon scowling fiercely under her foot, while four-and-twenty dishevelled damsels sang a song of exultation, to the barbaric music of a tattoo on their shields.

All went well that night, and when at last the girls doffed crown and helmet, they confided to one another the firm opinion that the success of the piece was in a great measure owing to their talent, their exertions, and went gaily home predicting for themselves careers as brilliant as those of Siddons and Rachel.[5]

It would be a pleasant task to paint the vicissitudes and victories of a successful actress; but Christie was no dramatic genius born to shine before the world and leave a name behind her. She had no talent except that which may be developed in any girl possessing the lively fancy, sympathetic nature, and ambitious spirit which make such girls naturally dramatic. This was to be only one of many experiences which were to show her her own weakness and strength, and through effort, pain, and disappointment fit her to play a nobler part on a wider stage.

For a few weeks Christie's illusions lasted; then she discovered that the new life was nearly as humdrum as the old, that her companions were ordinary men and women, and her bright hopes were growing as dim as her tarnished shield. She grew unutterably weary of "The Castle of the Sun," and

---

[5]Actresses Sarah Kemble Siddons (1755–1831) and Mlle. Rachel (stage name of Elisa Felix (1820–1848).

found the "Demon's Daughter" an unmitigated bore. She was not tired of the profession, only dissatisfied with the place she held in it, and eager to attempt a part that gave some scope for power and passion.

Mrs. Black wisely reminded her that she must learn to use her wings before she tried to fly, and comforted her with stories of celebrities who had begun as she was beginning, yet who had suddenly burst from their grub-like obscurity to adorn the world as splendid butterflies.

"We'll stand by you, Kit; so keep up your courage, and do your best. Be clever to every one in general, old Sharp in particular, and when a chance comes, have your wits about you and grab it. That's the way to get on," said Lucy, as sagely as if she had been a star for years.

"If I had beauty I should stand a better chance," sighed Christie, surveying herself with great disfavor, quite unconscious that to a cultivated eye the soul of beauty was often visible in that face of hers, with its intelligent eyes, sensitive mouth, and fine lines about the forehead, making it a far more significant and attractive countenance than that of her friend, possessing only piquant prettiness.

"Never mind, child; you've got a lovely figure, and an actress's best feature,—fine eyes and eyebrows. I heard old Kent say so, and he's a judge. So make the best of what you've got, as I do," answered Lucy, glancing at her own comely little person with an air of perfect resignation.

Christie laughed at the adviser, but wisely took the advice, and though she fretted in private, was cheerful and alert in public. Always modest, attentive, and obliging, she soon became a favorite with her mates, and, thanks to Lucy's good offices with Mr. Sharp, whose favorite she was, Christie got promoted sooner than she otherwise would have been.

A great Christmas spectacle was brought out the next season, and Christie had a good part in it. When that was over she thought there was no hope for her, as the regular company was full and a different sort of performance was to begin. But just then her chance came, and she "grabbed it." The first soubrette[6] died suddenly, and in the emergency Mr. Sharp offered the place to Christie till he could fill it to his mind. Lucy was second soubrette, and had hoped for this promotion; but Lucy did not sing well. Christie had a good voice, had taken lessons and much improved of late, so she had the preference and resolved to stand the test so well that this temporary elevation should become permanent.

She did her best, and though many of the parts were distasteful to her she got through them successfully, while now and then she had one which she thoroughly enjoyed. Her Tilly Slowboy[7] was a hit, and a proud girl was

---

[6]In dramatic comedy, the stock character of a young flirtatious maid.

[7]A children's nurse in *The Cricket on the Heath* (1845) by Charles Dickens.

Christie when Kent, the comedian, congratulated her on it, and told her he had seldom seen it better done.

To find favor in Kent's eyes was an honor indeed, for he belonged to the old school, and rarely condescended to praise modern actors. His own style was so admirable that he was justly considered the first comedian in the country, and was the pride and mainstay of the old theatre where he had played for years. Of course he possessed much influence in that little world, and being a kindly man used it generously to help up any young aspirant who seemed to him deserving.

He had observed Christie, attracted by her intelligent face and modest manners, for in spite of her youth there was a native refinement about her that made it impossible for her to romp and flirt as some of her mates did. But till she played Tilly he had not thought she possessed any talent. That pleased him, and seeing how much she valued his praise, and was flattered by his notice, he gave her the wise but unpalatable advice always offered young actors. Finding that she accepted it, was willing to study hard, work faithfully, and wait patiently, he predicted that in time she would make a clever actress, never a great one.

Of course Christie thought he was mistaken, and secretly resolved to prove him a false prophet by the triumphs of her career. But she meekly bowed to his opinion; this docility pleased him, and he took a paternal sort of interest in her, which, coming from the powerful favorite, did her good service with the higher powers, and helped her on more rapidly than years of meritorious effort.

Toward the end of that second season several of Dickens's dramatized novels were played, and Christie earned fresh laurels. She loved those books, and seemed by instinct to understand and personate the humor and pathos of many of those grotesque creations. Believing she had little beauty to sacrifice, she dressed such parts to the life, and played them with a spirit and ease that surprised those who had considered her a dignified and rather dull young person.

"I'll tell you what it is, Sharp, that girl is going to make a capital character actress. When her parts suit, she forgets herself entirely and does admirably well. Her Miggs[8] was nearly the death of me to-night. She's got that one gift, and it's a good one. You'd better give her a chance, for I think she'll be a credit to the old concern."

Kent said that,—Christie heard it, and flew to Lucy, waving Miggs's cap for joy as she told the news.

---

[8]A minor character in Dickens's novel *Barnaby Rudge* (1841).

"What did Mr. Sharp say?" asked Lucy, turning round with her face half "made-up."

"He merely said 'Hum,' and smiled. Wasn't that a good sign?" said Christie, anxiously.

"Can't say," and Lucy touched up her eyebrows as if she took no interest in the affair.

Christie's face fell, and her heart sunk at the thought of failure; but she kept up her spirits by working harder than ever, and soon had her reward. Mr. Sharp's "Hum" did mean yes, and the next season she was regularly engaged, with a salary of thirty dollars a week.

It was a grand step, and knowing that she owed it to Kent, Christie did her utmost to show that she deserved his good opinion. New trials and temptations beset her now, but hard work and an innocent nature kept her safe and busy. Obstacles only spurred her on to redoubled exertion, and whether she did well or ill, was praised or blamed, she found a never-failing excitement in her attempts to reach the standard of perfection she had set up for herself. Kent did not regret his patronage. Mr. Sharp was satisfied with the success of the experiment, and Christie soon became a favorite in a small way, because behind the actress the public always saw a woman who never "forgot the modesty of nature."

But as she grew prosperous in outward things, Christie found herself burdened with a private cross that tried her very much. Lucy was no longer her friend; something had come between them, and a steadily increasing coldness took the place of the confidence and affection which had once existed. Lucy was jealous for Christie had passed her in the race. She knew she could not fill the place Christie had gained by favor, and now held by her own exertions, still she was bitterly envious, though ashamed to own it.

Christie tried to be just and gentle, to prove her gratitude to her first friend, and to show that her heart was unchanged. But she failed to win Lucy back and felt herself injured by such unjust resentment. Mrs. Black took her daughter's part, and though they preserved the peace outwardly the old friendliness was quite gone.

Hoping to forget this trouble in excitement Christie gave herself entirely to her profession, finding in it a satisfaction which for a time consoled her.

But gradually she underwent the sorrowful change which comes to strong natures when they wrong themselves through ignorance or wilfulness.

Pride and native integrity kept her from the worst temptations of such a life, but to the lesser ones she yielded, growing selfish, frivolous, and vain,— intent on her own advancement, and careless by what means she reached it. She had no thought now beyond her art, no desire beyond the commendation of those whose opinion was serviceable, no care for any one but herself.

Her love of admiration grew by what it fed on, till the sound of applause became the sweetest music to her ear. She rose with this hope, lay down with this satisfaction, and month after month passed in this feverish life, with no wish to change it, but a growing appetite for its unsatisfactory delights, an ever-increasing forgetfulness of any higher aspiration than dramatic fame.

"Give me joy, Lucy, I'm to have a benefit next week! Everybody else has had one, and I've played for them all, so no one seemed to begrudge me my turn when dear old Kent proposed it," said Christie, coming in one night still flushed and excited with the good news.

"What shall you have?" asked Lucy, trying to look pleased, and failing decidedly.

" 'Masks and Faces.'[9] I've always wanted to play Peg, and it has good parts for you and Kent, and St. George. I chose it for that reason, for I shall need all the help I can get to pull me through, I dare say."

The smile vanished entirely at this speech, and Christie was suddenly seized with a suspicion that Lucy was not only jealous of her as an actress, but as a woman. St. George was a comely young actor who usually played lovers' parts with Christie, and played them very well, too, being possessed of much talent, and a gentleman. They had never thought of falling in love with each other, though St. George wooed and won Christie night after night in vaudeville and farce. But it was very easy to imagine that so much mock passion had a basis of truth, and Lucy evidently tormented herself with this belief.

"Why didn't you choose Juliet: St. George would do Romeo so well?" said Lucy, with a sneer.

"No, that is beyond me. Kent says Shakespeare will never be my line, and I believe him. I should think you'd be satisfied with 'Masks and Faces,' for you know Mabel gets her husband safely back in the end," answered Christie, watching the effect of her words.

"As if I wanted the man! No, thank you, other people's leavings won't suit me," cried Lucy, tossing her head, though her face belied her words.

"Not even though he has 'heavenly eyes,' 'distracting legs,' and 'a melting voice?' " asked Christie maliciously, quoting Lucy's own rapturous speeches when the new actor came.

"Come, come, girls, don't quarrel. I won't 'ave it in me room. Lucy's tired to death, and it's not nice of you, Kitty, to come and crow over her this way," said Mamma Black, coming to the rescue, for Lucy was in tears, and Christie looking dangerous.

---

[9]This 1852 play by Charles Reade concerns Irish actress and impressionist Margaret Woffington (1718–1760).

"It's impossible to please you, so I'll say good-night," and Christie went to her room with resentment burning hotly in her heart.

As she crossed the chamber her eye fell on her own figure reflected in the long glass, and with a sudden impulse she turned up the gas, wiped the rouge from her cheeks, pushed back her hair, and studied her own face intently for several moments. It was pale and jaded now, and all its freshness seemed gone; hard lines had come about the mouth, a feverish disquiet filled the eyes, and on the forehead seemed to lie the shadow of a discontent that saddened the whole face. If one could believe the testimony of that countenance things were not going well with Christie, and she owned it with a regretful sigh, as she asked herself, "Am I what I hoped I should be? No, and it is my fault. If three years of this life have made me this, what shall I be in ten? A fine actress perhaps, but how good a woman?"

With gloomy eyes fixed on her altered face she stood a moment struggling with herself. Then the hard look returned, and she spoke out defiantly, as if in answer to some warning voice within herself. "No one cares what I am, so why care myself? Why not go on and get as much fame as I can? Success gives me power if it cannot give me happiness, and I must have some reward for my hard work. Yes! a gay life and a short one, then out with the lights and down with the curtain!"

But in spite of her reckless words Christie sobbed herself to sleep that night like a child who knows it is astray, yet cannot see the right path or hear its mother's voice calling it home.

On the night of the benefit, Lucy was in a most exasperating mood, Christie in a very indignant one, and as they entered their dressing-room they looked as if they might have played the Rival Queens[10] with great effect. Lucy offered no help and Christie asked none, but putting her vexation resolutely out of sight fixed her mind on the task before her.

As the pleasant stir began all about her, actress-like, she felt her spirits rise, her courage increase with every curl she fastened up, every gay garment she put on, and soon smiled approvingly at herself, for excitement lent her cheeks a better color than rouge, her eyes shone with satisfaction, and her heart beat high with the resolve to make a hit or die.

Christie needed encouragement that night, and found it in the hearty welcome that greeted her, and the full house, which proved how kind a regard was entertained for her by many who knew her only by a fictitious name. She felt this deeply, and it helped her much, for she was vexed with many trials those before the footlights knew nothing of.

---

[10]Allusion to Nathaniel Lee's *Alexander the Great, or, The Rival Queen* (1678), a play about murderous strife between the Alexander's wives.

The other players were full of kindly interest in her success, but Lucy took a naughty satisfaction in harassing her by all the small slights and unanswerable provocations which one actress has it in her power to inflict upon another.

Christie was fretted almost beyond endurance, and retaliated by an ominous frown when her position allowed, threatening asides when a moment's by-play favored their delivery, and angry protests whenever she met Lucy off the stage.

But in spite of all annoyances she had never played better in her life. She liked the part, and acted the warm-hearted, quick-witted, sharp-tongued Peg with a spirit and grace that surprised even those who knew her best. Especially good was she in the scenes with Triplet, for Kent played the part admirably, and cheered her on with many an encouraging look and word. Anxious to do honor to her patron and friend she threw her whole heart into the work; in the scene where she comes like a good angel to the home of the poor playwright, she brought tears to the eyes of her audience; and when at her command Triplet strikes up a jig to amuse the children she "covered the buckle" in gallant style, dancing with all the frolicsome *abandon* of the Irish orange-girl who for a moment forgot her grandeur and her grief.

That scene was her best, for it is full of those touches of nature that need very little art to make them effective; and when a great bouquet fell with a thump at Christie's feet, as she paused to bow her thanks for an encore, she felt that she had reached the height of earthly bliss.

In the studio scene Lucy seemed suddenly gifted with unsuspected skill; for when Mabel kneels to the picture, praying her rival to give her back her husband's heart, Christie was amazed to see real tears roll down Lucy's cheeks, and to hear real love and longing thrill her trembling words with sudden power and passion.

"That is not acting. She does love St. George, and thinks I mean to keep him from her. Poor dear! I'll tell her all about it to-night, and set her heart at rest," thought Christie; and when Peg left the frame, her face expressed the genuine pity that she felt, and her voice was beautifully tender as she promised to restore the stolen treasure.

Lucy felt comforted without knowing why, and the piece went smoothly on to its last scene. Peg was just relinquishing the repentant husband to his forgiving wife with those brave words of hers, when a rending sound above their heads made all look up and start back; all but Lucy, who stood bewildered. Christie's quick eye saw the impending danger, and with a sudden spring she caught her friend from it. It was only a second's work, but it cost her much; for in the act, down crashed one of the mechanical contrivances used in a late spectacle, and in its fall stretched Christie stunned and senseless on the stage.

A swift uprising filled the house with tumult; a crowd of actors hurried forward, and the panic-stricken audience caught glimpses of poor Peg lying mute and pallid in Mabel's arms, while Vane wrung his hands, and Triplet audibly demanded, "Why the devil somebody didn't go for a doctor?"

Then a brilliant view of Mount Parnassus,[11] with Apollo and the Nine Muses in full blast, shut the scene from sight, and soon Mr. Sharp appeared to ask their patience till the after-piece was ready, for Miss Douglas was too much injured to appear again. And with an unwonted expression of feeling, the little man alluded to "the generous act which perhaps had changed the comedy to a tragedy and robbed the beneficiary of her well-earned reward at their hands."

All had seen the impulsive spring toward, not from, the danger, and this unpremeditated action won heartier applause than Christie ever had received for her best rendering of more heroic deeds.

But she did not hear the cordial round they gave her. She had said she would "make a hit or die;" and just then it seemed as if she had done both, for she was deaf and blind to the admiration and the sympathy bestowed upon her as the curtain fell on the first, last benefit she ever was to have.

[1873]

---

[11]In Greek mythology, Mount Parnassus is the home of the Muses and the god Apollo.

Amiri Baraka
[1934–   ]

AMIRI BARAKA *was born LeRoi Jones in Newark, New Jersey. After attending Howard University, he served in the United States Air Force. In the 1950s, Baraka began his poetic career in association with the literary avant-garde of the period. He lived in Greenwich Village during the late fifties, associating with Beat poets such as Allen Ginsberg and Frank O'Hara. He was also influenced by Charles Olson, the leader of an experimental group of poets and artists working at Black Mountain College. At this time, he believed that poetry should seek its own form, and rejected traditional forms such as the sonnet or the sestina. His play,* Dutchman, *won an Obie award in 1964, which brought him national recognition.*

After the assassination of Malcolm X in 1965, Jones became a Black Nationalist, moving to Harlem and ending his association with white culture. His book Black Magic, *published in 1967, emblematized his break and subsequent powerful identification with blackness, and black people as "a race, a culture, a Nation." He established the Black Repertory Theater Arts School in Harlem. After nearly ten years of this association, Baraka reversed his position and declared himself a Third-World Marxist, rejecting the ideas of black separatism and violence against whites and white institutions. Rather, he came to believe in the destruction of the capitalist state and the institution of a socialist community; he defended art as "a weapon of revolution." His work during this period, after 1974, included* Hard Facts, Poetry for the Advanced, *and* What Was the Relationship of the Lone Ranger and the Means of Production? *Profoundly revisionist of dominant cultural forms, Baraka has sought throughout his career to write in such a way that readers can find the means, through language, to envision an alternative to social arrangements as they are—an artistic practice the author has called revolutionary.*

Ka 'Ba

AMIRI BARAKA

A closed window looks down
on a dirty courtyard, and black people
call across or scream across or walk across
defying physics in the stream of their will
Our world is full of sound   5
Our world is more lovely than anyone's
tho we suffer, and kill each other
and sometimes fail to walk the air

We are beautiful people
with african imaginations   10
full of masks and dances and swelling chants
with african eyes, and noses, and arms,
though we sprawl in grey chains in a place
full of winters, when what we want is sun.
We have been captured,   15
brothers. And we labor
to make our getaway, into
the ancient image, into a new

correspondence with ourselves
and our black family. We need magic   20
now we need the spells, to raise up
return, destroy, and create. What will be

the sacred words?

[1969]

Reprinted from *Black Magic Poetry*, by permission of Sterling Lord Literistic. Copyright
© 1969 by Amiri Baraka.

Elizabeth Bishop
[1911–1979]

ELIZABETH BISHOP *was born in Worcester, Massachusetts. Before her first birthday, her father died, and by the time she was five, her mother had been committed to a mental hospital, after a series of nervous collapses. Elizabeth was raised by her mother's family in Great Village, Nova Scotia until she was six, after which her father's family, who lived in Worcester and Boston, took her in. She attended Vassar; through a connection with the Vassar librarian, she met the poet Marianne Moore, twenty-four years her senior, and they became lifelong friends. Moore's was the first of many literary friendships for Bishop—she had a lasting friendship with Robert Lowell, and she had acquaintances and admirers such as Randall Jarrell, Donald Hall, James Merrill, and many others in the literary world.*

Bishop's earliest publications were in the Vassar undergraduate magazine, which she helped to found, along with novelist Mary McCarthy and others. Moore also published several of Bishop's poems in an anthology called Trial Balances *in 1935. She worked slowly; some of poems, such as "The Map" and "The Man-Moth," written when she lived in New York in 1936, did not see publication until her first volume,* North and South, *came out in 1946. A second volume,* A Cold Spring, *was published in 1955—this book won the Pulitzer Prize in 1956. In the intervening years, she lived in both Europe and Key West, Florida. In 1951, she began a long residency of about eighteen years in Brazil, with her lover Lota de Macedo Soares; she lived in Rio de Janeiro and, later, Ouro Prêto. Many poems in* Questions of Travel *(1965) take as their subject matter these years in Brazil.*

In 1967, Soares died of an overdose of tranquilizers, a loss that was devastating to Bishop, but she persisted to write and publish. A volume titled Complete Poems *was published in 1969, which included all her previously published poems as well as several new pieces; this book won the National Book Award of 1970. She accepted a teaching position at Harvard, where she taught for several years. Her last collection,* Geography III, *was published in 1976, and won the Book Critics Circle Award for 1977. She was at work on another volume, tentatively titled "Grandmother's Glass Eye," along with a book-length poem,* Elegy, *when she died in 1979. Four poems that were to be a part of the new collection—"Santarem," "North Haven," "Pink Dog," and "Sonnet"—were finished at that point; these poems were included in* The Complete Poems, 1927–1979, *published in 1983.*

Bishop's poems are cherished by generations of readers for their fresh, unstudied diction and their directness and warmth. Reviewing Geography III, *poet Alfred Corn noted that Bishop's work exhibited "a radiant patience few people ever achieve and few writers ever successfully render. The poems are works of philosophic beauty and calm, illuminated by that 'laughter in the soul' that belongs to the best part of the comic genius." James Merrill noted in his review of the posthumous* The Complete Poems 1927–1979 *that most of Bishop's poems are in the first person, and often that "I" is someone else—"the Riverman, or Robinson Crusoe." Merrill goes on to remark that "because [Bishop] is to no least degree concerned with making herself any more remarkable than, as the author of these poems, she already is, hers is a purified, transparent 'I,' which readers may take as their virtual own." These remarks suggest something of the high critical esteem in which Bishop's work is held, but also the reason why so many readers treasure the poems—for their playfulness, their matter-of-factness, their modesty, and for the marvels they introduce.*

Exchanging Hats

ELIZABETH BISHOP

Unfunny uncles who insist
in trying on a lady's hat,
—oh, even if the joke falls flat,
we share your slight transvestite twist

in spite of our embarrassment.   5
Costume and custom are complex.
The headgear of the other sex
inspires us to experiment.

Anandrous aunts, who, at the beach
with paper plates upon your laps,   10
keep putting on the yachtsmen's caps
with exhibitionistic screech,

the visors hanging o'er the ear
so that the golden anchors drag,
—the tides of fashion never lag.   15
Such caps may not be worn next year.

Or you who don the paper plate
itself, and put some grapes upon it,
or sport the Indian's feather bonnet,
—perversities may aggravate   20

the natural madness of the hatter.
And if the opera hats collapse
and crowns grow draughty, then, perhaps,
he thinks what might a miter matter?

Reprinted from *The Collected Poems: 1927-1979*, by permission of Farrar, Straus and Giroux, LLC. Copyright © 1979, 1983 by Alice Helen Methfessel.

Unfunny uncle, you who wore a   25
hat too big, or one too many,
tell us, can't you, are there any
stars inside your black fedora?

Aunt exemplary and slim,
with avernal eyes, we wonder   30
what slow changes they see under
their vast, shady, turned-down brim.

[1956]

Manners

ELIZABETH BISHOP

for a Child of 1918

My grandfather said to me
as we sat on the wagon seat,
"Be sure to remember to always
speak to everyone you meet."

We met a stranger on foot.   5
My grandfather's whip tapped his hat.
"Good day, sir. Good day. A fine day."
And I said it and bowed where I sat.

Then we overtook a boy we knew
with his big pet crow on his shoulder.   10
"Always offer everyone a ride;
don't forget that when you get older,"

my grandfather said. So Willy
climbed up with us, but the crow
gave a "Caw!" and flew off. I was worried.   15
How would he know where to go?

But he flew a little way at a time
from fence post to fence post, ahead;
and when Willy whistled he answered.
"A fine bird," my grandfather said,   20

"and he's well brought up. See, he answers
nicely when he's spoken to.
Man or beast, that's good manners.
Be sure that you both always do."

Reprinted from *The Collected Poems: 1927-1979,* by permission of Farrar, Straus and Giroux, LLC. Copyright © 1979, 1983 by Alice Helen Methfessel.

When automobiles went by,   *25*
the dust hid the people's faces,
but we shouted "Good day! Good day!
Fine day!" at the top of our voices.

When we came to Hustler Hill,
he said that the mare was tired,   *30*
so we all got down and walked,
as our good manners required.

[1965]

Poem

ELIZABETH BISHOP

About the size of an old-style dollar bill,
American or Canadian,
mostly the same whites, gray greens, and steel grays
—this little painting (a sketch for a larger one?)
has never earned any money in its life. 5
Useless and free, it has spent seventy years
as a minor family relic
handed along collaterally to owners
who looked at it sometimes, or didn't bother to.

It must be Nova Scotia; only there 10
does one see gabled wooden houses
painted that awful shade of brown.
The other houses, the bits that show, are white.
Elm trees, low hills, a thin church steeple
—that gray-blue wisp—or is it? In the foreground 15
a water meadow with some tiny cows,
two brushstrokes each, but confidently cows;
two minuscule white geese in the blue water,
back-to-back, feeding, and a slanting stick.
Up closer, a wild iris, white and yellow, 20
fresh-squiggled from the tube.
The air is fresh and cold; cold early spring
clear as gray glass; a half inch of blue sky
below the steel-gray storm clouds.
(They were the artist's specialty.) 25
A specklike bird is flying to the left.
Or is it a flyspeck looking for a bird?

Reprinted from *The Collected Poems: 1927-1979*, by permission of Farrar, Straus and Giroux, LLC. Copyright © 1979, 1983 by Alice Helen Methfessel.

Heavens, I recognize the place, I know it!
It's behind—I can almost remember the farmer's name.
His barn backed on that meadow. There it is,   30
titanium white, one dab. The hint of steeple,
filaments of brush-hairs, barely there,
must be the Presbyterian church.
Would that be Miss Gillespie's house?
Those particular geese and cows   35
are naturally before my time.
A sketch done in an hour, "in one breath,"
once taken from a trunk and handed over.
Would you like this? I'll probably never
have room to hang these things again.   40
Your Uncle George, no, mine, my Uncle George,
he'd be your great-uncle, left them all with Mother
when he went back to England.
You know, he was quite famous, an R.A. . . .

I never knew him. We both knew this place,   45
apparently, this literal small backwater,
looked at it long enough to memorize it,
our years apart. How strange. And it's still loved,
or its memory is (it must have changed a lot).
Our visions coincided—"visions" is   50
too serious a word—our looks, two looks:
art "copying from life" and life itself,
life and the memory of it so compressed
they've turned into each other. Which is which?
Life and the memory of it cramped,   55
dim, on a piece of Bristol board,
dim, but how live, how touching in detail
—the little that we get for free,
the little of our earthly trust. Not much.
About the size of our abidance   60
along with theirs: the munching cows,
the iris, crisp and shivering, the water
still standing from spring freshets,
the yet-to-be-dismantled elms, the geese.

[1976]

The Fish

ELIZABETH BISHOP

I caught a tremendous fish
and held him beside the boat
half out of water, with my hook
fast in a corner of his mouth.
He didn't fight.   5
He hadn't fought at all.
He hung a grunting weight,
battered and venerable
and homely. Here and there
his brown skin hung in strips   10
like ancient wallpaper,
and its pattern of darker brown
was like wallpaper:
shapes like full-blown roses
stained and lost through age.   15
He was speckled with barnacles,
fine rosettes of lime,
and infested
with tiny white sea-lice,
and underneath two or three   20
rags of green weed hung down.
While his gills were breathing in
the terrible oxygen
—the frightening gills,
fresh and crisp with blood,   25
that can cut so badly—
I thought of the coarse white flesh
packed in like feathers,
the big bones and the little bones,
the dramatic reds and blacks   30
of his shiny entrails,

Reprinted from *The Collected Poems: 1927-1979*, by permission of Farrar, Straus and Giroux, LLC. Copyright © 1979, 1983 by Alice Helen Methfessel.

and the pink swim-bladder
like a big peony.
I looked into his eyes
which were far larger than mine   35
but shallower, and yellowed,
the irises backed and packed
with tarnished tinfoil
seen through the lenses
of old scratched isinglass.   40
They shifted a little, but not
to return my stare.
—It was more like the tipping
of an object toward the light.
I admired his sullen face,   45
the mechanism of his jaw,
and then I saw
that from his lower lip
—if you could call it a lip—
grim, wet, and weaponlike,   50
hung five old pieces of fish-line,
or four and a wire leader
with the swivel still attached,
with all their five big hooks
grown firmly in his mouth.   55
A green line, frayed at the end
where he broke it, two heavier lines,
and a fine black thread
still crimped from the strain and snap
when it broke and he got away.   60
Like medals with their ribbons
frayed and wavering,
a five-haired beard of wisdom
trailing from his aching jaw.
I stared and stared   65
and victory filled up
the little rented boat,
from the pool of bilge
where oil had spread a rainbow
around the rusted engine   70
to the bailer rusted orange,
the sun-cracked thwarts,

the oarlocks on their strings,
the gunnels—until everything
was rainbow, rainbow, rainbow!   *75*
And I let the fish go.

[1940]

George Gordon, Lord Byron
[1788–1824]

No poet is larger than **GEORGE GORDON, LORD BYRON,** *the son of a dissolute aristocrat, mad Jack Byron, and an Aberdeen heiress, Byron received the most erratic of upbringings. His father faded from his life when he was very young, and his mother both doted on him and punished him physically and emotionally. He was sent off to school at age ten in Aberdeen but soon moved on to the best of educations at Harrow and Cambridge. He was a fine student and excellent athlete despite a malformed foot, a flaw that he resented and worked hard to overcome. He also quickly became known as a lady's man, a reputation that was to follow him most of his life. At Cambridge he published his first poems,* Hours of Idleness *(1807), which were not well reviewed in the* Edinburgh Review. *Byron struck back with* English Bards and Scotch Reviewers *(1809), the work that proclaimed him one of the great satirists of his day, a reputation that he upheld during his lifetime, and still holds. He began his grand tour of the Continent upon leaving Cambridge in 1808 and returned with the much celebrated* Childe Harold *(1812), a work that was extremely popular, for it portrayed Europe as it was in the lively days after revolution and in times of great change. He continued to write exotic poems of the Near East,* The Bride of Abydos *(1813),* The Corsair *(1814),* The Siege of Corinth *(1816), and* Parisina *(1816). The poems gave the reading world the Byronic hero and heroine, lovers who would risk all for love and adventure, characters out of an adventure movie. In 1815 he married Anne Milbanke and became father to Ada, but the marriage was soon over. Rumor had it that the marriage had broken up over Byron's half sister, Augusta Leigh, but no proof exists. The public chose to believe the worst, and Byron, angry, fled England for good.*

His travels produced more of Childe Harold *and a poetic drama,* Manfred *(1817). He is said to have had many lady loves in Venice where he lived and wrote until he met the Countess Teresa Guiccioli. He became a part of her family and moved with her around Italy, settling in Genoa in 1822. Living with her, he wrote* The Prisoner of Chillon, The Vision of Judgment, *and most significantly, his greatest work,* Don Juan. Don Juan *still amazes and delights readers, for it combines biting satire with pensive romanticism in ways that surprise and entrance readers of each generation. Byron can be alternately warm and sentimental and cold and sneering. In 1824, he joined the fight for the Greek war of liberation against the Turks, and died suddenly of a fever at the age of thirty-six. It was not required that a romantic poet die young, but it did seem to seal his reputation in the future.*

She Walks in Beauty[1]

GEORGE GORDON, LORD BYRON

1

She walks in beauty, like the night
   Of cloudless climes and starry skies;
And all that's best of dark and bright
   Meet in her aspect and her eyes:
Thus mellowed to that tender light   5
   Which heaven to gaudy day denies.

2

One shade the more, one ray the less,
   Had half impaired the nameless grace
Which waves in every raven tress,
   Or softly lightens o'er her face;
Where thoughts serenely sweet express   10
   How pure, how dear their dwelling place.

3

And on that cheek, and o'er that brow,
   So soft, so calm, yet eloquent,
The smiles that win, the tints that glow,   15
   But tell of days in goodness spent,
A mind at peace with all below,
   A heart whose love is innocent!

[1815]

---

[1]The "she" in the poem is Lady Wilmot Horton. Byron spotted her at a ball wearing black clothes for mourning.

First published in *Hebrew Melodies* in 1815.

Kate Chopin
[1851–1904]

Born in St. Louis to an Irish immigrant father and a French Creole mother,
KATE CHOPIN *enjoyed a life of wealth and privilege. During her early years she
was influenced heavily by a number of strong women; after her father's death in
1855, Kate was reared by her mother, grandmother, and great-grandmother.
Although her upbringing was conventional according to genteel Southern standards, she exhibited an independent spirit at an early age, preferring her books
and writing tablet to dancing with shallow young men. Regardless of her tastes,
at nineteen she wed a Louisiana businessman, Oscar Chopin, to whom she was
happily married for twelve years before his untimely death. A young widow with
six children, Chopin returned to St. Louis and began writing. Her first stories
were published in 1889, followed by a novel,* At Fault, *in 1890.*

Chopin gained national attention with the publication in 1894 of Bayou
Folk, *a collection of stories that featured settings and characters culled from her
years in Louisiana among French Creoles. Soon she was being compared to other
"local color" writers—writers who focus on the cultures and customs of specific
areas of the country—such as Sarah Orne Jewett and Hamlin Garland. Critics
also recognized the influence of French writer Guy de Maupassant, as well as
Americans Nathaniel Hawthorne and Walt Whitman, in Chopin's work. In 1897
a second collection,* A Night in Acadie, *was greeted with equal enthusiasm by
readers and critics alike. Both turned on the author in 1899, however, when her
novel* The Awakening *was published. Exploring the sexual and social rebellion of
protagonist Edna Pointelleir, a young wife and mother, the novel challenged
existing moral standards and shocked the public. Chopin was accused of fostering
immoral behavior with her uncritical depiction of Edna, who chooses suicide
rather than succumb to the rigid requirements of marriage and motherhood in
turn-of-the-century New Orleans. Reception of the novel was so harsh that
Chopin's publisher cancelled publication of her next volume of short stories,* A
Voice and a Vocation, *in 1899.*

Chopin was devastated by the negative response to The Awakening, *which
she considered (as do many contemporary critics) her best work. Although she
had published twenty poems, almost a hundred short stories—including children's stories, two novels, a play, and several critical essays—in a ten-year period,
she wrote very little after 1900. When she died of a brain hemorrhage at age 53,
her contributions to American literature were almost forgotten. Her reputation
was revived in 1969 with the publication of* The Complete Works of Kate
Chopin, *edited by Per Seyersted. Late twentieth-century critics recognized the
existential quality of Chopin's work, as well as her courageous social criticism,*

particularly with regard to women's lives. Chopin's women, from the peasant Calixta in "The Storm" to the middle-class Mrs. Mallard in "The Story of an Hour," exhibit an independence and vitality rarely found in late nineteenth century female characters. Chopin's prose is considered as vividly poetic as that of Hawthorne, and her characters as complex as those of Henry James. In the past several decades she has been recognized as one of the most significant writers in the American canon.

The Awakening

KATE CHOPIN

I

A GREEN AND YELLOW parrot, which hung in a cage outside the door, kept repeating over and over;

"*Allez vous-en! Allez vous-en! Sapristi!*[1] That's all right!"

He could speak a little Spanish, and also a language which nobody understood, unless it was the mocking-bird that hung on the other side of the door, whistling his fluty notes out upon the breeze with maddening persistence.

Mr. Pontellier, unable to read his newspaper with any degree of comfort, arose with an expression and an exclamation of disgust. He walked down the gallery and across the narrow "bridges" which connected the Lebrun cottages one with the other. He had been seated before the door of the main house. The parrot and the mockingbird were the property of Madame Lebrun, and they had the right to make all the noise they wished. Mr. Pontellier had the privilege of quitting their society when they ceased to be entertaining.

He stopped before the door of his own cottage, which was the fourth one from the main building and next to the last. Seating himself in a wicker rocker which was there, he once more applied himself to the task of reading the newspaper. The day was Sunday; the paper was a day old. The Sunday papers had not yet reached Grand Isle. He was already acquainted with the market reports, and he glanced restlessly over the editorials and bits of news which he had not had time to read before quitting New Orleans the day before.

Mr. Pontellier wore eye-glasses. He was a man of forty, of medium height and rather slender build; he stooped a little. His hair was brown and straight, parted on one side. His beard was neatly and closely trimmed.

Once in a while he withdrew his glance from the newspaper and looked about him. There was more noise than ever over at the house. The main building was called "the house," to distinguish it from the cottages. The chattering

---

[1]Go away! Go away! For God's sake! [All foreign terms are French.]

First published in 1899.

and whistling birds were still at it. Two young girls, the Farival twins, were playing a duet from "Zampa" upon the piano. Madame Lebrun was bustling in and out, giving orders in a high key to a yard-boy whenever she got inside the house, and directions in an equally high voice to a dining-room servant whenever she got outside. She was a fresh, pretty woman, clad always in white with elbow sleeves. Her starched skirts crinkled as she came and went. Farther down, before one of the cottages, a lady in black was walking demurely up and down, telling her beads. A good many persons of the *pension*[2] had gone over to the *Chênière Caminada* in Beaudelet's lugger to hear mass. Some young people were out under the water-oaks playing croquet. Mr. Pontellier's two children were there—sturdy little fellows of four and five. A quadroon nurse followed them about with a far-away, meditative air.

Mr. Pontellier finally lit a cigar and began to smoke, letting the paper drag idly from his hand. He fixed his gaze upon a white sunshade that was advancing at snail's pace from the beach. He could see it plainly between the gaunt trunks of the water-oaks and across the stretch of yellow camomile. The gulf looked far away, melting hazily into the blue of the horizon. The sunshade continued to approach slowly. Beneath its pink-lined shelter were his wife, Mrs. Pontellier, and young Robert Lebrun. When they reached the cottage, the two seated themselves with some appearance of fatigue upon the upper step of the porch, facing each other, each leaning against a supporting post.

"What folly! to bathe at such an hour in such heat!" exclaimed Mr. Pontellier. He himself had taken a plunge at daylight. That was why the morning seemed long to him.

"You are burnt beyond recognition," he added, looking at his wife as one looks at a valuable piece of personal property which has suffered some damage. She held up her hands, strong, shapely hands, and surveyed them critically, drawing up her lawn sleeves above the wrists. Looking at them reminded her of her rings, which she had given to her husband before leaving for the beach. She silently reached out to him, and he, understanding, took the rings from his vest pocket and dropped them into her open palm. She slipped them upon her fingers; then clasping her knees, she looked across at Robert and began to laugh. The rings sparkled upon her fingers. He sent back an answering smile.

"What is it?" asked Pontellier, looking lazily and amused from one to the other. It was some utter nonsense; some adventure out there in the water, and they both tried to relate it at once. It did not seem half so amusing when told.

---

[2]A small hotel.

They realized this, and so did Mr. Pontellier. He yawned and stretched himself. Then he got up, saying he had half a mind to go over to Klein's hotel and play a game of billiards.

"Come go along, Lebrun," he proposed to Robert. But Robert admitted quite frankly that he preferred to stay where he was and talk to Mrs. Pontellier.

"Well, send him about his business when he bores you, Edna," instructed her husband as he prepared to leave.

"Here, take the umbrella," she exclaimed, holding it out to him. He accepted the sunshade, and lifting it over his head descended the steps and walked away.

"Coming back to dinner?" his wife called after him. He halted a moment and shrugged his shoulders. He felt in his vest pocket; there was a ten-dollar bill there. He did not know; perhaps he would return for the early dinner and perhaps he would not. It all depended upon the company which he found over at Klein's and the size of "the game." He did not say this, but she understood it, and laughed, nodding good-bye to him.

Both children wanted to follow their father when they saw him starting out. He kissed them and promised to bring back bonbons and peanuts.

II

Mrs. Pontellier's eyes were quick and bright; they were a yellowish brown, about the color of her hair. She had a way of turning them swiftly upon an object and holding them there as if lost in some inward maze of contemplation or thought.

Her eyebrows were a shade darker than her hair. They were thick and almost horizontal, emphasizing the depth of her eyes. She was rather handsome than beautiful. Her face was captivating by reason of a certain frankness of expression and a contradictory subtle play of features. Her manner was engaging.

Robert rolled a cigarette. He smoked cigarettes because he could not afford cigars, he said. He had a cigar in his pocket which Mr. Pontellier had presented him with, and he was saving it for his after-dinner smoke.

This seemed quite proper and natural on his part. In coloring he was not unlike his companion. A clean-shaved face made the resemblance more pronounced than it would otherwise have been. There rested no shadow of care upon his open countenance. His eyes gathered in and reflected the light and languor of the summer day.

Mrs. Pontellier reached over for a palm-leaf fan that lay on the porch and began to fan herself, while Robert sent between his lips light puffs from his cigarette. They chatted incessantly: about the things around them; their amusing adventure out in the water—it had again assumed its entertaining aspect;

about the wind, the trees, the people who had gone to the *Chênière;* about the children playing croquet under the oaks, and the Farival twins, who were now performing the overture to "The Poet and the Peasant."

Robert talked a good deal about himself. He was very young, and did not know any better. Mrs. Pontellier talked a little about herself for the same reason. Each was interested in what the other said. Robert spoke of his intention to go to Mexico in the autumn, where fortune awaited him. He was always intending to go to Mexico, but some way never got there. Meanwhile he held on to his modest position in a mercantile house in New Orleans, where an equal familiarity with English, French and Spanish gave him no small value as a clerk and correspondent.

He was spending his summer vacation, as he always did, with his mother at Grand Isle. In former times, before Robert could remember, "the house" had been a summer luxury of the Lebruns. Now, flanked by its dozen or more cottages, which were always filled with exclusive visitors from the *"Quartier Français,"* it enabled Madame Lebrun to maintain the easy and comfortable existence which appeared to be her birthright.

Mrs. Pontellier talked about her father's Mississippi plantation and her girlhood home in the old Kentucky blue-grass country. She was an American woman, with a small infusion of French which seemed to have been lost in dilution. She read a letter from her sister, who was away in the East, and who had engaged herself to be married. Robert was interested, and wanted to know what manner of girls the sisters were, what the father was like, and how long the mother had been dead.

When Mrs. Pontellier folded the letter it was time for her to dress for the early dinner.

"I see Léonce isn't coming back," she said, with a glance in the direction whence her husband had disappeared. Robert supposed he was not, as there were a good many New Orleans club men over at Klein's.

When Mrs. Pontellier left him to enter her room, the young man descended the steps and strolled over toward the croquet players, where, during the half-hour before dinner, he amused himself with the little Pontellier children, who were very fond of him.

III

It was eleven o'clock that night when Mr. Pontellier returned from Klein's hotel. He was in an excellent humor, in high spirits, and very talkative. His entrance awoke his wife, who was in bed and fast asleep when he came in. He talked to her while he undressed, telling her anecdotes and bits of news and gossip that he had gathered during the day. From his trousers pockets he took a fistful of crumpled banknotes and a good deal of silver coin, which he piled on the bureau indiscriminately with keys, knife, handkerchief, and whatever else happened to be in his pockets. She was overcome with sleep, and answered him with little half utterances.

He thought it very discouraging that his wife, who was the sole object of his existence, evinced so little interest in things which concerned him, and valued so little his conversation.

Mr. Pontellier had forgotten the bonbons and peanuts for the boys. Notwithstanding he loved them very much, and went into the adjoining room where they slept to take a look at them and make sure that they were resting comfortably. The result of his investigation was far from satisfactory. He turned and shifted the youngsters about in bed. One of them began to kick and talk about a basket full of crabs.

Mr. Pontellier returned to his wife with the information that Raoul had a high fever and needed looking after. Then he lit a cigar and went and sat near the open door to smoke it.

Mrs. Pontellier was quite sure Raoul had no fever. He had gone to bed perfectly well, she said, and nothing had ailed him all day. Mr. Pontellier was too well acquainted with fever symptoms to be mistaken. He assured her the child was consuming[3] at that moment in the next room.

He reproached his wife with her inattention, her habitual neglect of the children. If it was not a mother's place to look after children, whose on earth was it? He himself had his hands full with his brokerage business. He could not be in two places at once; making a living for his family on the street, and staying at home to see that no harm befell them. He talked in a monotonous, insistent way.

Mrs. Pontellier sprang out of bed and went into the next room. She soon came back and sat on the edge of the bed, leaning her head down on the pillow. She said nothing, and refused to answer her husband when he questioned her. When his cigar was smoked out he went to bed, and in half a minute he was fast asleep.

Mrs. Pontellier was by that time thoroughly awake. She began to cry a little, and wiped her eyes on the sleeve of her *peignoir*.[4] Blowing out the candle, which her husband had left burning, she slipped her bare feet into a pair of satin *mules* at the foot of the bed and went out on the porch, where she sat down in the wicker chair and began to rock gently to and fro.

It was then past midnight. The cottages were all dark. A single faint light gleamed out from the hallway of the house. There was no sound abroad except

---

[3]Being consumed by fever.

[4]A light, loose dressing gown worn by women.

the hooting of an old owl in the top of a water-oak, and the everlasting voice of the sea, that was not uplifted at that soft hour. It broke like a mournful lullaby upon the night.

The tears came so fast to Mrs. Pontellier's eyes that the damp sleeve of her *peignoir* no longer served to dry them. She was holding the back of her chair with one hand; her loose sleeve had slipped almost to the shoulder of her uplifted arm. Turning, she thrust her face, steaming and wet, into the bend of her arm, and she went on crying there, not caring any longer to dry her face, her eyes, her arms. She could not have told why she was crying. Such experiences as the foregoing were not uncommon in her married life. They seemed never before to have weighed much against the abundance of her husband's kindness and a uniform devotion which had come to be tacit and self-understood.

An indescribable oppression, which seemed to generate in some unfamiliar part of her consciousness, filled her whole being with a vague anguish. It was like a shadow, like a mist passing across her soul's summer day. It was strange and unfamiliar; it was a mood. She did not sit there in-wardly upbraiding her husband, lamenting at Fate, which had directed her footsteps to the path which they had taken. She was just having a good cry all to herself. The mosquitoes made merry over her, biting her firm, round arms and nipping at her bare insteps.

The little stinging, buzzing imps succeeded in dispelling a mood which might have held her there in the darkness half a night longer.

The following morning Mr. Pontellier was up in good time to take the rockaway[5] which was to convey him to the steamer at the wharf. He was returning to the city to his business, and they would not see him again at the Island till the coming Sunday. He had regained his composure, which seemed to have been somewhat impaired the night before. He was eager to be gone, as he looked forward to a lively week in Carondelet Street.

Mr. Pontellier gave his wife half of the money which he had brought away from Klein's hotel the evening before. She liked money as well as most women, and accepted it with no little satisfaction.

"It will buy a handsome wedding present for Sister Janet!" she exclaimed, smoothing out the bills as she counted them one by one.

"Oh! we'll treat Sister Janet better than that, my dear," he laughed, as he prepared to kiss her good-by.

The boys were tumbling about, clinging to his legs, imploring that numerous things be brought back to them. Mr. Pontellier was a great favorite, and ladies, men, children, even nurses, were always on hand to say good-by to

---

[5]A horse-drawn carriage.

him. His wife stood smiling and waving, the boys shouting, as he disappeared in the old rockaway down the sandy road.

A few days later a box arrived for Mrs. Pontellier from New Orleans. It was from her husband. It was filled with *friandises*, with luscious and toothsome bits—the finest of fruits, *patés*, a rare bottle or two, delicious syrups, and bonbons in abundance.

Mrs. Pontellier was always very generous with the contents of such a box; she was quite used to receiving them when away from home. The patés and fruit were brought to the dining-room; the bonbons were passed around. And the ladies, selecting with dainty and discriminating fingers and a little greedily, all declared that Mr. Pontellier was the best husband in the world. Mrs. Pontellier was forced to admit that she knew of none better.

IV

It would have been a difficult matter for Mr. Pontellier to define to his own satisfaction or any one else's wherein his wife failed in her duty toward their children. It was something which he felt rather than perceived, and he never voiced the feeling without subsequent regret and ample atonement.

If one of the little Pontellier boys took a tumble whilst at play, he was not apt to rush crying to his mother's arms for comfort; he would more likely pick himself up, wipe the water out of his eyes and the sand out of his mouth, and go on playing. Tots as they were, they pulled together and stood their ground in childish battles with doubled fists and uplifted voices, which usually prevailed against the other brother-tots. The quadroon nurse was looked upon as a huge encumbrance, only good to button up waists and panties and to brush and part hair; since it seemed to be a law of society that their hair must be parted and brushed.

In short, Mrs. Pontellier was not a mother-woman. The mother-women seemed to prevail that summer at Grand Isle. It was easy to know them, fluttering about with extended, protecting wings when any harm, real or imaginary, threatened their precious brood. They were women who idolized their children, worshiped their husbands, and esteemed it a holy privilege to efface themselves as individuals and grow wings as ministering angels.

Many of them were delicious in the rôle; one of them was the embodiment of every womanly grace and charm. If her husband did not adore her, he was a brute, deserving of death by slow torture. Her name was Adèle Ratignolle. There are no words to describe her save the old ones that have served so often to picture the bygone heroine of romance and the fair lady of our dreams. There was nothing subtle or hidden about her charms; her beauty was all there, flaming and apparent; the spun-gold hair that comb nor confining pin could restrain; the blue eyes that were like nothing but sapphires; two lips that pouted, that were so red one could only think of cherries or some other delicious crimson fruit in looking at them. She was growing a little stout, but it did not seem to detract an iota from the grace of every step, pose, gesture. One would not have wanted her white neck a mite less full or her beautiful arms more slender. Never were hands more exquisite than hers, and it was joy to look at them when she threaded her needle or adjusted her gold thimble to her tapered middle finger as she sewed away on the little night-drawers or fashioned a bodice or a bib.

Madame Ratignolle was very fond of Mrs. Pontellier, and often she took her sewing and went over to sit with her in the afternoons. She was sitting there the afternoon of the day the box arrived from New Orleans. She had possession of the rocker, and she was busily engaged in sewing upon a diminutive pair of night-drawers.

She had brought the pattern of the drawers for Mrs. Pontellier to cut out—a marvel of construction, fashioned to enclose a baby's body so effectually that only two small eyes might look out from the garment, like an Eskimo's. They were designed for winter wear, when treacherous drafts came down chimneys and insidious currents of deadly cold found their way through key-holes.

Mrs. Pontellier's mind was quite at rest concerning the present material needs of her children, and she could not see the use of anticipating and making winter night garments the subject of her summer meditations. But she did not want to appear unamiable and uninterested, so she had brought forth newspapers, which she spread upon the floor of the gallery, and under Madame Ratignolle's directions she had cut a pattern of the impervious garment.

Robert was there, seated as he had been the Sunday before, and Mrs. Pontellier also occupied her former position on the upper step, leaning list-lessly against the post. Beside her was a box of bonbons, which she held out at intervals to Madame Ratignolle.

That lady seemed at a loss to make a selection, but finally settled upon a stick of nougat, wondering if it were not too rich; whether it could possibly hurt her. Madame Ratignolle had been married seven years. About every two years she had a baby. At that time she had three babies, and was beginning to think of a fourth one. She was always talking about her "condition." Her "condition" was in no way apparent, and no one would have known a thing about it but for her persistence in making it the subject of conversation.

Robert started to reassure her, asserting that he had known a lady who had subsisted upon nougat during the entire—but seeing the color mount into Mrs. Pontellier's face he checked himself and changed the subject.

Mrs. Pontellier, though she had married a Creole, was not thoroughly at home in the society of Creoles; never before had she been thrown so intimately among them. There were only Creoles that summer at Lebrun's. They all knew each other, and felt like one large family, among whom existed the most amicable relations. A characteristic which distinguished them and which impressed Mrs. Pontellier most forcibly was their entire absence of prudery. Their freedom of expression was at first incomprehensible to her, though she had no difficulty in reconciling it with a lofty chastity which in the Creole woman seems to be inborn and unmistakable.

Never would Edna Pontellier forget the shock with which she heard Madame Ratignolle relating to old Monsieur Farival the harrowing story of one of her *accouchements*,[6] withholding no intimate detail. She was growing accustomed to like shocks, but she could not keep the mounting color back from her cheeks. Oftener than once her coming had interrupted the droll story with which Robert was entertaining some amused group of married women.

A book had gone the rounds of the *pension*. When it came her turn to read it, she did so with profound astonishment. She felt moved to read the book in secret and solitude, though none of the others had done so—to hide it from view at the sound of approaching footsteps. It was openly criticized and freely discussed at table. Mrs. Pontellier gave over being astonished, and concluded that wonders would never cease.

V

They formed a congenial group sitting there that summer afternoon— Madame Ratignolle sewing away, often stopping to relate a story or incident with much expressive gesture of her perfect hands; Robert and Mrs. Pontellier sitting idle, exchanging occasional words, glances or smiles which indicated a certain advanced stage of intimacy and *camaraderie*.

He had lived in her shadow during the past month. No one thought anything of it. Many had predicted that Robert would devote himself to Mrs. Pontellier when he arrived. Since the age of fifteen, which was eleven years before, Robert each summer at Grand Isle had constituted himself the devoted attendant of some fair dame or damsel. Sometimes it was a young girl, again a widow; but as often as not it was some interesting married woman.

For two consecutive seasons he lived in the sunlight of Mademoiselle Duvigné's presence. But she died between summers; then Robert posed as an inconsolable, prostrating himself at the feet of Madame Ratignolle for

---

[6]Giving birth

whatever crumbs of sympathy and comfort she might be pleased to vouchsafe.

Mrs. Pontellier liked to sit and gaze at her fair companion as she might look upon a faultless Madonna.

"Could any one fathom the cruelty beneath that fair exterior?" murmured Robert. "She knew that I adored her once, and she let me adore her. It was 'Robert, come; go; stand up; sit down; do this; do that; see if the baby sleeps; my thimble, please, that I left God knows where. Come and read Daudet to me while I sew.' "

"*Par exemple!*[7] I never had to ask. You were always there under my feet, like a troublesome cat."

"You mean like an adoring dog. And just as soon as Ratignolle appeared on the scene, then it *was* like a dog. '*Passez! Adieu! Allez vous-en!*' "[8]

"Perhaps I feared to make Alphonse jealous," she interjoined, with excessive naïveté. That made them all laugh. The right hand jealous of the left! The heart jealous of the soul! But for that matter, the Creole husband is never jealòus; with him the gangrene passion is one which has become dwarfed by disuse.

Meanwhile Robert, addressing Mrs. Pontellier, continued to tell of his one time hopeless passion for Madame Ratignolle; of sleepless nights, of consuming flames till the very sea sizzled when he took his daily plunge. While the lady at the needle kept up a little running, contemptuous comment:

"*Blagueur—farceur—gros bête, va!*"[9]

He never assumed this serio-comic tone when alone with Mrs. Pontellier. She never knew precisely what to make of it; at that moment it was impossible for her to guess how much of it was jest and what proportion was earnest. It was understood that he had often spoken words of love to Madame Ratignolle, without any thought of being taken seriously. Mrs. Pontellier was glad he had not assumed a similar rôle toward herself. It would have been unacceptable and annoying.

Mrs. Pontellier had brought her sketching materials, which she sometimes dabbled with in an unprofessional way. She liked the dabbling. She felt in it satisfaction of a kind which no other employment afforded her.

She had long wished to try herself on Madame Ratignolle. Never had that lady seemed a more tempting subject than at that moment, seated there like some sensuous Madonna, with the gleam of the fading day enriching her splendid color.

---

[7]Indeed!

[8]Go! Good-bye! Go away!

[9]Joker—clown—beast, go!

Robert crossed over and seated himself upon the step below Mrs. Pontellier, that he might watch her work. She handled her brushes with a certain ease and freedom which came, not from long and close acquaintance with them, but from a natural aptitude. Robert followed her work with close attention, giving forth little ejaculatory expressions of appreciation in French, which he addressed to Madame Ratignolle.

"*Mais ce n'est pas mal! Elle s'y connait, elle a de la force, oui.*"[10]

During his oblivious attention he once quietly rested his head against Mrs. Pontellier's arm. As gently she repulsed him. Once again he repeated the offense. She could not but believe it to be thoughtlessness on his part; yet that was no reason she should submit to it. She did not remonstrate, except again to repulse him quietly but firmly. He offered no apology.

The picture completed bore no resemblance to Madame Ratignolle. She was greatly disappointed to find that it did not look like her. But it was a fair enough piece of work, and in many respects satisfying.

Mrs. Pontellier evidently did not think so. After surveying the sketch critically she drew a broad smudge of paint across its surface, and crumpled the paper between her hands.

The youngsters came tumbling up the steps, the quadroon following at the respectful distance which they required her to observe. Mrs. Pontellier made them carry her paints and things into the house. She sought to detain them for a little talk and some pleasantry. But they were greatly in earnest. They had only come to investigate the contents of the bonbon box. They accepted without murmuring what she chose to give them, each holding out two chubby hands scoop-like, in the vain hope that they might be filled; and then away they went.

The sun was low in the west, and the breeze soft and languorous that came up from the south, charged with the seductive odor of the sea. Children, freshly befurbelowed,[11] were gathering for their games under the oaks. Their voices were high and penetrating.

Madame Ratignolle folded her sewing, placing thimble, scissors and thread all neatly together in the roll, which she pinned securely. She complained of faintness. Mrs. Pontellier flew for the cologne water and a fan. She bathed Madame Ratignolle's face with cologne, while Robert plied the fan with unnecessary vigor.

The spell was soon over, and Mrs. Pontellier could not help wondering if there were not a little imagination responsible for its origin, for the rose tint had never faded from her friend's face.

---

[10]Not bad! She knows what she's doing, she's quite good.

[11]Dressed in frilly clothing.

She stood watching the fair woman walk down the long line of galleries with the grace and majesty which queens are sometimes supposed to possess. Her little ones ran to meet her. Two of them clung about her white skirts, the third she took from its nurse and with a thousand endearments bore it along in her own fond, encircling arms. Though, as everybody well knew, the doctor had forbidden her to lift so much as a pin!

"Are you going bathing?" asked Robert of Mrs. Pontellier. It was not so much a question as a reminder.

"Oh, no," she answered with a tone of indecision. "I'm tired; I think not." Her glance wandered from his face away toward the Gulf, whose sonorous murmur reached her like a loving but imperative entreaty.

"Oh, come!" he insisted. "You mustn't miss your bath. Come on. The water must be delicious; it will not hurt you. Come."

He reached up for her big, rough straw hat that hung on a peg outside the door, and put it on her head. They descended the steps, and walked away together toward the beach. The sun was low in the west and the breeze was soft and warm.

VI

Edna Pontellier could not have told why, wishing to go to the beach with Robert, she should in the first place have declined, and in the second place have followed in obedience to one of the two contradictory impulses which impelled her.

A certain light was beginning to dawn dimly within her,—the light which, showing the way, forbids it.

At that early period it served but to bewilder her. It moved her to dreams, to thoughtfulness, to the shadowy anguish which had overcome her the midnight when she had abandoned herself to tears.

In short, Mrs. Pontellier was beginning to realize her position in the universe as a human being, and to recognize her relations as an individual to the world within and about her. This may seem like a ponderous weight of wisdom to descend upon the soul of a young woman of twenty-eight—perhaps more wisdom than the Holy Ghost is usually pleased to vouchsafe to any woman.

But the beginning of things, of a world especially, is necessarily vague, tangled, chaotic, and exceedingly disturbing. How few of us ever emerge from such beginning! How many souls perish in its tumult!

The voice of the sea is seductive; never ceasing, whispering, clamoring, murmuring, inviting the soul to wander for a spell in abysses of solitude; to lose itself in mazes of inward contemplation.

The voice of the sea speaks to the soul. The touch of the sea is sensuous, enfolding the body in its soft, close embrace.

VII

Mrs. Pontellier was not a woman given to confidences, a characteristic hitherto contrary to her nature. Even as a child she had lived her own small life all within herself. At a very early period she had apprehended instinctively the dual life—that outward existence which conforms, the inward life which questions.

That summer at Grand Isle she began to loosen a little the mantle of reserve that had always enveloped her. There may have been—there must have been—influences, both subtle and apparent, working in their several ways to induce her to do this; but the most obvious was the influence of Adèle Ratignolle. The excessive physical charm of the Creole had first attracted her, for Edna had a sensuous susceptibility to beauty. Then the candor of the woman's whole existence, which every one might read, and which formed so striking a contrast to her own habitual reserve—this might have furnished a link. Who can tell what metals the gods use in forging the subtle bond which we call sympathy, which we might as well call love.

The two women went away one morning to the beach together, arm in arm, under the huge white sunshade. Edna had prevailed upon Madame Ratignolle to leave the children behind, though she could not induce her to relinquish a diminutive roll of needlework, which Adèle begged to be allowed to slip into the depths of her pocket. In some unaccountable way they had escaped from Robert.

The walk to the beach was no inconsiderable one, consisting as it did of a long, sandy path, upon which a sporadic and tangled growth that bordered it on either side made frequent and unexpected inroads. There were acres of yellow camomile reaching out on either hand. Further away still, vegetable gardens abounded, with frequent small plantations of orange or lemon trees intervening. The dark green clusters glistened from afar in the sun.

The women were both of goodly height, Madame Ratignolle possessing the more feminine and matronly figure. The charm of Edna Pontellier's physique stole insensibly upon you. The lines of her body were long, clean and symmetrical; it was a body which occasionally fell into splendid poses; there was no suggestion of the trim stereotyped fashion-plate about it. A casual and indiscriminating observer, in passing, might not cast a second glance upon the figure. But with more feeling and discernment he would have recognized the noble beauty of its modeling, and the graceful severity of poise and movement, which made Edna Pontellier different from the crowd.

She wore a cool muslin that morning—white, with a waving vertical line of brown running through it; also a white linen collar and the big straw hat which she had taken from the peg outside the door. The hat rested any way on her yellow-brown hair, that waved a little, was heavy, and clung close to her head.

Madame Ratignolle, more careful of her complexion, had twined a gauze veil about her head. She wore doeskin gloves, with gauntlets that protected her wrists. She was dressed in pure white, with a fluffiness of ruffles that became her. The draperies and fluttering things which she wore suited her rich, luxuriant beauty as a greater severity of line could not have done.

There were a number of bath-houses along the beach, of rough but solid construction, built with small, protecting galleries facing the water. Each house consisted of two compartments, and each family at Lebrun's possessed a compartment for itself, fitted out with all the essential paraphernalia of the bath and whatever other conveniences the owners might desire. The two women had no intention of bathing; they had just strolled down to the beach for a walk and to be alone and near the water. The Pontellier and Ratignolle compartments adjoined one another under the same roof.

Mrs. Pontellier had brought down her key through force of habit. Unlocking the door of her bath-room she went inside, and soon emerged, bringing a rug, which she spread upon the floor of the gallery, and two huge hair pillows covered with crash, which she placed against the front of the building.

The two seated themselves there in the shade of the porch, side by side, with their backs against the pillows and their feet extended. Madame Ratignolle removed her veil, wiped her face with a rather delicate handkerchief, and fanned herself with the fan which she always carried suspended somewhere about her person by a long, narrow ribbon. Edna removed her collar and opened her dress at the throat. She took the fan from Madame Ratignolle and began to fan both herself and her companion. It was very warm, and for a while they did nothing but exchange remarks about the heat, the sun, the glare. But there was a breeze blowing, a choppy, stiff wind that whipped the water into froth. It fluttered the skirts of the two women and kept them for a while engaged in adjusting, readjusting, tucking in, securing hair-pins and hat-pins. A few persons were sporting some distance away in the water. The beach was very still of human sound at that hour. The lady in black was reading her morning devotions on the porch of a neighboring bath-house. Two young lovers were exchanging their hearts' yearnings beneath the children's tent, which they had found unoccupied.

Edna Pontellier, casting her eyes about, had finally kept them at rest upon the sea. The day was clear and carried the gaze out as far as the blue sky went; there were a few white clouds suspended idly over the horizon. A lateen sail was visible in the direction of Cat Island, and others to the south seemed almost motionless in the far distance.

"Of whom—of what are you thinking?" asked Adéle of her companion, whose countenance she had been watching with a little amused attention, arrested by the absorbed expression which seemed to have seized and fixed every feature into a statuesque repose.

"Nothing," returned Mrs. Pontellier, with a start, adding at once: "How stupid! But it seems to me it is the reply we make instinctively to such a question. Let me see," she went on, throwing back her head and narrowing her fine eyes till they shone like two vivid points of light. "Let me see. I was really not conscious of thinking of anything; but perhaps I can retrace my thoughts."

"Oh! never mind!" laughed Madame Ratignolle. "I am not quite so exacting. I will let you off this time. It is really too hot to think, especially to think about thinking."

"But for the fun of it," persisted Edna. "First of all, the sight of the water stretching so far away, those motionless sails against the blue sky, made a delicious picture that I just wanted to sit and look at it. The hot wind beating in my face made me think—without any connection that I can trace—of a summer day in Kentucky, of a meadow that seemed as big as the ocean to the very little girl walking through the grass, which was higher than her waist. She threw out her arms as if swimming when she walked, beating the tall grass as one strikes out in the water. Oh, I see the connection now!"

"Where were you going that day in Kentucky, walking through the grass?"

"I don't remember now. I was just walking diagonally across a big field. My sun-bonnet obstructed the view. I could see only the stretch of green before me, and I felt as if I must walk on forever, without coming to the end of it. I don't remember whether I was frightened or pleased. I must have been entertained."

"Likely as not it was Sunday," she laughed; "and I was running away from prayers, from the Presbyterian service, read in a spirit of gloom by my father that chills me yet to think of."

"And have you been running away from prayer ever since, *ma chére?*" asked Madame Ratignolle, amused.

"No! oh, no!" Edna hastened to say. "I was a little unthinking child in those days, just following a misleading impulse without question. On the contrary, during one period of my life religion took a firm hold upon me; after I was twelve and until—until—why, I suppose until now, though I never thought much about it—just driven along by habit. But do you know," she broke off, turning her quick eyes upon Madame Ratignolle and leaning forward a little so as to bring her face quite close to that of her companion, "sometimes I feel this summer as if I were walking through the green meadow again; idly, aimlessly, unthinking and unguided."

Madame Ratignolle laid her hand over that of Mrs. Pontellier, which was near her. Seeing that the hand was not withdrawn, she clasped it firmly and warmly. She even stroked it a little fondly, with the other hand, murmuring in an undertone, "*Pauvre chérie.*"[12]

The action was at first a little confusing to Edna, but she soon lent herself readily to the Creole's gentle caress. She was not accustomed to an outward and spoken expression of affection, either in herself or in others. She and her younger sister, Janet, had quarreled a good deal through force of unfortunate habit. Her older sister, Margaret, was matronly and dignified, probably from having assumed matronly and housewifely responsibilities too early in life, their mother having died when they were quite young. Margaret was not effusive: she was practical. Edna had had an occasional girl friend, but whether accidentally or not, they seemed to have been all of one type—the self-contained. She never realized that the reserve of her own character had much, perhaps everything, to do with this. Her most intimate friend at school had been one of rather exceptional intellectual gifts, who wrote fine-sounding essays, which Edna admired and strove to imitate; and with her she talked and glowed over the English classics, and sometimes held religious and political controversies.

Edna often wondered at one propensity which sometimes had inwardly disturbed her without causing any outward show or manifestation on her part. At a very early age—perhaps it was when she traversed the ocean of waving grass—she remembered that she had been passionately enamored of a dignified and sad-eyed cavalry officer who visited her father in Kentucky. She could not leave his presence when he was there, nor remove her eyes from his face, which was something like Napoleon's, with a lock of black hair falling across the forehead. But the cavalry officer melted imperceptibly out of her existence.

At another time her affections were deeply engaged by a young gentleman who visited a lady on a neighboring plantation. It was after they went to Mississippi to live. The young man was engaged to be married to the young lady, and they sometimes called upon Margaret, driving over of afternoons in a buggy. Edna was a little miss, just merging into her teens; and the realization that she herself was nothing, nothing, nothing to the engaged young man was a bitter affliction to her. But he, too, went the way of dreams.

She was a grown young woman when she was overtaken by what she supposed to be the climax of her fate. It was when the face and figure of a great tragedian began to haunt her imagination and stir her senses. The persistence

---

[12]Poor dear

of the infatuation lent it an aspect of genuineness. The hopelessness of it colored it with the lofty tones of a great passion.

The picture of the tragedian stood enframed upon her desk. Any one may possess the portrait of a tragedian without exciting suspicion or comment. (This was a sinister reflection which she cherished.) In the presence of others she expressed admiration for his exalted gifts, as she handed the photograph around and dwelt upon the fidelity of the likeness. When alone she sometimes picked it up and kissed the cold glass passionately.

Her marriage to Léonce Pontellier was purely an accident, in this respect resembling many other marriages which masquerade as the decrees of Fate. It was in the midst of her secret great passion that she met him. He fell in love, as men are in the habit of doing, and pressed his suit with an earnestness and an ardor which left nothing to be desired. He pleased her; his absolute devotion flattered her. She fancied there was a sympathy of thought and taste between them, in which fancy she was mistaken. Add to this the violent opposition of her father and her sister Margaret to her marriage with a Catholic, and we need seek no further for the motives which led her to accept Monsieur Pontellier for her husband.

The acme of bliss, which would have been a marriage with the tragedian, was not for her in this world. As the devoted wife of a man who worshiped her, she felt she would take her place with a certain dignity in the world of reality, closing the portals forever behind her upon the realm of romance and dreams.

But it was not long before the tragedian had gone to join the cavalry officer and the engaged young man and a few others; and Edna found herself face to face with the realities. She grew fond of her husband, realizing with some unaccountable satisfaction that no trace of passion or excessive and fictitious warmth colored her affection, thereby threatening its dissolution.

She was fond of her children in an uneven, impulsive way. She would sometimes gather them passionately to her heart; she would sometimes forget them. The year before they had spent part of the summer with their grandmother Pontellier in Iberville. Feeling secure regarding their happiness and welfare, she did not miss them except with an occasional intense longing. Their absence was a sort of relief, though she did not admit this, even to herself. It seemed to free her of a responsibility which she had blindly assumed and for which Fate had not fitted her.

Edna did not reveal so much as all this to Madame Ratignolle that summer day when they sat with faces turned to the sea. But a good part of it escaped her. She had put her head down on Madame Ratignolle's shoulder. She was flushed and felt intoxicated with the sound of her own voice and the unaccustomed taste of candor. It muddled her like wine, or like a first breath of freedom.

There was the sound of approaching voices. It was Robert, surrounded by a troop of children, searching for them. The two little Pontelliers were with him, and he carried Madame Ratignolle's little girl in his arms. There were other children beside, and two nurse-maids followed, looking disagreeable and resigned.

The women at once rose and began to shake out their draperies and relax their muscles. Mrs. Pontellier threw the cushions and rug into the bathhouse. The children all scampered off to the awning, and they stood there in a line, gazing upon the intruding lovers, still exchanging their vows and sighs. The lovers got up, with only a silent protest, and walked slowly away somewhere else.

The children possessed themselves of the tent, and Mrs. Pontellier went over to join them.

Madame Ratignolle begged Robert to accompany her to the house; she complained of cramp in her limbs and stiffness of the joints. She leaned draggingly upon his arm as they walked.

VIII

"Do me a favor, Robert," spoke the pretty woman at his side, almost as soon as she and Robert had started on their slow, homeward way. She looked up in his face, leaning on his arm beneath the encircling shadow of the umbrella which he had lifted.

"Granted; as many as you like," he returned, glancing down into her eyes that were full of thoughtfulness and some speculation.

"I only ask for one; let Mrs. Pontellier alone."

"*Tiens!*" he exclaimed, with a sudden, boyish laugh. "*Voilà que Madame Ratignolle est jalouse!*"[13]

"Nonsense! I'm in earnest; I mean what I say. Let Mrs. Pontellier alone."

"Why?" he asked; himself growing serious at his companion's solicitation.

"She is not one of us; she is not like us. She might make the unfortunate blunder of taking you seriously."

His face flushed with annoyance, and taking off his soft hat he began to beat it impatiently against his leg as he walked. "Why shouldn't she take me seriously?" he demanded sharply. "Am I a comedian, a clown, a jack-in-the-box? Why shouldn't she? You Creoles! I have no patience with you! Am I always to be regarded as a feature of an amusing programme? I hope Mrs. Pontellier does take me seriously. I hope she has discernment enough to find in me something besides the *blagueur*. If I thought there was any doubt—"

---

[13]Look, Madame Ratignolle is jealous!

100

"Oh, enough, Robert!" she broke into his heated outburst. "You are not thinking of what you are saying. You speak with about as little reflection as we might expect from one of those children down there playing in the sand. If your intentions to any married women here were ever offered with any attention of being convincing, you would not be the gentleman we all know you to be, and you would be unfit to associate with the wives and daughters of the people who trust you."

Madame Ratignolle had spoken what she believed to be the law and the gospel. The young man shrugged his shoulders impatiently.

"Oh! well! That isn't it," slamming his hat down vehemently upon his head. "You ought to feel that such things are not flattering to say to a fellow."

"Should our whole intercourse consist of an exchange of compliments? *Ma foi!*"[14]

"It isn't pleasant to have a woman tell you—" he went on, unheedingly, but breaking off suddenly: "Now if I were like Arobin—you remember Alcée Arobin and that story of the consul's wife at Biloxi?" And he related the story of Alcée Arobin and the consul's wife; and another about the tenor of the French Opera, who received letters which should never have been written; and still other stories, grave and gay, till Mrs. Pontellier and her possible propensity for taking young men seriously was apparently forgotten.

Madame Ratignolle, when they had regained her cottage, went in to take the hour's rest which she considered helpful. Before leaving her, Robert begged her pardon for the impatience—he called it rudeness—with which he had received her well-meant caution.

"You made one mistake, Adèle," he said, with a light smile; "there is no earthly possibility of Mrs. Pontellier ever taking me seriously. You should have warned me against taking myself seriously. Your advice might then have carried some weight and given me subject for some reflection. *Au revoir.* But you look tired," he added, solicitously. "Would you like a cup of bouillon? Shall I stir you a toddy? Let me mix you a toddy with a drop of Angostura."

She acceded to the suggestion of bouillon, which was grateful and acceptable. He went himself to the kitchen, which was a building apart from the cottages and lying to the rear of the house. And he himself brought her the golden-brown bouillon, in a dainty Sévres cup, with a flaky cracker or two on the saucer.

She thrust a bare, white arm from the curtain which shielded her open door, and received the cup from his hands. She told him he was a *bon garçon*[15] and she meant it. Robert thanked her and turned away toward "the house."

---

[14]Good Lord!

[15]Good boy

The lovers were just entering the grounds of the *pension*. They were leaning toward each other as the water-oaks bent from the sea. There was not a particle of earth beneath their feet. Their heads might have been turned upside-down, so absolutely did they tread upon blue ether. The lady in black, creeping behind them, looked a trifle paler and more jaded than usual. There was no sign of Mrs. Pontellier and the children. Robert scanned the distance for any such apparition. They would doubtless remain away till the dinner hour. The young man ascended to his mother's room. It was situated at the top of the house, made up of odd angles and a queer, sloping ceiling. Two broad dormer windows looked out toward the Gulf, and as far across it as man's eye might reach. The furnishings of the room were light, cool, and practical.

Madame Lebrun was busily engaged at the sewing-machine. A little black girl sat on the floor, and with her hands worked the treadle of the machine. The Creole woman does not take any chances which may be avoided of imperiling her health.

Robert went over and seated himself on the broad sill of one of the dormer windows. He took a book from his pocket and began energetically to read it, judging by the precision and frequency with which he turned the leaves. The sewing-machine made a resounding clatter in the room; it was of a ponderous, by-gone make. In the lulls, Robert and his mother exchanged bits of desultory conversation.

"Where is Mrs. Pontellier?"

"Down at the beach with the children."

"I promised to lend her the Goncourt. Don't forget to take it down when you go; it's there on the bookshelf over the small table." Clatter, clatter, clatter, bang! for the next five or eight minutes.

"Where is Victor going with the rockaway?"

"The rockaway? Victor?"

"Yes; down there in front. He seems to be getting ready to drive away somewhere."

"Call him." Clatter, clatter!

Robert uttered a shrill, piercing whistle which might have been heard back at the wharf.

"He won't look up."

Madame Lebrun flew to the window. She called "Victor!" She waved a handkerchief and called again. The young fellow below got into the vehicle and started the horse off at a gallop.

Madame Lebrun went back to the machine, crimson with annoyance. Victor was the younger son and brother—a *tête montée*,[16] with a temper which invited violence and a will which no ax could break.

---

[16]Impulsive young man.

"Whenever you say the word I'm ready to thrash any amount of reason into him that he's able to hold."

"If your father had only lived!" Clatter, clatter, clatter, clatter, bang! It was a fixed belief with Madame Lebrun that the conduct of the universe and all things pertaining thereto would have been manifestly of a more intelligent and higher order had not Monsieur Lebrun been removed to other spheres during the early years of their married life.

"What do you hear from Montel?" Montel was a middle-aged gentleman whose vain ambition and desire for the past twenty years had been to fill the void which Monsieur Lebrun's taking off had left in the Lebrun household. Clatter, clatter, bang, clatter!

"I have a letter somewhere," looking in the machine drawer and finding the letter in the bottom of the work-basket. "He says to tell you he will be in Vera Cruz the beginning of next month"—clatter, clatter!—"and if you still have the intention of joining him"—bang! clatter, clatter, bang!

"Why didn't you tell me so before, mother? You know I wanted—" Clatter, clatter, clatter!

"Do you see Mrs. Pontellier starting back with the children? She will be in late to luncheon again. She never starts to get ready for luncheon till the last minute." Clatter, clatter! "Where are you going?"

"Where did you say the Goncourt was?"

IX

Every light in the hall was ablaze; every lamp turned as high as it could be without smoking the chimney or threatening explosion. The lamps were fixed at intervals against the wall, encircling the whole room. Some one had gathered orange and lemon branches, and with these fashioned graceful festoons between. The dark green of the branches stood out and glistened against the white muslin curtains which draped the windows, and which puffed, floated, and flapped at the capricious will of a stiff breeze that swept up from the Gulf.

It was Saturday night a few weeks after the intimate conversation held between Robert and Mrs. Ratignolle on their way from the beach. An unusual number of husbands, fathers, and friends had come down to stay over Sunday; and they were being suitably entertained by their families, with the material help of Madame Lebrun. The dining tables had all been removed to one end of the hall, and the chairs ranged about in rows and in clusters. Each little family group had had its say and exchanged its domestic gossip earlier in the evening. There was now an apparent disposition to relax; to widen the circle of confidences and give a more general tone to the conversation.

Many of the children had been permitted to sit up beyond their usual bedtime. A small band of them were lying on their stomachs on the floor looking at the colored sheets of the comic papers which Mr. Pontellier had brought down. The little Pontellier boys were permitting them to do so, and making their authority felt.

Music, dancing, and a recitation or two were the entertainments furnished, or rather, offered. But there was nothing systematic about the programme, no appearance of prearrangement nor even premeditation.

At an early hour in the evening the Farival twins were prevailed upon to play the piano. They were girls of fourteen, always clad in the Virgin's colors, blue and white, having been dedicated to the Blessed Virgin at their baptism. They played a duet from "Zampa," and at the earnest solicitation of every one present followed it with the overture to "The Poet and the Peasant."

"*Allez vous-en! Sapristi!*" shrieked the parrot outside the door. He was the only being present who possessed sufficient candor to admit that he was not listening to these gracious performances for the first time that summer. Old Monsieur Farival, grandfather of the twins, grew indignant over the interruption, and insisted upon having the bird removed and consigned to regions of darkness. Victor Lebrun objected; and his decrees were as immutable as those of Fate. The parrot fortunately offered no further interruption to the entertainment, the whole venom of his nature apparently having been cherished up and hurled against the twins in that one impetuous outburst.

Later a young brother and sister gave recitations, which every one present had heard many times at winter evening entertainments in the city.

A little girl performed a skirt dance in the center of the floor. The mother played her accompaniments and at the same time watched her daughter with greedy admiration and nervous apprehension. She need have had no apprehension. The child was mistress of the situation. She had been properly dressed for the occasion in black tulle and black silk tights. Her little neck and arms were bare, and her hair, artificially crimped, stood out like fluffy black plumes over her head. Her poses were full of grace, and her little black-shod toes twinkled as they shot out and upward with a rapidity and suddenness which were bewildering.

But there was no reason why every one should not dance. Madame Ratignolle could not, so it was she who gaily consented to play for the others. She played very well, keeping excellent waltz time and infusing an expression into the strains which was indeed inspiring. She was keeping up her music on account of the children, she said; because she and her husband both considered it a means of brightening the home and making it attractive.

Almost every one danced but the twins, who could not be induced to separate during the brief period when one or the other should be whirling around the room in the arms of a man. They might have danced together, but they did not think of it.

The children were sent to bed. Some went submissively; others with shrieks and protests as they were dragged away. They had been permitted to sit up till after the ice-cream, which naturally marked the limit of human indulgence.

The ice-cream was passed around with cake—gold and silver cake arranged on platters in alternate slices; it had been made and frozen during the afternoon back of the kitchen by two black women, under the supervision of Victor. It was pronounced a great success—excellent if it had only contained a little less vanilla or a little more sugar, if it had been frozen a degree harder, and if the salt might have been kept out of portions of it. Victor was proud of his achievement, and went about recommending it and urging every one to partake of it to excess.

After Mrs. Pontellier had danced twice with her husband, once with Robert, and once with Monsieur Ratignolle, who was thin and tall and swayed like a reed in the wind when he danced, she went out on the gallery and seated herself on the low window-sill, where she commanded a view of all that went on in the hall and could look out toward the Gulf. There was a soft effulgence in the east. The moon was coming up, and its mystic shimmer was casting a million lights across the distant, restless water.

"Would you like to hear Mademoiselle Reisz play?" asked Robert, coming out on the porch where she was. Of course Edna would like to hear Mademoiselle Reisz play, but she feared it would be useless to entreat her.

"I'll ask her," he said. "I'll tell her that you want to hear her. She likes you. She will come." He turned and hurried away to one of the far cottages, where Mademoiselle Reisz was shuffling away. She was dragging a chair in and out of her room, and at intervals objecting to the crying of a baby, which a nurse in the adjoining cottage was endeavoring to put to sleep. She was a disagreeable little woman, no longer young, who had quarreled with almost every one, owing to a temper which was self-assertive and a disposition to trample upon the rights of others. Robert prevailed upon her without any too great difficulty.

She entered the hall with him during a lull in the dance. She made an awkward, imperious little bow as she went in. She was a homely woman, with a small weazened face and body and eyes that glowed. She had absolutely no taste in dress, and wore a batch of rusty black lace with a bunch of artificial violets pinned to the side of her hair.

"Ask Mrs. Pontellier what she would like to hear me play," she requested of Robert. She sat perfectly still before the piano, not touching the keys, while

Robert carried her message to Edna at the window. A general air of surprise and genuine satisfaction fell upon every one as they saw the pianist enter. There was a settling down, and a prevailing air of expectancy everywhere. Edna was a trifle embarrassed at being thus signaled out for the imperious little woman's favor. She would not dare to choose, and begged that Mademoiselle Riesz would please herself in her selections.

Edna was what she herself called very fond of music. Musical strains, well rendered, had a way of evoking pictures in her mind. She sometimes liked to sit in the room of mornings when Madame Ratignolle played or practiced. One piece which that lady played Edna had entitled "Solitude." It was a short, plaintive, minor strain. The name of the piece was something else, but she called it "Solitude." When she heard it there came before her imagination the figure of a man standing beside a desolate rock on the seashore. He was naked. His attitude was one of hopeless resignation as he looked toward a distant bird winging its flight away from him.

Another piece called to her mind a dainty young woman clad in an Empire gown, taking mincing dancing steps as she came down a long avenue between tall hedges. Again, another reminded her of children at play, and still another of nothing on earth but a demure lady stroking a cat.

The very first chords which Mademoiselle Reisz struck upon the piano sent a keen tremor down Mrs. Pontellier's spinal column. It was not the first time she had heard an artist at the piano. Perhaps it was the first time she was ready, perhaps the first time her being was tempered to take an impress of the abiding truth.

She waited for the material pictures which she thought would gather and blaze before her imagination. She waited in vain. She saw no pictures of solitude, of hope, of longing, or of despair. But the very passions themselves were aroused within her soul, swaying it, lashing it, as the waves daily beat upon her splendid body. She trembled, she was choking, and the tears blinded her.

Mademoiselle had finished. She arose, and bowing her stiff, lofty bow, she went away, stopping for neither thanks nor applause. As she passed along the gallery she patted Edna upon the shoulder.

"Well, how did you like my music?" she asked. The young woman was unable to answer; she pressed the hand of the pianist convulsively. Mademoiselle Reisz perceived her agitation and even her tears. She patted her again upon the shoulder as she said:

"You are the only one worth playing for. Those others? Bah!" and she went shuffling and sidling on down the gallery toward her room.

But she was mistaken about "those others." Her playing had aroused a fever of enthusiasm. "What passion!" "What an artist!" "I have always said no one could play Chopin like Mademoiselle Reisz!" "That last prelude! Bon Dieu![17] It shakes a man!"

It was growing late, and there was a general disposition to disband. But some one, perhaps it was Robert, thought of a bath at that mystic hour and under that mystic moon.

X

At all events Robert proposed it, and there was not a dissenting voice. There was not one but was ready to follow when he led the way. He did not lead the way, however, he directed the way; and he himself loitered behind with the lovers, who had betrayed a disposition to linger and hold themselves apart. He walked between them, whether with malicious or mischievous intent was not wholly clear, even to himself.

The Pontelliers and Ratignolles walked ahead; the women leaning upon the arms of their husbands. Edna could hear Robert's voice behind them, and could sometimes hear what he said. She wondered why he did not join them. It was unlike him not to. Of late he had sometimes held away from her for an entire day, redoubling his devotion upon the next and the next, as though to make up for hours that had been lost. She missed him the days when some pretext served to take him away from her, just as one misses the sun on a cloudy day without having thought much about the sun when it was shining.

The people walked in little groups toward the beach. They talked and laughed; some of them sang. There was a band playing down at Klein's hotel, and the strains reached them faintly, tempered by the distance. There were strange, rare odors abroad—a tangle of the sea smell and of weeds and damp, new-plowed earth, mingled with the heavy perfume of a field of white blossoms somewhere near. But the night sat lightly upon the sea and the land. There was no weight of darkness, there were no shadows. The white light of the moon had fallen upon the world like the mystery and the softness of sleep.

Most of them walked into the water as though into a native element. The sea was quiet now, and swelled lazily in broad billows that melted into one another and did not break except upon the beach in little foamy crests that coiled back like slow, white serpents.

Edna had attempted all summer to learn to swim. She had received instructions from both the men and women; in some instances from the children. Robert had pursued a system of lessons almost daily; and he was nearly

---

[17]Good God!

at the point of discouragement in realizing the futility of his efforts. A certain ungovernable dread hung about her when in the water, unless there was a hand near by that might reach out and reassure her.

But that night she was like the little tottering, stumbling, clutching child, who of a sudden realizes its powers, and walks for the first time alone, boldly and with over-confidence. She could have shouted for joy. She did shout for joy, as with a sweeping stroke or two she lifted her body to the surface of the water.

A feeling of exultation overtook her, as if some power of significant import had been given to her to control the working of her body and her soul. She grew daring and reckless, overestimating her strength. She wanted to swim far out, where no woman had swum before.

Her unlooked-for achievement was the subject of wonder, applause, and admiration. Each one congratulated himself that his special teachings had accomplished this desired end.

"How easy it is!" she thought. "It is nothing," she said aloud; "why did I not discover before that it was nothing? Think of the time I have lost splashing about like a baby!" She would not join the groups in their sports and bouts, but intoxicated with her newly conquered power, she swam out alone.

She turned her face seaward to gather in an impression of space and solitude, which the vast expanse of water, meeting and melting with the moonlit sky, conveyed to her excited fancy. As she swam she seemed to be reaching out for the unlimited in which to lose herself.

Once she turned and looked toward the shore, toward the people she had left there. She had not gone any great distance—that is, what would have been a great distance for an experienced swimmer. But to her unaccustomed vision the stretch of water behind her assumed the aspect of a barrier which her unaided strength would never be able to overcome.

A quick vision of death smote her soul, and for a second time appalled and enfeebled her senses. But by an effort she rallied her staggering faculties and managed to regain the land.

She made no mention of her encounter with death and her flash of terror, except to say to her husband, "I thought I should have perished out there alone."

"You were not so very far, my dear; I was watching you," he told her.

Edna went at once to the bath-house, and she had put on her dry clothes and was ready to return home before the others had left the water. She started to walk away alone. They all called to her and shouted to her. She waved a dissenting hand, and went on, paying no further heed to their renewed cries which sought to detain her.

"Sometimes I am tempted to think that Mrs. Pontellier is capricious," said Madame Lebrun, who was amusing herself immensely and feared that Edna's abrupt departure might put an end to the pleasure.

"I know she is," assented Mr. Pontellier; "sometimes, not often."

Edna had not traversed a quarter of the distance on her way home before she was overtaken by Robert.

"Did you think I was afraid?" she asked him, without a shade of annoyance.

"No; I knew you weren't afraid."

"Then why did you come? Why didn't you stay out there with the others?"

"I never thought of it."

"Thought of what?"

"Of anything. What difference does it make?"

"I'm very tired," she uttered, complainingly.

"I know you are."

"You don't know anything about it. Why should you know? I never was so exhausted in my life. But it isn't unpleasant. A thousand emotions have swept through me to-night. I don't comprehend half of them. Don't mind what I'm saying; I am just thinking aloud. I wonder if I shall ever be stirred again as Mademoiselle Reisz's playing moved me to-night. I wonder if any night on earth will ever again be like this one. It is like a night in a dream. The people about me are like some uncanny, half-human beings. There must be spirits abroad tonight."

"There are," whispered Robert. "Didn't you know this was the twenty-eighth of August?"

"The twenty-eight of August?"

"Yes. On the twenty-eighth of August, at the hour of midnight, and if the moon is shining—the moon must be shining—a spirit that has haunted these shores for ages rises up from the Gulf. With its own penetrating vision the spirit seeks some one mortal worthy to hold him company, worthy of being exalted for a few hours into realms of the semi-celestials. His search has always hitherto been fruitless, and he has sunk back, disheartened, into the sea. But tonight he found Mrs. Pontellier. Perhaps he will never wholly release her from the spell. Perhaps she will never again suffer a poor, unworthy earthling to walk in the shadow of her divine presence."

"Don't banter me," she said, wounded at what appeared to be his flippancy. He did not mind the entreaty, but the tone with its delicate note of pathos was like a reproach. He could not explain; he could not tell her that he had penetrated her mood and understood. He said nothing except to offer her his arm, for, by her own admission, she was exhausted. She had been walking alone with her arms hanging limp, letting her white skirts trail along the dewy path. She took his arm, but she did not lean upon it. She let her hand lie listlessly, as though her thoughts were elsewhere—somewhere in advance of her body, and she was striving to overtake them.

Robert assisted her into the hammock which swung from the post before her door out to the trunk of a tree.

"Will you stay out here and wait for Mr. Pontellier?" he asked.

"I'll stay out here. Good-night."

"Shall I get you a pillow?"

"There's one here," she said, feeling about, for they were in the shadow.

"It must be soiled; the children have been tumbling it about."

"No matter." And having discovered the pillow, she adjusted it beneath her head. She extended herself in the hammock with a deep breath of relief. She was not a supercilious or an over-dainty woman. She was not much given to reclining in the hammock, and when she did so it was with no catlike suggestion of voluptuous ease, but with a beneficent repose which seemed to invade her whole body.

"Shall I stay with you till Mr. Pontellier comes?" asked Robert, seating himself on the outer edge of one of the steps and taking hold of the hammock rope which was fastened to the post.

"If you wish. Don't swing the hammock. Will you get my white shawl which I left on the window-sill over at the house?"

"Are you chilly?"

"No; but I shall be presently."

"Presently?" he laughed. "Do you know what time it is? How long are you going to stay out here?"

"I don't know. Will you get the shawl?"

"Of course I will," he said, rising. He went over to the house, walking along the grass. She watched his figure pass in and out of the strips of moonlight. It was past midnight. It was very quiet.

When he returned with the shawl she took it and kept it in her hand. She did not put it around her.

"Did you say I should stay till Mr. Pontellier came back?"

"I said you might if you wished to."

He seated himself again and rolled a cigarette, which he smoked in silence. Neither did Mrs. Pontellier speak. No multitude of words could have been more significant than those moments of silence, or more pregnant with the first-felt throbbings of desire.

When the voices of the bathers were heard approaching, Robert said goodnight. She did not answer him. He thought she was asleep. Again she watched his figure pass in and out of the strips of moonlight as he walked away.

XI

"What are you doing out here, Edna? I thought I should find you in bed," said her husband, when he discovered her lying there. He had walked up with Madame Lebrun and left her at the house. His wife did not reply.

"Are you asleep?" he asked, bending down close to look at her.

"No." Her eyes gleamed bright and intense, with no sleepy shadows, as they looked into his.

"Do you know it is past one o'clock? Come on," and he mounted the steps and went into their room.

"Edna!" called Mr. Pontellier from within, after a few moments had gone by.

"Don't wait for me," she answered. He thrust his head through the door.

"You will take cold out there," he said irritably. "What folly is this? Why don't you come in?"

"It isn't cold; I have my shawl."

"The mosquitoes will devour you."

"There are no mosquitoes."

She heard him moving about the room; every sound indicating impatience and irritation. Another time she would have gone in at his request. She would, through habit, have yielded to his desire; not with any sense of submission or obedience to his compelling wishes, but unthinkingly, as we walk, move, sit, stand, go through the daily treadmill of the life which has been portioned out to us.

"Edna, dear, are you not coming in soon?" he asked again, this time fondly, with a note of entreaty.

"No; I am going to stay out here."

"This is more than folly," he blurted out. "I can't permit you to stay out there all night. You must come in the house instantly."

With a writhing motion she settled herself more securely in the hammock. She perceived that her will had blazed up, stubborn and resistant. She could not at that moment have done other than denied and resisted. She wondered if her husband had ever spoken to her like that before, and if she had submitted to his command. Of course she had; she remembered that she had. But she could not realize why or how she should have yielded, feeling as she then did.

"Léonce, go to bed," she said. "I mean to stay out here. I don't wish to go in, and I don't intend to. Don't speak to me like that again; I shall not answer you."

Mr. Pontellier had prepared for bed, but he slipped on an extra garment. He opened a bottle of wine, of which he kept a small and select supply in a buffet of his own. He drank a glass of wine and went out on the gallery and offered a glass to his wife. She did not wish any. He drew up a rocker, hoisted his slippered feet on the rail, and proceeded to smoke a cigar. He smoked two cigars; then he went inside and drank another glass of wine. Mrs. Pontellier again declined to accept a glass when it was offered to her. Mr. Pontellier once more seated himself with elevated feet, and after a reasonable interval of time smoked some more cigars.

Edna began to feel like one who awakens gradually out of a dream, a delicious, grotesque, impossible dream, to feel again the realities pressing into her soul. The physical need for sleep began to overtake her; the exuberance which had sustained and exalted her spirit left her helpless and yielding to the conditions which crowded her in.

The stillest hour of the night had come, the hour before dawn, when the world seems to hold its breath. The moon hung low, and had turned from silver to copper in the sleeping sky. The old owl no longer hooted, and the water-oaks had ceased to moan as they bent their heads.

Edna arose, cramped from lying so long and still in the hammock. She tottered up the steps, clutching feebly at the post before passing into the house.

"Are you coming in, Léonce?" she asked, turning her face toward her husband.

"Yes, dear," he answered, with a glance following a misty puff of smoke. "Just as soon as I have finished my cigar."

XII

She slept but a few hours. They were troubled and feverish hours, disturbed with dreams that were intangible, that eluded her, leaving only an impression upon her half-awakened senses of something unattainable. She was up and dressed in the cool of the early morning. The air was invigorating and steadied somewhat her faculties. However, she was not seeking refreshment or help from any source, either external or from within. She was blindly following whatever impulse moved her, as if she had placed herself in alien hands for direction, and freed her soul of responsibility.

Most of the people at that early hour were still in bed and asleep. A few, who intended to go over to the *Chênière* for mass, were moving about. The lovers, who had laid their plans the night before, were already strolling toward the wharf. The lady in black, with her Sunday prayer-book, velvet and gold-clasped, and her Sunday silver beads, was following them at no great distance. Old Monsieur Farival was up, and was more than half inclined to do anything that suggested itself. He put on his big straw hat, and taking his umbrella from the stand in the hall, followed the lady in black, never overtaking her.

The little negro girl who worked Madame Lebrun's sewing-machine was sweeping the galleries with long, absent-minded strokes of the broom. Edna sent her up into the house to awaken Robert.

"Tell him I am going to the *Chênière*. The boat is ready; tell him to hurry."

He had soon joined her. She had never sent for him before. She had never asked for him. She had never seemed to want him before. She did not appear conscious that she had done anything unusual in commanding his presence. He was apparently equally unconscious of anything extraordinary in the situation. But his face was suffused with a quiet glow when he met her.

They went together back to the kitchen to drink coffee. There was no time to wait for any nicety of service. They stood outside the window and the cook passed them their coffee and a roll, which they drank and ate from the window-sill. Edna said it tasted good. She had not thought of coffee nor of anything. He told her he had often noticed that she lacked forethought.

"Wasn't it enough to think of going to the *Chênière* and waking you up?" she laughed. "Do I have to think of everything?—as Léonce says when he's in a bad humor. I don't blame him; he'd never be in a bad humor if it weren't for me."

They took a short cut across the sands. At a distance they could see the curious procession moving toward the wharf—the lovers, shoulder to shoulder, creeping; the lady in black, gaining steadily upon them; old Monsieur Farival, losing ground inch by inch, and a young barefooted Spanish girl, with a red kerchief on her head and a basket on her arm, bringing up the rear.

Robert knew the girl, and he talked to her a little in the boat. No one present understood what they said. Her name was Mariequita. She had a round, sly, piquant face and pretty black eyes. Her hands were small, and she kept them folded over the handle of her basket. Her feet were broad and coarse. She did not strive to hide them. Edna looked at her feet, and noticed the sand and slime between her brown toes.

Beaudelet grumbled because Mariequita was there, taking up so much room. In reality he was annoyed at having old Monsieur Farival, who considered himself the better sailor of the two. But he would not quarrel with so old a man as Monsieur Farival, so he quarreled with Mariequita. The girl was deprecatory at one moment, appealing to Robert. She was saucy the next, moving her head up and down, making "eyes" at Robert and making "mouths" at Beaudelet.

The lovers were all alone. They saw nothing, they heard nothing. The lady in black was counting her beads for the third time. Old Monsieur Farival talked incessantly of what he knew about handling a boat, and of what Beaudelet did not know on the same subject.

Edna liked it all. She looked Mariequita up and down, from her ugly brown toes to her pretty black eyes, and back again.

"Why does she look at me like that?" inquired the girl of Robert.

"Maybe she thinks you are pretty. Shall I ask her?"

"No. Is she your sweetheart?"

"She's a married lady, and has two children."

"Oh! well! Francisco ran away with Sylvano's wife, who had four children. They took all his money and one of the children and stole his boat."

"Shut up!"

"Does she understand?"

"Oh, hush!"

"Are those two married over there—leaning on each other?"

"Of course not," laughed Robert.

"Of course not," echoed Mariequita, with a serious, confirmatory bob of the head.

The sun was high up and beginning to bite. The swift breeze seemed to Edna to bury the sting of it into the pores of her face and hands. Robert held his umbrella over her.

As they went cutting sidewise through the water, the sails bellied taut, with the wind filling and overflowing them. Old Monsieur Farival laughed sardonically at something as he looked at the sails, and Beaudelet swore at the old man under his breath.

Sailing across the bay to the *Chênière Caminada*, Edna felt as if she were being borne away from some anchorage which had held her fast, whose chains had been loosening—had snapped the night before when the mystic spirit was abroad, leaving her free to drift whithersoever she chose to set her sails. Robert spoke to her incessantly; he no longer noticed Mariequita. The girl had shrimps in her bamboo basket. They were covered with Spanish moss. She beat the moss down impatiently, and muttered to herself sullenly.

"Let us go to Grand Terre to-morrow," said Robert in a low voice.

"What shall we do there?"

"Climb up the hill to the old fort and look at the little wriggling gold snakes, and watch the lizards sun themselves."

She gazed away toward Grande Terre and thought she would like to be alone there with Robert, in the sun, listening to the ocean's roar and watching the slimy lizards writhe in and out among the ruins of the old fort.

"And the next day or the next we can sail to the Bayou Brulow," he went on.

"What shall we do there?"

"Anything—cast bait for fish."

"No; we'll go back to Grande Terre. Let the fish alone."

"We'll go wherever you like," he said. "I'll have Tonie come over and help me patch and trim my boat. We shall not need Beaudelet nor any one. Are you afraid of the pirogue?"[18]

"Oh, no."

"Then I'll take you some night on the pirogue when the moon shines. Maybe your Gulf spirit will whisper to you in which of these islands the treasures are hidden—direct you to the very spot, perhaps."

"And in a day we should be rich!" she laughed. "I'd give it all to you, the pirate gold and every bit of treasure we could dig up. I think you would know how to spend it. Pirate gold isn't a thing to be hoarded or utilized. It is something to squander and throw to the four winds, for the fun of seeing the golden specks fly."

"We'd share it, and scatter it together," he said. His face flushed.

They all went together up to the quaint little Gothic church of Our Lady of Lourdes, gleaming all brown and yellow with paint in the sun's glare.

Only Beaudelet remained behind, tinkering at his boat, and Mariequita walked away with her basket of shrimps, casting a look of childish ill-humor and reproach at Robert from the corner of her eye.

XIII

A feeling of oppression and drowsiness overcame Edna during the service. Her head began to ache, and the lights on the altar swayed before her eyes. Another time she might have made an effort to regain her composure; but her one thought was to quit the stifling atmosphere of the church and reach the open air. She arose, climbing over Robert's feet with a muttered apology. Old Monsieur Farival, flurried, curious, stood up, but upon seeing that Robert had followed Mrs. Pontellier, he sank back into his seat. He whispered an anxious inquiry of the lady in black, who did not notice him or reply, but kept her eyes fastened upon the pages of her velvet prayer-book.

"I felt giddy and almost overcome," Edna said, lifting her hands instinctively to her head and pushing her straw hat up from her forehead. "I couldn't have stayed through the service." They were outside in the shadow of the church. Robert was full of solicitude.

"It was folly to have thought of going in the first place, let alone staying. Come over to Madame Antoine's; you can rest there." He took her arm and led her away, looking anxiously and continuously down into her face.

How still it was, with only the voice of the sea whispering through the reeds that grew in the salt-water pools! The long line of little gray, weather-

---

[18]A canoe

beaten houses nestled peacefully among the orange trees. It must always have been God's day on that low, drowsy island, Edna thought. They stopped, leaning over a jagged fence made of sea-drift, to ask for water. A youth, a mild-faced Acadian, was drawing water from the cistern, which was nothing more than a rusty buoy, with an opening on one side, sunk in the ground. The water which the youth handed to them in a tin pail was not cold to taste, but it was cool to her heated face, and it greatly revived and refreshed her.

Madame Antoine's cot was at the far end of the village. She welcomed them with all the native hospitality, as she would have opened her door to let the sunlight in. She was fat, and walked heavily and clumsily across the floor. She could speak no English, but when Robert made her understand that the lady who accompanied him was ill and desired to rest, she was all eagerness to make Edna feel at home and to dispose of her comfortably.

The whole place was immaculately clean, and the big, four-posted bed, snow-white, invited one to repose. It stood in a small side room which looked out across a narrow grass plot toward the shed, where there was a disabled boat lying keel upward.

Madame Antoine had not gone to mass. Her son Tonie had, but she supposed he would soon be back, and she invited Robert to be seated and wait for him. But he went and sat outside the door and smoked. Madame Antoine busied herself in the large front room preparing dinner. She was boiling mullets over a few red coals in the huge fireplace.

Edna, left alone in the little side room, loosened her clothes, removing the greater part of them. She bathed her face, her neck and arms in the basin that stood between the windows. She took off her shoes and stockings and stretched herself in the very center of the high, white bed. How luxurious it felt to rest thus in a strange, quaint bed, with its sweet country odor of laurel lingering about the sheets and mattress! She stretched her strong limbs that ached a little. She ran her fingers through her loosened hair for a while. She looked at her round arms as she held them straight up and rubbed them one after the other, observing closely, as if it were something she saw for the first time, the fine, firm quality and texture of her flesh. She clasped her hands easily above her head, and it was thus she fell asleep.

She slept lightly at first, half awake and drowsily attentive to the things about her. She could hear Madame Antoine's heavy, scraping tread as she walked back and forth on the sanded floor. Some chickens were clucking outside the windows, scratching for bits of gravel in the grass. Later she half heard the voices of Robert and Tonie talking under the shed. She did not stir. Even her eyelids rested numb and heavily over her sleepy eyes. The voices went on—Tonie's slow, Acadian drawl, Robert's quick, soft, smooth French. She understood French imperfectly unless directly addressed, and the voices were only part of the other drowsy, muffled sounds lulling her senses.

When Edna awoke it was with the conviction that she had slept long and soundly. The voices were hushed under the shed. Madame Antoine's step was no longer to be heard in the adjoining room. Even the chickens had gone elsewhere to scratch and cluck. The mosquito bar was drawn over her; the old woman had come in while she slept and let down the bar. Edna rose quietly from the bed, and looking between the curtains of the window, she saw by the slanting rays of the sun that the afternoon was far advanced. Robert was out there under the shed, reclining in the shade against the sloping keel of the overturned boat. He was reading from a book. Tonic was no longer with him. She wondered what had become of the rest of the party. She peeped out at him two or three times as she stood washing herself in the little basin between the windows.

Madame Antoine had lain some coarse, clean towels upon a chair, and had placed a box of *poudre de riz*[19] within easy reach. Edna dabbed the powder upon her nose and cheeks as she looked at herself closely in the little distorted mirror which hung on the wall above the basin. Her eyes were bright and wide awake and her face glowed.

When she had completed her toilet she walked into the adjoining room. She was very hungry. No one was there. But there was a cloth spread upon the table that stood against the wall, and a cover was laid for one, with a crusty brown loaf and a bottle of wine beside the plate. Edna bit a piece from the brown loaf, tearing it with her strong, white teeth. She poured some of the wine into the glass and drank it down. Then she went softly out of doors, and plucking an orange from the low-hanging bough of a tree, threw it at Robert, who did not know she was awake and up.

An illumination broke over his whole face when he saw her and joined her under the orange tree.

"How many years have I slept?" she inquired. "The whole island seems changed. A new race of beings must have sprung up, leaving only you and me as past relics. How many ages ago did Madame Antoine and Tonie die? and when did our people from Grand Isle disappear from the earth?"

He familiarly adjusted a ruffle upon her shoulder.

"You have slept precisely one hundred years. I was left here to guard your slumbers; and for one hundred years I have been out under the shed reading a book. The only evil I couldn't prevent was to keep a broiled fowl from drying up."

"If it has turned to stone, still will I eat it," said Edna, moving with him into the house. "But really, what has become of Monsieur Farival and the others?"

---

[19]Talcum powder

"Gone hours ago. When they found that you were sleeping they thought it best not to awake you. Any way, I wouldn't have let them. What was I here for?"

"I wonder if Léonce will be uneasy!" she speculated, as she seated herself at table.

"Of course not; he knows you are with me," Robert replied, as he busied himself among sundry pans and covered dishes which had been left standing on the hearth.

"Where are Madame Antoine and her son?" asked Edna.

"Gone to Vespers, and to visit some friends, I believe. I am to take you back in Tonie's boat whenever you are ready to go."

He stirred the smoldering ashes till the broiled fowl began to sizzle afresh. He served her with no mean repast, dripping the coffee anew and sharing it with her. Madame Antoine had cooked little else than the mullets, but while Edna slept Robert had foraged the island. He was childishly gratified to discover her appetite, and to see the relish with which she ate the food which he had procured for her.

"Shall we go right away?" she asked, after draining her glass and brushing together the crumbs of the crusty loaf.

"The sun isn't as low as it will be in two hours," he answered.

"The sun will be gone in two hours."

"Well, let it go; who cares!"

They waited a good while under the orange trees, till Madame Antoine came back, panting, waddling, with a thousand apologies to explain her absence. Tonie did not dare to return. He was shy, and would not willingly face any woman except his mother.

It was very pleasant to stay there under the orange trees, while the sun dipped lower and lower, turning the western sky to flaming copper and gold. The shadows lengthened and crept out like stealthy, grotesque monsters across the grass.

Edna and Robert both sat upon the ground—that is, he lay upon the ground beside her, occasionally picking at the hem of her muslin gown.

Madame Antoine seated her fat body, broad and squat, upon a bench beside the door. She had been talking all the afternoon, and had wound herself up to the story-telling pitch.

And what stories she told them! But twice in her life she had left the *Chênière Caminada*, and then for the briefest span. All her years she had squatted and waddled there upon the island, gathering legends of the Baratarians and the sea. The night came on, with the moon to lighten it. Edna could hear the whispering voices of dead men and the click of muffled gold.

When she and Robert stepped into Tonie's boat, with the red lateen sail, misty spirit forms were prowling in the shadows and among the reeds, and upon the water were phantom ships, speeding to cover.

XIV

The youngest boy, Etienne, had been very naughty, Madame Ratignolle said, as she delivered him into the hands of his mother. He had been unwilling to go to bed and had made a scene; whereupon she had taken charge of him and pacified him as well as she could. Raoul had been in bed and asleep for two hours.

The youngster was in his long white nightgown, that kept tripping him up as Madame Ratignolle led him along by the hand. With the other chubby fist he rubbed his eyes, which were heavy with sleep and ill humor. Edna took him in her arms, and seating herself in the rocker, began to coddle and caress him, calling him all manner of tender names, soothing him to sleep.

It was not more than nine o'clock. No one had yet gone to bed but the children.

Léonce had been very uneasy at first, Madame Ratignolle said, and had wanted to start at once for the *Chênière*. But Monsieur Farival had assured him that his wife was only overcome with sleep and fatigue, that Tonie would bring her safely back later in the day; and he had thus been dissuaded from crossing the bay. He had gone over to Klein's, looking up some cotton broker whom he wished to see in regard to securities, exchanges, stocks, bonds, or something of the sort, Madame Ratignolle did not remember what. He said he would not remain away late. She herself was suffering from heat and oppression, she said. She carried a bottle of salts and a large fan. She would not consent to remain with Edna, for Monsieur Ratignolle was alone, and he detested above all things to be left alone.

When Etienne had fallen asleep Edna bore him into the back room, and Robert went and lifted the mosquito bar that she might lay the child comfortably in his bed. The quadroon had vanished. When they emerged from the cottage Robert bade Edna good-night.

"Do you know we have been together the whole livelong day, Robert— since early this morning?" she said at parting.

"All but the hundred years when you were sleeping. Good-night."

He pressed her hand and went away in the direction of the beach. He did not join any of the others, but walked alone toward the Gulf.

Edna stayed outside, awaiting her husband's return. She had no desire to sleep or to retire; nor did she feel like going over to sit with the Ratignolle, or to join Madame Lebrun and a group whose animated voices reached her as they sat in conversation before the house. She let her mind wander back over her stay at Grand Isle; and she tried to discover wherein this summer had been different from any and every other summer of her life. She could only realize that she herself—her present self—was in some way different from the other self. That she was seeing with different eyes and making the acquaintance of new conditions in herself that colored and changed her environment, she did not yet suspect.

She wondered why Robert had gone away and left her. It did not occur to her to think he might have grown tired of being with her the livelong day. She was not tired, and she felt that he was not. She regretted that he had gone. It was so much more natural to have him stay when he was not absolutely required to leave her.

As Edna waited for her husband she sang low a little song that Robert had sung as they crossed the bay. It began with "Ah! *Si tu savais*,"[20] and every verse ended with "*si tu savais*."

Robert's voice was not pretentious. It was musical and true. The voice, the notes, the whole refrain haunted her memory.

XV

When Edna entered the dining-room one evening a little late, as was her habit, an unusually animated conversation seemed to be going on. Several persons were talking at once, and Victor's voice was predominating, even over that of his mother. Edna had returned late from her bath, had dressed in some haste, and her face was flushed. Her head, set off by her dainty white gown, suggested a rich, rare blossom. She took her seat at table between old Monsieur Farival and Madame Ratignolle.

As she seated herself and was about to begin to eat her soup, which had been served when she entered the room, several persons informed her simultaneously that Robert was going to Mexico. She laid her spoon down and looked about her bewildered. He had been with her, reading to her all the morning, and had never even mentioned such a place as Mexico. She had not seen him during the afternoon; she had heard some one say he was at the house, upstairs with his mother. This she had thought nothing of, though she was surprised when he did not join her later in the afternoon, when she went down to the beach.

She looked across at him, where he sat beside Madame Lebrun, who presided. Edna's face was a blank picture of bewilderment, which she never thought of disguising. He lifted his eyebrows with the pretext of a smile as he returned her glance. He looked embarrassed and uneasy.

---

[20]Ah, if you only knew.

"When is he going?" she asked of everybody in general, as if Robert were not there to answer for himself.

"To-night!" "This very evening!" "Did you ever!" "What possesses him!" were some of the replies she gathered, uttered simultaneously in French and English.

"Impossible!" she exclaimed. "How can a person start off from Grand Isle to Mexico at a moment's notice, as if he were going over to Klein's or to the wharf or down to the beach?"

"I said all along I was going to Mexico; I've been saying so for years!" cried Robert, in an excited and irritable tone, with the air of a man defending himself against a swarm of stinging insects.

Madame Lebrun knocked on the table with her knife handle.

"Please let Robert explain why he is going, and why he is going tonight," she called out. "Really, this table is getting to be more and more like Bedlam every day, with everybody talking at once. Sometimes—I hope God will forgive me—but positively, sometimes I wish Victor would lose the power of speech."

Victor laughed sardonically as he thanked his mother for her holy wish, of which he failed to see the benefit to anybody, except that it might afford her a more ample opportunity and license to talk herself.

Monsieur Farival thought that Victor should have been taken out in midocean in his earliest youth and drowned. Victor thought there would be more logic in thus disposing of old people with an established claim for making themselves universally obnoxious. Madame Lebrun grew a trifle hysterical; Robert called his brother some sharp, hard names.

"There's nothing much to explain, mother," he said; though he explained, nevertheless—looking chiefly at Edna—that he could only meet the gentleman whom he intended to join at Vera Cruz by taking such and such a steamer, which left New Orleans on such a day; that Beaudelet was going out with his lugger-load of vegetables that night, which gave him an opportunity of reaching the city and making his vessel in time.

"But when did you make up your mind to all this?" demanded Monsieur Farival.

"This afternoon," returned Robert, with as shade of annoyance.

"At what time this afternoon?" persisted the old gentleman, with nagging determination, as if he were cross-questioning a criminal in a court of justice.

"At four o'clock this afternoon, Monsieur Farival," Robert replied, in a high voice and with a lofty air, which reminded Edna of some gentleman on the stage.

She had forced herself to eat most of her soup, and now she was picking the flaky bits of a *court bouillon*[21] with her fork.

---

[21] Fish broth

The lovers were profiting by the general conversation on Mexico to speak in whispers of matters which they rightly considered were interesting to no one but themselves. The lady in black had once received a pair of prayer-beads of curious workmanship from Mexico, with very special indulgence attached to them, but she had never been able to ascertain whether the indulgence extended outside the Mexican border. Father Fochel of the Cathedral had attempted to explain it; but he had not done so to her satisfaction. And she begged that Robert would interest himself, and discover, if possible, whether she was entitled to the indulgence accompanying the remarkably curious Mexican prayer-beads.

Madame Ratignolle hoped that Robert would exercise extreme caution in dealing with the Mexicans, who, she considered, were a treacherous people, unscrupulous and revengeful. She trusted she did them no injustice in thus condemning them as a race. She had known personally but one Mexican, who made and sold excellent tamales, and whom she would have trusted implicitly, so soft-spoken was he. One day he was arrested for stabbing his wife. She never knew whether he had been hanged or not.

Victor had grown hilarious, and was attempting to tell an anecdote about a Mexican girl who served chocolate one winter in a restaurant in Dauphine Street. No one would listen to him but old Monsieur Farival, who went into convulsions over the droll story.

Edna wondered if they had all gone mad, to be talking and clamoring at that rate. She herself could think of nothing to say about Mexico or the Mexicans.

"At what time do you leave?" she asked Robert.

"At ten," he told her. "Beaudelet wants to wait for the moon."

"Are you all ready to go?"

"Quite ready. I shall only take a hand-bag, and shall pack my trunk in the city."

He turned to answer some question put to him by his mother, and Edna, having finished her black coffee, left the table.

She went directly to her room. The little cottage was close and stuffy after leaving the outer air. But she did not mind; there appeared to be a hundred different things demanding her attention indoors. She began to set the toilet-stand to rights, grumbling at the negligence of the quadroon, who was in the adjoining room putting the children to bed. She gathered together stray garments that were hanging on the backs of chairs, and put each where it belonged in closet or bureau drawer. She changed her gown for a more comfortable and commodious wrapper. She rearranged her hair, combing and brushing it with unusual energy. Then she went in and assisted the quadroon in getting the boys to bed.

They were very playful and inclined to talk—to do anything but lie quiet and go to sleep. Edna sent the quadroon away to her supper and told her she need not return. Then she sat and told the children a story. Instead of soothing it excited them, and added to their wakefulness. She left them in heated argument, speculating about the conclusion of the tale which their mother promised to finish the following night.

The little black girl came in to say that Madame Lebrun would like to have Mrs. Pontellier go and sit with them over at the house till Mr. Robert went away. Edna returned answer that she had already undressed, that she did not feel quite well, but perhaps she would go over to the house later. She started to dress again, and got as far advanced as to remove her *peignoir*. But changing her mind once more she resumed the *peignoir*, and went outside and sat down before her door. She was over-heated and irritable, and fanned herself energetically for a while. Madame Ratignolle came down to discover what was the matter.

"All that noise and confusion at the table must have upset me," replied Edna, "and moreover, I hate shocks and surprises. The idea of Robert starting off in such a ridiculously sudden and dramatic way! As if it were a matter of life and death! Never saying a word about it all morning when he was with me."

"Yes," agreed Madame Ratignolle. "I think it was showing us all—you especially—very little consideration. It wouldn't have surprised me in any of the others; those Lebruns are all given to heroics. But I must say I should never have expected such a thing from Robert. Are you not coming down? Come on, dear; it doesn't look friendly."

"No," said Edna, a little sullenly. "I can't go to the trouble of dressing again; I don't feel like it."

"You needn't dress; you look all right; fasten a belt around your waist. Just look at me!"

"No," persisted Edna; "but you go on. Madame Lebrun might be offended if we both stayed away."

Madame Ratignolle kissed Edna good-night, and went away, being in truth rather desirous of joining in the general and animated conversation which was still in progress concerning Mexico and the Mexicans.

Somewhat later Robert came up, carrying his hand-bag.

"Aren't you feeling well?" he asked.

"Oh, well enough. Are you going right away?"

He lit a match and looked at his watch. "In twenty minutes," he said. The sudden and brief flare of the match emphasized the darkness for a while. He sat down upon a stool which the children had left out on the porch.

"Get a chair," said Edna.

"This will do," he replied. He put on his soft hat and nervously took it off again, and wiping his face with his handkerchief, complained of the heat.

"Take the fan," said Edna, offering it to him.

"Oh, no! Thank you. It does no good; you have to stop fanning some time, and feel all the more uncomfortable afterward."

"That's one of the ridiculous things which men always say. I have never known one to speak otherwise of fanning. How long will you be gone?"

"Forever, perhaps. I don't know. It depends upon a good many things."

"Well, in case it shouldn't be forever, how long will it be?"

"I don't know."

"This seems to me perfectly preposterous and uncalled for. I don't like it. I don't understand your motive for silence and mystery, never saying a word to me about it this morning." He remained silent, not offering to defend himself. He only said, after a moment:

"Don't part with me in an ill-humor. I never knew you to be out of patience with me before."

"I don't want to part in any ill-humor," she said. "But can't you understand? I've grown used to seeing you, to having you with me all the time, and your action seems unfriendly, even unkind. You don't even offer an excuse for it. Why, I was planning to be together, thinking of how pleasant it would be to see you in the city next winter."

"So was I," he blurted. "Perhaps that's the—" He stood up suddenly and held out his hand. "Good-by, my dear Mrs. Pontellier; good-by. You won't—I hope you won't completely forget me." She clung to his hand, striving to detain him.

"Write to me when you get there, won't you, Robert?" she entreated.

"I will, thank you. Good-by."

How unlike Robert! The merest acquaintance would have said something more emphatic than "I will, thank you; good-by," to such a request.

He had evidently already taken leave of the people over at the house, for he descended the steps and went to join Beaudelet, who was out there with an oar across his shoulder waiting for Robert. They walked away in the darkness. She could only hear Beaudelet's voice; Robert had apparently not even spoken a word of greeting to his companion.

Edna bit her handkerchief convulsively, striving to hold back and to hide, even from herself as she would have hidden from another, the emotion which was troubling—tearing—her. Her eyes were brimming with tears.

For the first time she recognized anew the symptoms of infatuation which she had felt incipiently as a child, as a girl in her earliest teens, and later as a young woman. The recognition did not lessen the reality, the poignancy of the revelation by any suggestion or promise of instability. The past was nothing to her; offered no lesson which she was willing to heed. The future was a mystery which she never attempted to penetrate. The present alone was significant; was hers, to torture her as it was doing then with the biting conviction that she had lost that which she had held, that she had been denied that which her impassioned, newly awakened being demanded.

XVI

"Do you miss your friend greatly?" asked Mademoiselle Reisz one morning as she came creeping up behind Edna, who had just left her cottage on her way to the beach. She spent much of her time in the water since she had acquired finally the art of swimming. As their stay at Grand Isle drew near its close, she felt that she could not give too much time to a diversion which afforded her the only real pleasurable moments that she knew. When Mademoiselle Reisz came and touched her upon the shoulder and spoke to her, the woman seemed to echo the thought which was ever in Edna's mind; or better, the feeling which constantly possessed her.

Robert's going had some way taken the brightness, the color, the meaning out of everything. The conditions of her life were in no way changed, but her whole existence was dulled, like a faded garment which seems to be no longer worth wearing. She sought him everywhere—in others whom she induced to talk about him. She went up in the mornings to Madame Lebrun's room, braving the clatter of the old sewing-machine. She sat there and chatted at intervals as Robert had done. She gazed around the room at the pictures and photographs hanging upon the wall, and discovered in some corner an old family album, which she examined with the keenest interest, appealing to Madame Lebrun for enlightenment concerning the many figures and faces which she discovered between its pages.

There was a picture of Madame Lebrun with Robert as a baby, seated in her lap, a round-faced infant with a fist in his mouth. The eyes alone in the baby suggested the man. And that was he also in kilts, at the age of five, wearing long curls and holding a whip in his hand. It made Edna laugh, and she laughed, too, at the portrait in his first long trousers; while another interested her, taken when he left for college, looking thin, long-faced, with eyes full of fire, ambition and great intentions. But there was no recent picture, none which suggested the Robert who had gone away five days ago, leaving a void and wilderness behind him.

"Oh, Robert stopped having his pictures taken when he had to pay for them himself! He found wiser use for his money, he says," explained Madame Lebrun. She had a letter from him, written before he left New Orleans. Edna wished to see the letter, and Madame Lebrun told her to look for it either on the table or the dresser, or perhaps it was on the mantelpiece.

The letter was on the bookshelf. It possessed the greatest interest and attraction for Edna; the envelope, its size and shape, the post-mark, the handwriting. She examined every detail of the outside before opening it. There were only a few lines, setting forth that he would leave the city that afternoon, that he had packed his trunk in good shape, that he was well, and sent her his love and begged to be affectionately remembered to all. There was no special message to Edna except a postscript saying that if Mrs. Pontellier desired to finish the book which he had been reading to her, his mother would find it in his room, among other books there on the table. Edna experienced a pang of jealousy because he had written to his mother rather than to her.

Every one seemed to take for granted that she missed him. Even her husband, when he came down the Saturday following Robert's departure, expressed regret that he had gone.

"How do you get on without him, Edna?" he asked.

"It's very dull without him," she admitted. Mr. Pontellier had seen Robert in the city, and Edna asked him a dozen questions or more. Where had they met? On Carondelet Street, in the morning. They had gone "in" and had a drink and a cigar together. What had they talked about? Chiefly about his prospects in Mexico, which Mr. Pontellier thought were promising. How did he look? How did he seem—grave, or gay, or how? Quite cheerful, and wholly taken up with the idea of his trip, which Mr. Pontellier found altogether natural in a young fellow about to seek fortune and adventure in a strange, queer country.

Edna tapped her foot impatiently, and wondered why the children persisted in playing in the sun when they might be under the trees. She went down and led them out of the sun, scolding the quadroon for not being more attentive.

It did not strike her as in the least grotesque that she should be making of Robert the object of conversation and leading her husband to speak of him. The sentiment which she entertained for Robert in no way resembled that which she felt for her husband, or had ever felt, or ever expected to feel. She had all her life long been accustomed to harbor thoughts and emotions which never voiced themselves. They had never taken the form of struggles. They belonged to her and were her own, and she entertained the conviction that she had a right to them and that they concerned no one but herself. Edna had once told Madame Ratignolle that she would never sacrifice herself for her children, or for any one. Then had followed a rather heated argument; the two women did not appear to understand each other or to be talking the same language. Edna tried to appease her friend, to explain.

"I would give up the unessential; I would give my money, I would give my life for my children; but I wouldn't give myself. I can't make it more clear; it's only something which I am beginning to comprehend, which is revealing itself to me."

"I don't know what you would call the essential, or what you mean by the unessential," said Madame Ratignolle, cheerfully; "but a woman who would give her life for her children could do no more than that—your Bible tells you so. I'm sure I couldn't do more than that."

"Oh, yes you could!" laughed Edna.

She was not surprised at Mademoiselle Reisz's question the morning that lady, following her to the beach, tapped her on the shoulder and asked if she did not greatly miss her young friend.

"Oh, good morning, Mademoiselle; is it you? Why, of course I miss Robert. Are you going down to bathe?"

"Why should I go down to bathe at the very end of the season when I haven't been in the surf all summer?" replied the woman, disagreeably.

"I beg your pardon," offered Edna, in some embarrassment, for she should have remembered that Mademoiselle Reisz's avoidance of the water had furnished a theme for much pleasantry. Some among them thought it was on account of her false hair, or the dread of getting the violets wet, while others attributed it to the natural aversion for water sometimes believed to accompany the artistic temperament. Mademoiselle offered Edna some chocolates in a paper bag, which she took from her pocket, by way of showing that she bore no ill feeling. She habitually ate chocolates for their sustaining quality; they contained much nutrient in small compass, she said. They saved her from starvation, as Madame Lebrun's table was utterly impossible; and no one save so impertinent a woman as Madame Lebrun could think of offering such food to people and requiring them to pay for it.

"She must feel very lonely without her son," said Edna, desiring to change the subject. "Her favorite son, too. It must have been quite hard to let him go."

Mademoiselle laughed maliciously.

"Her favorite son! Oh, dear! Who could have been imposing such a tale upon you? Aline Lebrun lives for Victor, and for Victor alone. She has spoiled him into the worthless creature he is. She worships him and the ground he walks on. Robert is very well in a way, to give up all the money he can earn to the family, and keep the barest pittance for himself. Favorite son, indeed! I miss the poor fellow myself, my dear. I liked to see him and to hear him about the place—the only Lebrun who is worth a pinch of salt. He comes to see me often in the city. I like to play to him. That Victor! hanging would be too good for him. It's a wonder Robert hasn't beaten him to death long ago."

"I thought he had great patience with his brother," offered Edna, glad to be talking about Robert, no matter what was said.

"Oh! he thrashed him well enough a year or two ago," said Mademoiselle. "It was about a Spanish girl, whom Victor considered that he had some sort of claim upon. He met Robert one day talking to the girl, or walking with her, or bathing with her, or carrying her basket—I don't remember what;—and he became so insulting and abusive that Robert gave him a thrashing on the spot that has kept him comparatively in order for a good while. It's about time he was getting another."

"Was her name Mariequita?" asked Edna.

"Mariequita—yes, that was it; Mariequita. I had forgotten. Oh, she's a sly one, and a bad one, that Mariequita!"

Edna looked down at Mademoiselle Reisz and wondered how she could have listened to her venom so long. For some reason she felt depressed, almost unhappy. She had not intended to go into the water; but she donned her bathing suit, and left Mademoiselle alone, seated under the shade of the children's tent. The water was growing cooler as the season advanced. Edna plunged and swam about with an abandon that thrilled and invigorated her. She remained a long time in the water, half hoping that Mademoiselle Reisz would not wait for her.

But Mademoiselle waited. She was very amiable during the walk back, and raved much over Edna's appearance in her bathing suit. She talked about music. She hoped that Edna would go to see her in the city, and wrote her address with the stub of a pencil on a piece of card which she found in her pocket.

"When do you leave?" asked Edna.

"Next Monday; and you?"

"The following week," answered Edna, adding, "It has been a pleasant summer, hasn't it, Mademoiselle?"

"Well," agreed Mademoiselle Reisz, with a shrug, "rather pleasant, if it hadn't been for the mosquitoes and the Farival twins."

XVII

The Pontelliers possessed a very charming home on Esplanade Street in New Orleans. It was a large, double cottage, with a broad front veranda, whose round, fluted columns supported the sloping roof. The house was painted a dazzling white; the outside shutters, or jalousies, were green. In the yard, which was kept scrupulously neat, were flowers and plants of every description which flourish in South Louisiana. Within doors the appointments were perfect after the conventional type. The softest carpets and rugs covered the floors; rich and tasteful draperies hung at doors and windows. There were paintings, selected with judgment and discrimination, upon the walls. The cut glass, the silver, the heavy damask which daily appeared upon the table were the envy of many women whose husbands were less generous than Mr. Pontellier.

Mr. Pontellier was very fond of walking about his house examining its various appointments and details, to see that nothing was amiss. He greatly valued his possessions, chiefly because they were his, and derived genuine pleasure from contemplating a painting, a statuette, a rare lace curtain—no matter what—after he had bought it and placed it among his household goods.

On Tuesday afternoons—Tuesday being Mrs. Pontellier's reception day—there was a constant stream of callers—women who came in carriages or in the street cars, or walked when the air was soft and distance permitted. A light-colored mulatto boy, in dress coat and bearing a diminutive silver tray for the reception of cards, admitted them. A maid, in white fluted cap, offered the callers liqueur, coffee, or chocolate, as they might desire. Mrs. Pontellier, attired in a handsome reception gown, remained in the drawing-room the entire afternoon receiving her visitors. Men sometimes called in the evening with their wives.

This had been the programme which Mrs. Pontellier had religiously followed since her marriage, six years before. Certain evenings during the week she and her husband attended the opera or sometimes the play.

Mr. Pontellier left his home in the mornings between nine and ten o'clock, and rarely returned before half-past six or seven in the evening—dinner being served at half-past seven.

He and his wife seated themselves at table one Tuesday evening, a few weeks after their return from Grand Isle. They were alone together. The boys were being put to bed; the patter of their bare, escaping feet could be heard occasionally, as well as the pursuing voice of the quadroon, lifted in mild protest and entreaty. Mrs. Pontellier did not wear her usual Tuesday reception gown; she was in ordinary house dress. Mr. Pontellier, who was observant about such things, noticed it, as he served the soup and handed it to the boy in waiting.

"Tired out, Edna? Whom did you have? Many callers?" he asked. He tasted his soup and began to season it with pepper, salt, vinegar, mustard—everything within reach.

"There were a good many," replied Edna, who was eating her soup with evident satisfaction. "I found their cards when I got home; I was out."

"Out!" exclaimed her husband, with something like genuine consternation in his voice as he laid down the vinegar cruet and looked at her through his glasses. "Why, what could have taken you out on Tuesday? What did you have to do?"

"Nothing. I simply felt like going out, and I went out."

"Well, I hope you left some suitable excuse," said her husband, some-what appeased, as he added a dash of cayenne pepper to the soup.

"No, I left no excuse. I told Joe to say I was out, that was all."

"Why, my dear, I should think you'd understand by this time that people don't do such things; we've got to observe *les convenances*[22] if we ever expect to get on and keep up with the procession. If you felt that you had to leave home this afternoon, you should have left some suitable explanation for your absence.

"This soup is really impossible; it's strange that woman hasn't learned yet to make a decent soup. Any free-lunch stand in town serves a better one. Was Mrs. Belthrop here?"

"Bring the tray with the cards, Joe. I don't remember who was here."

The boy retired and returned after a moment, bringing the tiny silver tray, which was covered with ladies' visiting cards. He handed it to Mrs. Pontellier.

"Give it to Mr. Pontellier," she said.

Joe offered the tray to Mr. Pontellier, and removed the soup.

Mr. Pontellier scanned the names of his wife's callers, reading some of them aloud, with comments as he read.

" 'The Misses Delasidas.' I worked a big deal in futures for their father this morning; nice girls; it's time they were getting married. 'Mrs. Belthrop.' I tell you what it is Edna; you can't afford to snub Mrs. Belthrop. Why, Belthrop could buy and sell us ten times over. His business is worth a good, round sum to me. You'd better write her a note. 'Mrs. James Highcamp.' Hugh! the less you have to do with Mrs. Highcamp, the better. 'Madame Laforcé.' Came all the way from Carrolton, too, poor old soul. 'Miss Wiggs,' 'Mrs. Eleanor Boltons.' " He pushed the cards aside.

"Mercy!" exclaimed Edna, who had been fuming. "Why are you taking the thing so seriously and making such a fuss over it?"

"I'm not making any fuss over it. But it's just such seeming trifles that we've got to take seriously; such things count."

The fish was scorched. Mr. Pontellier would not touch it. Edna said she did not mind a little scorched taste. The roast was in some way not to his fancy, and he did not like the manner in which the vegetables were served.

"It seems to me," he said, "we spend money enough in this house to procure at least one meal a day which a man could eat and retain his self-respect."

"You used to think the cook was a treasure," returned Edna, indifferently.

"Perhaps she was when she first came; but cooks are only human. They need looking after, like any other class of persons that you employ. Suppose I

---

[22]The social conventions.

didn't look after the clerks in my office, just let them run things their own way; they'd soon make a nice mess of me and my business."

"Where are you going?" asked Edna, seeing that her husband arose from table without having eaten a morsel except a taste of the highly-seasoned soup.

"I'm going to get my dinner at the club. Good night." He went into the hall, took his hat and stick from the stand, and left the house.

She was somewhat familiar with such scenes. They had often made her very unhappy. On a few previous occasions she had been completely deprived of any desire to finish her dinner. Sometimes she had gone into the kitchen to administer a tardy rebuke to the cook. Once she went to her room and studied the cookbook during an entire evening, finally writing out a menu for the week, which left her harassed with a feeling that, after all, she had accomplished no good that was worth the name.

But that evening Edna finished her dinner alone, with forced deliberation. Her face was flushed and her eyes flamed with some inward fire that lighted them. After finishing her dinner she went to her room, having instructed the boy to tell any other callers that she was indisposed.

It was a large, beautiful room, rich and picturesque in the soft, dim light which the maid had turned low. She went and stood at an open window and looked out upon the deep tangle of the garden below. All the mystery and witchery of the night seemed to have gathered there amid the perfumes and the dusky and tortuous outlines of flowers and foliage. She was seeking herself and finding herself in just such sweet, half-darkness which met her moods. But the voices were not soothing that came to her from the darkness and the sky above and the stars. They jeered and sounded mournful notes without promise, devoid even of hope. She turned back into the room and began to walk to and fro down its whole length, without stopping, without resting. She carried in her hands a thin handkerchief, which she tore into ribbons, rolled into a ball, and flung from her. Once she stopped, and taking off her wedding ring, flung it upon the carpet. When she saw it lying there, she stamped her heel upon it, striving to crush it. But her small boot heel did not make an indenture, not a mark upon the little glittering circlet.

In a sweeping passion she seized a glass vase from the table and flung it upon the tiles of the hearth. She wanted to destroy something. The crash and clatter were what she wanted to hear.

A maid, alarmed at the din of breaking glass, entered the room to discover what was the matter.

"A vase fell upon the hearth," said Edna. "Never mind; leave it till morning."

"Oh! you might get some of the glass in your feet, ma'am," insisted the young woman, picking up bits of the broken vase that were scattered upon the carpet. "And here's your ring, ma'am, under the chair."

Edna held out her hand, and taking the ring, slipped it upon her finger.

XVIII

The following morning Mr. Pontellier, upon leaving for his office, asked Edna if she would not meet him in town in order to look at some new fixtures for the library.

"I hardly think we need new fixtures, Léonce. Don't let us get anything new; you are too extravagant. I don't believe you ever think of saving or putting by."

"The way to become rich is to make money, my dear Edna, not to save it," he said. He regretted that she did not feel inclined to go with him and select new fixtures. He kissed her good-by, and told her she was not looking well and must take care of herself. She was unusually pale and very quiet.

She stood on the front veranda as he quitted the house, and absently picked a few sprays of jessamine that grew upon a trellis near by. She inhaled the odor of the blossoms and thrust them into the bosom of her white morning gown. The boys were dragging along the banquette[23] a small "express wagon," which they had filled with blocks and sticks. The quadroon was following them with little quick steps, having assumed a fictitious animation and alacrity for the occasion. A fruit vendor was crying his wares in the street.

Edna looked straight before her with a self-absorbed expression upon her face. She felt no interest in anything about her. The street, the children, the fruit vendor, the flowers growing there under her eyes, were all part and parcel of an alien world which had suddenly become antagonistic.

She went back into the house. She had thought of speaking to the cook concerning her blunders of the previous night; but Mr. Pontellier had saved her that disagreeable mission, for which she was so poorly fitted. Mr. Pontellier's arguments were usually convincing with those whom he employed. He left home feeling quite sure that he and Edna would sit down that evening, and possibly a few subsequent evenings, to a dinner deserving of the name.

Edna spent an hour or two in looking over some of her old sketches. She could see their shortcomings and defects, which were glaring in her eyes. She tried to work a little, but found she was not in the humor. Finally she gathered together a few of the sketches—those which she considered the least discred-

---

[23]The sidewalk

itable; and she carried them with her when, a little later, she dressed and left the house. She looked handsome and distinguished in her street gown. The tan of the seashore had left her face, and her forehead was smooth, white, and polished beneath her heavy, yellow-brown hair. There were a few freckles on her face, and a small, dark mole near the under lip and one on the temple, half-hidden in her hair.

As Edna walked along the street she was thinking of Robert. She was still under the spell of her infatuation. She had tried to forget him, realizing the inutility of remembering. But the thought of him was like an obsession, ever pressing itself upon her. It was not that she dwelt upon details of their acquaintance, or recalled in any special or peculiar way his personality; it was his being, his existence, which dominated her thought, fading sometimes as if it would melt into the mist of the forgotten, reviving again with an intensity which filled her with an incomprehensible longing.

Edna was on her way to Madame Ratignolle's. Their intimacy, begun at Grand Isle, had not declined, and they had seen each other with some frequency since their return to the city. The Ratignolles lived at no great distance from Edna's home, on the corner of a side street, where Monsieur Ratignolle owned and conducted a drug store which enjoyed a steady and prosperous trade. His father had been in the business before him, and Monsieur Ratignolle stood well in the community and bore an enviable reputation for integrity and clear-headedness. His family lived in commodious apartments over the store, having an entrance on the side within the *porte cochère*.[24] There was something which Edna thought very French, very foreign, about their whole manner of living. In the large and pleasant salon which extended across the width of the house, the Ratignolles entertained their friends once a fortnight with a *soirée musicale*,[25] sometimes diversified by card-playing. There was a friend who played upon the 'cello. One brought his flute and another his violin, while there were some who sang and a number who performed upon the piano with various degrees of taste and agility. The Ratignolles' *soirées musicales* were widely known, and it was considered a privilege to be invited to them.

Edna found her friend engaged in assorting the clothes which had returned that morning from the laundry. She at once abandoned her occupation upon seeing Edna, who had been ushered without ceremony into her presence.

"Cité can do it as well as I; it is really her business," she explained to Edna, who apologized for interrupting her. And she summoned a young black woman, whom she instructed, in French, to be very careful in checking off the

---

[24]A permanent awning to protect people from rain.

[25]A musical evening.

list which she handed her. She told her to notice particularly if a fine linen handkerchief of Monsieur Ratignolle's, which was missing last week, had been returned; and to be sure to set to one side such pieces as required mending and darning.

Then placing an arm around Edna's waist, she led her to the front of the house, to the salon, where it was cool and sweet with the odor of great roses that stood upon the hearth in jars.

Madame Ratignolle looked more beautiful than ever there at home, in a négligée which left her arms almost wholly bare and exposed the rich, melting curves of her white throat.

"Perhaps I shall be able to paint your picture some day," said Edna with a smile when they were seated. She produced the roll of sketches and started to unfold them. "I believe I ought to work again. I feel as if I wanted to be doing something. What do you think of them? Do you think it worth while to take it up again and study some more? I might study for a while with Laidpore."

She knew that Madame Ratignolle's opinion in such a matter would be next to valueless, that she herself had not alone decided, but determined; but she sought the words of praise and encouragement that would help her to put heart into her venture.

"Your talent is immense, dear!"

"Nonsense!" protested Edna, well pleased.

"Immense, I tell you," persisted Madame Ratignolle, surveying the sketches one by one, at close range, then holding them at arm's length, narrowing her eyes, and dropping her head on one side. "Surely, this Bavarian peasant is worthy of framing; and this basket of apples! Never have I seen anything more lifelike. One might almost be tempted to reach out a hand and take one."

Edna could not control a feeling which bordered upon complacency at her friend's praise, even realizing, as she did, its true worth. She retained a few of the sketches, and gave all the rest to Madame Ratignolle, who appreciated the gift far beyond its value and proudly exhibited the pictures to her husband when he came up from the store a little later for his midday dinner.

Mr. Ratignolle was one of those men who are called the salt of the earth. His cheerfulness was unbounded, and it was matched by his goodness of heart, his broad charity, and common sense. He and his wife spoke English with an accent which was only discernible through its un-English emphasis and a certain carefulness and deliberation. Edna's husband spoke English with no accent whatever. The Ratignolles understood each other perfectly. If ever the fusion of two human beings into one has been accomplished on this sphere it was surely in their union.

As Edna seated herself at table with them she thought, "Better a dinner of herbs," though it did not take her long to discover that it was no dinner of herbs, but a delicious repast, simple, choice, and in every way satisfying.

Monsieur Ratignolle was delighted to see her, though he found her looking not so well as at Grand Isle, and he advised a tonic. He talked a good deal on various topics, a little politics, some city news and neighborhood gossip. He spoke with an animation and earnestness that gave an exaggerated importance to every syllable he uttered. His wife was keenly interested in everything he said, laying down her fork the better to listen, chiming in, taking the words out of his mouth.

Edna felt depressed rather than soothed after leaving them. The little glimpse of domestic harmony which had been offered her, gave her no regret, no longing. It was not a condition of life which fitted her, and she could see in it but an appalling and hopeless ennui. She was moved by a kind of commiseration for Madame Ratignolle,—a pity for that colorless existence which never uplifted its possessor beyond the region of blind contentment, in which no moment of anguish ever visited her soul, in which she would never have the taste of life's delirium. Edna vaguely wondered what she meant by "life's delirium." It had crossed her thought like some unsought extraneous impression.

XIX

Edna could not help but think that it was very foolish, very childish, to have stamped upon her wedding ring and smashed the crystal vase upon the tiles. She was visited by no more outbursts, moving her to such futile expedients. She began to do as she liked and to feel as she liked. She completely abandoned her Tuesdays at home, and did not return the visits of those who had called upon her. She made no ineffectual efforts to conduct her household *en bonne ménagère*,[26] going and coming as it suited her fancy, and, so far as she was able, lending herself to any passing caprice.

Mr. Pontellier had been a rather courteous husband so long as he met a certain tacit submissiveness in his wife. But her new and unexpected line of conduct completely bewildered him. It shocked him. Then her absolute disregard for her duties as a wife angered him. When Mr. Pontellier became rude, Edna grew insolent. She had resolved never to take another step backward.

"It seems to me the utmost folly for a woman at the head of a household, and the mother of children, to spend in an atelier[27] days which would be better employed contriving for the comfort of her family."

---

[26]A good housekeeper.

[27]An artist's studio.

"I feel like painting," answered Edna. "Perhaps I shan't always feel like it."

"Then in God's name paint! but don't let the family go to the devil. There's Madame Ratignolle; because she keeps up her music, she doesn't let everything else go to chaos. And she's more of a musician than you are a painter."

"She isn't a musician, and I'm not a painter. It isn't on account of painting that I let things go."

"On account of what, then?"

"Oh! I don't know. Let me alone; you bother me."

It sometimes entered Mr. Pontellier's mind to wonder if his wife were not growing a little unbalanced mentally. He could see plainly that she was not herself. That is, he could not see that she was becoming herself and daily casting aside that fictitious self which we assume like a garment with which to appear before the world.

Her husband let her alone as she requested, and went away to his office. Edna went up to her atelier—a bright room in the top of the house. She was working with great energy and interest, without accomplishing anything, however, which satisfied her even in the smallest degree. For a time she had the whole household enrolled in the service of art. The boys posed for her. They thought it amusing at first, but the occupation soon lost its attractiveness when they discovered that it was not a game arranged especially for their entertainment. The quadroon sat for hours before Edna's palette, patient as a savage, while the house-maid took charge of the children, and the drawing-room went undusted. But the house-maid, too, served her term as model when Edna perceived that the young woman's back and shoulders were molded on classic lines, and that her hair, loosened from its confining cap, became an inspiration. While Edna worked she sometimes sang low the little air, "*Ah! si tu savais!*"

It moved her with recollections. She could hear again the ripple of the water, the flapping sail. She could see the glint of the moon upon the bay, and could feel the soft, gusty beating of the hot south wind. A subtle current of desire passed through her body, weakening her hold upon the brushes and making her eyes burn.

There were days when she was very happy without knowing why. She was happy to be alive and breathing, when her whole being seemed to be one with the sunlight, the color, the odors, the luxuriant warmth of some perfect Southern day. She liked then to wander alone into strange and unfa-miliar places. She discovered many a sunny, sleepy corner, fashioned to dream in. And she found it good to dream and to be alone and unmolested.

There were days when she was unhappy, she did not know why,—when it did not seem worth while to be glad or sorry, to be alive or dead; when life appeared to her like a grotesque pandemonium and humanity like worms struggling blindly toward inevitable annihilation. She could not work on such a day, nor weave fancies to stir her pulses and warm her blood.

XX

It was during such a mood that Edna hunted up Mademoiselle Reisz. She had not forgotten the rather disagreeable impression left upon her by their last interview; but she nevertheless felt a desire to see her—above all, to listen while she played upon the piano. Quite early in the afternoon she started upon her quest for the pianist. Unfortunately she had mislaid or lost Mademoiselle Reisz's card, and looking up her address in the city directory, she found that the woman lived on Bienville Street, some distance away. The directory which fell into her hands was a year or more old, however, and upon reaching the number indicated, Edna discovered that the house was occupied by a respectable family of mulattoes who had *chambres garnies*[28] to let. They had been living there for six months, and knew absolutely nothing of a Mademoiselle Reisz. In fact, they knew nothing of any of their neighbors; their lodgers were all people of the highest distinction, they assured Edna. She did not linger to discuss class distinctions with Madame Pouponne, but hastened to a neighboring grocery store, feeling sure that Mademoiselle would have left her address with the proprietor.

He knew Mademoiselle Reisz a good deal better than he wanted to know her, he informed his questioner. In truth, he did not want to know her at all, or anything concerning her—the most disagreeable and unpopular woman who ever lived in Bienville Street. He thanked heaven she had left the neighborhood, and was equally thankful that he did not know where she had gone.

Edna's desire to see Mademoiselle Reisz had increased tenfold since these unlooked-for obstacles had arisen to thwart it. She was wondering who could give her the information she sought, when it suddenly occurred to her that Madame Lebrun would be the one most likely to do so. She knew it was useless to ask Madame Ratignolle, who was on the most distant terms with the musician, and preferred to know nothing concerning her. She had once been almost as emphatic in expressing herself upon the subject as the corner grocer.

Edna knew that Madame Lebrun had returned to the city, for it was the middle of November. And she also knew where the Lebruns lived, on Chartres Street.

Their home from the outside looked like a prison, with iron bars before the door and lower windows. The iron bars were a relic of the old *régime*, and

---

[28]Furnished rooms

no one had ever thought of dislodging them. At the side was a high fence enclosing the garden. A gate or door opening upon the street was locked. Edna rang the bell at this side garden gate, and stood upon the banquette, waiting to be admitted.

It was Victor who opened the gate for her. A black woman, wiping her hands upon her apron, was close at his heels. Before she saw them Edna could hear them in altercation, the woman—plainly an anomaly—claiming the right to be allowed to perform her duties, one of which was to answer the bell.

Victor was surprised and delighted to see Mrs. Pontellier, and he made no attempt to conceal either his astonishment or his delight. He was a dark-browed, good-looking youngster of nineteen, greatly resembling his mother, but with ten times her impetuosity. He instructed the black woman to go at once and inform Madame Lebrun that Mrs. Pontellier desired to see her. The woman grumbled a refusal to do part of her duty when she had not been permitted to do it all, and started back to her interrupted task of weeding the garden. Whereupon Victor administered a rebuke in the form of a volley of abuse, which, owing to its rapidity and incoherence, was all but incomprehensible to Edna. Whatever it was, the rebuke was convincing, for the woman dropped her hoe and went mumbling into the house.

Edna did not wish to enter. It was very pleasant there on the side porch, where there were chairs, a wicker lounge, and a small table. She seated herself, for she was tired from her long tramp; and she began to rock gently and smooth out the folds of her silk parasol. Victor drew up his chair beside her. He at once explained that the black woman's offensive conduct was all due to imperfect training, as he was not there to take her in hand. He had only come up from the island the morning before, and expected to return next day. He stayed all winter at the island; he lived there, and kept the place in order and got things ready for the summer visitors.

But a man needed occasional relaxation, he informed Mrs. Pontellier, and every now and again he drummed up a pretext to bring him to the city. My! but he had had a time of it the evening before! He wouldn't want his mother to know, and he began to talk in a whisper. He was scintillant with recollections. Of course, he couldn't think of telling Mrs. Pontellier all about it, she being a woman and not comprehending such things. But it all began with a girl peeping and smiling at him through the shutters as he passed by. Oh! but she was a beauty! Certainly he smiled back, and went up and talked to her. Mrs. Pontellier did not know him if she supposed he was one to let an opportunity like that escape him. Despite herself, the youngster amused her. She must have betrayed in her look some degree of interest or entertainment. The boy grew more daring, and Mrs. Pontellier might have found herself, in a little while, listening to a highly colored story but for the timely appearance of Madame Lebrun.

That lady was still clad in white, according to her custom of the summer. Her eyes beamed an effusive welcome. Would not Mrs. Pontellier go inside? Would she partake of some refreshment? Why had she not been there before? How was that dear Mr. Pontellier and how were those sweet children? Had Mrs. Pontellier ever known such a warm November?

Victor went and reclined on the wicker lounge behind his mother's chair, where he commanded a view of Edna's face. He had taken her parasol from her hands while he spoke to her, and he now lifted it and twirled it above him as he lay on his back. When Madame Lebrun complained that it was *so* dull coming back to the city; that she saw *so* few people now; that even Victor, when he came up from the island for a day or two, had *so* much to occupy him and engage his time; then it was that the youth went into contortions on the lounge and winked mischievously at Edna. She somehow felt like a confederate in crime, and tried to look severe and disapproving.

There had been but two letters from Robert, with little in them, they told her. Victor said it was really not worth while to go inside for the letters, when his mother entreated him to go in search of them. He remembered the contents, which in truth he rattled off very glibly when put to the test.

One letter was written from Vera Cruz and the other from the City of Mexico. He had met Montel, who was doing everything toward his advancement. So far, the financial situation was no improvement over the one he had left in New Orleans, but of course the prospects were vastly better. He wrote of the City of Mexico, the buildings, the people and their habits, the conditions of life which he found there. He sent his love to the family. He enclosed a check to his mother, and hoped she would affectionately remember him to all his friends. That was about the substance of the two letters. Edna felt that if there had been a message for her, she would have received it. The despondent frame of mind in which she had left home began again to overtake her, and she remembered that she wished to find Mademoiselle Reisz.

Madame Lebrun knew where Mademoiselle Reisz lived. She gave Edna the address, regretting that she would not consent to stay and spend the remainder of the afternoon, and pay a visit to Mademoiselle Reisz some other day. The afternoon was already well advanced.

Victor escorted her out upon the banquette, lifted her parasol, and held it over her while he walked to the car with her. He entreated her to bear in mind that the disclosures of the afternoon were strictly confidential. She laughed and bantered him a little, remembering too late that she should have been dignified and reserved.

"How handsome Mrs. Pontellier looked!" said Madame Lebrun to her son.

"Ravishing!" he admitted. "The city atmosphere has improved her. Some way she doesn't seem like the same woman."

XXI

Some people contended that the reason Mademoiselle Reisz always chose apartments up under the roof was to discourage the approach of beggars, peddlers and callers. There were plenty of windows in her little front room. They were for the most part dingy, but as they were nearly always open it did not make so much difference. They often admitted into the room a good deal of smoke and soot; but at the same time all the light and air that there was came through them. From her windows could be seen the crescent of the river, the masts of ships and the big chimneys of the Mississippi steamers. A magnificent piano crowded the apartment. In the next room she slept, and in the third and last she harbored a gasoline stove on which she cooked her meals when disinclined to descend to the neighboring restaurant. It was there also that she ate, keeping her belongings in a rare old buffet, dingy and battered from a hundred years of use.

When Edna knocked at Mademoiselle Reisz's front room door and entered, she discovered that person standing beside the window, engaged in mending or patching an old prunella gaiter. The little musician laughed all over when she saw Edna. Her laugh consisted of a contortion of the face and all the muscles of the body. She seemed strikingly homely, standing there in the afternoon light. She still wore the shabby lace and the artificial bunch of violets on the side of her head.

"So you remembered me at last," said Mademoiselle. "I had said to myself, 'Ah, bah! she will never come.' "

"Did you want me to come?" asked Edna with a smile.

"I had not thought much about it," answered Mademoiselle. The two had seated themselves on a little bumpy sofa which stood against the wall. "I am glad, however, that you came. I have the water boiling back there, and was just about to make some coffee. You will drink a cup with me. And how is *la belle dame?* Always handsome! always healthy! always contented!" She took Edna's hand between her strong wiry fingers, holding it loosely without warmth, and executing a sort of double theme upon the back and palm.

"Yes," she went on; "I sometimes thought: 'She will never come. She promised as those women in society always do, without meaning it. She will not come.' For I really don't believe you like me, Mrs. Pontellier."

"I don't know whether I like you or not," replied Edna, gazing down at the little woman with a quizzical look.

The candor of Mrs. Pontellier's admission greatly pleased Mademoiselle Reisz. She expressed her gratification by repairing forthwith to the region of the gasoline stove and rewarding her guest with the promised cup of coffee. The coffee and the biscuit accompanying it proved very acceptable to Edna, who had declined refreshment at Madame Lebrun's and was now beginning to feel hungry. Mademoiselle set the tray which she brought in upon a small table near at hand, and seated herself once again on the lumpy sofa.

"I have had a letter from your friend," she remarked, as she poured a little cream into Edna's cup and handed it to her.

"My friend?"

"Yes, your friend Robert. He wrote to me from the City of Mexico."

"Wrote to *you?*" repeated Edna in amazement, stirring her coffee absently.

"Yes, to me. Why not? Don't stir all the warmth out of your coffee; drink it. Though the letter might as well have been sent to you; it was nothing but Mrs. Pontellier from beginning to end."

"Let me see it," requested the young woman, entreatingly.

"No; a letter concerns no one but the person who writes it and the one to whom it is written."

"Haven't you just said it concerned me from beginning to end?"

"It was written about you, not to you. 'Have you seen Mrs. Pontellier? How is she looking?' he asks. 'As Mrs. Pontellier says,' or 'as Mrs. Pontellier once said.' 'If Mrs. Pontellier should call upon you, play for her that Impromptu of Chopin's, my favorite. I heard it here a day or two ago, but not as you play it. I should like to know how it affects her,' and so on, as if he supposed we were constantly in each other's society."

"Let me see the letter."

"Oh, no."

"Have you answered it?"

"No."

"Let me see the letter."

"No, and again, no."

"Then play the Impromptu for me."

"It is growing late; what time do you have to be home?"

"Time doesn't concern me. Your question seems a little rude. Play the Impromptu."

"But you have told me nothing of yourself. What are you doing?"

"Painting!" laughed Edna. "I am becoming an artist. Think of it!"

"Ah! an artist! You have pretensions. Madame."

"Why pretensions? Do you think I could not become an artist?"

"I do not know you well enough to say. I do not know your talent or your temperament. To be an artist includes much; one must possess many gifts—

absolute gifts—which have not been acquired by one's own effort. And, more-over, to succeed, the artist must possess the courageous soul."

"What do you mean by the courageous soul?"

"Courageous, *ma foi!*[29] The brave soul. The soul that dares and defies."

"Show me the letter and play for me the Impromptu. You see that I have persistence. Does that quality count for anything in art?"

"It counts with a foolish old woman whom you have captivated," replied Mademoiselle, with her wriggling laugh.

The letter was right there at hand in the drawer of the little table upon which Edna had just placed her coffee cup. Mademoiselle opened the drawer and drew forth the letter, the topmost one. She placed it in Edna's hands, and without further comment arose and went to the piano.

Mademoiselle played a soft interlude. It was an improvisation. She sat low at the instrument, and the lines of her body settled into ungraceful curves and angles that gave it an appearance of deformity. Gradually and imperceptibly the interlude melted into the soft opening minor chords of the Chopin Impromptu.

Edna did not know when the Impromptu began or ended. She sat in the sofa corner reading Robert's letter by the fading light. Mademoiselle had glided from the Chopin into the quivering love-notes of Isolde's song, and back again to the Impromptu with its soulful and poignant longing.

The shadows deepened in the little room. The music grew strange and fantastic—turbulent, insistent, plaintive and soft with entreaty. The shadows grew deeper. The music filled the room. It floated out upon the night, over the housetops, the crescent of the river, losing itself in the silence of the upper air.

Edna was sobbing, just as she had wept one midnight at Grand Isle when strange, new voices awoke in her. She arose in some agitation to take her departure. "May I come again, Mademoiselle?" she asked at the threshold.

"Come whenever you feel like it. Be careful; the stairs and landings are dark; don't stumble."

Mademoiselle reentered and lit a candle. Robert's letter was on the floor. She stooped and picked it up. It was crumpled and damp with tears. Mademoiselle smoothed the letter out, restored it to the envelope, and replaced it in the table drawer.

XXII

One morning on his way into town, Mr. Pontellier stopped at the house of his old friend and family physician, Doctor Mandelet. The Doctor was a semi-retired physician, resting, as the saying is, upon his laurels. He bore a

---

[29]My faith!

reputation for wisdom rather than skill—leaving the active practice of medicine to his assistants and younger contemporaries—and was much sought for in matters of consultation. A few families, united to him by bonds of friendship, he still attended when they required the services of a physician. The Pontelliers were among these.

Mr. Pontellier found the Doctor reading at the open window of his study. His house stood rather far back from the street, in the center of a delightful garden, so that it was quiet and peaceful at the old gentleman's study window. He was a great reader. He stared up disapprovingly over his eye-glasses as Mr. Pontellier entered, wondering who had the temerity to disturb him at that hour of the morning.

"Ah, Pontellier! Not sick, I hope. Come and have a seat. What news do you bring this morning?" He was quite portly, with a profusion of gray hair, and small blue eyes which age had robbed of much of their brightness but none of their penetration.

"Oh! I'm never sick, Doctor. You know that I come of tough fiber—of that old Creole race of Pontelliers that dry up and finally blow away. I came to consult—no, not precisely to consult—to talk to you about Edna. I don't know what ails her."

"Madame Pontellier not well?" marveled the Doctor. "Why, I saw her—I think it was a week ago—walking along Canal Street, the picture of health, it seemed to me."

"Yes, yes; she seems quite well," said Mr. Pontellier, leaning forward and whirling his stick between his two hands; "but she doesn't act well. She's odd, she's not like herself. I can't make her out, and I thought perhaps you'd help me."

"How does she act?" inquired the doctor.

"Well, it isn't easy to explain," said Mr. Pontellier, throwing himself back in his chair. "She lets the housekeeping go to the dickens."

"Well, well; women are not all alike, my dear Pontellier. We've got to consider—"

"I know that; I told you I couldn't explain. Her whole attitude—toward me and everybody and everything—has changed. You know I have a quick temper, but I don't want to quarrel or be rude to a woman, especially my wife; yet I'm driven to it, and feel like ten thousand devils after I've made a fool of myself. She's making it devilishly uncomfortable for me," he went on nervously. "She's got some sort of notion in her head concerning the eternal rights of women; and—you understand—we meet in the morning at the breakfast table."

The old gentleman lifted his shaggy eyebrows, protruded his thick nether lip, and tapped the arms of his chair with his cushioned fingertips.

"What have you been doing to her, Pontellier?"

Doing! *Parbleu!*[30]

"Has she," asked the Doctor, with a smile, "has she been associating of late with a circle of pseudo-intellectual women—super-spiritual superior beings? My wife has been telling me about them."

"That's the trouble," broke in Mr. Pontellier, "she hasn't been associating with any one. She has abandoned her Tuesdays at home, has thrown over all her acquaintances, and goes tramping about by herself, moping in the street-cars, getting in after dark. I tell you she's peculiar. I don't like it; I feel a little worried over it."

This was a new aspect for the Doctor. "Nothing hereditary?" he asked, seriously. "Nothing peculiar about her family antecedents, is there?"

"Oh, no indeed! She comes of sound old Presbyterian Kentucky stock. The old gentleman, her father, I have heard, used to atone for his weekday sins with his Sunday devotions. I know for a fact, that his race horses literally ran away with the prettiest bit of Kentucky farming land I ever laid eyes upon. Margaret—you know Margaret—she has all the Presbyterianism undiluted. And the youngest is something of a vixen. By the way, she gets married in a couple of weeks from now."

"Send your wife up to the wedding," exclaimed the Doctor, foreseeing a happy solution. "Let her stay among her own people for a while; it will do her good."

"That's what I want her to do. She won't go to the marriage. She says a wedding is one of the most lamentable spectacles on earth. Nice thing for a woman to say to her husband!" exclaimed Mr. Pontellier, fuming anew at the recollection.

"Pontellier," said the Doctor, after a moment's reflection, "let your wife alone for a while. Don't bother her, and don't let her bother you. Woman, my dear friend, is a very peculiar and delicate organism—a sensitive and highly organized woman, such as I know Mrs. Pontellier to be, is especially peculiar. It would require an inspired psychologist to deal successfully with them. And when ordinary fellows like you and me attempt to cope with their idiosyncrasies the result is bungling. Most women are moody and whimsical. This is some passing whim of your wife, due to some cause or causes which you and I needn't try to fathom. But it will pass happily over, especially if you let her alone. Send her around to see me."

"Oh! I couldn't do that; there'd be no reason for it," objected Mr. Pontellier.

"Then I'll go around and see her," said the Doctor. "I'll drop in to dinner some evening *en bon ami*."[31]

---

[30]For heaven's sake!

[31]As a good friend.

"Do! by all means," urged Mr. Pontellier. "What evening will you come? Say Thursday. Will you come Thursday?" he asked, rising to take his leave.

"Very well; Thursday. My wife may possibly have some engagement for me Thursday. In case she has, I shall let you know. Otherwise, you may expect me."

Mr. Pontellier turned before leaving to say:

"I am going to New York on business very soon. I have a big scheme on hand, and want to be on the field proper to pull the ropes and handle the ribbons. We'll let you in on the inside if you say so, Doctor," he laughed.

"No, I thank you, my dear sir," returned the Doctor. "I leave such ventures to you younger men with the fever of life still in your blood."

"What I wanted to say," continued Mr. Pontellier, with his hand on the knob; "I may have to be absent a good while. Would you advise me to take Edna along?"

"By all means, if she wishes to go. If not, leave her here. Don't contradict her. The mood will pass, I assure you. It may take a month, two, three months—possibly longer, but it will pass; have patience."

"Well, good-by, *à jeudi*,"[32] said Mr. Pontellier, as he let himself out.

The doctor would have liked during the course of conversation to ask, "Is there any man in the case?" but he knew his Creole too well to make such a blunder as that.

He did not resume his book immediately, but sat for a while meditatively looking out into the garden.

XXIII

Edna's father was in the city, and had been with them several days. She was not very warmly or deeply attached to him, but they had certain tastes in common, and when together they were companionable. His coming was in the nature of a welcome disturbance; it seemed to furnish a new direction for her emotions.

He had come to purchase a wedding ring for his daughter, Janet, and an outfit for himself in which he might make a creditable appearance at her marriage. Mr. Pontellier had selected the bridal gift, as every one immediately connected with him always deferred to his taste in such matters. And his suggestions on the question of dress—which too often assumes the nature of a problem—were of inestimable value to his father-in-law. But for the past few days the old gentleman had been upon Edna's hands, and in his society she

---

[32]Until Thursday

was becoming acquainted with a new set of sensations. He had been a colonel in the Confederate army, and still maintained, with the title, the military bearing which had always accompanied it. His hair and mustache were white and silky, emphasizing the rugged bronze of his face. He was tall and thin, and wore his coats padded, which gave a fictitious breadth and depth to his shoulders and chest. Edna and her father looked very distinguished together, and excited a good deal of notice during their perambulations. Upon his arrival she began by introducing him to her atelier and making a sketch of him. He took the whole matter very seriously. If her talent had been ten-fold greater than it was, it would not have surprised him, convinced as he was that he had bequeathed to all of his daughters the germs of a masterful capability, which only depended upon their own efforts to be directed toward successful achievement.

Before her pencil he sat rigid and unflinching, as he had faced the cannon's mouth in days gone by. He resented the intrusion of the children, who gaped with wondering eyes at him, sitting so stiff up there in their mother's bright atelier. When they drew near he motioned them away with an expressive action of the foot, loath to disturb the fixed lines of his countenance, his arms, or his rigid shoulders.

Edna, anxious to entertain him, invited Mademoiselle Reisz to meet him, having promised him a treat in her piano playing; but Mademoiselle declined the invitation. So together they attended a *soirée musicale* at the Ratignolles'. Monsieur and Madame Ratignolle made much of the Colonel, installing him as the guest of honor and engaging him at once to dine with them the following Sunday, or any day which he might select. Madame coquetted with him in the most captivating and naïve manner, with eyes, gestures, and a profusion of compliments, till the Colonel's old head felt thirty years younger on his padded shoulders. Edna marveled, not comprehending. She herself was almost devoid of coquetry.

There were one or two men whom she observed at the *soirée musicale;* but she would never have felt moved to any kittenish display to attract their notice—to any feline or feminine wiles to express herself toward them. Their personality attracted her in an agreeable way. Her fancy selected them, and she was glad when a lull in the music gave them an opportunity to meet her and talk with her. Often on the street the glance of strange eyes had lingered in her memory, and sometimes had disturbed her.

Mr. Pontellier did not attend these *soirée musicales*. He considered them *bourgeois*, and found more diversion at the club. To Madame Ratignolle he said the music dispensed at her *soirées* was too "heavy," too far beyond his untrained comprehension. His excuse flattered her. But she disapproved of Mr. Pontellier's club, and she was frank enough to tell Edna so.

"It's a pity Mr. Pontellier doesn't stay home more in the evenings. I think you would be more—well, if you don't mind my saying it—more united, if he did."

"Oh! dear no!" said Edna, with a blank look in her eyes. "What should I do if he stayed home? We wouldn't have anything to say to each other."

She had not much of anything to say to her father, for that matter; but he did not antagonize her. She discovered that he interested her, though she realized that he might not interest her long; and for the first time in her life she felt as if she were thoroughly acquainted with him. He kept her busy serving him and ministering to his wants. It amused her to do so. She would not permit a servant or one of the children to do anything for him which she might do herself. Her husband noticed, and thought it was the expression of a deep filial attachment which he had never suspected.

The Colonel drank numerous "toddies" during the course of the day, which left him, however, imperturbed. He was an expert at concocting strong drinks. He had even invented some, to which he had given fantastic names, and for whose manufacture he required diverse ingredients that it devolved upon Edna to procure for him.

When Doctor Mandelet dined with the Pontelliers on Thursday he could discern in Mrs. Pontellier no trace of that morbid condition which her husband had reported to him. She was excited and in a manner radiant. She and her father had been to the race course, and their thoughts when they seated themselves at table were still occupied with the events of the afternoon, and their talk was still of the track. The Doctor had not kept pace with turf affairs. He had certain recollections of racing in what he called "the good old times" when the Lecompte stables flourished, and he drew upon this fund of memories so that he might not be left out and seem wholly devoid of the modern spirit. But he failed to impose upon the Colonel, and was even far from impressing him with this trumped-up knowledge of bygone days. Edna had staked her father on his last venture, with the most gratifying results to both of them. Besides, they had met some very charming people, according to the Colonel's impressions. Mrs. Mortimer Merriman and Mrs. James Highcamp, who were there with Alcée Arobin, had joined them and had enlivened the hours in a fashion that warmed him to think of.

Mr. Pontellier himself had no particular leaning toward horse-racing, and was even rather inclined to discourage it as a pastime, especially when he considered the fate of that blue-grass farm in Kentucky. He endeavored in a general way, to express a particular disapproval, and only succeeded in arousing the ire and opposition of his father-in-law. A petty dispute followed, in which Edna warmly espoused her father's cause and the Doctor remained neutral.

He observed his hostess attentively from under his shaggy brows, and noted a subtle change which had transformed her from the listless woman he had known into a being who, for the moment, seemed palpitant with the forces of life. Her speech was warm and energetic. There was no repression in her glance or gesture. She reminded him of some beautiful, sleek animal waking up in the sun.

The dinner was excellent. The claret was warm and the champagne was cold, and under their beneficent influence the threatened unpleasantness melted and vanished with the fumes of the wine.

Mr. Pontellier warmed up and grew reminiscent. He told some amusing plantation experiences, recollections of old Iberville and his youth, when he hunted 'possum in company with some friendly darky; thrashed the pecan trees, shot the grosbec, and roamed the woods and fields in mischievous idleness.

The Colonel, with little sense of humor and of the fitness of things, related a somber episode of those dark and bitter days, in which he had acted a conspicuous part and always formed a central figure. Nor was the Doctor happier in his selection, when he told the old, ever new and curious story of the waning of a woman's love, seeking strange, new channels, only to return to its legitimate source after days of fierce unrest. It was one of the many little human documents which had been unfolded to him during his long career as a physician. The story did not seem especially to impress Edna. She had one of her own to tell, of a woman who paddled away with her lover one night in a pirogue and never came back. They were lost amid the Baratarian Islands, and no one ever heard of them or found trace of them from that day to this. It was a pure invention. She said that Madame Antoine had related it to her. That, also, was an invention. Perhaps it was a dream she had had. But every glowing word seemed real to those who listened. They could feel the hot breath of the Southern night; they could hear the long sweep of the pirogue through the glistening moonlit water, the beating of birds' wings, rising startled from among the reeds in the saltwater pools; they could see the faces of the lovers, pale, close together, rapt in oblivious forgetfulness, drifting into the unknown.

The champagne was cold, and its subtle fumes played fantastic tricks with Edna's memory that night.

Outside, away from the glow of the fire and the soft lamplight, the night was chill and murky. The Doctor doubled his old-fashioned cloak across his breast as he strode home through the darkness. He knew his fellow-creatures better than most men; knew that inner life which so seldom unfolds itself to unanointed eyes. He was sorry he had accepted Pontellier's invitation. He was growing old, and beginning to need rest and an imperturbed spirit. He did not want the secrets of other lives thrust upon him.

"I hope it isn't Arobin," he muttered to himself as he walked. "I hope to heaven it isn't Alcée Arobin."

XXIV

Edna and her father had a warm, and almost violent dispute upon the subject of her refusal to attend her sister's wedding. Mr. Pontellier declined to interfere, to interpose either his influence or his authority. He was following Doctor Mandelet's advice, and letting her do as she liked. The Colonel reproached his daughter for her lack of filial kindness and respect, her want of sisterly affection and womanly consideration. His arguments were labored and unconvincing. He doubted if Janet would accept any excuse—forgetting that Edna had offered none. He doubted if Janet would ever speak to her again, and he was sure Margaret would not.

Edna was glad to be rid of her father when he finally took himself off with his wedding garments and his bridal gifts, with his padded shoulders, his Bible reading, his "toddies" and ponderous oaths.

Mr. Pontellier followed him closely. He meant to stop at the wedding on his way to New York and endeavor by every means which money and love could devise to atone somewhat for Edna's incomprehensible action.

"You are too lenient, too lenient by far, Léonce," asserted the Colonel. "Authority, coercion are what is needed. Put you foot down good and hard; the only way to manage a wife. Take my word for it."

The Colonel was perhaps unaware that he had coerced his own wife into her grave. Mr. Pontellier had a vague suspicion of it which he thought it needless to mention at that late day.

Edna was not so consciously gratified at her husband's leaving home as she had been over the departure of her father. As the day approached when he was to leave her for a comparatively long stay, she grew melting and affectionate, remembering his many acts of consideration and his repeated expressions of an ardent attachment. She was solicitous about his health and his welfare. She bustled around, looking after his clothing, thinking about heavy underwear, quite as Madame Ratignolle would have done under similar circumstances. She cried when he went away, calling him her dear, good friend, and she was quite certain she would grow lonely before very long and go to join him in New York.

But after all, a radiant peace settled upon her when she at last found herself alone. Even the children were gone. Old Madame Pontellier had come herself and carried them off to Iberville with their quadroon. The old Madame did not venture to say she was afraid they would be neglected during Léonce's absence; she hardly ventured to think so. She was hungry for them—even a little fierce in her attachment. She did not want them to be wholly "children of the pavement," she always said when begging to have them for a space. She wished them to know the country, with its streams, its fields, its woods, its freedom, so delicious to the young. She wished them to taste something of the life their father had lived and known and loved when he, too, was a little child.

When Edna was at last alone, she breathed a big, genuine sigh of relief. A feeling that was unfamiliar but very delicious came over her. She walked all through the house, from one room to another, as if inspecting it for the first time. She tried the various chairs and lounges, as if she had never sat and reclined upon them before. And she perambulated around the outside of the house, investigating, looking to see if windows and shutters were secure and in order. The flowers were like new acquaintances; she approached them in a familiar spirit, and made herself at home among them. The garden walks were damp, and Edna called to the maid to bring out her rubber sandals. And there she stayed, and stooped, digging around the plants, trimming, picking dead, dry leaves. The children's little dog came out, interfering, getting in her way. She scolded him, laughed at him, played with him. The garden smelled so good and looked so pretty in the afternoon sunlight. Edna plucked all the bright flowers she could find, and went into the house with them, she and the little dog.

Even the kitchen assumed a sudden interesting character which she had never before perceived. She went in to give directions to the cook, to say that the butcher would have to bring much less meat, that they would require only half their usual quantity of bread, of milk and groceries. She told the cook that she herself would be greatly occupied during Mr. Pontellier's absence, and she begged her to take all thought and responsibility of the larder upon her own shoulders.

That night Edna dined alone. The candelabra, with a few candles in the center of the table, gave all the light she needed. Outside the circle of light in which she sat, the large dining-room looked solemn and shadowy. The cook, placed upon her mettle, served a delicious repast—a luscious tenderloin broiled *à point*.[33] The wine tasted good; the *marron glacé*[34] seemed to be just what she wanted. It was so pleasant, too, to dine in a comfortable *peignoir*.

She thought a little sentimentally about Léonce and the children, and wondered what they were doing. As she gave a dainty scrap or two to the doggie, she talked intimately to him about Etienne and Raoul. He was beside himself with astonishment and delight over these companionable advances, and showed his appreciation by his little quick, snappy barks and a lively agitation.

---

[33]To a turn, perfectly.

[34]Glazed chestnuts

Then Edna sat in the library after dinner and read Emerson until she grew sleepy. She realized that she had neglected her reading, and determined to start anew upon a course of improving studies, now that her time was completely her own to do with as she liked.

After a refreshing bath, Edna went to bed. And as she snuggled comfortably beneath the eiderdown a sense of restfulness invaded her, such as she had not known before.

XXV

When the weather was dark and cloudy Edna could not work. She needed the sun to mellow and temper her mood to the sticking point. She had reached a stage when she seemed to be no longer feeling her way, working, when in the humor, with sureness and ease. And being devoid of ambition, and striving not toward accomplishment, she drew satisfaction from the work in itself.

On rainy or melancholy days Edna went out and sought the society of the friends she had made at Grand Isle. Or else she stayed indoors and nursed a mood with which she was becoming too familiar for her own comfort and peace of mind. It was not despair; but it seemed to her as if life were passing by, leaving its promise broken and unfulfilled. Yet there were other days when she listened, was led on and deceived by fresh promises which her youth held out to her.

She went again to the races, and again. Alcée Arobin and Mrs. Highcamp called for her one bright afternoon in Arobin's drag. Mrs. Highcamp was a worldly but unaffected, intelligent, slim, tall blonde woman in the forties, with an indifferent manner and blue eyes that stared. She had a daughter who served her as a pretext for cultivating the society of young men of fashion. Alcée Arobin was one of them. He was a familiar figure at the race course, the opera, the fashionable clubs. There was a perpetual smile in his eyes, which seldom failed to awaken a corresponding cheerfulness in any one who looked into them and listened to his good-humored voice. His manner was quiet, and at times a little insolent. He possessed a good figure, a pleasing face, not overburdened with depth of thought or feeling; and his dress was that of the conventional man of fashion.

He admired Edna extravagantly, after meeting her at the races with her father. He had met her before on other occasions, but she had seemed to him unapproachable until that day. It was at his instigation that Mrs. Highcamp called to ask her to go with them to the Jockey Club to witness the turf event of the season.

There were possibly a few track men out there who knew the race horse as well as Edna, but there was certainly none who knew it better. She sat between her two companions as one having authority to speak. She laughed at Arobin's pretensions, and deplored Mrs. Highcamp's ignorance. The race horse was a friend and intimate associate of her childhood. The atmosphere of the stable and the breath of the blue grass paddock revived in her memory and lingered in her nostrils. She did not perceive that she was talking like her father as the sleek geldings ambled in review before them. She played for very high stakes, and fortune favored her. The fever of the game flamed in her cheeks and eyes, and it got into her blood and into her brain like an intoxicant. People turned their heads to look at her, and more than one lent an attentive ear to her utterances, hoping thereby to secure the elusive but ever-desired "tip." Arobin caught the contagion of excitement which drew him to Edna like a magnet. Mrs. Highcamp remained, as usual, unmoved, with her indifferent stare and uplifted eyebrows.

Edna stayed and dined with Mrs. Highcamp upon being urged to do so. Arobin also remained and sent away his drag.

The dinner was quiet and uninteresting, save for the cheerful efforts of Arobin to enliven things. Mrs. Highcamp deplored the absence of her daughter from the races, and tried to convey to her what she had missed by going to the "Dante reading" instead of joining them. The girl held a geranium leaf up to her nose and said nothing, but looked knowing and noncommittal. Mr. Highcamp was a plain, bald-headed man, who only talked under compulsion. He was unresponsive. Mrs. Highcamp was full of delicate courtesy and consideration toward her husband. She addressed most of her conversation to him at table. They sat in the library after dinner and read the evening papers together under the droplight; while the younger people went into the drawing-room near by and talked. Miss Highcamp played some selections from Grieg upon the piano. She seemed to have apprehended all of the composer's coldness and none of his poetry. While Edna listened she could not help wondering if she had lost her taste for music.

When the time came for her to go home, Mr. Highcamp grunted a lame offer to escort her, looking down at his slippered feet with tactless concern. It was Arobin who took her home. The car ride was long, and it was late when they reached Esplanade Street. Arobin asked permission to enter for a second to light his cigarette—his match safe was empty. He filled his match safe, but did not light his cigarette until he left her, after she had expressed her willingness to go to the races with him again.

Edna was neither tired nor sleepy. She was hungry again, for the Highcamp dinner, though of excellent quality, had lacked abundance. She rummaged in the larder and brought forth a slice of Gruyère and some crackers. She opened a bottle of beer which she found in the icebox. Edna felt extremely restless and excited. She vacantly hummed a fantastic tune as she poked at the wood embers on the hearth and munched a cracker.

She wanted something to happen—something, anything; she did not know what. She regretted that she had not made Arobin stay a half hour to talk over the horses with her. She counted the money she had won. But there was nothing else to do, so she went to bed, and tossed there for hours in a sort of monotonous agitation.

In the middle of the night she remembered that she had forgotten to write her regular letter to her husband; and she decided to do so next day and tell him about her afternoon at the Jockey Club. She lay wide awake composing a letter which was nothing like the one which she wrote next day. When the maid awoke her in the morning Edna was dreaming of Mr. Highcamp playing the piano at the entrance of a music store on Canal Street, while his wife was saying to Alcée Arobin, as they boarded an Esplanade Street car:

"What a pity that so much talent has been neglected! but I must go."

When, a few days later, Alcée Arobin again called for Edna in his drag, Mrs. Highcamp was not with him. He said they would pick her up. But as that lady had not been apprised of his intention of picking her up, she was not at home. The daughter was just leaving the house to attend the meeting of a branch Folk Lore Society, and regretted that she could not accompany them. Arobin appeared nonplused, and asked Edna if there were any one else she cared to ask.

She did not deem it worth while to go in search of any of the fashionable acquaintances from whom she had withdrawn herself. She thought of Madame Ratignolle, but knew that her fair friend did not leave the house, except to take a languid walk around the block with her husband after night-fall. Mademoiselle Reisz would have laughed at such a request from Edna. Madame Lebrun might have enjoyed the outing, but for some reason Edna did not want her. So they went alone, she and Arobin.

The afternoon was intensely interesting to her. The excitement came back upon her like a remittent fever. Her talk grew familiar and confidential. It was no labor to become intimate with Arobin. His manner invited easy confidence. The preliminary stage of becoming acquainted was one which he always endeavored to ignore when a pretty and engaging woman was concerned.

He stayed and dined with Edna. He stayed and sat beside the wood fire. They laughed and talked; and before it was time to go he was telling her how different life might have been if he had known her years before. With ingenuous frankness he spoke of what a wicked, ill-disciplined boy he had been, and impulsively drew up his cuff to exhibit upon his wrist the scar from a saber cut which he had received in a duel outside of Paris when he was nineteen. She touched his hand as she scanned the red cicatrice on the inside of his white wrist. A quick impulse that was somewhat spasmodic impelled her fingers to close in a sort of clutch upon his hand. He felt the pressure of her pointed nails in the flesh of his palm.

She arose hastily and walked toward the mantel.

"The sight of a wound or scar always agitates and sickens me," she said. "I shouldn't have looked at it."

"I beg your pardon," he entreated, following her; "it never occurred to me that it might be repulsive."

He stood close to her, and the effrontery in his eyes repelled the old, vanishing self in her, yet drew all her awakening sensuousness. He saw enough in her face to impel him to take her hand and hold it while he said his lingering good night.

"Will you go to the races again?" he asked.

"No," she said. "I've had enough of the races. I don't want to lose all the money I've won, and I've got to work when the weather is bright, instead of—"

"Yes; work; to be sure. You promised to show me your work. What morning may I come up to your atelier? To-morrow?"

"No!"

"Day after?"

"No, no."

"Oh, please don't refuse me! I know something of such things. I might help you with a stray suggestion or two."

"No. Good night. Why don't you go after you have said good night? I don't like you," she went on in a high, excited pitch, attempting to draw away her hand. She felt that her words lacked dignity and sincerity, and she knew that he felt it.

"I'm sorry you don't like me. I'm sorry I offended you. How have I offended you? What have I done? Can't you forgive me?" And he bent and pressed his lips upon her hand as if he wished never more to withdraw them.

"Mr. Arobin," she complained. "I'm greatly upset by the excitement of the afternoon; I'm not myself. My manner must have misled you in some way. I wish you to go, please." She spoke in a monotonous, dull tone. He took his hat from the table, and stood with eyes turned from her, looking into the dying fire. For a moment or two he kept an impressive silence.

"Your manner has not misled me, Mrs. Pontellier," he said finally. "My own emotions have done that. I couldn't help it. When I'm near you, how could I help it? Don't think anything of it, don't bother, please. You see, I go when you command me. If you wish me to stay away, I shall do so. If you let me come back, I—oh! you will let me come back?"

He cast one appealing glance at her, to which she made no response. Alcée Arobin's manner was so genuine that it often deceived even himself.

Edna did not care or think whether it were genuine or not. When she was alone she looked mechanically at the back of her hand which he had kissed so warmly. Then she leaned her head down on the mantelpiece. She felt somewhat like a woman who in a moment of passion is betrayed into an act of infidelity, and realizes the significance of the act without being wholly awakened from its glamour. The thought was passing vaguely through her mind, "What would he think?"

She did not mean her husband; she was thinking of Robert Lebrun. Her husband seemed to her now like a person whom she had married without love as an excuse.

She lit a candle and went up to her room. Alcée Arobin was absolutely nothing to her. Yet his presence, his manners, the warmth of his glances, and above all the touch of his lips upon her hand had acted like a narcotic upon her.

She slept a languorous sleep, interwoven with vanishing dreams.

XXVI

Alcée Arobin wrote Edna an elaborate note of apology, palpitant with sincerity. It embarrassed her; for in a cooler, quieter moment it appeared to her absurd that she should have taken his action so seriously, so dramatically. She felt sure that the significance of the whole occurrence had lain in her own self-consciousness. If she ignored his note it would give undue importance to a trivial affair. If she replied to it in a serious spirit it would still leave in his mind the impression that she had in a susceptible moment yielded to his influence. After all, it was no great matter to have one's hand kissed. She was provoked at his having written the apology. She answered in as light and bantering a spirit as she fancied it deserved, and said she would be glad to have him look in upon her at work whenever he felt the inclination and his business gave him the opportunity.

He responded at once by presenting himself at her home with all his disarming naïveté. And then there was scarcely a day which followed that she did not see him or was not reminded of him. He was prolific in pretexts. His attitude became one of good-humored subservience and tacit adoration. He was ready at all times to submit to her moods, which were as often kind as they were cold. She grew accustomed to him. They became intimate and friendly by imperceptible degrees, and then by leaps. He sometimes talked in a way that astonished her at first and brought the crimson into her face; in a way that pleased her at last, appealing to the animalism that stirred impatiently within her.

There was nothing which so quieted the turmoil in Edna's senses as a visit to Mademoiselle Reisz. It was then, in the presence of that personality which was offensive to her, that the woman, by her divine art, seemed to reach Edna's spirit and set it free.

It was misty, with heavy, lowering atmosphere, one afternoon, when Edna climbed the stairs to the pianist's apartments under the roof. Her clothes were dripping with moisture. She felt chilled and pinched as she entered the room. Mademoiselle was poking at a rusty stove that smoked a little and warmed the room indifferently. She was endeavoring to heat a pot of chocolate on the stove. The room looked cheerless and dingy to Edna as she entered. A bust of Beethoven, covered with a hood of dust, scowled at her from the mantelpiece.

"Ah! here comes the sunlight!" exclaimed Mademoiselle, rising from her knees before the stove. "Now it will be warm and bright enough; I can let the fire alone."

She closed the stove door with a bang, and approaching, assisted in removing Edna's dripping mackintosh.

"You are cold; you look miserable. The chocolate will soon be hot. But would you rather have a taste of brandy? I have scarcely touched the bottle which you brought me for my cold." A piece of red flannel was wrapped around Mademoiselle's throat; a stiff neck compelled her to hold her head on one side.

"I will take some brandy," said Edna, shivering as she removed her gloves and overshoes. She drank the liquor from the glass as a man would have done. Then flinging herself upon the uncomfortable sofa she said, "Mademoiselle, I am going to move away from my house on Esplanade Street."

"Ah!" ejaculated the musician, neither surprised nor especially interested. Nothing ever seemed to astonish her very much. She was endeavoring to adjust the bunch of violets which had become loose from its fastening in her hair. Edna drew her down upon the sofa, and taking a pin from her own hair, secured the shabby artificial flowers in their accustomed place.

"Aren't you astonished?"

"Passably. Where are you going? to New York? to Iberville? to your father in Mississippi? where?"

"Just two steps away," laughed Edna, "in a little four-room house around the corner. It looks so cozy, so inviting and restful, whenever I pass by; and it's for rent. I'm tired looking after that big house. It never seemed like mine, any-way—like home. It's too much trouble. I have to keep too many servants. I am tired bothering with them."

"That is not your true reason, *ma belle*. There is no use in telling me lies. I don't know your reason, but you have not told me the truth." Edna did not protest or endeavor to justify herself.

"The house, the money that provides for it, are not mine. Isn't that enough reason?"

"They are your husband's," returned Mademoiselle, with a shrug and a malicious elevation of the eyebrows.

"Oh! I see there is no deceiving you. Then let me tell you: It is a caprice. I have a little money of my own from my mother's estate, which my father sends me by driblets. I won a large sum this winter on the races, and I am beginning to sell my sketches. Laidpore is more and more pleased with my work; he says it grows in force and individuality. I cannot judge of that myself, but I feel that I have gained in ease and confidence. However, as I said, I have sold a good many through Laidpore. I can live in the tiny house for little or nothing, with one servant. Old Celestine, who works occasionally for me, says she will come stay with me and do my work. I know I shall like it, like the feeling of freedom and independence."

"What does your husband say?"

"I have not told him yet. I only thought of it this morning. He will think I am demented, no doubt. Perhaps you think so."

Mademoiselle shook her head slowly. "Your reason is not yet clear to me," she said.

Neither was it quite clear to Edna herself; but it unfolded itself as she sat for a while in silence. Instinct had prompted her to put away her husband's bounty in casting off her allegiance. She did not know how it would be when he returned. There would have to be an understanding, an explanation. Conditions would some way adjust themselves, she felt; but whatever came, she had resolved never again to belong to another than herself.

"I shall give a grand dinner before I leave the old house!" Edna exclaimed. "You will have to come to it, Mademoiselle. I will give you everything that you like to eat and drink. We shall sing and laugh and be merry for once." And she uttered a sigh that came from the very depths of her being.

If Mademoiselle happened to have received a letter from Robert during the interval of Edna's visits, she would give her the letter unsolicited. And she would seat herself at the piano and play as her humor prompted her while the young woman read the letter.

The little stove was roaring; it was red-hot, and the chocolate in the tin sizzled and sputtered. Edna went forward and opened the stove door, and Mademoiselle rising, took a letter from under the bust of Beethoven and handed it to Edna.

"Another! so soon!" she exclaimed, her eyes filled with delight. "Tell me, Mademoiselle, does he know that I see his letters?"

"Never in the world! He would be angry and would never write to me again if he thought so. Does he write to you? Never a line. Does he send you a message? Never a word. It is because he loves you, poor fool, and is trying to forget you, since you are not free to listen to him or to belong to him."

"Why do you show me his letters, then?"

"Haven't you begged for them? Can I refuse you anything? Oh! you cannot deceive me," and Mademoiselle approached her beloved instrument and began to play. Edna did not at once read the letter. She sat holding it in her hand, while the music penetrated her whole being like an effulgence, warming and brightening the dark places of her soul. It prepared her for joy and exultation.

"Oh!" she exclaimed, letting the letter fall to the floor. "Why did you not tell me?" She went and grasped Mademoiselle's hands up from the keys. "Oh! unkind! malicious! Why did you not tell me?"

"That he was coming back? No great news, *ma foi*. I wonder he did not come long ago."

"But when, when?" cried Edna, impatiently. "He does not say when."

"He says 'very soon.' You know as much about it as I do; it is all in the letter."

"But why? Why is he coming? Oh, if I thought—" and she snatched the letter from the floor and turned the pages this way and that way, looking for the reason, which was left untold.

"If I were young and in love with a man," said Mademoiselle, turning on the stool and pressing her wiry hands between her knees as she looked down at Edna, who sat on the floor holding the letter, "it seems to me he would have to be some *grand esprit*[35] a man with lofty aims and ability to reach them; one who stood high enough to attract the notice of his fellowmen. It seems to me if I were young and in love I should never deem a man of ordinary caliber worthy of my devotion."

"Now it is you who are telling lies and seeking to deceive me, Mademoiselle; or else you have never been in love, and know nothing about it. Why," went on Edna, clasping her knees and looking up into Mademoiselle's twisted face, "do you suppose a woman knows why she loves? Does she select? Does she say to herself: 'Go to! Here is a distinguished statesman with presidential possibilities; I shall proceed to fall in love with him.' Or, 'I shall set my heart upon this musician, whose fame is on every tongue?' Or, 'This financier, who controls the world's money markets?'"

"You are purposely misunderstanding me, *ma reine*.[36] Are you in love with Robert?"

"Yes," said Edna. It was the first time she had admitted it, and a glow overspread her face, blotching it with red spots.

"Why?" asked her companion. "Why do you love him when you ought not to?"

---

[35]Noble spirit, or soul.

[36]My queen, my dear.

Edna, with a motion or two, dragged herself on her knees before Mademoiselle Reisz, who took the glowing face between her two hands.

"Why? Because his hair is brown and grows away from his temples; because he opens and shuts his eyes, and his nose is a little out of drawing; because he has two lips and a square chin, and a little finger which he can't straighten from having played baseball too energetically in his youth. Because—"

"Because you do, in short," laughed Mademoiselle. "What will you do when he comes back?" she asked.

"Do? Nothing, except feel glad and happy to be alive."

She was already glad and happy to be alive at the mere thought of his return. The murky, lowering sky, which had depressed her a few hours before, seemed bracing and invigorating as she splashed through the streets on her way home.

She stopped at a confectioner's and ordered a huge box of bonbons for the children in Iberville. She slipped a card in the box, on which she scribbled a tender message and sent an abundance of kisses.

Before dinner in the evening Edna wrote a charming letter to her husband, telling him of her intention to move for a while into the little house around the block, and to give a farewell dinner before leaving, regretting that he was not there to share it, to help her out with the menu and assist her in entertaining the guests. Her letter was brilliant and brimming with cheerfulness.

XXVII

"What is the matter with you?" asked Arobin that evening. "I never found you in such a happy mood." Edna was tired by that time, and was reclining on the lounge before the fire.

"Don't you know the weather prophet has told us we shall see the sun pretty soon?"

"Well, that ought to be reason enough," he acquiesced. "You wouldn't give me another if I sat here all night imploring you." He sat close to her on a low tabouret, and as he spoke his fingers lightly touched the hair that fell a little over her forehead. She liked the touch of his fingers through her hair, and closed her eyes sensitively.

"One of these days," she said, "I'm going to pull myself together for a while and think—try to determine what character of a woman I am; for, candidly, I don't know. By all the codes which I am acquainted with, I am a devilishly wicked specimen of the sex. But some way I can't convince myself that I am. I must think about it."

"Don't. What's the use? Why should you bother thinking about it when I can tell you what manner of woman you are." His lingers strayed occasionally down to her warm, smooth cheeks and firm chin, which was growing a little full and double.

"Oh, yes! You will tell me that I am adorable; everything that is captivating. Spare yourself the effort."

"No; I shan't tell you anything of the sort, though I shouldn't be lying if I did."

"Do you know Mademoiselle Reisz?" she asked irrelevantly.

"The pianist? I know her by sight. I've heard her play."

"She says queer things sometimes in a bantering way that you don't notice at the time and you find yourself thinking about afterward."

"For instance?"

"Well, for instance, when I left her to-day, she put her arms around me and felt my shoulder blades, to see if my wings were strong, she said. 'The bird that would soar above the level plain of tradition and prejudice must have strong wings. It is a sad spectacle to see the weaklings bruised, exhausted, fluttering back to earth.' "

"Whither would you soar?"

"I'm not thinking of any extraordinary flights. I only half comprehend her."

"I've heard she's partially demented," said Arobin.

"She seems to me wonderfully sane," Edna replied.

"I'm told she's extremely disagreeable and unpleasant. Why have you introduced her at a moment when I desired to talk of you?"

"Oh! talk of me if you like," cried Edna, clasping her hands beneath her head; "but let me think of something else while you do."

"I'm jealous of your thoughts to-night. They're making you a little kinder than usual; but some way I feel as if they were wandering, as if they were not here with me." She only looked at him and smiled. His eyes were very near. He leaned upon the lounge with an arm extended across her, while the other hand still rested upon her hair. They continued silently to look into each other's eyes. When he leaned forward and kissed her, she clasped his head, holding his lips to hers.

It was the first kiss of her life to which her nature had really responded. It was a flaming torch that kindled desire.

XXVIII

Edna cried a little that night after Arobin left her. It was only one phase of the multitudinous emotions which had assailed her. There was with her an overwhelming feeling of irresponsibility. There was the shock of the unexpected and the unaccustomed. There was her husband's reproach looking at her from the external things around her which he had provided for her external existence. There was Robert's reproach making itself felt by a quicker, fiercer, more overpowering love, which had awakened within her toward him. Above all, there was understanding. She felt as if a mist had been lifted from her eyes, enabling her to look upon and comprehend the significance of life, that monster made up of beauty and brutality. But among the conflicting sensations which assailed her, there was neither shame nor remorse. There was a dull pang of regret because it was not the kiss of love which had inflamed her, because it was not love which had held this cup of life to her lips.

XXIX

Without even waiting for an answer from her husband regarding his opinion or wishes in the matter, Edna hastened her preparations for quitting her home on Esplanade Street and moving into the little house around the block. A feverish anxiety attended her every action in that direction. There was no moment of deliberation, no interval of repose between the thought and its fulfillment. Early upon the morning following those hours passed in Arobin's society, Edna set about securing her new abode and hurrying her arrangements for occupying it. Within the precincts of her home she felt like one who has entered and lingered within the portals of some forbidden temple in which a thousand muffled voices bade her begone.

Whatever was her own in the house, everything she had acquired aside from her husband's bounty, she caused to be transported to the other house, supplying simple and meager deficiencies from her own resources.

Arobin found her with rolled sleeves, working in company with the house-maid when he looked in during the afternoon. She was splendid and robust, and had never appeared handsomer than in the old blue gown, with a red silk handkerchief knotted at random around her head to protect her hair from the dust. She was mounted upon a high step-ladder, unhooking a picture from the wall when he entered. He had found the front door open, and had followed his ring by walking in unceremoniously.

"Come down!" he said. "Do you want to kill yourself?" She greeted him with affected carelessness, and appeared absorbed in her occupation.

If he had expected to find her languishing, reproachful, or indulging in sentimental tears, he must have been greatly surprised.

He was no doubt prepared for any emergency, ready for any one of the foregoing attitudes, just as he bent himself easily and naturally to the situation which confronted him.

"Please come down," he insisted, holding the ladder and looking up at her.

"No," she answered; "Ellen is afraid to mount the ladder. Joe is working over at the 'pigeon house'—that's the name Ellen gives it, because it's so small and looks like a pigeon house—and some one has to do this."

Arobin pulled off his coat, and expressed himself ready and willing to tempt fate in her place. Ellen brought him one of her dust-caps, and went into contortions of mirth, which she found it impossible to control, when she saw him put it on before the mirror as grotesquely as he could. Edna herself could not refrain from smiling when she fastened it at his request. So it was he who in turn mounted the ladder, unhooking pictures and curtains, and dislodging ornaments as Edna directed. When he had finished he took off his dust-cap and went out to wash his hands.

Edna was sitting on the tabouret, idly brushing the tips of a feather duster along the carpet when he came in again.

"Is there anything more you will let me do?" he asked.

"That is all," she answered. "Ellen can manage the rest." She kept the young woman occupied in the drawing-room, unwilling to be left alone with Arobin.

"What about the dinner?" he asked; "the grand event, the *coup d'état?*"

"It will be day after to-morrow. Why do you call it the '*coup d'état?*' Oh! it will be very fine; all my best of everything—crystal, silver and gold, Sèvres, flowers, music, and champagne to swim in. I'll let Léonce pay the bills. I wonder what he'll say when he sees the bills."

"And you ask me why I call it a *coup d'état?*" Arobin put on his coat, and he stood before her and asked if his cravat was plumb. She told him it was, looking no higher than the tip of his collar.

"When do you go to the 'pigeon house?'—with all due acknowledgement to Ellen."

"Day after to-morrow, after the dinner. I shall sleep there."

"Ellen, will you very kindly get me a glass of water?" asked Arobin. "The dust in the curtains, if you will pardon me for hinting such a thing, has parched my throat to a crisp."

"While Ellen gets the water," said Edna, rising, "I will say good-by and let you go. I must get rid of this grime, and I have a million things to do and think of."

"When shall I see you?" asked Arobin, seeking to detain her, the maid having left the room.

"At the dinner, of course. You are invited."

"Not before?—not to-night or to-morrow morning or to-morrow noon or night? or the day after morning or noon? Can't you see yourself, without my telling you, what an eternity it is?"

He had followed her into the hall and to the foot of the stairway, looking up at her as she mounted with her face half turned to him.

"Not an instant sooner," she said. But she laughed and looked at him with eyes that at once gave him courage to wait and made it torture to wait.

XXX

Though Edna had spoken of the dinner as a grand affair, it was in truth a very small affair and very select, in so much as the guests invited were few and were selected with discrimination. She had counted upon an even dozen seating themselves at her round mahogany board, forgetting for the moment that Madame Ratignolle was to the last degree *souffrante*[37] and unpresentable, and not foreseeing that Madame Lebrun would send a thousand regrets at the last moment. So there were only ten, after all, which made a cozy, comfortable number.

There were Mr. and Mrs. Merriman, a pretty, vivacious little woman in the thirties; her husband, a jovial fellow, something of a shallow-pate, who laughed a good deal at other people's witticisms, and had thereby made himself extremely popular. Mrs. Highcamp had accompanied them. Of course, there was Alcée Arobin; and Mademoiselle Reisz had consented to come. Edna had sent her a fresh bunch of violets with black lace trimmings for her hair. Monsieur Ratignolle brought himself and his wife's excuses. Victor Lebrun, who happened to be in the city, bent upon relaxation, had accepted with alacrity. There was a Miss Mayblunt, no longer in her teens, who looked at the world through lorgnettes and with the keenest interest. It was thought and said that she was intellectual; it was suspected of her that she wrote under a *nom de guerre*.[38] She had come with a gentleman by the name of Gouvernail, connected with one of the daily papers, of whom nothing special could be said, except that he was observant and seemed quiet and inoffensive. Edna herself made the tenth, and at half-past eight they seated themselves at table, Arobin and Monsieur Ratignolle on either side of their hostess.

Mrs. Highcamp sat between Arobin and Victor Lebrun. Then came Mrs. Merriman, Mr. Gouvernail, Miss Mayblunt, Mr. Merriman, and Mademoiselle Reisz next to Monsieur Ratignolle.

There was something extremely gorgeous about the appearance of the table, an effect of splendor conveyed by a cover of pale yellow satin under strips of lacework. There were wax candles in massive brass candelabra, burning softly under yellow silk shades; full, fragrant roses, yellow and red,

[37]Ill

[38]Pseudonym

abounded. There were silver and gold, as she had said there would be, and crystal which glittered like the gems which the women wore.

The ordinary stiff dining chairs had been discarded for the occasion and replaced by the most commodious and luxurious which could be collected throughout the house. Mademoiselle Reisz, being exceedingly diminutive, was elevated upon cushions, as small children are sometimes hoisted at table upon bulky volumes.

"Something new, Edna?" exclaimed Miss Mayblunt, with lorgnette directed toward a magnificent cluster of diamonds that sparkled, that almost sputtered, in Edna's hair, just over the center of her forehead.

"Quite new; 'brand' new, in fact; a present from my husband. It arrived this morning from New York. I may as well admit that this is my birthday, and that I am twenty-nine. In good time I expect you to drink my health. Meanwhile, I shall ask you to begin with this cocktail, composed—would you say 'composed?' " with an appeal to Miss Mayblunt—"composed by my father in honor of Sister Janet's wedding."

Before each guest stood a tiny glass that looked and sparkled like a garnet gem.

"Then, all things considered," spoke Arobin, "it might not be amiss to start out by drinking the Colonel's health in the cocktail which he composed, on the birthday of the most charming of women—the daughter whom he invented."

Mr. Merriman's laugh at this sally was such a genuine outburst and so contagious that it started the dinner with an agreeable swing that never slackened.

Miss Mayblunt begged to be allowed to keep her cocktail untouched before her, just to look at. The color was marvelous! She could compare it to nothing she had ever seen, and the garnet lights which it emitted were unspeakably rare. She pronounced the Colonel an artist, and stuck to it.

Monsieur Ratignolle was prepared to take things seriously: the *mets*, the *entremets*,[39] the service, the decorations, even the people. He looked up from his pompano and inquired of Arobin if he were related to the gentleman of that name who formed one of the firm of Laitner and Arobin, lawyers. The young man admitted that Laitner was a warm personal friend, who permitted Arobin's name to decorate the firm's letterheads and to appear upon a shingle that graced Perdido Street.

"There are so many inquisitive people and institutions abounding," said Arobin, "that one is really forced as a matter of convenience these days to assume the virtue of an occupation if he has it not."

---

[39]The main dishes, the side dishes.

Monsieur Ratignolle stared a little, and turned to ask Mademoiselle Reisz if she considered the symphony concerts up to the standard which had been set the previous winter. Mademoiselle Reisz answered Monsieur Ratignolle in French, which Edna thought a little rude, under the circumstances, but characteristic. Mademoiselle had only disagreeable things to say of the symphony concerts, and insulting remarks to make of all the musicians of New Orleans, singly and collectively. All her interest seemed to be centered upon the delicacies placed before her.

Mr. Merriman said that Mr. Arobin's remark about inquisitive people reminded him of a man from Waco the other day at the St. Charles Hotel—but as Mr. Merriman's stories were always lame and lacking point, his wife seldom permitted him to complete them. She interrupted him to ask if he remembered the name of the author whose book she had bought the week before to send to a friend in Geneva. She was talking "books" with Mr. Gouvernail and trying to draw from him his opinion upon current literary topics. Her husband told the story of the Waco man privately to Miss Mayblunt, who pretended to be greatly amused and to think it extremely clever.

Mrs. Highcamp hung with languid but unaffected interest upon the warm and impetuous volubility of her left-hand neighbor, Victor Lebrun. Her attention was never for a moment withdrawn from him after seating herself at table; and when he turned to Mrs. Merriman, who was prettier and more vivacious than Mrs. Highcamp, she waited with easy indifference for an opportunity to reclaim his attention. There was the occasional sound of music, of mandolins, sufficiently removed to be an agreeable accompaniment rather than an interruption to the conversation. Outside the soft, monotonous splash of a fountain could be heard; the sound penetrated into the room with the heavy odor of jessamine that came through the open windows.

The golden shimmer of Edna's satin gown spread in rich folds on either side of her. There was a soft fall of lace encircling her shoulders. It was the color of her skin, without the glow, the myriad living tints that one may sometimes discover in vibrant flesh. There was something in her attitude, in her whole appearance when she leaned her head against the high-backed chair and spread her arms, which suggested the regal woman, the one who rules, who looks on, who stands alone.

But as she sat there amid her guests, she felt the old ennui overtaking her; the hopelessness which so often assailed her, which came upon her like an obsession, like something extraneous, independent of volition. It was something which announced itself; a chill breath that seemed to issue from some vast cavern wherein discords wailed. There came over her the acute longing which always summoned into her spiritual vision the presence of the beloved one, overpowering her at once with a sense of the unattainable.

The moments glided on, while a feeling of good fellowship passed around the circle like a mystic cord, holding and binding these people together with jest and laughter. Monsieur Ratignolle was the first to break the pleasant charm. At ten o'clock he excused himself. Madame Ratignolle was waiting for him at home. She was *bien souffrante*, and she was filled with vague dread, which only her husband's presence could allay.

Mademoiselle Reisz arose with Monsieur Ratignolle, who offered to escort her to the car. She had eaten well; she had tasted the good, rich wines, and they must have turned her head, for she bowed pleasantly to all as she withdrew from table. She kissed Edna upon the shoulder, and whispered: "*Bonne nuit, ma reine; soyez sage.*"[40] She had been a little bewildered upon rising, or rather, descending from her cushions, and Monsieur Ratignolle gallantly took her arm and led her away.

Mrs. Highcamp was weaving a garland of roses, yellow and red. When she had finished the garland, she laid it lightly upon Victor's black curls. He was reclining far back in the luxurious chair, holding a glass of champagne to the light.

As if a magician's wand had touched him, the garland of roses transformed him into a vision of Oriental beauty. His cheeks were the color of crushed grapes, and his dusky eyes glowed with a languishing fire.

"*Sapristi!*" exclaimed Arobin.

But Mrs. Highcamp had one more touch to add to the picture. She took from the back of her chair a white silken scarf, with which she had covered her shoulders in the early part of the evening. She draped it across the boy in graceful folds, and in a way to conceal his black, conventional evening dress. He did not seem to mind what she did to him, only smiled showing a faint gleam of white teeth, while he continued to gaze with narrowing eyes at the light through his glass of champagne.

"Oh! to be able to paint in color rather than in words!" exclaimed Miss Mayblunt, losing herself in a rhapsodic dream as she looked at him.

" 'There was a graven image of Desire
Painted with red blood on a ground of gold.' "

murmured Gouvernail, under his breath.

The effect of the wine upon Victor was to change his accustomed volubility into silence. He seemed to have abandoned himself to a reverie, and to be seeing pleasing visions in the amber bead.

"Sing," entreated Mrs. Highcamp. "Won't you sing to us?"

---

[40]Good night, my queen; be well.

166

"Let him alone," said Arobin.

"He's posing," offered Mr. Merriman; "let him have it out."

"I believe he's paralyzed," laughed Mrs. Merriman. And leaning over the youth's chair, she took the glass from his hand and held it to his lips. He sipped the wine slowly, and when he had drained the glass she laid it upon the table and wiped his lips with her little filmy handkerchief.

"Yes, I'll sing for you," he said, turning in his chair toward Mrs. Highcamp. He clasped his hands behind his head, and looking up at the ceiling began to hum a little, trying his voice like a musician tuning an instrument. Then, looking at Edna, he began to sing:

"Ah! si tu savais!"

"Stop!" she cried, "don't sing that. I don't want you to sing it," and she laid her glass so impetuously and blindly upon the table as to shatter it against a carafe. The wine spilled over Arobin's legs and some of it trickled down upon Mrs. Highcamp's black gauze gown. Victor had lost all idea of courtesy, or else he thought his hostess was not in earnest, for he laughed and went on:

"Ah! si tu savais
Ce que tes yeux me disent"—[41]

"Oh! you mustn't! you mustn't," exclaimed Edna, and pushing back her chair she got up, and going behind him placed her hand over his mouth. He kissed the soft palm that pressed upon his lips.

"No, no, I won't, Mrs. Pontellier. I didn't know you meant it," looking up at her with caressing eyes. The touch of his lips was like a pleasing sting to her hand. She lifted the garland of roses from his head and flung it across the room.

"Come, Victor; you've posed long enough. Give Mrs. Highcamp her scarf."

Mrs. Highcamp undraped her scarf from about him with her own hands. Miss Mayblunt and Mr. Gouvernail suddenly conceived the notion that it was time to say good night. And Mr. and Mrs. Merriman wondered how it could be so late.

Before parting from Victor, Mrs. Highcamp invited him to call upon her daughter, who she knew would be charmed to meet him and talk French and sing French songs with him. Victor expressed his desire and intention to call upon Miss Highcamp at the first opportunity which presented itself. He asked if Arobin were going his way. Arobin was not.

---

[41]Ah! If you only knew what your eyes say to me.

The mandolin players had long since stolen away. A profound stillness had fallen upon the broad, beautiful street. The voices of Edna's disbanding guests jarred like a discordant note upon the quiet harmony of the night.

XXXI

"Well?" questioned Arobin, who had remained with Edna after the others had departed.

"Well," she reiterated, and stood up, stretching her arms, and feeling the need to relax her muscles after having been so long seated.

"What next?" he asked.

"The servants are all gone. They left when the musicians did. I have dismissed them. The house has to be closed and locked, and I shall trot around to the pigeon house, and shall send Celestine over in the morning to straighten things up."

He looked around, and began to turn out some of the lights.

"What about upstairs?" he inquired.

"I think it is all right; but there may be a window or two unlatched. We had better look; you might take a candle and see. And bring me my wrap and hat on the foot of the bed in the middle room."

He went up with the light, and Edna began closing doors and windows. She hated to shut in the smoke and the fumes of the wine. Arobin found her cape and hat, which he brought down and helped her to put on.

When everything was secured and the lights put out, they left through the front door, Arobin locking it and taking the key, which he carried for Edna. He helped her down the steps.

"Will you have a spray of jessamine?" he asked, breaking off a few blossoms as he passed.

"No; I don't want anything."

She seemed disheartened, and had nothing to say. She took his arm, which he offered her, holding up the weight of her satin gown with the other hand. She looked down, noticing the black line of his leg moving in and out so close to her against the yellow shimmer of her gown. There was the whistle of a railway train somewhere in the distance, and the midnight bells were ringing. They met no one in their short walk.

The "pigeon-house" stood behind a locked gate, and a shallow *parterre*[42] that had been somewhat neglected. There was a small front porch, upon which a long window and the front door opened. The door opened directly

---

[42] A formal garden.

into the parlor; there was no side entry. Back in the yard was a room for servants, in which old Celestine had been ensconced.

Edna had left a lamp burning low upon the table. She had succeeded in making the room look habitable and homelike. There were some books on the table and a lounge near at hand. On the floor was a fresh matting, covered with a rug or two; and on the walls hung a few tasteful pictures. But the room was filled with flowers. These were a surprise to her. Arobin had sent them, and had had Celestine distribute them during Edna's absence. Her bedroom was adjoining, and across a small passage were the dining-room and kitchen.

Edna seated herself with every appearance of discomfort.

"Are you tired?" he asked.

"Yes, and chilled, and miserable. I feel as if I had been wound up to a certain pitch—too tight—and something inside of me had snapped."

She had rested her head against the table upon her bare arm.

"You want to rest," he said, "and to be quiet. I'll go; I'll leave you and let you rest."

"Yes," she replied.

He stood up beside her and smoothed her hair with his soft, magnetic hand. His touch conveyed to her a certain physical comfort. She could have fallen quietly asleep there if he had continued to pass his hand over her hair. He brushed the hair upward from the nape of her neck.

"I hope you will feel better and happier in the morning," he said. "You have tried to do too much in the past few days. The dinner was the last straw; you might have dispensed with it."

"Yes," she admitted; "it was stupid."

"No, it was delightful; but it has worn you out." His hand strayed to her beautiful shoulders, and he could feel the response of her flesh to his touch. He seated himself beside her and kissed her lightly on the shoulder.

"I thought you were going away," she said, in an uneven voice.

"I am, after I have said good night."

"Good night," she murmured.

He did not answer, except to continue to caress her. He did not say good night until she had become supple to his gentle, seductive entreaties.

XXXII

When Mr. Pontellier learned of his wife's intention to abandon her home and take up her residence elsewhere he immediately wrote her a letter of unqualified disapproval and remonstrance. She had given reasons which he was unwilling to acknowledge as adequate. He hoped she had not acted upon her rash impulse; and he begged her to consider first, foremost, and above all else, what people would say. He was not dreaming of scandal when he uttered this warning; that was a thing which would never have entered into his mind to consider in connection with his wife's name or his own. He was simply thinking of his financial integrity. It might get noised about that the Pontelliers had met with reverses, and were forced to conduct their *ménage*[43] on a humbler scale than heretofore. It might do incalculable mischief to his business prospects.

But remembering Edna's whimsical turn of mind of late, and foreseeing that she had immediately acted upon her impetuous determination, he grasped the situation with his usual promptness and handled it with his well-known business tact and cleverness.

The same mail which brought to Edna his letter of disapproval carried instructions—the most minute instructions—to a well-known architect concerning the remodeling of his home, changes which he had long contemplated, and which he desired carried forward during his temporary absence.

Expert and reliable packers and movers were engaged to convey the furniture, carpets, pictures—everything movable, in short—to places of security. And in an incredibly short time the Pontellier house was turned over to the artisans. There was to be an addition—a small snuggery; there was to be frescoing, and hardwood flooring was to be put into such rooms as had not yet been subjected to this improvement.

Furthermore, in one of the daily papers appeared a brief notice to the effect that Mr. and Mrs. Pontellier were contemplating a summer sojourn abroad, and that their handsome residence on Esplanade Street was undergoing sumptuous alterations, and would not be ready for occupancy until their return. Mr. Pontellier had saved appearances!

Edna admired the skill of his maneuver, and avoided any occasion to balk his intentions. When the situation as set forth by Mr. Pontellier was accepted and taken for granted, she was apparently satisfied that it should be so.

The pigeon-house pleased her. It at once assumed the intimate character of a home, while she herself invested it with a charm which it reflected like a warm glow. There was with her a feeling of having descended in the social scale, with a corresponding sense of having risen in the spiritual. Every step, which she took toward relieving herself from obligations added to her strength and expansion as an individual. She began to look with her own eyes; to see and to apprehend the deeper undercurrents of life. No longer was she content to "feed upon opinion" when her own soul had invited her.

After a little while, a few days, in fact, Edna went up and spent a week with her children in Iberville. They were delicious February days, with all the summer's promise hovering in the air.

---

[43]Household

How glad she was to see the children! She wept for very pleasure when she felt their little arms clasping her; their hard, ruddy cheeks pressed against her own glowing cheeks. She looked into their faces with hungry eyes that could not be satisfied with looking. And what stories they had to tell their mother! About the pigs, the cows, the mules! About riding to the mill behind Gluglu; fishing back in the lake with their Uncle Jasper; picking pecans with Lidie's little black brood, and hauling chips in their little express wagon. It was a thousand times more fun to haul real chips for old lame Susie's real fire than to drag painted blocks along the banquette on Esplanade Street!

She went with them herself to see the pigs and the cows, to look at the darkies laying the cane, to thrash the pecan trees, and catch fish in the back lake. She lived with them a whole week long, giving them all of herself, and gathering and filling herself with their young existence. They listened, breathless, when she told them the house in Esplanade Street was crowded with workmen, hammering, nailing, sawing, and filling the place with clatter. They wanted to know where their bed was; what had been done with their rocking-horse; and where did Joe sleep, and where had Ellen gone, and the cook? But, above all, they were fired with a desire to see the little house around the block. Was there any place to play? Were there any boys next door? Raoul, with pessimistic foreboding, was convinced that there were only girls next door. Where would they sleep, and where would papa sleep? She told them the fairies would fix it all right.

The old Madame was charmed with Edna's visit, and showered all manner of delicate attentions upon her. She was delighted to know that the Esplanade Street house was in a dismantled condition. It gave her the promise and pretext to keep the children indefinitely.

It was with a wrench and a pang that Edna left her children. She carried away with her the sound of their voices and the touch of their cheeks. All along the journey homeward their presence lingered with her like the memory of a delicious song. But by the time she had regained the city the song no longer echoed in her soul. She was again alone.

XXXIII

It happened sometimes when Edna went to see Mademoiselle Reisz that the little musician was absent, giving a lesson or making some small necessary household purchase. The key was always left in a secret hiding-place in the entry, which Edna knew. If Mademoiselle happened to be away, Edna would usually enter and wait for her return.

When she knocked at Mademoiselle Reisz's door one afternoon there was no response; so unlocking the door, as usual, she entered and found the apartment deserted, as she had expected. Her day had been quite filled up, and it was for a rest, for a refuge, and to talk about Robert, that she sought out her friend.

She had worked at her canvas—a young Italian character study—all the morning, completing the work without the model; but there had been many interruptions, some incident to her modest housekeeping, and others of a social nature.

Madame Ratignolle had dragged herself over, avoiding the too public thoroughfares, she said. She complained that Edna had neglected her much of late. Besides, she was consumed with curiosity to see the little house and the manner in which it was conducted. She wanted to hear all about the dinner party; Monsieur Ratignolle had left *so* early. What had happened after he left? The champagne and grapes which Edna sent over were *too* delicious. She had so little appetite; they had refreshed and toned her stomach. Where on earth was she going to put Mr. Pontellier in that little house, and the boys? And then she made Edna promise to go to her when her hour of trial overtook her.

"At any time—any time of the day or night, dear," Edna assured her.

Before leaving Madame Ratignolle said:

"In some way you seem to me like a child, Edna. You seem to act without a certain amount of reflection which is necessary in this life. That is the reason I want to say you mustn't mind if I advise you to be a little careful while you are living here alone. Why don't you have some one come and stay with you? Wouldn't Mademoiselle Reisz come?"

"No; she wouldn't wish to come, and I shouldn't want her always with me."

"Well, the reason—you know how evil-minded the world is—some one was talking of Alcée Arobin visiting you. Of course, it wouldn't matter if Mr. Arobin had not such a dreadful reputation. Monsieur Ratignolle was telling me that his attentions alone are considered enough to ruin a woman's name."

"Does he boast of his successes?" asked Edna, indifferently, squinting at her picture.

"No, I think not. I believe he is a decent fellow as far as that goes. But his character is so well known among the men. I shan't be able to come back and see you; it was very, very imprudent to-day."

"Mind the step!" cried Edna.

"Don't neglect me," entreated Madame Ratignolle; "and don't mind what I said about Arobin, or having some one to stay with you."

"Of course not," Edna laughed. "You may say anything you like to me." They kissed each other good-by. Madame Ratignolle had not far to go, and Edna stood on the porch a while watching her walk down the street.

Then in the afternoon Mrs. Merriman and Mrs. Highcamp had made their "party call." Edna felt that they might have dispensed with the formality. They had also come to invite her to play *vingt-et-un*[44] one evening at Mrs. Merriman's. She was asked to go early, to dinner, and Mr. Merriman or Mr. Arobin would take her home. Edna accepted in a half-hearted way. She sometimes felt very tired of Mrs. Highcamp and Mrs. Merriman.

Late in the afternoon she sought refuge with Mademoiselle Reisz, and stayed there alone, waiting for her, feeling a kind of repose invade her with the very atmosphere of the shabby, unpretentious little room.

Edna sat at the window, which looked out over the house-tops and across the river. The window frame was filled with pots of flowers, and she sat and picked the dry leaves from a rose geranium. The day was warm, and the breeze which blew from the river was very pleasant. She removed her hat and laid it on the piano. She went on picking the leaves and digging around the plants with her hat pin. Once she thought she heard Mademoiselle Reisz approaching. But it was a young black girl, who came in, bringing a small bundle of laundry, which she deposited in the adjoining room, and went away.

Edna seated herself at the piano, and softly picked out with one hand the bars of a piece of music which lay open before her. A half-hour went by. There was the occasional sound of people going and coming in the lower hall. She was growing interested in her occupation of picking out the aria, when there was a second rap at the door. She vaguely wondered what these people did when they found Mademoiselle's door locked.

"Come in," she called, turning her face toward the door. And this time it was Robert Lebrun who presented himself. She attempted to rise; she could not have done so without betraying the agitation which mastered her at sight of him, so she fell back upon the stool, only exclaiming, "Why, Robert!"

He came and clasped her hand, seemingly without knowing what he was saying or doing.

"Mrs. Pontellier! How do you happen—oh! how well you look! Is Mademoiselle Reisz not here? I never expected to see you."

"When did you come back?" asked Edna in an unsteady voice, wiping her face with her handkerchief. She seemed ill at ease on the piano stool, and he begged her to take the chair by the window. She did so, mechanically, while he seated himself on the stool.

"I returned day before yesterday," he answered, while he leaned his arm on the keys, bringing forth a crash of discordant sound.

"Day before yesterday!" she repeated, aloud; and went on thinking to herself, "day before yesterday," in a sort of an uncomprehending way. She had

---

[44]The card game twenty-one.

pictured him seeking her at the very first hour, and he had lived under the same sky since day before yesterday; while only by accident had he stumbled upon her. Mademoiselle must have lied when she said, "Poor fool, he loves you."

"Day before yesterday," she repeated, breaking off a spray of Mademoiselle's geranium; "then if you had not met me here to-day you wouldn't—when—that is, didn't you mean to come and see me?"

"Of course, I should have gone to see you. There have been so many things—" he turned the leaves of Mademoiselle's music nervously. "I started in at once yesterday with the old firm. After all there is as much chance for me here as there was there—that is, I might find it profitable some day. The Mexicans were not very congenial."

So he had come back because the Mexicans were not congenial; because business was as profitable here as there; because of reason, and not because he cared to be near her. She remembered the day she sat on the floor, turning the pages of his letter, seeking the reason which was left untold.

She had not noticed how he looked—only feeling his presence; but she turned deliberately and observed him. After all, he had been absent but a few months, and was not changed. His hair—the color of hers—waved back from his temples in the same way as before. His skin was not more burned than it had been at Grand Isle. She found in his eyes, when he looked at her for one silent moment, the same tender caress, with an added warmth and entreaty which had not been there before—the same glance which had penetrated to the sleeping places of her soul and awakened them.

A hundred times Edna had pictured Robert's return, and imagined their first meeting. It was usually at her home, whither he had sought her out at once. She always fancied him expressing or betraying in some way his love for her. And here, the reality was that they sat ten feet apart, she at the window, crushing geranium leaves in her hand and smelling them, he twirling around on the piano stool, saying:

"I was very much surprised to hear of Mr. Pontellier's absence; it's a wonder Mademoiselle Reisz did not tell me; and your moving—mother told me yesterday. I should think you would have gone to New York with him, or to Iberville with the children, rather than be bothered here with housekeeping. And you are going abroad, too, I hear. We shan't have you at Grand Isle next summer; it won't seem—do you see much of Mademoiselle Reisz? She often spoke of you in the few letters she wrote."

"Do you remember that you promised to write to me when you went away?" A flush overspread his whole face.

"I couldn't believe that my letters would be of any interest to you."

"That is an excuse; it isn't the truth." Edna reached for her hat on the piano. She adjusted it, sticking the hat pin through the heavy coil of hair with some deliberation.

"Are you not going to wait for Mademoiselle Reisz?" asked Robert.

"No; I have found when she is absent this long, she is liable not to come back till late." She drew on her gloves, and Robert picked up his hat.

"Won't you wait for her?" asked Edna.

"Not if you think she will not be back till late," adding, as if suddenly aware of some discourtesy in his speech "and I should miss the pleasure of walking home with you." Edna locked the door and put the key back in its hiding-place.

They went together, picking their way across muddy streets and sidewalks encumbered with the cheap display of small tradesmen. Part of the distance they rode in the car, and after disembarking, passed the Pontellier mansion, which looked broken and half torn asunder. Robert had never known the house, and looked at it with interest.

"I never knew you in your home," he remarked.

"I am glad you did not."

"Why?" She did not answer. They went on around the corner, and it seemed as if her dreams were coming true after all, when he followed her into the little house.

"You must stay and dine with me, Robert. You see I am all alone, and it is so long since I have seen you. There is so much I want to ask you."

She took off her hat and gloves. He stood irresolute, making some excuse about his mother who expected him; he even muttered something about an engagement. She struck a match and lit the lamp in the table; it was growing dusk. When he saw her face in the lamp-light, looking pained, with all the soft lines gone out of it, he threw his hat aside and seated himself.

"Oh! you know I want to stay if you will let me!" he exclaimed. All the softness came back. She laughed, and went and put her hand on his shoulder.

"This is the first moment you have seemed like the old Robert. I'll go tell Celestine." She hurried away to tell Celestine to set an extra place. She even sent her off in search of some added delicacy which she had not thought of for herself. And she recommended great care in dripping the coffee and having the omelet done to a proper turn.

When she reentered, Robert was turning over magazines, sketches and things that lay upon the table in great disorder. He picked up a photograph, and exclaimed:

"Alcée Arobin! What on earth is his picture doing here?"

"I tried to make a sketch of his head one day," answered Edna, "and he thought the photograph might help me. It was at the other house. I thought it had been left there. I must have picked it up with my drawing materials."

"I should think you would give it back to him if you have finished with it."

"Oh! I have a great many such photographs. I never think of returning them. They don't amount to anything." Robert kept on looking at the picture.

"It seems to me—do you think his head worth drawing? Is he a friend of Mr. Pontellier's? You never said you knew him."

"He isn't a friend of Mr. Pontellier's; he's a friend of mine. I always knew him—that is, it is only of late that I know him pretty well. But I'd rather talk about you, and know what you have been seeing and doing and feeling out there in Mexico." Robert threw aside the picture.

"I've been seeing the waves and the white beach of Grand Isle; the quiet, grassy street of the *Chênière Caminada*; the old fort at Grande Terre. I've been working like a machine, and feeling like a lost soul. There was nothing interesting."

She leaned her head upon her hand to shade her eyes from the light.

"And what have you been seeing and doing and feeling all these days?" he asked.

"I've been seeing the waves and the white beach of Grand Isle; the quiet, grassy street of the *Chênière*; the old sunny fort at Grande Terre. I've been working with a little more comprehension than a machine, and still feeling like a lost soul. There was nothing interesting."

"Mrs. Pontellier, you are cruel," he said, with feeling, closing his eyes and resting his head back in his chair. They remained in silence till old Celestine announced dinner.

XXXIV

The dining-room was very small. Edna's round mahogany would have almost filled it. As it was there was but a step or two from the little table to the kitchen, to the mantel, the small buffet, and the side door that opened out on the narrow brick-paved yard.

A certain degree of ceremony settled upon them with the announcement of dinner. There was no return to personalities. Robert related incidents of his sojourn in Mexico, and Edna talked of events likely to interest him, which had occurred during his absence. The dinner was of ordinary quality, except for the few delicacies which she had sent out to purchase. Old Celestine, with a bandana *tignon* twisted about her head, hobbled in and out, taking a personal interest in everything; and she lingered occasionally to talk patois[45] with Robert, whom she had known as a boy.

---

[45] A regional dialect based on English, French, Spanish, and American Indian.

He went out to a neighboring cigar stand to purchase cigarette papers, and when he came back he found that Celestine had served the black coffee in the parlor.

"Perhaps I shouldn't have come back," he said. "When you are tired of me, tell me to go."

"You never tire me. You must have forgotten the hours and hours at Grand Isle in which we grew accustomed to each other and used to being together."

"I have forgotten nothing at Grand Isle," he said, not looking at her, but rolling a cigarette. His tobacco pouch, which he laid upon the table, was a fantastic embroidered silk affair, evidently the handiwork of a woman.

"You used to carry your tobacco in a rubber pouch," said Edna, picking up the pouch and examining the needlework.

"Yes; it was lost."

"Where did you buy this one? In Mexico?"

"It was given to me by a Vera Cruz girl; they are very generous," he replied, striking a match and lighting his cigarette.

"They are very handsome, I suppose, those Mexican women; very picturesque, with their black eyes and their lace scarfs."

"Some are; others are hideous. Just as you find women everywhere."

"What was she like—the one who gave you the pouch? You must have known her very well."

"She was very ordinary. She wasn't of the slightest importance. I knew her well enough."

"Did you visit at her house? Was it interesting? I should like to know and hear about the people you met, and the impressions they made on you."

"There are some people who leave impressions not so lasting as the imprint of an oar upon the water."

"Was she such a one?"

"It would be ungenerous for me to admit that she was of that order and kind." He thrust the pouch back in his pocket, as if to put away the subject with the trifle which had brought it up.

Arobin dropped in with a message from Mrs. Merriman, to say that the card party was postponed on account of the illness of one of her children.

"How do you do, Arobin?" said Robert, rising from the obscurity.

"Oh! Lebrun. To be sure! I heard yesterday you were back. How did they treat you down in Mexique?"

"Fairly well."

"But not well enough to keep you there. Stunning girls, though, in Mexico. I thought I should never get away from Vera Cruz when I was down there a couple of years ago."

"Did they embroider slippers and tobacco pouches and hat-bands and things for you?" asked Edna.

"Oh! my! no! I didn't get so deep in their regard. I fear they made more impression on me than I made on them."

"You were less fortunate than Robert, then."

"I am always less fortunate than Robert. Has he been imparting tender confidences?"

"I've been imposing myself long enough," said Robert, rising, and shaking hands with Edna. "Please convey my regards to Mr. Pontellier when you write."

He shook hands with Arobin and went away.

"Fine fellow, that Lebrun," said Arobin when Robert had gone. "I never heard you speak of him."

"I knew him last summer at Grand Isle," she replied. "Here is that photograph of yours. Don't you want it?"

"What do I want with it? Throw it away." She threw it back on the table.

"I'm not going to Mrs. Merriman's," she said. "If you see her, tell her so. But perhaps I had better write. I think I shall write now, and say that I am sorry her child is sick, and tell her not to count on me."

"It would be a good scheme," acquiesced Arobin. "I don't blame you; stupid lot!"

Edna opened the blotter, and having procured paper and pen, began to write the note. Arobin lit a cigar and read the evening paper, which he had in his pocket.

"What is the date?" she asked. He told her.

"Will you mail this for me when you go out?"

"Certainly." He read to her little bits out of the newspaper, while she straightened things on the table.

"What do you want to do?" he asked, throwing aside the paper. "Do you want to go out for a walk or a drive or anything? It would be a fine night to drive."

"No; I don't want to do anything but just be quiet. You go away and amuse yourself. Don't stay."

"I'll go away if I must; but I shan't amuse myself. You know that I only live when I am near you."

He stood up to bid her good night.

"Is that one of the things you always say to women?"

"I have said it before, but I don't think I ever came so near meaning it," he answered with a smile. There were no warm lights in her eyes; only a dreamy, absent look.

"Good night. I adore you. Sleep well," he said, and he kissed her hand and went away.

She stayed alone in a kind of reverie—a sort of stupor. Step by step she lived over every instant of the time she had been with Robert after he had entered Mademoiselle Reisz's door. She recalled his words, his looks. How few and meager they had been for her hungry heart! A vision—a transcendently seductive vision of a Mexican girl arose before her. She writhed with a jealous pang. She wondered when he would come back. He had not said he would come back. She had been with him, had heard his voice and touched his hand. But some way he had seemed nearer to her off there in Mexico.

XXXV

The morning was full of sunlight and hope. Edna could see before her no denial—only the promise of excessive joy. She lay in bed awake, with bright eyes full of speculation. "He loves you, poor fool." If she could but get that conviction firmly fixed in her mind, what mattered about the rest? She felt she had been childish and unwise the night before in giving herself over to despondency. She recapitulated the motives which no doubt explained Robert's reserve. They were not insurmountable; they would not hold if he really loved her; they could not hold against her own passion, which he must come to realize in time. She pictured him going to his business that morning. She even saw how he was dressed; how he walked down one street, and turned the corner of another; saw him bending over his desk, talking to people who entered the office, going to his lunch, and perhaps watching for her on the street. He would come to her in the afternoon or evening, sit and roll his cigarette, talk a little, and go away as he had done the night before. But how delicious it would be to have him there with her! She would have no regrets, nor seek to penetrate his reserve if he still chose to wear it.

Edna ate her breakfast only half dressed. The maid brought her a delicious printed scrawl from Raoul, expressing his love, asking her to send him some bonbons, and telling her they had found that morning ten tiny white pigs all lying in a row beside Lidie's big white pig.

A letter also came from her husband, saying he hoped to be back early in March, and then they would get ready for that journey abroad which he had promised her so long, which he felt now fully able to afford; he felt able to travel as people should, without any thought of small economies—thanks to his recent speculations in Wall Street.

Much to her surprise she received a note from Arobin, written at midnight from the club. It was to say good morning to her, to hope she had slept well, to assure her of his devotion, which he trusted she in some faintest manner returned.

All these letters were pleasing to her. She answered the children in a cheerful frame of mind, promising them bonbons, and congratulating them upon their happy find of the little pigs.

She answered her husband with friendly evasiveness,—not with any fixed design to mislead him, only because all sense of reality had gone out of her life; she had abandoned herself to Fate, and awaited the consequences with indifference.

To Arobin's note she made no reply. She put it under Celestine's stovelid.

Edna worked several hours with much spirit. She saw no one but a picture dealer, who asked her if it were true that she was going abroad to study in Paris.

She said possibly she might, and he negotiated with her for some Parisian studies to reach him in time for the holiday trade in December.

Robert did not come that day. She was keenly disappointed. He did not come the following day, nor the next. Each morning she awoke with hope, and each night she was a prey to despondency. She was tempted to seek him out. But far from yielding to the impulse, she avoided any occasion which might throw her in his way. She did not go to Mademoiselle Reisz's nor pass by Madame Lebrun's, as she might have done if he had still been in Mexico.

When Arobin, one night, urged her to drive with him, she went—out to the lake, on the Shell Road. His horses were full of mettle, and even a little unmanageable. She liked the rapid gait at which they spun along, and the quick, sharp sound of the horses' hoofs on the hard road. They did not stop anywhere to eat or to drink. Arobin was not needlessly imprudent. But they ate and they drank when they regained Edna's little dining-room—which was comparatively early in the evening.

It was late when he left her. It was getting to be more than a passing whim with Arobin to see her and be with her. He had detected the latent sensuality, which unfolded under his delicate sense of her nature's requirements like a torpid, torrid, sensitive blossom.

There was no despondency when she fell asleep that night; nor was there hope when she awoke in the morning.

XXXVI

There was a garden out in the suburbs; a small, leafy corner, with a few green tables under the orange trees. An old cat slept all day on the stone step in the sun, and an old *mulatresse*[46] slept her idle hours away in her chair at the open window, till some one happened to knock on one of the green tables. She had

---

[46]A woman of mixed race.

milk and cream cheese to sell, and bread and butter. There was no one who could make such excellent coffee or fry a chicken so golden brown as she.

The place was too modest to attract the attention of people of fashion, and so quiet as to have escaped the notice of those in search of pleasure and dissipation. Edna had discovered it accidentally one day when the highboard gate stood ajar. She caught sight of a little green table, blotched with the checkered sunlight that filtered through the quivering leaves overhead. Within she had found the slumbering *mulatresse*, the drowsy cat, and a glass of milk which reminded her of the milk she had tasted in Iberville.

She often stopped there during her perambulations; sometimes taking a book with her, and sitting an hour or two under the trees when she found the place deserted. Once or twice she took a quiet dinner there alone, having instructed Celestine beforehand to prepare no dinner at home. It was the last place in the city where she would have expected to meet any one she knew.

Still she was not astonished when, as she was partaking of a modest dinner late in the afternoon, looking into an open book, stroking the cat, which had made friends with her—she was not greatly astonished to see Robert come in at the tall garden gate.

"I am destined to see you only by accident," she said, shoving the cat off the chair beside her. He was surprised, ill at ease, almost embarrassed at meeting her thus so unexpectedly.

"Do you come here often?" he asked.

"I almost live here," she said.

"I used to drop in very often for a cup of Catiche's good coffee. This is the first time since I came back."

"She'll bring you a plate, and you will share my dinner. There's always enough for two—even three." Edna had intended to be indifferent and as reserved as he when she met him; she had reached the determination by a laborious train of reasoning, incident to one of her despondent moods. But her resolve melted when she saw him before her, seated there beside her in the little garden, as if a designing Providence had led him into her path.

"Why have you kept away from me, Robert?" she asked, closing the book that lay open upon the table.

"Why are you so personal, Mrs. Pontellier? Why do you force me to idiotic subterfuges?" he exclaimed with sudden warmth. "I suppose there's no use telling you I've been very busy, or that I've been sick, or that I've been to see you and not found you at home. Please let me off with any of these excuses."

"You are the embodiment of selfishness," she said. "You save yourself something—I don't know what—but there is some selfish motive, and in sparing yourself you never consider for a moment what I think, or how I feel your neglect and indifference. I suppose this is what you would call unwomanly; but

I have got into a habit of expressing myself. It doesn't matter to me, and you may think me unwomanly if you like."

"No; I only think you cruel, as I said the other day. Maybe not intentionally cruel; but you seem to be forcing me into disclosures which can result in nothing; as if you would have me bare a wound for the pleasure of looking at it, without the intention or power of healing it."

"I'm spoiling your dinner, Robert; never mind what I say. You haven't eaten a morsel."

"I only came in for a cup of coffee." His sensitive face was all disfigured with excitement.

"Isn't this a delightful place?" she remarked. "I am so glad it has never actually been discovered. It is so quiet, so sweet, here. Do you notice there is scarcely a sound to be heard? It's so out of the way; and a good walk from the car. However, I don't mind walking. I always feel so sorry for women who don't like to walk; they miss so much—so many rare little glimpses of life; and we women learn so little of life on the whole.

"Catiche's coffee is always hot. I don't know how she manages it, here in open air. Celestine's coffee gets cold bringing it from the kitchen to the dining-room. Three lumps! How can you drink it so sweet? Take some of the cress with your chop; it's so biting and crisp. Then there's the advantage of being able to smoke with your coffee out here. Now, in the city—aren't you going to smoke?"

"After a while," he said, laying a cigar on the table.

"Who gave it to you?" she laughed.

"I bought it. I suppose I'm getting reckless; I bought a whole box." She was determined not to be personal again and make him uncomfortable.

The cat made friends with him, and climbed into his lap when he smoked his cigar. He stroked her silky fur, and talked a little about her. He looked at Edna's book, which he had read; and he told her the end, to save her the trouble of wading through it, he said.

Again he accompanied her back to her home; and it was after dusk when they reached the little "pigeon-house." She did not ask him to remain, which he was grateful for, as it permitted him to stay without the discomfort of blundering through an excuse which he had no intention of considering. He helped her to light the lamp; then she went into her room to take off her hat and to bathe her face and hands.

When she came back Robert was not examining the pictures and magazines as before; he sat off in the shadow, leaning his head back on the chair as if in a reverie. Edna lingered a moment beside the table, arranging the books there. Then she went across the room to where he sat. She bent over the arm of his chair and called his name.

"Robert," she said, "are you asleep?"

"No," he answered, looking up at her.

She leaned over and kissed him—a soft, cool, delicate kiss, whose voluptuous sting penetrated his whole being—then she moved away from him. He followed, and took her in his arms, just holding her close to him. She put her hand up to his face and pressed his cheek against her own. The action was full of love and tenderness. He sought her lips again. Then he drew her down upon the sofa beside him and held her hand in both of his.

"Now you know," he said, "now you know what I have been fighting against since last summer at Grand Isle; what drove me away and drove me back again."

"Why have you been fighting against it?" she asked. Her face glowed with soft lights.

"Why? Because you were not free; you were Léonce Pontellier's wife. I couldn't help loving you if you were ten times his wife; but so long as I went away from you and kept away I could help telling you so." She put her free hand up to his shoulder, and then against his cheek, rubbing it softly. He kissed her again. His face was warm and flushed.

"There in Mexico I was thinking of you all the time, and longing for you."

"But not writing to me," she interrupted.

"Something put into my head that you cared for me; and I lost my senses. I forgot everything but a wild dream of your some way becoming my wife."

"Your wife!"

"Religion, loyalty, everything would give way if only you cared."

"Then you must have forgotten that I was Léonce Pontellier's wife."

"Oh! I was demented, dreaming of wild, impossible things, recalling men who had set their wives free, we have heard of such things."

"Yes, we have heard of such things."

"I came back full of vague, mad intentions. And when I got here—"

"When you got here you never came near me!" She was still caressing his cheek.

"I realized what a cur I was to dream of such a thing, even if you had been willing."

She took his face between her hands and looked into it as if she would never withdraw her eyes more. She kissed him on the forehead, the eyes, the cheeks, and the lips.

"You have been a very, very foolish boy, wasting your time dreaming of impossible things when you speak of Mr. Pontellier setting me free! I am no longer one of Mr. Pontellier's possessions to dispose of or not. I give myself where I choose. If he were to say, 'Here, Robert, take her and be happy; she is yours,' I should laugh at you both."

His face grew a little white. "What do you mean?" he asked.

There was a knock at the door. Old Celestine came in to say that Madame Ratignolle's servant had come around the back way with a message that Madame had been taken sick and begged Mrs. Pontellier to go to her immediately.

"Yes, yes," said Edna, rising; "I promised. Tell her yes—to wait for me. I'll go back with her."

"Let me walk over with you," offered Robert.

"No," she said; "I will go with the servant." She went into her room to put on her hat, and when she came in again she sat once more upon the sofa beside him. He had not stirred. She put her arms about his neck.

"Good-by, my sweet Robert. Tell me good-by." He kissed her with a degree of passion which had not before entered into his caress, and strained her to him.

"I love you," she whispered, "only you; no one but you. It was you who woke me last summer out of a life-long, stupid dream. Oh! you have made me so unhappy with your indifference. Oh! I have suffered, suffered! Now you are here we shall love each other, my Robert. We shall be everything to each other. Nothing else in the world is of any consequence. I must go to my friend; but you will wait for me? No matter how late; you will wait for me, Robert?"

"Don't go; don't go! Oh! Edna, stay with me," he pleaded. "Why should you go? Stay with me, stay with me."

"I shall come back as soon as I can; I shall find you here." She buried her face in his neck, and said good-by again. Her seductive voice, together with his great love for her, had enthralled his senses, had deprived him of every impulse but the longing to hold her and keep her.

XXXVII

Edna looked in at the drug store. Monsieur Ratignolle was putting up a mixture himself, very carefully, dropping a red liquid into a tiny glass. He was grateful to Edna for having come; her presence would be a comfort to his wife. Madame Ratignolle's sister, who had always been with her at such trying times, had not been able to come up from the plantation, and Adèle had been inconsolable until Mrs. Pontellier so kindly promised to come to her. The nurse had been with them at night for the past week, as she lived a great distance away. And Dr. Mandelet had been coming and going all the afternoon. They were then looking for him any moment.

Edna hastened upstairs by a private stairway that led from the rear of the store to the apartment above. The children were all sleeping in a back room. Madame Ratignolle was in the salon, whither she had strayed in her suffering impatience. She sat on the sofa, clad in an ample white *peignoir*, holding a handkerchief tight in her hand with a nervous clutch. Her face was drawn and pinched, her sweet blue eyes haggard and unnatural. All her beautiful hair had been drawn back and plaited. It lay in a long braid on the sofa pillow, coiled like a golden serpent. The nurse, a comfortable looking *Griffe*[47] woman in white apron and cap, was urging her to return to her bedroom.

"There is no use, there is no use," she said at once to Edna. "We must get rid of Mandelet; he is getting too old and careless. He said he would be here at half-past seven; now it must be eight. See what time it is, Joséphine."

The woman was possessed of a cheerful nature, and refused to take any situation too seriously, especially a situation with which she was so familiar. She urged Madame to have courage and patience. But Madame only set her teeth hard into her under lip, and Edna saw the sweat gather in beads on her white forehead. After a moment or two she uttered a profound sigh and wiped her face with the handkerchief rolled in a ball. She appeared exhausted. The nurse gave her a fresh handkerchief, sprinkled with cologne water.

"This is too much!" she cried. "Mandelet ought to be killed! Where is Alphonse? Is it possible I am to be abandoned like this—neglected by every one?"

"Neglected, indeed!" exclaimed the nurse. Wasn't she there? And here was Mrs. Pontellier leaving, no doubt, a pleasant evening at home to devote to her? And wasn't Monsieur Ratignolle coming that very instant through the hall? And Joséphine was quite sure she had heard Doctor Mandelet's coupé. Yes, there it was, down at the door.

Adèle consented to go back to her room. She sat on the edge of a little low couch next to her bed.

Doctor Mandelet paid no attention to Madame Ratignolle's upbraidings. He was accustomed to them at such times, and was too well convinced of her loyalty to doubt it.

He was glad to see Edna, and wanted her to go with him into the salon and entertain him. But Madame Ratignolle would not consent that Edna should leave her for an instant. Between agonizing moments, she chatted a little, and said it took her mind off her sufferings.

Edna began to feel uneasy. She was seized with a vague dread. Her own like experiences seemed far away, unreal, and only half remembered. She recalled faintly an ecstasy of pain, the heavy odor of chloroform, a stupor which had deadened sensation, and an awakening to find a little new life to which she had given being, added to the great unnumbered multitude of souls that come and go.

She began to wish she had not come; her presence was not necessary. She might have invented a pretext for staying away; she might even invent a pretext now for going. But Edna did not go. With an inward agony, with a

---

[47]Mixed-race

flaming, outspoken revolt against the ways of Nature, she witnessed the scene of torture.

She was still stunned and speechless with emotion when later she leaned over her friend to kiss her and softly say good-by. Adèle, pressing her cheek, whispered in an exhausted voice: "Think of the children, Edna. Oh, think of the children! Remember them!"

XXXVIII

Edna still felt dazed when she got outside in the open air. The Doctor's coupè had returned for him and stood before the *porte cochère*. She did not wish to enter the coupè, and told Doctor Mandelet she would walk; she was not afraid, and would go alone. He directed his carriage to meet him at Mrs. Pontellier's, and he started to walk home with her.

Up—away up, over the narrow street between the tall houses, the stars were blazing. The air was mild and caressing, but cool with the breath of spring and the night. They walked slowly, the Doctor with a heavy, measured tread and his hands behind him; Edna, in an absent-minded way, as she had walked one night at Grand Isle, as if her thoughts had gone ahead of her and she was striving to overtake them.

"You shouldn't have been there, Mrs. Pontellier," he said. "That was no place for you. Adèle is full of whims at such times. There were a dozen women she might have had with her, unimpressionable women. I felt that it was cruel, cruel. You shouldn't have gone."

"Oh, well!" she answered, indifferently. "I don't know that it matters after all. One has to think of the children some time or other; the sooner the better."

"When is Léonce coming back?"

"Quite soon. Some time in March."

"And you are going abroad?"

"Perhaps—no, I am not going. I'm not going to be forced into doing things. I don't want to go abroad. I want to be let alone. Nobody has any right—except children, perhaps—and even then, it seems to me—or it did seem—" She felt that her speech was voicing the incoherency of her thoughts, and stopped abruptly.

"The trouble is," sighed the Doctor, grasping her meaning intuitively, "that youth is given up to illusions. It seems to be a provision of Nature; a decoy to secure mothers for the race. And Nature takes no account of moral consequences, or arbitrary conditions which we create, and which we feel obliged to maintain at any cost."

"Yes," she said. "The years that are gone seem like dreams—if one might go on sleeping and dreaming—but to wake up and find—oh! well! perhaps it is better to wake up after all, even to suffer, rather than to remain a dupe to illusions all one's life."

"It seems to me, my dear child," said the Doctor at parting, holding her hand, "you seem to me to be in trouble. I am not going to ask for your confidence. I will only say that if ever you feel moved to give it to me, perhaps I might help you. I know I would understand, and I tell you there are not many who would—not many, my dear."

"Some way I don't feel moved to speak of things that trouble me. Don't think I am ungrateful or that I don't appreciate your sympathy. There are periods of despondency and suffering which take possession of me. But I don't want anything but my own way. That is wanting a good deal, of course, when you have to trample upon the lives, the hearts, the prejudices of others—but no matter—still, I shouldn't want to trample upon the little lives. Oh! I don't know what I'm saying, Doctor. Good night. Don't blame me for anything."

"Yes, I will blame you if you don't come and see me soon. We will talk of things you never have dreamt of talking about before. It will do us both good. I don't want you to blame yourself, whatever comes. Good night, my child."

She let herself in at the gate, but instead of entering she sat upon the step of the porch. The night was quiet and soothing. All the tearing emotion of the last few hours seemed to fall away from her like a somber, uncomfortable garment, which she had but to loosen to be rid of. She went back to that hour before Adèle had sent for her; and her senses kindled afresh in thinking of Robert's words, the pressure of his arms, and the feeling of his lips upon her own. She could picture at that moment no greater bliss on earth than possession of the beloved one. His expression of love had already given him to her in part. When she thought that he was there at hand, waiting for her, she grew numb with the intoxication of expectancy. It was so late; he would be asleep perhaps. She would awaken him with a kiss. She hoped he would be asleep that she might arouse him with her caresses.

Still, she remembered Adèle's voice whispering, "Think of the children; think of them." She meant to think of them; that determination had driven into her soul like a death wound—but not to-night. To-morrow would be time to think of everything.

Robert was not waiting for her in the little parlor. He was nowhere at hand. The house was empty. But he had scrawled on a piece of paper that lay in the lamplight:

"I love you. Good-by—because I love you."

Edna grew faint when she read the words. She went and sat on the sofa. Then she stretched herself out there, never uttering a sound. She did not sleep. She did not go to bed. The lamp sputtered and went out. She was still awake in the morning, when Celestine unlocked the kitchen door and came in to light the fire.

XXXIX

Victor, with hammer and nails and scraps of scantling, was patching a corner of one of the galleries. Mariequita sat near by, dangling her legs, watching him work, and handing him nails from the tool-box. The sun was beating down upon them. The girl covered her head with her apron folded into a square pad. They had been talking for an hour or more. She was never tired of hearing Victor describe the dinner at Mrs. Pontellier's. He exaggerated every detail, making it appear a veritable Lucullean feast. The flowers were in tubs, he said. The champagne was quaffed from huge golden goblets. Venus rising from the foam could have presented no more entrancing a spectacle than Mrs. Pontellier, blazing with beauty and diamonds at the head of the board, while the other women were all of them youthful houris,[48] possessed of incomparable charms.

She got it into her head that Victor was in love with Mrs. Pontellier, and he gave her evasive answers, framed so as to confirm her belief. She grew sullen and cried a little, threatening to go off and leave him to his fine ladies. There were a dozen men crazy about her at the *Chênière;* and since it was the fashion to be in love with married people, why, she could run away any time she liked to New Orleans with Célina's husband.

Célina's husband was a fool, a coward, and a pig, and to prove it to her, Victor intended to hammer his head into a jelly the next time he encountered him. This assurance was very consoling to Mariequita. She dried her eyes, and grew cheerful at the prospect.

They were still talking of the dinner and the allurements of city life when Mrs. Pontellier herself slipped around the corner of the house. The two youngsters stayed dumb with amazement before what they considered to be an apparition. But it was really she in flesh and blood, looking tired and a little travel-strained.

"I walked up from the wharf," she said, "and heard the hammering. I supposed it was you, mending the porch. It's a good thing. I was always tripping over those loose planks last summer. How dreary and deserted everything looks!"

It took Victor some time to comprehend that she had come in Beaudelet's lugger, that she had come alone, and for no purpose but to rest.

"There's nothing fixed up yet, you see. I'll give you my room; it's the only place."

"Any corner will do," she assured him.

---

[48]The virgins in paradise, according to the Koran.

"And if you can stand Philomel's cooking," he went on, "though I might try to get her mother while you are here. Do you think she would come?" turning to Mariequita.

Mariequita thought that perhaps Philomel's mother might come for a few days, and money enough.

Beholding Mrs. Pontellier make her appearance, the girl had at once suspected a lovers' rendezvous. But Victor's astonishment was so genuine, and Mrs. Pontellier's indifference so apparent, that the disturbing notion did not lodge long in her brain. She contemplated with the greatest interest this woman who gave the most sumptuous dinners in America, and who had all the men in New Orleans at her feet.

"What time will you have dinner?" asked Edna. "I'm very hungry; but don't get anything extra."

"I'll have it ready in little or no time," he said, bustling and packing away his tools. "You may go to my room to brush up and rest yourself. Mariequita will show you."

"Thank you," said Edna. "But, do you know, I have a notion to go down to the beach and take a good wash and even a little swim, before dinner?"

"The water is too cold!" they both exclaimed. "Don't think of it."

"Well, I might go down and try—dip my toes in. Why, it seems to me the sun is hot enough to have warmed the very depths of the ocean. Could you get me a couple of towels? I'd better go right away, so as to be back in time. It would be a little too chilly if I waited till this afternoon."

Mariequita ran over to Victor's room, and returned with some towels, which she gave to Edna.

"I hope you have fish for dinner," said Edna, as she started to walk away; "but don't do anything extra if you haven't."

"Run and find Philomel's mother," Victor instructed the girl. "I'll go to the kitchen and see what I can do. By Gimminy! Women have no consideration! She might have sent me word."

Edna walked on down to the beach rather mechanically, not noticing anything special except that the sun was hot. She was not dwelling upon any particular train of thought. She had done all the thinking which was necessary after Robert went away, when she lay awake upon the sofa till morning.

She had said over and over to herself: "To-day it is Arobin; to-morrow it will be some one else. It makes no difference to me, it doesn't matter about Léonce Pontellier—but Raoul and Etienne!" She understood now clearly what she had meant long ago when she said to Adèle Ratignolle that she would give up the unessential, but she would never sacrifice herself for her children.

Despondency had come upon her there in the wakeful night, and had never lifted. There was no one thing in the world that she desired. There was no human being whom she wanted near her except Robert; and she even realized that the day would come when he, too, and the thought of him would melt out of her existence, leaving her alone. The children appeared before her like antagonists who had overcome her; who had overpowered and sought to drag her into the soul's slavery for the rest of her days. But she knew a way to elude them. She was not thinking of these things when she walked down to the beach.

The water of the Gulf stretched out before her, gleaming with the million lights of the sun. The voice of the sea is seductive, never ceasing, whispering, clamoring, murmuring, inviting the soul to wander in abysses of solitude. All along the white beach, up and down, there was no living thing in sight. A bird with a broken wing was beating the air above, reeling, fluttering, circling disabled down, down to the water.

Edna had found her old bathing suit still hanging, faded, upon its accustomed peg.

She put it on, leaving her clothing in the bath-house. But when she was there beside the sea, absolutely alone, she cast the unpleasant, pricking garments from her, and for the first time in her life she stood naked in the open air, at the mercy of the sun, the breeze that beat upon her, and the waves that invited her.

How strange and awful it seemed to stand naked under the sky! how delicious! She felt like some new-born creature, opening its eyes in a familiar world that it had never known.

The foamy wavelets curled up to her white feet, and coiled like serpents above her ankles. She walked out. The water was chill, but she walked on. The water was deep, but she lifted her white body and reached out for a long, sweeping stroke. The touch of the sea is sensuous, enfolding the body in its soft, close embrace.

She went on and on. She remembered the night she swam far out, and recalled the terror that seized her at the fear of being unable to regain the shore. She did not look back now, but went on and on, thinking of the blue-grass meadow that she had traversed when a little child, believing that it had no beginning and no end.

Her arms and legs were growing tired.

She thought of Léonce and the children. They were a part of her life. But they need not have thought that they could possess her, body and soul. How Mademoiselle Reisz would have laughed, perhaps sneered, if she knew! "And you call yourself an artist! What pretensions, Madame! The artist must possess the courageous soul that dares and defies."

Exhaustion was pressing upon and overpowering her.

"Good-by—because I love you." He did not know; he did not understand. He would never understand. Perhaps Doctor Mandelet would have understood if she had seen him—but it was too late; the shore was far behind her, and her strength was gone.

She looked into the distance, and the old terror flamed up for an instant, then sank again. Edna heard her father's voice and her sister Margaret's. She heard the barking of an old dog that was chained to the sycamore tree. The spurs of the cavalry officer clanged as he walked across the porch. There was the hum of bees, and the musky odor of pinks filled the air.

[1899]

Lucille Clifton
[1936–2010]

LUCILLE CLIFTON *was born in Depew, Michigan to working class parents. Educated at Howard University and later at Fredonia State Teacher's College, she studied drama and worked as an actor as well as a writer. She shares some of the stylistic and thematic characteristics of other poets in the Black Aesthetic school, such as lower case letters, concise lines, sparse punctuation, and patterns of repetition, as well as the valorization of African-American culture and vernacular language. She won the YW-YMHA Poetry Center Discovery Award in 1969—poet Robert Hayden entered her poetry in the competition—which launched her career with the publication of the volume* Good Times. *Her writing career was prolific and much lauded. She wrote volumes of fiction, poetry, and memoir, as well as books for children. Her* Generations: A Memoir *(1976) gives an account of her family's history through the period of slavery. Her book* Good Woman: Poems and a Memoir *(1987) collected her poems and was a Pulitzer Prize nominee as well as winner of the Juniper Prize. Clifton served as the Poet Laureate of the state of Maryland from 1979 to 1982. More recent books include* Next: New Poems *(1987) and* The Book of Light *(1993).*

Homage to My Hips

LUCILLE CLIFTON

these hips are big hips
they need space to
move around in.
they don't fit into little
petty places. these hips   5
are free hips.
they don't like to be held back.
these hips have never been enslaved,
they go where they want to go
they do what they want to do.   10
these hips are mighty hips.
these hips are magic hips.
I have know them
to put a spell on a man and
spin him like a top!   15

[1980]

Reprinted from *Good Woman: Poems and a Memoir 1969-1980,* by permission of Curtis Brown, Ltd. Copyright © 1980, 1987 by Lucille Clifton.

Samuel Taylor Coleridge

[1772–1834]

Born in Ottery St. Mary, Devonshire, **SAMUEL TAYLOR COLERIDGE** *was the precocious son of the mild-mannered village vicar. The doting father died when Coleridge was nine, and the youth was sent off to school at Christ's Hospital. Both Coleridge's friend, Charles Lamb, and Coleridge himself recount those early years at school as lonely and sorrowful. Coleridge did in fact receive an excellent early education that led him to Jesus College, Cambridge, where he began as a good student but then lost focus, one time even running off with the Light Dragoons (a military outfit) using the pseudonyn, Silas Tomkyn Comberbacke. His friends had to buy him back from the outfit. Eventually he left Cambridge (1794) and joined poet Robert Southey in the strange adventure of setting up a utopian community in Pennsylvania. When this failed, he and Southey married sisters, Edith and Sarah Fricker. The chief claim to fame of these two women is being satirized in Lord Byron's* Don Juan. *Coleridge wandered off to meet the poet William Wordsworth and his sister, just after publishing his first book of poems,* Juvenile Poems *(1796). In 1797 he published two of his best poems,* The Rime of the Ancient Mariner *and* Christabel. *The Rime* *is one of the best-loved of all poems, but* Christabel *is more obscure, a poem about a hypnotic woman who turns into a serpent. The fragment breaks off leaving the reader entranced but unsatisfied. In 1798 he wrote his famous fragment poem* Kubla Khan *and published the* Lyrical Ballads *with Wordsworth. This work is considered the watershed moment in Romanticism. Before 1798 poets still are a part of an earlier era, but after the Preface lays out a sort of credo, theory, and definition for the Romantic poets, the writers move on within the collective constraints of that definition. The Wordsworth siblings and Coleridge then journeyed to Gottingen where Coleridge quickly learned German, read Kantian philosophy, and translated Friedrich Schiller's drama,* Wallenstein. *Soon he followed the Wordsworths back to England and joined them in the country life in Keswick. There he become addicted to opium and wrote two depressing works,* Dejection, an Ode *(1802) and* Youth and Age *(1828). Having licked his opium habit, he moved on to the lecture circuit and spoke widely about his theories of literature, especially creating a Romantic setting of Shakespeare's plays that still tends to dominate critical opinion. He was far better at talking about his ideas than he was at writing them down. He planned a work on theology and several longer poems, but no more were written, and in fact,* The Rime of the Ancient Mariner *is the only long poem Coleridge completed. He did however write two outstanding prose works, his* Biographia Literaria *(1817), in which he illuminates much about his relationship with Wordworth, and* Table Talk, *conversations written down that are among the best of their kind.*

Kubla Khan[1]
or, a Vision in a Dream. A Fragment

SAMUEL TAYLOR COLERIDGE

THE FOLLOWING FRAGMENT is here published at the request of a poet of great and deserved celebrity [Lord Byron], and, as far as the Author's own opinions are concerned, rather as a psychological curiosity, than on the ground of any supposed poetic merits.

In the summer of the year 1797, the Author, then in ill health, had retired to a lonely farm-house between Porlock and Linton, on the Exmoor confines of Somerset and Devonshire. In consequence of a slight indisposition, an anodyne had been prescribed, from the effects of which he fell asleep in his chair at the moment that he was reading the following sentence, or words of the same substance, in "Purchas's Pilgrimage": "Here the Khan Kubla commanded a palace to be built, and a stately garden thereunto. And thus ten miles of fertile ground were inclosed with a wall." The Author continued for about three hours in a profound sleep, at least of the external senses, during which time he has the most vivid confidence, that he could not have composed less than from two to three hundred lines; if that indeed can be called composition in which all the images rose up before him as things, with a parallel production of the correspondent expressions, without any sensation or consciousness of effort. On awaking he appeared to himself to have a distinct recollection of the whole, and taking his pen, ink, and paper, instantly and eagerly wrote down the lines that are here preserved. At this moment he was unfortunately called out by a person on business from Porlock, and detained by him above an hour, and on his return to his room, found, to his no small surprise and mortification, that though he still retained some vague and dim recollection of the general purport of the vision, yet, with the exception of some eight or ten scattered lines and images, all the rest had passed away like the images on the

---

[1] The poet claims that he took medicine for a stomach upset, then read in a book lines about Kubla Khan's pleasure dome. He says that he woke up in a vision, wrote down what is here, got up to go to his room, and then lost the rest of the story—not exactly "the dog ate my homework" but close. Coleridge was not a finisher.

Composed in either 1797 or 1798 and first published in 1816 with "Christabel" and "The Pains of Sleep."

surface of a stream into which a stone has been cast, but, alas! without the after restoration of the latter!

> Then all the charm
> Is broken—all that phantom-world so fair
> Vanishes, and a thousand circlets spread,

> And each mis-shape the other. Stay awhile,
> Poor youth! who scarcely dar'st lift up thine eyes—   5
> The stream will soon renew its smoothness, soon
> The visions will return! And lo, he stays,
> And soon the fragments dim of lovely forms
> Come trembling back, unite, and now once more
> The pool becomes a mirror.   10

Yet from the still surviving recollections in his mind, the Author has frequently purposed to finish for himself what had been originally, as it were, given to him. Αὔριον ἄδιον ἄσω: [tomorrow I shall sing a sweeter song]: but the to-morrow is yet to come.

> In Xanadu did Kubla Khan
> A stately pleasure-dome decree:
> Where Alph, the sacred river, ran
> Through caverns measureless to man
>> Down to a sunless sea.   5
> So twice five miles of fertile ground
> With walls and towers were girdled round:
> And here were gardens bright with sinuous rills,
> Where blossomed many an incense-bearing tree;
> And there were forests ancient as the hills,   10
> Enfolding sunny spots of greenery.
>> But oh! that deep romantic chasm which slanted
> Down the green hill athwart a cedarn cover!
> A savage place! as holy and enchanted
> As e'er beneath a waning moon was haunted   15
> By woman wailing for her demon-lover!
> And from this chasm, with ceaseless turmoil seething,
> As if this earth in fast thick pants were breathing,
> A mighty fountain momently was forced:
> Amid whose swift half-intermitted burst   20
> Huge fragments vaulted like rebounding hail,

Or chaffy grain beneath the thresher's flail:
And 'mid these dancing rocks at once and ever
It flung up momently the sacred river.
Five miles meandering with a mazy motion   25
Through wood and dale the sacred river ran,
Then reached the caverns measureless to man,
And sank in tumult to a lifeless ocean:
And 'mid this tumult Kubla heard from far
Ancestral voices prophesying war!   30
   The shadow of the dome of pleasure
   Floated midway on the waves;
   Where was heard the mingled measure
   From the fountain and the caves.
It was a miracle of rare device,   35
A sunny pleasure-dome with caves of ice!

   A damsel with a dulcimer
   In a vision once I saw:
   It was an Abyssinian maid,
   And on her dulcimer she played,   40
   Singing of Mount Abora.
   Could I revive within me
   Her symphony and song,
   To such a deep delight 'twould win me,
That with music loud and long,   45
I would build that dome in air,
That sunny dome! those caves of ice!
And all who heard should see them there,
And all should cry, Beware! Beware!
His flashing eyes, his floating hair!   50
Weave a circle round him thrice,
And close your eyes with holy dread,
For he on honey-dew hath fed,
And drunk the milk of Paradise.

[1797]

Joseph Conrad
[1857–1924]

JOSEPH CONRAD (*born Teodor Josef Konrad Korzeniowski*) *was born to politically active Polish nationalist parents. After Poland's failed rebellion against Russian rule in 1863, his father was exiled to northern Russia, where Conrad's mother died. After returning to Poland his father died in 1869 and Conrad was raised by an uncle who recommended that he go to sea. Despite the rest of his family's objections, Conrad did so in 1874, and pursued a lively and various career as a mariner for the next twenty years. As early as 1892 he seems to have been pondering the idea of using his seagoing adventures as the basis for fiction, and his ultimate decision to give up the sea for the pen probably stems both from his dissatisfaction at his prospects for advancements and from complications arising from his best-known adventure: his tenure as the captain of a steamboat working for a Belgian trading company on the Congo River. On this voyage he became seriously ill; after recuperating in Brussels and London he decided to devote his life to writing. It is one of the most striking twists in a striking life that a man born speaking Polish could become one of the greatest prose stylists of the English language.*

Conrad's first novel, Almayer's Folly, *was published in 1895, followed by* An Outcast of the Islands *in 1896. Both of these are regarded as apprentice works; but by the time he published* The Nigger of the Narcissus *in 1897 and* Lord Jim *in 1900, his facility with narrative and with the English language were established. In 1902 he published his most celebrated and important short work—the novella* Heart of Darkness, *based on his adventure on the Congo. Conrad here explores one of his central themes, the idea of human corruptibility. It is a concern that Conrad would treat in many of his books, including the major work,* Nostromo, *published in 1904. Although Conrad's work is best known for nautical settings, his novels* The Secret Agent *(1907) and* Under Western Eyes *(1911) delve into political subject matter. In later works such as "The Secret Sharer" (1912),* The Rescue *(1920) and* The Rover *(1923), however, Conrad demonstrated his continuing devotion to the sea, his primary source of inspiration. In "The Secret Sharer" Conrad revisits concepts central to earlier sea pieces like* Lord Jim: *the ambiguity and subjectivity of personal experience and the difficulty of maintaining absolute moral standards.*

Throughout much of his career Conrad's works were neither critical nor popular successes, but with the publication in 1913 of Chance *he began to gain recognition. From this time until his death he was able to overcome the financial problems that plagued him as a writer. When he died in 1924, Conrad left an unfinished novel,* Suspense, *which was published in the following year. Conrad's life and work persist as a site of contest between warring critical viewpoints.* Heart of Darkness *has been castigated in recent times by commentators such as Edward Said and the famous Nigerian novelist Chinua Achebe, both of whom argue that the novel ultimately reaffirms Victorian racism and colonialism. At the same time, however, the novel is still widely read, assigned in classrooms around the world, and it is routinely nominated one of the finest literary works of all time.*

—David L. G. Arnold, *University of Wisconsin, Stevens Point*

Heart of Darkness

JOSEPH CONRAD

1

THE NELLIE, A CRUISING yawl, swung to her anchor without a flutter of the sails, and was at rest. The flood had made, the wind was nearly calm, and being bound down the river, the only thing for it was to come to and wait for the turn of the tide.

The sea-reach of the Thames stretched before us like the beginning of an interminable waterway. In the offing[1] the sea and the sky were welded together without a joint, and in the luminous space the tanned sails of the barges drifting up with the tide seemed to stand still in red clusters of canvas sharply peaked, with gleams of varnished sprits. A haze rested on the low shores that ran out to sea in vanishing flatness. The air was dark above Gravesend,[2] and farther back stiff seemed condensed into a mournful gloom, brooding motionless over the biggest, and the greatest, town on earth.

The Director of Companies was our captain and our host. We four affectionately watched his back as he stood in the bows looking to seaward. On the whole river there was nothing that looked half so nautical. He resembled a pilot, which to a seaman is trustworthiness personified. It was difficult to realize his work was not out there in the luminous estuary, but behind him, within the brooding gloom.

Between us there was, as I have already said somewhere, the bond of the sea. Besides holding our hearts together through long periods of separation, it had the effect of making us tolerant of each other's yarns—and even convictions.

---

[1]This nautical term denotes the part of the sea visible from land or the stretch of deep water a sufficient distance from the shore for safe navigation.

[2]Located on the south bank of the river Thames, Gravesend is a port-town twenty-four miles east of London.

Heart of Darkness was first published serially in *Blackwood's Magazine* in February, March and April of 1899, and was reprinted in the United States the following year as an eight-part series in *The Living Age* (June 16-Aug. 4, 1900). It was revised before its first appearance in book form in *Youth and Two Other Stories* (1902).

The Lawyer—the best of old fellows—had, because of his many years and many virtues, the only cushion on deck, and was lying on the only rug. The Accountant had brought out already a box of dominoes, and was toying architecturally with the bones. Marlow sat cross-legged right aft, leaning against the mizzen-mast. He had sunken cheeks, a yellow complexion, a straight back, an ascetic aspect, and, with his arms dropped, the palms of hands outwards, resembled an idol. The Director, satisfied the anchor had good hold, made his way aft and sat down amongst us. We exchanged a few words lazily. Afterwards there was silence on board the yacht. For some reason or other we did not begin that game of dominoes. We felt meditative, and fit for nothing but placid staring. The day was ending in a serenity of still and exquisite brilliance. The water shone pacifically; the sky, without a speck, was a benign immensity of unstained light; the very mist on the Essex marshes was like a gauzy and radiant fabric, hung from the wooded rises inland, and draping the low shores in diaphanous folds. Only the gloom to the west, brooding over the upper reaches, became more sombre every minute, as if angered by the approach of the sun.

And at last, in its curved and imperceptible fall, the sun sank low, and from glowing white changed to a dull red without rays and without heat, as if about to go out suddenly, stricken to death by the touch of that gloom brooding over a crowd of men.

Forthwith a change came over the waters, and the serenity became less brilliant but more profound. The old river in its broad reach rested unruffled at the decline of day, after ages of good service done to the race that peopled its banks, spread out in the tranquil dignity of a waterway leading to the uttermost ends of the earth. We looked at the venerable stream not in the vivid flush of a short day that comes and departs for ever, but in the august light of abiding memories. And indeed nothing is easier for a man who has, as the phrase goes, 'followed the sea' with reverence and affection, than to evoke the great spirit of the past upon the lower reaches of the Thames. The tidal current runs to and fro in its unceasing service, crowded with memories of men and ships it had borne to the rest of home or to the battles of the sea. It had known and served all the men of whom the nation is proud, from Sir Francis Drake to Sir John Franklin,[3] knights all, titled and untitled—the great knights-errant of the sea. It had borne all the ships whose names are like jewels flashing in the night of time, from the *Golden Hind* returning with her round flanks full of treasure, to be visited by the Queen's Highness and thus pass out of the gigantic tale, to the *Erebus* and *Terror,* bound on other conquests—and

---

[3]Sir John Franklin (1786–1847) commanded the ships *Erebus* and the *Terror* on an ill-fated 1845 Arctic expedition. British privateer and naval hero Sir Francis Drake (1540–1596), captain of the ship *Golden Hind*, was knighted by Queen Elizabeth as the first Englishman to circumnavigate the globe.

that never returned. It had known the ships and the men. They had sailed from Deptford, from Greenwich, from Erith—the adventurers and the settlers; kings' ships and the ships of men on 'Change;[4] captains, admirals, the dark 'interlopers' of the Eastern trade, and the commissioned 'generals' of East India fleets. Hunters for gold or pursuers of fame, they all had gone out on that stream, bearing the sword, and often the torch, messengers of the might within the land, bearers of a spark from the sacred fire. What greatness had not floated on the ebb of that river into the mystery of an unknown earth! ... The dreams of men, the seed of commonwealths, the germs of empires.

The sun set; the dusk fell on the stream, and lights began to appear along the shore. The Chapman lighthouse, a three-legged thing erect on a mud-flat, shone strongly. Lights of ships moved in the fairway[5]—a great stir of lights going up and going down. And farther west on the upper reaches the place of the monstrous town was still marked ominously on the sky, a brooding gloom in sunshine, a lurid glare under the stars.

'And this also,' said Marlow suddenly, 'has been one of the dark places of the earth.'

He was the only man of us who still 'followed the sea'. The worst that could be said of him was that he did not represent his class. He was a seaman, but he was a wanderer, too, while most seamen lead, if one may so express it, a sedentary life. Their minds are of the stay-at-home order, and their home is always with them—the ship; and so is their country—the sea. One ship is very much like another, and the sea is always the same. In the immutability of their surroundings the foreign shores, the foreign faces, the changing immensity of life, glide past, veiled not by a sense of mystery but by a slightly disdainful ignorance; for there is nothing mysterious to a seaman unless it be the sea itself, which is the mistress of his existence and as inscrutable as Destiny. For the rest, after his hours of work, a casual stroll or a casual spree on shore suffices to unfold for him the secret of a whole continent, and generally he finds the secret not worth knowing. The yarns of seamen have a direct simplicity, the whole meaning of which lies within the shell of a cracked nut. But Marlow was not typical (if his propensity to spin yarns be excepted), and to him the meaning of an episode was not inside like a kernel but outside, enveloping the tale which brought it out only as a glow brings out a haze, in the likeness of one of these misty halos that sometimes are made visible by the spectral illumination of moonshine.

---

[4]Stock Exchange

[5]Navigable channel for ships entering and exiting a harbor or river.

His remark did not seem at all surprising. It was just like Marlow. It was accepted in silence. No one took the trouble to grunt even; and presently he said, very slow—

'I was thinking of very old times, when the Romans first came here, nineteen hundred years ago—the other day . . . Light came out of this river since—you say Knights? Yes; but it is like a running blaze on a plain, like a flash of lightning in the clouds. We live in the flicker—may it last as long as the old earth keeps rolling! But darkness was here yesterday. Imagine the feelings of a commander of a fine—what d'ye call 'em?—trireme[6] in the Mediterranean, ordered suddenly to the north; run overland across the Gauls in a hurry; put in charge of one of these craft the legionaries—a wonderful lot of handy men they must have been, too—used to build, apparently by the hundred, in a month or two, if we may believe what we read. Imagine him here—the very end of the world, a sea the colour of lead, a sky the colour of smoke, a kind of ship about as rigid as a concertina—and going up this river with stores, or orders, or what you like. Sand-banks, marshes, forests, savages,—precious little to eat fit for a civilized man, nothing but Thames water to drink. No Falernian wine[7] here, no going ashore. Here and there a military camp lost in a wilderness, like a needle in a bundle of hay—cold, fog, tempests, disease, exile, and death—death skulking in the air, in the water, in the bush. They must have been dying like flies here. Oh, yes—he did it. Did it very well, too, no doubt, and without thinking much about it either, except afterwards to brag of what he had done through his time, perhaps. They were men enough to face the darkness. And perhaps he was cheered by keeping his eye on a chance of promotion to the fleet at Ravenna[8] by-and-by, if he had good friends in Rome and survived the awful climate. Or think of a decent young citizen in a toga—perhaps too much dice, you know—coming out here in the train of some prefect, or tax-gatherer, or trader even, to mend his fortunes. Land in a swamp, march through the woods, and in some inland post feel the savagery, the utter savagery, had closed round him,—all that mysterious life of the wilderness that stirs in the forest, in the jungles, in the hearts of wild men. There's no initiation either into such mysteries. He has to live in the midst of the incomprehensible, which is also detestable. And it has a fascination, too, that goes to work upon him. The fascination of the abomination—you know, imagine the growing regrets, the longing to escape, the powerless disgust, the surrender, the hate.'

---

[6]Ancient Greek and Roman galley or warship having three ranks of oars.

[7]This southern Italian wine was highly esteemed by ancient Romans.

[8]In ancient times, the port-city of Ravenna served as the seat of the Roman Empire.

He paused.

'Mind,' he began again, lifting one arm from the elbow, the palm of the hand outwards, so that, with his legs folded before him, he had the pose of a Buddha preaching in European clothes and without a lotus-flower—'Mind, none of us would feel exactly like this. What saves us is efficiency—the devotion to efficiency. But these chaps were not much account, really. They were no colonists; their administration was merely a squeeze, and nothing more, I suspect. They were conquerors, and for that you want only brute force—nothing to boast of, when you have it, since your strength is just an accident arising from the weakness of others. They grabbed what they could get for the sake of what was to be got. It was just robbery with violence, aggravated murder on a great scale, and men going at it blind—as is very proper for those who tackle a darkness. The conquest of the earth, which mostly means the taking it away from those who have a different complexion or slightly flatter noses than ourselves, is not a pretty thing when you look into it too much. What redeems it is the idea only. An idea at the back of it; not a sentimental pretence but an idea; and an unselfish belief in the idea—something you can set up, and bow down before, and offer a sacrifice to . . .'

He broke off. Flames glided in the river, small green flames, red flames, white flames, pursuing, overtaking, joining, crossing each other—then separating slowly or hastily. The traffic of the great city went on in the deepening night upon the sleepless river. We looked on, waiting patiently—there was nothing else to do till the end of the flood; but it was only after a long silence, when he said, in a hesitating voice, 'I suppose you fellows remember I did once turn fresh-water sailor for a bit,' that we knew we were fated, before the ebb began to run, to hear about one of Marlow's inconclusive experiences.

'I don't want to bother you much with what happened to me personally,' he began, showing in this remark the weakness of many tellers of tales who seem so often unaware of what their audience would best like to hear; 'yet to understand the effect of it on me you ought to know how I got out there, what I saw, how I went up that river to the place where I first met the poor chap. It was the farthest point of navigation and the culminating point of my experience. It seemed somehow to throw a kind of light on everything about me—and into my thoughts. It was sombre enough, too—and pitiful—not extraordinary in any way—not very clear either. No, not very clear. And yet it seemed to throw a kind of light.

'I had then, as you remember, just returned to London after a lot of Indian Ocean, Pacific, China Seas—a regular dose of the East—six years or so, and I was loafing about, hindering you fellows in your work and invading your homes, just as though I had got a heavenly mission to civilize you. It was very fine for a time, but after a bit I did get tired of resting. Then I began to look for a ship—I should think the hardest work on earth. But the ships wouldn't even look at me. And I got tired of that game, too.

'Now when I was a little chap I had a passion for maps. I would look for hours at South America, or Africa, or Australia, and lose myself in all the glories of exploration. At that time there were many blank spaces on the earth, and when I saw one that looked particularly inviting on a map (but they all look that) I would put my finger on it and say, When I grow up I will go there. The North Pole was one of these places, I remember. Well, I haven't been there yet, and shall not try now. The glamour's off. Other places were scattered about the Equator, and in every sort of latitude all over the two hemispheres. I have been in some of them, and . . . well, we won't talk about that. But there was one yet—the biggest, the most blank, so to speak—that I had a hankering after.

'True, by this time it was not a blank space any more. It had got filled since my boyhood with rivers and lakes and names. It had ceased to be a blank space of delightful mystery—a white patch for a boy to dream gloriously over. It had become a place of darkness. But there was in it one river especially, a mighty big river, that you could see on the map, resembling an immense snake uncoiled, with its head in the sea, its body at rest curving afar over a vast country, and its tail lost in the depths of the land. And as I looked at the map of it in a shop-window, it fascinated me as a snake would a bird—a silly little bird. Then I remembered there was a big concern, a Company for trade on that river. Dash it all! I thought to myself, they can't trade without using some kind of craft on that lot of fresh water—steamboats! Why shouldn't I try to get charge of one? I went on along Fleet Street, [9] but could not shake off the idea. The snake had charmed me.

'You understand it was a Continental concern, that Trading society; but I have a lot of relations living on the Continent, because it's cheap and not so nasty as it looks, they say.

'I am sorry to own I began to worry them. This was already a fresh departure for me. I was not used to get things that way, you know. I always went my own road and on my own legs where I had a mind to go. I wouldn't have believed it of myself; but, then—you see—I felt somehow I must get there by hook or by crook. So I worried them. The men said "My dear fellow," and did nothing. Then—would you believe it?—I tried the women. I, Charlie Marlow, set the women to work—to get a job. Heavens! Well, you see, the notion drove me. I had an aunt, a dear enthusiastic soul. She wrote: "It will be delightful. I am ready to do anything, anything for you. It is a glorious idea. I know the wife of a very high personage in the Administration, and also a man who has

---

[9]Former site of the national press, London's famous Fleet Street is historically associated with the business of journalism.

lots of influence with," etc., etc. She was determined to make no end of fuss to get me appointed skipper of a river steamboat, if such was my fancy.

'I got my appointment—of course; and I got it very quick. It appears the Company had received news that one of their captains had been killed in a scuffle with the natives. This was my chance, and it made me the more anxious to go. It was only months and months afterwards, when I made the attempt to recover what was left of the body, that I heard the original quarrel arose from a misunderstanding about some hens. Yes, two black hens. Fresleven—that was the fellow's name, a Dane—thought himself wronged somehow in the bargain, so he went ashore and started to hammer the chief of the village with a stick. Oh, it didn't surprise me in the least to hear this, and at the same time to be told that Fresleven was the gentlest, quietest creature that ever walked on two legs. No doubt he was; but he had been a couple of years already out there engaged in the noble cause, you know, and he probably felt the need at last of asserting his self-respect in some way. Therefore he whacked the old nigger mercilessly, while a big crowd of his people watched him, thunderstruck, till some man—I was told the chief's son—in desperation at hearing the old chap yell, made a tentative jab with a spear at the white man—and of course it went quite easy between the shoulder-blades. Then the whole population cleared into the forest, expecting all kinds of calamities to happen, while, on the other hand, the steamer Fresleven commanded left also in a bad panic, in charge of the engineer, I believe. Afterwards nobody seemed to trouble much about Fresleven's remains, till I got out and stepped into his shoes. I couldn't let it rest, though; but when an opportunity offered at last to meet my predecessor, the grass growing through his ribs was tall enough to hide his bones. They were all there. The supernatural being had not been touched after he fell. And the village was deserted, the huts gaped black, rotting, all askew within the fallen enclosures. A calamity had come to it, sure enough. The people had vanished. Mad terror had scattered them, men, women, and children, through the bush, and they had never returned. What became of the hens I don't know either. I should think the cause of progress got them, anyhow. However, through this glorious affair I got my appointment, before I had fairly begun to hope for it.

'I flew around like mad to get ready, and before forty-eight hours I was crossing the Channel to show myself to my employers, and sign the contract. In a very few hours I arrived in a city that always makes me think of a whited sepulchre.[10] Prejudice no doubt. I had no difficulty in finding the Company's

---

[10]In the *King James Bible*, Christ says, "Woe unto you, scribes and Pharisees, hypocrites! for ye are like unto whited sepulchres, which indeed appear beautiful outward, but are within full of dead men's bones, and of all uncleanness" (Matthew 23:37).

offices. It was the biggest thing in the town, and everybody I met was full of it. They were going to run an over-sea empire, and make no end of coin by trade.

'A narrow and deserted street in deep shadow, high houses, innumerable windows with venetian blinds, a dead silence, grass sprouting between the stones, imposing carriage archways right and left, immense double doors standing ponderously ajar. I slipped through one of these cracks, went up a swept and ungarnished staircase, as arid as a desert, and opened the first door I came to. Two women, one fat and the other slim, sat on straw-bottomed chairs, knitting black wool. The slim one got up and walked straight at me— still knitting with downcast eyes—and only just as I began to think of getting out of her way, as you would for a somnambulist, stood still, and looked up. Her dress was as plain as an umbrella-cover, and she turned round without a word and preceded me into a waiting-room. I gave my name, and looked about. Deal table in the middle, plain chairs all round the walls, on one end a large shining map, marked with all the colours of a rainbow. There was a vast amount of red—good to see at any time, because one knows that some real work is done in there, a deuce of a lot of blue, a little green, smears of orange, and, on the East Coast, a purple patch, to show where the jolly pioneers of progress drink the jolly lager-beer. However, I wasn't going into any of these. I was going into the yellow. Dead in the centre. And the river was there—fascinating—deadly—like a snake. Ough! A door opened, a white-haired secretarial head, but wearing a compassionate expression, appeared, and a skinny forefinger beckoned me into the sanctuary. Its light was dim, and a heavy writing-desk squatted in the middle. From behind that structure came out an impression of pale plumpness in a frock-coat. The great man himself. He was five feet six, I should judge, and had his grip on the handle-end of ever so many millions. He shook hands, I fancy, murmured vaguely, was satisfied with my French. *Bon voyage.*

'In about forty-five seconds I found myself again in the waiting-room with the compassionate secretary, who, full of desolation and sympathy, made me sign some document. I believe I undertook amongst other things not to disclose any trade secrets. Well, I am not going to.

'I began to feel slightly uneasy. You know I am not used to such ceremonies, and there was something ominous in the atmosphere. It was just as though I had been let into some conspiracy—I don't know—something not quite right; and I was glad to get out. In the outer room the two women knitted black wool feverishly. People were arriving, and the younger one was walking back and forth introducing them. The old one sat on her chair. Her flat cloth slippers were propped up on a foot-warmer, and a cat reposed on her lap. She wore a starched white affair on her head, had a wart on one cheek, and silver-rimmed spectacles hung on the tip of her nose. She glanced at me above the glasses. The swift and indifferent placidity of that look troubled me. Two youths with foolish and cheery countenances were being piloted over, and she threw at them the same quick glance of unconcerned wisdom. She seemed to know all about them and about me, too. An eerie feeling came over me. She seemed uncanny and fateful. Often far away there I thought of these two, guarding the door of Darkness, knitting black wool as for a warm pall, one introducing, introducing continuously to the unknown, the other scrutinizing the cheery and foolish faces with unconcerned old eyes. *Ave!* Old knitter of black wool. *Morituri te salutant.*[11] Not many of those she looked at ever saw her again—not half, by a long way.

'There was yet a visit to the doctor. "A simple formality," assured me the secretary, with an air of taking an immense part in all my sorrows. Accordingly a young chap wearing his hat over the left eyebrow, some clerk I suppose—there must have been clerks in the business, though the house was as still as a house in a city of the dead—came from somewhere upstairs, and led me forth. He was shabby and careless, with ink-stains on the sleeves of his jacket, and his cravat was large and billowy, under a chin shaped like the toe of an old boot. It was a little too early for the doctor, so I proposed a drink, and thereupon he developed a vein of joviality. As we sat over our vermouths he glorified the Company's business, and by-and-by I expressed casually my surprise at him not going out there. He became very cool and collected all at once. "I am not such a fool as I look, quoth Plato to his disciples," he said sententiously, emptied his glass with great resolution, and we rose.

'The old doctor felt my pulse, evidently thinking of something else the while. "Good, good for there," he mumbled, and then with a certain eagerness asked me whether I would let him measure my head. Rather surprised, I said Yes, when he produced a thing like calipers and got the dimensions back and front and every way, taking notes carefully. He was an unshaven little man in a threadbare coat like a gaberdine, with his feet in slippers, and I thought him a harmless fool. "I always ask leave, in the interests of science, to measure the crania of those going out there," he said. "And when they come back, too?" I asked. "Oh, I never see them," he remarked; "and, moreover, the changes take place inside, you know." He smiled, as if at some quiet joke. "So you are going out there. Famous. Interesting, too." He gave me a searching glance, and made another note. "Ever any madness in your family?" he asked, in a matter-of-fact tone. I felt very annoyed. "Is that question in the interests of science, too?" "It would be," he said, without taking notice of my irritation, "interesting for science to watch the mental changes of individuals, on the spot, but . . ." "Are you

---

[11]Latin: "Hail, those who are about to die salute you"; salutation given to emperor by Roman gladiators entering the arena.

an alienist?"[12] I interrupted. "Every doctor should be—a little," answered that original, imperturbably. "I have a little theory which you Messieurs who go out there must help me to prove. This is my share in the advantages my country shall reap from the possession of such a magnificent dependency. The mere wealth I leave to others. Pardon my questions, but you are the first Englishman coming under my observation . . ." I hastened to assure him I was not in the least typical. "If I were," said I, "I wouldn't be talking like this with you." "What you say is rather profound, and probably erroneous," he said, with a laugh. "Avoid irritation more than exposure to the sun. Adieu. How do you English say, eh? Good-bye. Ah! Good-bye. Adieu. In the tropics one must before everything keep calm." . . . He lifted a warning forefinger . . . "*Du calme, du calme. Adieu.*"

'One thing more remained to do—say good-bye to my excellent aunt. I found her triumphant. I had a cup of tea—the last decent cup of tea for many days—and in a room that most soothingly looked just as you would expect a lady's drawing-room to look, we had a long quiet chat by the fireside. In the course of these confidences it became quite plain to me I had been represented to the wife of the high dignitary, and goodness knows to how many more people besides, as an exceptional and gifted creature—a piece of good fortune for the Company—a man you don't get hold of every day. Good heavens! and I was going to take charge of a two-penny-half-penny river steamboat with a penny whistle attached! It appeared, however, I was also one of the Workers, with a capital—you know. Something like an emissary of light, something like a lower sort of apostle. There had been a lot of such rot let loose in print and talk just about that time, and the excellent woman, living right in the rush of all that humbug, got carried off her feet. She talked about "weaning those ignorant millions from their horrid ways," till, upon my word, she made me quite uncomfortable. I ventured to hint that the Company was run for profit.

' "You forget, dear Charlie, that the labourer is worthy of his hire," she said, brightly. It's queer how out of touch with truth women are. They live in a world of their own, and there had never been anything like it, and never can be. It is too beautiful altogether, and if they were to set it up it would go to pieces before the first sunset. Some confounded fact we men have been living contentedly with ever since the day of creation would start up and knock the whole thing over.

'After this I got embraced, told to wear flannel, be sure to write often, and so on—and I left. In the street—I don't know why—a queer feeling came to me that I was an impostor. Old thing that I, who used to clear out for any part of the world at twenty-four hours' notice, with less thought than most men

[12]Victorian term for a doctor specializing in mental disease.

give to the crossing of a street, had a moment—I won't say of hesitation, but of startled pause, before this commonplace affair. The best way I can explain it to you is by saying that, for a second or two, I felt as though, instead of going to the centre of a continent, I were about to set off for the centre of the earth.

'I left in a French steamer, and she called in every blamed port they have out there, for, as far as I could see, the sole purpose of landing soldiers and custom-house officers. I watched the coast. Watching a coast as it slips by the ship is like thinking about an enigma. There it is before you—smiling, frowning, inviting, grand, mean, insipid, or savage, and always mute with an air of whispering, Come and find out. This one was almost featureless, as if still in the making, with an aspect of monotonous grimness. The edge of a colossal jungle, so dark-green as to be almost black, fringed with white surf, ran straight, like a ruled fine, far, far away along a blue sea whose glitter was blurred by a creeping mist. The sun was fierce, the land seemed to glisten and drip with steam. Here and there greyish-whitish specks showed up clustered inside the white surf, with a flag flying above them perhaps. Settlements some centuries old, and still no bigger than pinheads on the untouched expanse of their background. We pounded along, stopped, landed soldiers; went on, landed custom-house clerks to levy toll in what looked like a God-forsaken wilderness, with a tin shed and a flag-pole lost in it; landed more soldiers—to take care of the custom-house clerks, presumably. Some, I heard, got drowned in the surf; but whether they did or not, nobody seemed particularly to care. They were just flung out there, and on we went. Every day the coast looked the same, as though we had not moved; but we passed various places—trading places—with names like Gran' Bassam, Little Popo; names that seemed to belong to some sordid farce acted in front of a sinister back-cloth. The idleness of a passenger, my isolation amongst all these men with whom I had no point of contact, the oily and languid sea, the uniform sombreness of the coast, seemed to keep me away from the truth of things, within the toil of a mournful and senseless delusion. The voice of the surf now and then was a positive pleasure, like the speech of a brother. It was something natural, that had its reason, that had a meaning. Now and then a boat from the shore gave one a momentary contact with reality. It was paddled by black fellows. You could see from afar the white of their eyeballs glistening. They shouted, sang; their bodies streamed with perspiration; they had faces like grotesque masks—these chaps; but they had bone, muscle, a wild vitality, an intense energy of movement, that was as natural and true as the surf along their coast. They wanted no excuse for being there. They were a great comfort to look at. For a time I would feel I belonged still to a world of straight-forward facts; but the feeling would not last long. Something would turn up to scare it away. Once, I remember, we came upon a man-of-war anchored off the coast. There wasn't even a shed there, and she was shelling the bush. It appears the French had one of their wars going on thereabouts. Her ensign dropped limp like a rag; the muzzles of the long six-inch guns stuck out all over the low hull; the greasy, slimy swell swung her up lazily and let her down, swaying her thin masts. In the empty immensity of earth, sky, and water, there she was, incomprehensible, firing into a continent. Pop, would go one of the six-inch guns; a small flame would dart and vanish, a little white smoke would disappear, a tiny projectile would give a feeble screech—and nothing happened. Nothing could happen. There was a touch of insanity in the proceeding, a sense of lugubrious drollery in the sight; and it was not dissipated by somebody on board assuring me earnestly there was a camp of natives—he called them enemies!—hidden out of sight somewhere.

'We gave her her letters (I heard the men in that lonely ship were dying of fever at the rate of three a-day) and went on. We called at some more places with farcical names, where the merry dance of death and trade goes on in a still and earthy atmosphere as of an overheated catacomb; all along the formless coast bordered by dangerous surf, as if Nature herself had tried to ward off intruders; in and out of rivers, streams of death in life, whose banks were rotting into mud, whose waters, thickened into slime, invaded the contorted mangroves, that seemed to writhe at us in the extremity of an impotent despair. Nowhere did we stop long enough to get a particularized impression, but the general sense of vague and oppressive wonder grew upon me. It was like a weary pilgrimage amongst hints for nightmares.

'It was upward of thirty days before I saw the mouth of the big river. We anchored off the seat of the government. But my work would not begin till some two hundred miles farther on. So as soon as I could I made a start for a place thirty miles higher up.

'I had my passage on a little sea-going steamer. Her captain was a Swede, and knowing me for a seaman, invited me on the bridge. He was a young man, lean, fair, and morose, with lanky hair and a shuffling gait. As we left the miserable little wharf, he tossed his head contemptuously at the shore. "Been living there?" he asked. I said, "Yes." "Fine lot these government chaps—are they not?" he went on, speaking English with great precision and considerable bitterness. "It is funny what some people will do for a few francs a-month. I wonder what becomes of that kind when it goes up country?" I said to him I expected to see that soon. "So-o-o!" he exclaimed. He shuffled athwart, keeping one eye ahead vigilantly. "Don't be too sure," he continued. "The other day I took up a man who hanged himself on the road. He was a Swede, too." "Hanged himself! Why, in God's name?" I cried. He kept on looking out watchfully. "Who knows? The sun too much for him, or the country perhaps."

'At last we opened a reach. A rocky cliff appeared, mounds of turned-up earth by the shore, houses on a hill, others with iron roofs, amongst a waste of excavations, or hanging to the declivity. A continuous noise of the rapids above hovered over this scene of inhabited devastation. A lot of people, mostly black and naked, moved about like ants. A jetty projected into the river. A blinding sunlight drowned all this at times in a sudden recrudescence of glare. "There's your Company's station," said the Swede, pointing to three wooden barrack-like structures on the rocky slope. "I will send your things up. Four boxes did you say? So. Farewell."

'I came upon a boiler wallowing in the grass, then found a path leading up the hill. It turned aside for the boulders, and also for an undersized railway-truck lying there on its back with its wheels in the air. One was off. The thing looked as dead as the carcass of some animal. I came upon more pieces of decaying machinery, a stack of rusty rails. To the left a clump of trees made a shady spot, where dark things seemed to stir feebly. I blinked, the path was steep. A horn tooted to the right, and I saw the black people run. A heavy and dull detonation shook the ground, a puff of smoke came out of the cliff, and that was all. No change appeared on the face of the rock. They were building a railway. The cliff was not in the way or anything; but this objectless blasting was all the work going on.

'A slight clinking behind me made me turn my head. Six black men advanced in a file, toiling up the path. They walked erect and slow, balancing small baskets full of earth on their heads, and the clink kept time with their footsteps. Black rags were wound round their loins, and the short ends behind waggled to and fro like tails. I could see every rib, the joints of their limbs were like knots in a rope; each had an iron collar on his neck, and all were connected together with a chain whose bights swung between them, rhythmically clinking. Another report from the cliff made me think suddenly of that ship of war I had seen firing into a continent. It was the same kind of ominous voice; but these men could by no stretch of imagination be called enemies. They were called criminals, and the outraged law, like the bursting shells, had come to them, an insoluble mystery from the sea. All their meagre breasts panted together, the violently dilated nostrils quivered, the eyes stared stonily uphill. They passed me within six inches, without a glance, with that complete, deathlike indifference of unhappy savages. Behind this raw matter one of the reclaimed, the product of the new forces at work, strolled despondently, carrying a rifle by its middle. He had a uniform jacket with one button off, and seeing a white man on the path, hoisted his weapon to his shoulder with alacrity. This was simple prudence, white men being so much alike at a distance that he could not tell who I might be. He was speedily reassured, and with a large, white, rascally grin, and a glance at his charge, seemed to take me into partnership in his exalted trust. After all, I also was a part of the great cause of these high and just proceedings.

'Instead of going up, I turned and descended to the left. My idea was to let that chain-gang get out of sight before I climbed the hill. You know I am not particularly tender; I've had to strike and to fend off. I've had to resist and to attack sometimes—that's only one way of resisting—without counting the exact cost, according to the demands of such sort of life as I had blundered into. I've seen the devil of violence, and the devil of greed, and the devil of hot desire; but, by all the stars! these were strong, lusty, red-eyed devils, that swayed and drove men—men, I tell you. But as I stood on this hillside, I foresaw that in the blinding sunshine of that land I would become acquainted with a flabby, pretending, weak-eyed devil of a rapacious and pitiless folly. How insidious he could be, too, I was only to find out several months later and a thousand miles farther. For a moment I stood appalled, as though by a warning. Finally I descended the hill, obliquely, towards the trees I had seen.

'I avoided a vast artificial hole somebody had been digging on the slope, the purpose of which I found it impossible to divine. It wasn't a quarry or a sandpit, anyhow. It was just a hole. It might have been connected with the philanthropic desire of giving the criminals something to do. I don't know. Then I nearly fell into a very narrow ravine, almost no more than a scar in the hillside. I discovered that a lot of imported drainage-pipes for the settlement had been tumbled in there. There wasn't one that was not broken. It was a wanton smash-up. At last I got under the trees. My purpose was to stroll into the shade for a moment; but no sooner within than it seemed to me I had stepped into the gloomy circle of some Inferno. The rapids were near, and an uninterrupted, uniform, headlong, rushing noise filled the mournful stillness of the grove, where not a breath stirred, not a leaf moved, with a mysterious sound—as though the tearing pace of the launched earth had suddenly become audible.

'Black shapes crouched, lay, sat between the trees leaning against the trunks, clinging to the earth, half coming out, half effaced within the dim light, in all the attitudes of pain, abandonment, and despair. Another mine on the cliff went off, followed by a slight shudder of the soil under my feet. The work was going on. The work! And this was the place where some of the helpers had withdrawn to die.

'They were dying slowly—it was very clear. They were not enemies, they were not criminals, they were nothing earthly now,—nothing but black shadows of disease and starvation, lying confusedly in the greenish gloom. Brought from all the recesses of the coast in all the legality of time contracts, lost in uncongenial surroundings, fed on unfamiliar food, they sickened, became inefficient, and were then allowed to crawl away and rest. These moribund shapes were free as air—and nearly as thin. I began to distinguish the gleam of the eyes under the trees. Then, glancing down, I saw a face near my hand. The black bones reclined at full length with one shoulder against the tree, and slowly the eyelids rose and the sunken eyes looked up at me, enormous and vacant, a kind of blind, white flicker in the depths of the orbs, which died out slowly. The man seemed young—almost a boy—but you know with them it's hard to tell. I found nothing else to do but to offer him one of my good Swede's ship's biscuits I had in my pocket. The fingers closed slowly on it and held—there was no other movement and no other glance. He had tied a bit of white worsted round his neck—Why? Where did he get it? Was it a badge—an ornament—a charm—a propitiatory act? Was there any idea at all connected with it? It looked starting round his black neck, this bit of white thread from beyond the seas.

'Near the same tree two more bundles of acute angles sat with their legs drawn up. One, with his chin propped on his knees, stared at nothing, in an intolerable and appalling manner: his brother phantom rested its forehead, as if overcome with a great weariness; and all about others were scattered in every pose of contorted collapse, as in some picture of a massacre or a pestilence. While I stood horror-struck, one of these creatures rose to his hands and knees, and went off on all-fours towards the river to drink. He lapped out of his hand, then sat up in the sunlight, crossing his shins in front of him, and after a time let his woolly head fall on his breastbone.

'I didn't want any more loitering in the shade, and I made haste towards the station. When near the buildings I met a white man, in such an unexpected elegance of get-up that in the first moment I took him for a sort of vision. I saw a high starched collar, white cuffs, a light alpaca jacket, snowy trousers, a clear necktie, and varnished boots. No hat. Hair parted, brushed, oiled, under a green-lined parasol held in a big white hand. He was amazing, and had a penholder behind his ear.

'I shook hands with this miracle, and I learned he was the Company's chief accountant, and that all the book-keeping was done at this station. He had come out for a moment, he said, "to get a breath of fresh air." The expression sounded wonderfully odd, with its suggestion of sedentary desk-life. I wouldn't have mentioned the fellow to you at all, only it was from his lips that I first heard the name of the man who is so indissolubly connected with the memories of that time. Moreover, I respected the fellow. Yes; I respected his collars, his vast cuffs, his brushed hair. His appearance was certainly that of a hairdresser's dummy; but in the great demoralization of the land he kept up his appearance. That's backbone. His starched collars and got-up shirt-fronts were achievements of character. He had been out nearly three years; and later, I could not help asking him how he managed to sport such linen. He had just the faintest blush, and said modestly, "I've been teaching one of the native women about the station. It was difficult. She had a distaste for the work." Thus this man had verily accomplished something. And he was devoted to his books, which were in apple-pie order.

'Everything else in the station was in a muddle—heads, things, buildings. Strings of dusty niggers with splay feet arrived and departed; a stream of manufactured goods, rubbishy cottons, beads, and brass wire sent into the depths of darkness, and in return came a precious trickle of ivory.

'I had to wait in the station for ten days—an eternity. I lived in a hut in the yard, but to be out of the chaos I would sometimes get into the accountant's office. It was built of horizontal planks, and so badly put together that, as he bent over his high desk, he was barred from neck to heels with narrow strips of sunlight. There was no need to open the big shutters to see. It was hot there, too; big flies buzzed fiendishly, and did not sting, but stabbed. I sat generally on the floor, while, of faultless appearance (and even slightly scented), perching on a high stool, he wrote. Sometimes he stood up for exercise. When a truckled-bed with a sick man (some invalid agent from up-country) was put in there, he exhibited a gentle annoyance. "The groans of this sick person," he said, "distract my attention. And without that it is extremely difficult to guard against clerical errors in this climate."

'One day he remarked, without lifting his head, "In the interior you will no doubt meet Mr Kurtz." On my asking who Mr Kurtz was, he said he was a first-class agent; and seeing my disappointment at this information, he added slowly, laying down his pen, "He is a very remarkable person." Further questions elicited from him that Mr Kurtz was at present in charge of a trading post, a very important one, in the true ivory-country, at "the very bottom of there. Sends in as much ivory as all the others put together . . ." He began to write again. The sick man was too ill to groan. The files buzzed in a great peace.

'Suddenly there was a growing murmur of voices and a great tramping of feet. A caravan had come in. A violent babble of uncouth sounds burst out on the other side of the planks. All the carriers were speaking together, and in the midst of the uproar the lamentable voice of the chief agent was heard "giving it up" tearfully for the twentieth time that day . . . He rose slowly. "What a frightful row," he said. He crossed the room gently to look at the sick man, and returning, said to me, "He does not hear." "What! Dead?" I asked, started. "No, not yet," he answered, with great composure. Then, alluding with a toss of the head to the tumult in the station yard, "When one has got to make correct entries, one comes to hate those savages—hate them to the death." He remained thoughtful for a moment. "When you see Mr Kurtz," he went on, "tell him from me that everything here"—he glanced at the desk—"is very satisfactory. I don't like to write to him—with those messengers of ours you never know who may get hold of your letter—at that Central Station." He stared at me for a moment with his mild, bulging eyes. "Oh, he will go far, very far," he began again. "He will be a somebody in the Administration before long. They, above—the Council in Europe, you know—mean him to be."

'He turned to his work. The noise outside had ceased, and presently in going out I stopped at the door. In the steady buzz of flies the homeward-bound agent was lying flushed and insensible; that other, bent over his books, was making correct entries of perfectly correct transactions, and fifty feet below the doorstep I could see the still tree-tops of the grove of death.

'Next day I left that station at last, with a caravan of sixty men, for a two-hundred-mile tramp.

'No use telling you much about that. Paths, paths, everywhere; a stamped-in network of paths spreading over the empty land, through long grass, through burnt grass, through thickets, down and up chilly ravines, up and down stony hills ablaze with heat; and a solitude, a solitude, nobody, not a hut. The population had cleared out a long time ago. Well, if a lot of mysterious niggers armed with all kinds of fearful weapons suddenly took to travelling on the road between Deal and Gravesend, catching the yokels right and left to carry heavy loads for them, I fancy every farm and cottage thereabouts would get empty very soon. Only here the dwellings were gone, too. Still I passed through several abandoned villages. There's something pathetically childish in the ruins of grass walls. Day after day, with the stamp and shuffle of sixty pair of bare feet behind me, each pair under a 60-lb. load. Camp, cook, sleep, strike camp, march. Now and then a carrier dead in harness, at rest in the long grass near the path, with an empty water-gourd and his long staff lying by his side. A great silence around and above. Perhaps on some quiet night the tremor of far-off drums, sinking, swelling, a tremor vast, faint; a sound weird, appealing, suggestive, and wild—and perhaps with as profound a meaning as the sound of bells in a Christian country. Once a white man in an unbuttoned uniform, camping on the path with an armed escort of lank Zanzibaris,[13] very hospitable and festive—not to say drunk. Was looking after the upkeep of the road, he declared. Can't say I saw any road or any upkeep, unless the body of a middle-aged negro, with a bullet-hole in the forehead, upon which I absolutely stumbled three miles farther on, may be considered as a permanent improvement. I had a white companion, too, not a bad chap, but rather too fleshy and with the exasperating habit of fainting on the hot hillsides, miles away from the least bit of shade and water. Annoying, you know, to hold your own coat like a parasol over a man's head while he is coming-to. I couldn't

---

[13]Zanzibar is an island off the east coast of Africa; its natives were often employed as mercenaries.

help asking him once what he meant by coming there at all. "To make money, of course. What do you think?" he said, scornfully. Then he got fever, and had to be carried in a hammock slung under a pole. As he weighed sixteen stone[14] I had no end of rows with the carriers. They jibbed, ran away, sneaked off with their loads in the night—quite a mutiny. So, one evening, I make a speech in English with gestures, not one of which was lost to the sixty pairs of eyes before me, and the next morning I started the hammock off in front all right. An hour afterwards I came upon the whole concern wrecked in a bush—man, hammock, groans, blankets, horrors. The heavy pole had skinned his poor nose. He was very anxious for me to kill somebody, but there wasn't the shadow of a carrier near. I remembered the old doctor,—"It would be interesting for science to watch the mental changes of individuals, on the spot." I felt I was becoming scientifically interesting. However, all that is to no purpose. On the fifteenth day I came in sight of the big river again, and hobbled into the Central Station. It was on a backwater surrounded by scrub and forest, with a pretty border of smelly mud on one side, and on the three others enclosed by a crazy fence of rushes. A neglected gap was all the gate it had, and the first glance at the place was enough to let you see the flabby devil was running the show. White men with long staves in their hands appeared languidly from amongst the buildings, strolling up to take a took at me, and then retired out of sight somewhere. One of them, a stout, excitable chap with black moustaches, informed me with great volubility and many digressions, as soon as I told him who I was, that my steamer was at the bottom of the river. I was thunderstruck. What, how, why? Oh, it was "all right." The "manager himself" was there. All quite correct. "Everybody had behaved splendidly! splendidly!"—"You must," he said in agitation, "go and see the general manager at once. He is waiting!"

'I did not see the real significance of that wreck at once. I fancy I see it now, but I am not sure—not at all. Certainly the affair was too stupid—when I think of it—to be altogether natural. Still . . . But at the moment it presented itself simply as a confounded nuisance. The steamer was sunk. They had started two days before in a sudden hurry up the river with the manager on board, in charge of some volunteer skipper, and before they had been out three hours they tore the bottom out of her on stones, and she sank near the south bank. I asked myself what I was to do there, now my boat was lost. As a matter of fact, I had plenty to do in fishing my command out of the river. I had to set about it the very next day. That, and the repairs when I brought the pieces to the station, took some months.

---

[14]224 pounds (a "stone" is unit of measurement that equals 14 pounds).

'My first interview with the manager was curious. He did not ask me to sit down after my twenty-mile walk that morning. He was commonplace in complexion, in features, in manners, and in voice. He was of middle size and of ordinary build. His eyes, of the usual blue, were perhaps remarkably cold, and he certainly could make his glance fall on one as trenchant and heavy as an axe. But even at these times the rest of his person seemed to disclaim the intention. Otherwise there was only an indefinable, faint expression of his lips, something stealthy—a smile—not a smile—I remember it, but I can't explain. It was unconscious, this smile was, though just after he had said something it got intensified for an instant. It came at the end of his speeches like a seal applied on the words to make the meaning of the commonest phrase appear absolutely inscrutable. He was a common trader, from his youth up employed in these parts—nothing more. He was obeyed, yet he inspired neither love nor fear, nor even respect. He inspired uneasiness. That was it! Uneasiness. Not a definite mistrust—just uneasiness—nothing more. You have no idea how effective such a . . . a . . . faculty can be. He had no genius for organizing, for initiative, or for order even. That was evident in such things as the deplorable state of the station. He had no learning, and no intelligence. His position had come to him—why? Perhaps because he was never ill . . . He had served three terms of three years out there . . . Because triumphant health in the general rout of constitutions is a kind of power in itself. When he went home on leave he rioted on a large scale—pompously. Jack ashore—with a difference—in externals only. This one could gather from his causal talk. He originated nothing, he could keep the routine going—that's all. But he was great. He was great by this little thing that it was impossible to tell what could control such a man. He never gave that secret away. Perhaps there was nothing within him. Such a suspicion made one pause—for out there there were no external checks. Once when various tropical diseases had laid low almost every "agent" in the station, he was heard to say, "Men who come out here should have no entrails." He sealed the utterance with the smile of his, as though it had been a door opening into a darkness he had in his keeping. You fancied you had seen things—but the seal was on. When annoyed at mealtimes by constant quarrels of the white men about precedence, he ordered an immense round table to be made, for which a special house had to be built. This was the station's mess-room. Where he sat was the first place—the rest were nowhere. One felt this to be his unalterable conviction. He was neither civil nor uncivil. He was quiet. He allowed his "boy"—an overfed young Negro from the coast—to treat the white men, under his very eyes, with provoking insolence.

'He began to speak as soon as he saw me. I had been very long on the road. He could not wait. Had to start without me. The upriver stations had to be relieved. There had been so many delays already that he did not know who was dead and who was alive, and how they got on—and so on, and so on. He paid no attention to my explanations, and, playing with a stick of sealing-wax, repeated several times that the situation was "very grave, very grave." There were rumours that a very important station was in jeopardy, and its chief, Mr Kurtz, was ill. Hoped it was not true. Mr Kurtz was . . . I felt weary and irritable. Hang Kurtz, I thought. I interrupted him by saying I had heard of Mr Kurtz on the coast. "Ah! So they talk of him down there," he murmured to himself. Then he began again, assuring me Mr Kurtz was the best agent he had, an exceptional man, of the greatest importance to the Company; therefore I could understand his anxiety. He was, he said, "very, very uneasy." Certainly he fidgeted on his chair a good deal, exclaimed, "Ah, Mr Kurtz!," broke the stick of sealing-wax and seemed dumbfounded by the accident. Next thing he wanted to know "how long it would take to" . . . I interrupted him again. Being hungry, you know, and kept on my feet, too, I was getting savage. "How could I tell?" I said. "I hadn't even seen the wreck yet—some months, no doubt." All this talk seemed to me so futile. "Some months," he said. "Well, let us say three months before we can make a start. Yes. That ought to do the affair." I flung out of his hut (he lived all alone in a clay hut with a sort of verandah) muttering to myself my opinion of him. He was a chattering idiot. Afterwards I took it back when it was borne in upon me startlingly with what extreme nicety he had estimated the time requisite for the "affair."

'I went to work the next day, turning, so to speak, my back on that station. In that way only it seemed to me I could keep my hold on the redeeming facts of life. Still, one must look about sometimes; and then I saw this station, these men strolling aimlessly about in the sunshine of the yard. I asked myself sometimes what it all meant. They wandered here and there with their absurd long staves in their hands, like a lot of faithless pilgrims bewitched inside a rotten fence. The word "ivory" rang in the air, was whispered, was sighed. You would think they were praying to it. A taint of imbecile rapacity blew through it all, like a whiff from some corpse. By Jove! I've never seen anything so unreal in my life. And outside, the silent wilderness surrounding this cleared speck on the earth struck me as something great and invincible, like evil or truth, waiting patiently for the passing away of this fantastic invasion.

'Oh, these months! Well, never mind. Various things happened. One evening a grass shed full of calico, cotton print, beads, and I don't know what else, burst into a blaze so suddenly that you would have thought the earth had opened to let an avenging fire consume all that trash. I was smoking my pipe quietly by my dismantled steamer, and saw them all cutting capers in the light, with their arms lifted high, when the stout man with moustaches came tearing down to the river, a tin pail in his hand, assured me that everybody was "behaving splendidly, splendidly," dipped about a quart of water and tore back again. I noticed there was a hole in the bottom of his pail.

'I strolled up. There was no hurry. You see the thing had gone off like a box of matches. It had been hopeless from the very first. The flame had leaped high, driven everybody back, lighted up everything—and collapsed. The shed was already a heap of embers glowing fiercely. A nigger was being beaten near by. They said he had caused the fire in some way; be that as it may, he was screeching most horribly. I saw him, later, for several days, sitting in a bit of shade looking very sick and trying to recover himself: afterwards he arose and went out—and the wilderness without a sound took him into its bosom again. As I approached the glow from the dark I found myself at the back of two men, talking. I heard the name of Kurtz pronounced, then the words, "take advantage of this unfortunate accident." One of the men was the manager. I wished him a good evening. "Did you ever see anything like it—eh? it is incredible," he said, and walked off. The other man remained. He was a first-class agent, young, gentlemanly, a bit reserved, with a forked little beard and a hooked nose. He was stand-offish with the other agents, and they on their side said he was the manager's spy upon them. As to me, I had hardly ever spoken to him before. We got into talk, and by-and-by we strolled away from the hissing ruins. Then he asked me to his room, which was in the main building of the station. He struck a match, and I perceived that this young aristocrat had not only a silver-mounted dressing-case but also a whole candle all to himself. Just at that time the manager was the only man supposed to have any right to candles. Native mats covered the clay walls; a collection of spears, assegais,[15] shields, knives was hung up in trophies. The business entrusted to this fellow was the making of bricks—so I had been informed; but there wasn't a fragment of a brick anywhere in the station, and he had been there more than a year—waiting. It seems he could not make bricks without something, I don't know what—straw maybe. Anyways, it could not be found there, and as it was not likely to be sent from Europe, it did not appear clear to me what he was waiting for. An act of special creation perhaps. However, they were all waiting—all the sixteen or twenty pilgrims of them—for something; and upon my word it did not seem an uncongenial occupation, from the way they took it, though the only thing that ever came to them was disease—as far as I could see. They beguiled the time by backbiting and intriguing against each other in a foolish kind of way. There was an air of plotting about that station, but nothing came of it, of course. It was as unreal as everything else—as the philanthropic pretence of the whole concern, as their talk, as their government, as their show of work. The only real feeling was a desire to get appointed to a

---

[15]A light lance or throwing spear attributed to the Bantu peoples of southern Africa.

trading post where ivory was to be had, so that they could earn percentages. They intrigued and slandered and hated each other only on that account—but as to effectually lifting a little finger—oh, no. By heavens! there is something after all in the world allowing one man to steal a horse while another must not look at a halter. Steal a horse straight out. Very well. He had done it. Perhaps he can ride. But there is a way of looking at a halter that would provoke the most charitable of saints into a kick.

'I had no idea why he wanted to be sociable, but as we chatted in there it suddenly occurred to me the fellow was trying to get at something—in fact, pumping me. He alluded constantly to Europe, to the people I was supposed to know there—putting leading questions as to my acquaintances in the sepulchral city, and so on. His little eyes glittered like mica discs—with curiosity—though he tried to keep up a bit of superciliousness. At first I was astonished, but very soon I became awfully curious to see what he would find out from me. I couldn't possibly imagine what I had in me to make it worth his while. It was very pretty to see how he baffled himself, for in truth my body was full only of chills, and my head had nothing in it but that wretched steamboat business. It was evident he took me for a perfectly shameless prevaricator. At last he got angry, and to conceal a movement of furious annoyance, he yawned. I rose. Then I noticed a small sketch in oils, on a panel, representing a woman, draped and blindfolded, carrying a lighted torch. The background was sombre—almost black. The movement of the woman was stately, and the effect of the torch-light on the face was sinister.

'It arrested me, and he stood by civilly, holding an empty half-pint champagne bottle (medical comforts) with the candle stuck in it. To my question he said Mr Kurtz had painted this—in this very station more than a year ago—while waiting for means to go to his trading post. "Tell me, pray," said I, "who is this Mr Kurtz?"

' "The chief of the Inner Station," he answered in a short tone, looking away. "Much obliged," I said, laughing. "And you are the brickmaker of the Central Station. Everyone knows that." He was silent for a while. "He is a prodigy," he said at last. "He is an emissary of pity, and science, and progress, and devil knows what else. We want," he began to declaim suddenly, "for the guidance of the cause entrusted to us by Europe, so to speak, higher intelligence, wide sympathies, a singleness of purpose." "Who says that?" I asked. "Lots of them," he replied. "Some even write that; and so *he* comes here, a special being, as you ought to know." "Why ought I to know?" I interrupted, really surprised. He paid no attention. "Yes. Today he is chief of the best station, next year he will be assistant-manager, two years more and . . . but I daresay you know what he will be in two years' time. You are of the new gang—the gang of virtue. The same people who sent him specially also recommended you.

Oh, don't say no. I've my own eyes to trust." Light dawned upon me. My dear aunt's influential acquaintances were producing an unexpected effect upon that young man. I nearly burst into a laugh. "Do you read the Company's confidential correspondence?" I asked. He hadn't word to say. It was great fun. "When Mr Kurtz," I continued, severely, "is General Manager, you won't have the opportunity."

'He blew the candle out suddenly, and we went outside. The moon he risen. Black figures strolled about listlessly, pouring water on the glow, whence proceeded a sound of hissing; steam ascended in the moonlight, the beaten nigger groaned something. "What a row the brute makes!" said the indefatigable man with the moustaches, appearing near us. "Serve him right. Transgression—punishment—bang! Pitiless, pitiless. That's the only way. This will prevent all conflagrations for the future. I was just telling the manager . . ." He noticed my companion, and became crestfallen all at once. "Not in bed yet," he said, with a kind of servile heartiness; "it's so natural. Ha! Danger—agitation." He vanished. I went on to the river-side, and the other followed me. I heard a scathing murmur at my ear, "Heap of muffs—go to." The pilgrims could be seen in knots gesticulating, discussing. Several had still their staves in their hands. I verily believe they took these sticks to bed with them. Beyond the fence the forest stood up spectrally in the moonlight, and through the dim stir, through the faint sounds of that lamentable courtyard, the silence of the land went home to one's very heart—its mystery, its greatness, the amazing reality of its concealed life. The hurt nigger moaned feebly somewhere near by, and then fetched a deep sigh that made me mend my pace away from there. I felt a hand introducing itself under my arm. "My dear sir," said the fellow, "I don't want to be misunderstood, and especially by you, who will see Mr Kurtz long before I can have that pleasure. I wouldn't like him to get a false idea of my disposition . . ."

'I let him run on, this papier-mâché Mephistopheles, and it seemed to me that if I tried to could poke my forefinger through him, and would find nothing inside but a little loose dirt, maybe. He, don't you see, had been planning to be assistant-manager by-and-by under the present man, and I could see that the coming of that Kurtz had upset them both not a little. He talked precipitately, and I did not try to stop him. I had my shoulders against the wreck of my steamer, hauled up on the slope like a carcass of some big river animal. The smell of mud, of primeval mud, by Jove! was in my nostrils, the high stillness of primeval forest was before my eyes; there were shiny patches on the black creek. The moon had spread over everything a thin layer of silver—over the rank grass, over the mud, upon the wall of matted vegetation standing higher than the wall of a temple, over the great river I could see through a sombre gap glittering, glittering, as it flowed broadly by without a murmur.

All this was great, expectant, mute, while the man jabbered about himself. I wondered whether the stillness on the face of the immensity looking at us two were meant as an appeal or as a menace. What were we who had strayed in here? Could we handle that dumb thing, or would it handle us? I felt how big, how confoundedly big, was that thing that couldn't talk, and perhaps was deaf as well. What was in there? I could see a little ivory coming out from there, and I had heard Mr Kurtz was in there. I had heard enough about it, too—God knows! Yet somehow it didn't bring any image with it—no more than if I had been told an angel or a fiend was in there. I believed it in the same way one of you might believe there are inhabitants in the planet Mars. I knew once a Scotch sailmaker who was certain, dead sure, there were people in Mars. If you asked him, for some idea how they looked and behaved, he would get shy and mutter something about "walking on all fours." If you as much as smiled, he would—though a man of sixty—offer to fight you. I would not have gone so far as to fight for Kurtz, but I went for him near enough to a lie. You know I hate, detest, and can't bear a lie, not because I am straighter than the rest of us, but simply because it appals me. There is a taint of death, a flavour of mortality in lies—which is exactly what I hate and detest in the world—what I want to forget. It makes me miserable and sick, like biting something rotten would do. Temperament, I suppose. Well, I went near enough to it by letting the young fool there believe anything he liked to imagine as to my influence in Europe. I became in an instant as much of a pretence as the rest of the bewitched pilgrims. This simply because I had a notion it somehow would be of help to that Kurtz whom at the time I did not see—you understand. He was just a word for me. I did not see the man in the name any more than you do. Do you see him? Do you see the story? Do you see anything? It seems to me I am trying to tell you a dream—making a vain attempt, because no relation of a dream can convey the dream-sensation, that commingling of absurdity, surprise, and bewilderment in a tremor of struggling revolt, that notion of being captured by the incredible which is of the very essence of dreams . . .'

He was silent for a while.

'. . . No, it is impossible; it is impossible to convey the life-sensation of any given epoch of one's existence—that which makes its truth, its meaning—its subtle and penetrating essence. It is impossible. We live, as we dream— alone . . .'

He paused again as if reflecting, then added—

'Of course in this you fellows see more than I could then. You see me, whom you know . . .'

It had become so pitch dark that we listeners could hardly see one another. For a long time already he, sitting apart, had been no more to us than a voice. There was not a word from anybody. The others might have been asleep, but I was awake. I listened, I listened on the watch for the sentence, for the word, that would give me the clue to the faint uneasiness inspired by this narrative that seemed to shape itself without human lips in the heavy night-air of the river.

'. . . Yes—I let him run on,' Marlow began again, 'and think what he pleased about the powers that were behind me. I did! And there was nothing behind me! There was nothing but that wretched, old, mangled steamboat I was leaning against, while he talked fluently about "the necessity for every man to get on." "And when one comes out here, you conceive, it is not to gaze at the moon." Mr Kurtz was a "universal genius," but even a genius would find it easier to work with "adequate tools—intelligent men." He did not make bricks—why, there was a physical impossibility in the way—as I was well aware, and if he did secretarial work for the manager, it was because "no sensible man rejects wantonly the confidence of his superiors." Did I see it? I saw it. What more did I want? What I really wanted was rivets, by heaven! Rivets. To get on with the work—to stop the hole. Rivets I wanted. There were cases of them down at the coast—cases—piled up—burst—split! You kicked a loose rivet at every second step in that station yard on the hillside. Rivets had rolled into the grove of death. You could fill your pockets with rivets for the trouble of stooping down—and there wasn't one rivet to be found where it was wanted. We had plates that would do, but nothing to fasten them with. And every week the messenger, a lone negro, letter-bag on shoulder and staff in hand, left our station for the coast. And several times a week a coast caravan came in with trade goods—ghastly glazed calico that made you shudder only to look at it, glass beads value about a penny a quart, confounded spotted cotton handkerchiefs. And no rivets. Three carriers could have brought all that was wanted to set that steamboat afloat.

'He was becoming confidential now, but I fancy my unresponsive attitude must have exasperated him at last, for he judged it necessary to inform me he feared neither God nor devil, let alone any mere man. I said I could see that very well, but what I wanted was a certain quantity of rivets—and rivets were what really Mr Kurtz wanted, if he had only known it. Now letters went to the coast every week . . . "My dear sir," he cried, "I write from dictation." I demanded rivets. There was a way—for an intelligent man. He changed his manner; became very cold, and suddenly began to talk about a hippopotamus; wondered whether sleeping on board the steamer (I stuck to my salvage night and day) I wasn't disturbed. There was an old hippo that had the bad habit of getting out on the bank and roaming at night over the station grounds. The pilgrims used to turn out in a body and empty every rifle they could lay hands on at him. Some even had sat up o' nights for him. All this energy was wasted, though. "That animal has a charmed life," he said; "but you can say this only of brutes in this country. No man—you apprehend me?—no man here bears a charmed life." He stood there for a moment in the moonlight with his delicate hooked nose set a little askew, and his mica eyes glittering without a wink, then, with a curt Good-night, he strode off. I could see he was disturbed and considerably puzzled, which made me feel more hopeful than I had been for days. It was a great comfort to turn from that chap to my influential friend, the battered, twisted, ruined, tin-pot steamboat. I clambered on board. She rang under my feet like an empty Huntley & Palmers biscuit-tin kicked along a gutter; she was nothing so solid in make, and rather less pretty in shape, but I had expended enough hard work on her to make me love her. No influential friend would have served me better. She had given me a chance to come out a bit—to find out what I could do. No, I don't like work. I had rather laze about and think of all the fine things that can be done. I don't like work,—no man does—but I like what is in the work,—the chance to find yourself. Your own reality—for yourself, not for others—what no other man can ever know. They can only see the mere show, and never can tell what it really means.

'I was not surprised to see somebody sitting aft, on the deck, with his legs dangling over the mud. You see I rather chummed with the few mechanics there were in that station, whom the other pilgrims naturally despised—on account of their imperfect manners, I suppose. This was the foreman—a boiler-maker by trade—a good worker. He was a lank, bony, yellow-faced man, with big intense eyes. His aspect was worried, and his head was as bald as the palm of my hand; but his hair in falling seemed to have stuck to his chin, and had prospered in the new locality, for his beard hung down to his waist. He was a widower with six young children (he had left them in charge of a sister of his to come out there), and the passion of his life was pigeon-flying. He was an enthusiast and a connoisseur. He would rave about pigeons. After work hours he used sometimes to come over from his hut for a talk about his children and his pigeons; at work, when he had to crawl in the mud under the bottom of the steamboat, he would tie up that beard of his in a kind of white serviette[16] he brought for the purpose. It had loops to go over his ears. In the evening he could be seen squatted on the bank rinsing that wrapper in the creek with great care, then spreading it solemnly on a bush to dry.

'I slapped him on the back and shouted "We shall have rivets!" He scrambled to his feet exclaiming "No! Rivets!" as though he couldn't believe his ears. Then in a low voice, "You . . . eh?" I don't know why we behaved like lunatics. I put my finger to the side of my nose and nodded mysteriously. "Good for you!" he cried, snapped his fingers above his head, lifting one foot. I tried a jig. We capered on the iron deck. A frightful clatter came out of that hulk, and the

---

[16]French: table napkin.

virgin forest on the other bank of the creek sent it back in a thundering roll upon the sleeping station. It must have made some of the pilgrims sit up in their hovels. A dark figure obscured the lighted doorway of the manager's hut, vanished, then, a second or so after, the doorway itself vanished, too. We stopped, and the silence driven away by the stamping of our feet flowed back again from the recesses of the land. The great wall of vegetation, an exuberant and entangled mass of trunks, branches, leaves, boughs, festoons, motionless in the moonlight, was like a rioting invasion of soundless life, a rolling wave of plants, piled up, crested, ready to topple over the creek, to sweep every little man of us out of his little existence. And it moved not. A deadened burst of mighty splashes and snorts reached us from afar, as though an ichthyosaurus[17] had been taking a bath of glitter in the great river. "After all," said the boiler-maker in a reasonable tone, "why shouldn't we get the rivets?" Why not, indeed! I did not know of any reason why we shouldn't. "They'll come in three weeks," I said, confidently.

'But they didn't. Instead of rivets there came an invasion, an infliction, a visitation. It came in sections during the next three weeks, each section headed by a donkey carrying a white man in new clothes and tan shoes, bowing from that elevation right and left to the impressed pilgrims. A quarrelsome band of footsore sulky niggers trod on the heels of the donkey; a lot of tents, camp-stools, tin boxes, white cases, brown bales would be shot down in the court-yard, and the air of mystery would deepen a little over the muddle of the station. Five such instalments came, with their absurd air of disorderly flight with the loot of innumerable outfit shops and provision stores, that, one would think, they were lugging, after a raid, into the wilderness for equitable division. It was an inextricable mess of things decent in themselves but that human folly made look like spoils of thieving.

'This devoted band called itself the Eldorado Exploring Expedition, and I believe they were sworn to secrecy. Their talk, however, was the talk of sordid buccaneers: it was reckless without hardihood, greedy without audacity, and cruel without courage; there was not an atom of foresight or of serious intention in the whole batch of them, and they did not seem aware these things are wanted for the work of the world. To tear treasure out of the bowels of the land was their desire, with no more moral purpose at the back of it than there is in burglars breaking into a safe. Who paid the expenses of the noble enterprise I don't know; but the uncle of our manager was leader of that lot.

'In exterior he resembled a butcher in a poor neighbourhood, and his eyes had a look of sleepy cunning. He carried his fat paunch with ostentation on his short legs, and during the time his gang infested the station spoke to no

---

[17]Prehistoric marine reptile resembling a crocodile.

one but his nephew. You could see these two roaming about all day long with their heads close together in an everlasting confab.

'I had given up worrying myself about the rivets. One's capacity for that kind of folly is more limited than you would suppose. I said Hang!—and let things slide. I had plenty of time for meditation, and now and then I would give some thought to Kurtz. I wasn't very interested in him. No. Still, I was curious to see whether this man, who had come out equipped with moral ideas of some sort, would climb to the top after all and how he would set about his work when there.'

2

'One evening as I was lying flat on the deck of my steamboat, I heard voices approaching—and there were the nephew and the uncle strolling along the bank. I laid my head on my arm again, and had nearly lost myself in a doze, when somebody said in my ear, as it were: "I am as harmless as a little child, but I don't like to be dictated to. Am I the manager—or am I not? I was ordered to send him there. It's incredible." . . . I became aware that the two were standing on the shore alongside the forepart of the steamboat, just below my head. I did not move; it did not occur to me to move: I was sleepy. "It *is* unpleasant," grunted the uncle. "He has asked the Administration to be sent there," said the other, "with the idea of showing what he could do; and I was instructed accordingly. Look at the influence that man must have. Is it not frightful?" They both agreed it was frightful, then made several bizarre remarks: "Make rain and fine weather—one man—the Council—by the nose"—bits of absurd sentences that got the better of my drowsiness, so that I had pretty near the whole of my wits about me when the uncle said, "The climate may do away with this difficulty for you. Is he alone there?" "Yes," answered the manager; "he sent his assistant down the river with a note to me in these terms: 'Clear this poor devil out of the country, and don't bother sending more of that sort. I had rather be alone than have the kind of men you can dispose of with me.' It was more than a year ago. Can you imagine such impudence!" "Anything since then?" asked the other, hoarsely. "Ivory," jerked the nephew; "lots of it—prime sort—lots—most annoying, from him." "And with that?" questioned the heavy rumble. "Invoice," was the reply fired out, so to speak. Then silence. They had been talking about Kurtz.

'I was broad awake by this time, but, lying perfectly at ease, remained still, having no inducement to change my position. "How did that ivory come all this way?" growled the elder man, who seemed very vexed. The other explained that it had come with a fleet of canoes in charge of an English half-caste clerk Kurtz had with him; that Kurtz had apparently intended to return himself, the station being by that time bare of goods and stores, but after coming three hundred miles, had suddenly decided to go back, which he started to do alone in a small dugout with four paddlers, leaving the half-caste to continue down the river with the ivory. The two fellows there seemed astounded at anybody attempting such a thing. They were at a loss for an adequate motive. As to me, I seemed to see Kurtz for the first time. It was a distinct glimpse: the dugout, four paddling savages, and the lone white man turning his back suddenly on the headquarters, on relief, on thoughts of home—perhaps; setting his face towards the depths of the wilderness, towards his empty and desolate station. I did not know the motive. Perhaps he was just simply a fine fellow who stuck to his work for its own sake. His name, you understand, had not been pronounced once. He was "that man." The half-caste, who, as far as I could see, had conducted a difficult trip with great prudence and pluck, was invariably alluded to as "that scoundrel." The "scoundrel" had reported that the "man" had been very ill—had recovered imperfectly . . . The two below me moved away then a few paces, and strolled back and forth at some little distance. I heard: "Military post—doctor—two hundred miles—quite alone now—unavoidable delays—nine months—no news—strange rumours." They approached again, just as the manager was saying, "No one, as far as I know, unless a species of wandering trader—a pestilential fellow, snapping ivory from the natives." Who was it they were talking about now? I gathered in snatches that this was some man supposed to be in Kurtz's district, and of whom the manager did not approve. "We will not be free from unfair competition till one of these fellows is hanged for an example," he said. "Certainly," grunted the other; "get him hanged! Why not? Anything—anything can be done in this country. That's what I say; nobody here, you understand, *here*, can endanger your position. And why? You stand the climate—you outlast them all. The danger is in Europe; but there before I left I took care to—" They moved off and whispered, then their voices rose again. "The extraordinary series of delays is not my fault. I did my best." The fat man sighed. "Very sad." "And the pestiferous absurdity of his talk," continued the other; "he bothered me enough when he was here. 'Each station should be like a beacon on the road towards better things, a centre for trade of course, but also for humanizing, improving, instructing.' Conceive you—that ass! And he wants to be manager! No, it's—" Here he got choked by excessive indignation, and I lifted my head the least bit. I was surprised to see how near they were—right under me. I could have spat upon their hats. They were looking on the ground, absorbed in thought. The manager was switching his leg with a slender twig: his sagacious relative lifted his head. "You have been well since you came out this time?" he asked. The other gave a start. "Who? I? Oh! Like a charm—like a charm. But the rest—oh, my goodness! All sick. They die so quick, too, that I haven't the time to send them out of the country—it's incredible!" "H'm. Just so," grunted the uncle. "Ah! my boy, trust to this—I say, trust to this." I saw him extend his short flipper of an arm for a gesture that took in the forest, the creek, the mud, the river—seemed to beckon with a dishonouring flourish before the sunlit face of the land a treacherous appeal to the lurking death, to the hidden evil, to the profound darkness of its heart. It was so startling that I leaped to my feet and looked back at the edge of the forest, as though I had expected an answer of some sort to that black display of confidence. You know the foolish notions that come to one sometimes. The high stillness confronted these two figures with its ominous patience, waiting for the passing away of a fantastic invasion.

'They swore aloud together—out of sheer fright, I believe—then pretending not to know anything of my existence, turned back to the station. The sun was low; and leaning forward side by side, they seemed to be tugging painfully uphill their two ridiculous shadows of unequal length, that trailed behind them slowly over the tall grass without bending a single blade.

'In a few days the Eldorado Expedition went into the patient wilderness, that closed upon it as the sea closes over a diver. Long afterwards the news came that all the donkeys were dead. I know nothing as to the fate of the less valuable animals. They, no doubt, like the rest of us, found what they deserved. I did not inquire. I was then rather excited at the prospect of meeting Kurtz very soon. When I say very soon I mean it comparatively. It was just two months from the day we left the creek when we came to the bank below Kurtz's station.

'Going up that river was like travelling back to the earliest beginnings of the world, when vegetation rioted on the earth and the big trees were kings. An empty stream, a great silence, an impenetrable forest. The air was warm, thick, heavy, sluggish. There was no joy in the brilliance of sunshine. The long stretches of the waterway ran on, deserted, into the gloom of overshadowed distances. On silvery sandbanks hippos and alligators sunned themselves side by side. The broadening waters flowed through a mob of wooded islands; you lost your way on that river as you would in a desert, and butted all day long against shoals, trying to find the channel, till you thought yourself bewitched and cut off for ever from everything you had known once—somewhere—far away—in another existence perhaps. There were moments when one's past came back to one, as it will sometimes when you have not a moment to spare to yourself; but it came in the shape of an unrestful and noisy dream, remembered with wonder amongst the overwhelming realities of this strange world of plants, and water, and silence. And this stillness of life did not in the least resemble a peace. It was the stillness of an implacable force brooding over an inscrutable intention. It looked at you with a vengeful aspect. I got used to it afterwards; I did not see it any more; I had no time. I had to keep guessing at the channel; I had to discern, mostly by inspiration, the signs of hidden banks; I watched for sunken stones; I was learning to clap my teeth smartly before my heart flew out, when I shaved by a fluke some infernal sly old snag that would have ripped the life out of the tin-pot steamboat and drowned all the pilgrims; I had to keep a look-out for the signs of dead wood we could cut up in the night for next day's steaming. When you have to attend to things of that sort, to the mere incidents of the surface, the reality—the reality, I tell you—fades. The inner truth is hidden—luckily, luckily. But I felt it all the same; I felt often its mysterious stillness watching me at my monkey tricks, just as it watches you fellows performing on your respective tight-ropes for—what is it? half-a-crown a tumble—'

'Try to be civil, Marlow,' growled a voice, and I knew there was at least one listener awake besides myself.

'I beg your pardon. I forgot the heartache which makes up the rest of the price. And indeed what does the price matter, if the trick be well done? You do your tricks very well. And I didn't do badly either, since I managed not to sink that steamboat on my first trip. It's a wonder to me yet. Imagine a blindfolded man set to drive a van over a bad road. I sweated and shivered over that business considerably, I can tell you. After all, for a seaman, to scrape the bottom of the thing that's supposed to float all the time under his care is the unpardonable sin. No one may know of it, but you never forget the thump—eh? A blow on the very heart. You remember it, you dream of it, you wake up at night and think of it—years after—and go hot and cold all over. I don't pretend to say that steamboat floated all the time. More than once she had to wade for a bit, with twenty cannibals splashing around and pushing. We had enlisted some of these chaps on the way for a crew. Fine fellows—cannibals—in their place. They were men one could work with, and I am grateful to them. And, after all, they did not eat each other before my face: they had brought along a provision of hippo-meat which went rotten, and made the mystery of the wilderness stink in my nostrils. Phoo! I can sniff it now. I had the manager on board and three or four pilgrims with their staves—all complete. Sometimes we came upon a station close by the bank, clinging to the skirts of the unknown, and the white men rushing out of a tumbledown hovel, with great gestures of joy and surprise and welcome, seemed very strange—had the appearance of being held there captive by a spell. The word ivory would ring in the air for a while—and on we went again into the silence, along empty reaches, round the still bends, between the high walls of our winding way, reverberating in hollow claps the ponderous beat of the stern-wheel. Trees, trees, millions of trees, massive, immense, running up high; and at their foot, hugging the bank against the stream, crept the little begrimed steamboat, like a sluggish beetle crawling on the floor of a lofty portico. It made you feel very small, very lost, and yet it was not altogether depressing, that feeling. After all, if you were small, the grimy beetle crawled on—which was just what you wanted it to do. Where the pilgrims imagined it crawled to I don't know. To some place where they expected to get something, I bet! For me it crawled towards Kurtz—exclusively; but when the steam-pipes started leaking we crawled very slow. The reaches opened before us and closed behind, as if the forest had stepped leisurely across the water to bar the way for our return. We penetrated deeper and deeper into the heart of darkness. It was very quiet there. At night sometimes the roll of drums behind the curtain of trees would run up the river and remain sustained faintly, as if hovering in the air high over our heads, till the first break of day. Whether it meant war, peace, or prayer we could not tell. The dawns were heralded by the descent of a chill stillness; the wood-cutters slept, their fires burned low; the snapping of a twig would make you start. We were wanderers on prehistoric earth, on an earth that wore the aspect of an unknown planet. We could have fancied ourselves the first of men taking possession of an accursed inheritance, to be subdued at the cost of profound anguish and of excessive toil. But suddenly, as we struggled round a bend, there would be a glimpse of rush walls, of peaked grass-roofs, a burst of yells, a whirl of black limbs, a mass of hands clapping, of feet stamping, of bodies swaying, of eyes rolling, under the droop of heavy and motionless foliage. The steamer toiled slowly on the edge of a black and incomprehensible frenzy. The prehistoric man was cursing us, praying to us, welcoming us—who could tell? We were cut off from the comprehension of our surroundings; we glided past like phantoms, wondering and secretly appalled, as sane men would be before an enthusiastic outbreak in a mad-house. We could not understand because we were too far and could not remember, because we were travelling in the night of first ages, of those ages that are gone, leaving hardly a sign—and no memories.

'The earth seemed unearthly. We are accustomed to look upon the shackled form of a conquered monster, but there—there you could look at a thing monstrous and free. It was unearthly, and the men were—No, they were not inhuman. Well, you know, that was the worst of it—this suspicion of their not being inhuman. It would come slowly to one. They howled and leaped, and spun, and made horrid faces; but what thrilled you was just the thought of their humanity—like yours—the thought of your remote kinship with this wild and passionate uproar. Ugly. Yes, it was ugly enough; but if you were man enough you would admit to yourself that there was in you just the faintest trace of a response to the terrible frankness of that noise, a dim suspicion of there being a meaning in it which you—you so remote from the night of first ages—could comprehend. And why not? The mind of man is capable of anything—because everything is in it, all the past as well as all the future. What was there after all? Joy, fear, sorrow, devotion, valour, rage—who can tell?—but truth—truth stripped of its cloak of time. Let the fool gape and shudder—the man knows, and can look on without a wink. But he must at least be as much of a man as these on the shore. He must meet that truth with his own true stuff—with his own inborn strength. Principles won't do. Acquisitions, clothes, pretty rags—rags that would fly off at the first good shake. No; you want a deliberate belief. An appeal to me in this fiendish row—is there? Very well; I hear; I admit, but I have a voice, too, and for good or evil mine is the speech that cannot be silenced. Of course, a fool, what with sheer fright and fine sentiments, is always safe. Who's that grunting? You wonder I didn't go ashore for a howl and a dance? Well, no—I didn't. Fine sentiments, you say? Fine sentiments, be hanged! I had no time. I had to mess about with white-lead and strips of woolen blanket helping to put bandages on those leaky steam-pipes—I tell you. I had to watch the steering, and circumvent those snags, and get the tin-pot along by hook or by crook. There was surface-truth enough in these things to save a wiser man. And between whiles I had to look after the savage who was fireman. He was an improved specimen; he could fire up a vertical boiler. He was there below me, and, upon my word, to look at him was as edifying as seeing a dog in a parody of breeches and a feather hat, walking on his hind-legs. A few months of training had done for that really fine chap. He squinted at the steam-gauge and at the water-gauge with an evident effort of intrepidity—and he had filed teeth, too, the poor devil, and the wool of his pate shaved into queer patterns, and three ornamental scars on each of his cheeks. He ought to have been clapping his hands and stamping his feet on the bank, instead of which he was hard at work, a thrall to strange witchcraft, full of improving knowledge. He was useful because he had been instructed; and what he knew was this—that should the water in that transparent thing disappear, the evil spirit inside the boiler would get angry through the greatness of his thirst, and take a terrible vengeance. So he sweated and fired up and watched the glass fearfully (with an impromptu charm, made of rags, tied to his arm, and a piece of polished bone, as big as a watch, stuck flatways through his lower lip), while the wooded banks slipped past us slowly, the short noise was left behind, the interminable miles of silence—and we crept on, towards Kurtz. But the snags were thick, the water was treacherous and shallow, the boiler seemed indeed to have a sulky devil in it, and thus neither that fireman nor I had any time to peer into our creepy thoughts.

'Some fifty miles below the Inner Station we came upon a hut of reeds, an inclined and melancholy pole, with the unrecognizable tatters of what had been a flag of some sort flying from it, and a neatly stacked wood-pile. This was unexpected. We came to the bank, and on the stack of firewood found a flat piece of board with some faded pencil-writing on it. When deciphered it said: "Wood for you. Hurry up. Approach cautiously." There was a signature, but it was illegible—not Kurtz—a much longer word. Hurry up. Where? Up the river? "Approach cautiously." We had not done so. But the warning could not have been meant for the place where it could be only found after approach. Something was wrong above. But what—and how much? That was the question. We commented adversely upon the imbecility of that telegraphic style. The bush around said nothing, and would not let us look very far, either. A torn curtain of red twill hung in the doorway of the hut, and flapped sadly in our faces. The dwelling was dismantled; but we could see a white man had lived there not very long ago. There remained a rude table—a plank on two posts; a heap of rubbish reposed in a dark corner, and by the door I picked up a book. It had lost its covers, and the pages had been thumbed into a state of extremely dirty softness; but the back had been lovingly stitched afresh with white cotton thread, which looked clean yet. It was an extraordinary find. Its title was, *An Inquiry into some Points of Seamanship*, by a man, Tower, Towson—some such name—Master in His Majesty's Navy. The matter looked dreary reading enough, with illustrative diagrams and repulsive tables of figures, and the copy was sixty years old. I handled this amazing antiquity with the greatest possible tenderness, lest it should dissolve in my hands. Within, Towson or Towser was inquiring earnestly into the breaking strain of ships' chains and tackle, and other such matters. Not a very enthralling book; but at the first glance you could see there a singleness of intention, an honest concern for the right way of going to work, which made these humble pages, thought out so many years ago, luminous with another than a professional light. The simple old sailor, with his talk of chains and purchases, made me forget the jungle and the pilgrims in a delicious sensation of having come upon something unmistakably real. Such a book being there was wonderful enough; but still more astounding were the notes pencilled in the margin, and plainly referring to the text. I couldn't believe my eyes! They were in cipher! Yes, it looked like cipher. Fancy a man lugging with him a book of that description into this nowhere and studying it—and making notes—in cipher at that! It was an extravagant mystery.

'I had been dimly aware for some time of a worrying noise, and when I lifted my eyes I saw the wood-pile was gone, and the manager, aided by all the pilgrims, was shouting at me from the river-side. I slipped the book into my pocket. I assure you to leave off reading was like tearing myself away from the shelter of an old and solid friendship.

'I started the lame engine ahead. "It must be this miserable trader—this intruder," exclaimed the manager, looking back malevolently at the place we had left. "He must be English," I said. "It will not save him from getting into trouble if he is not careful," muttered the manager darkly. I observed with assumed innocence that no man was safe from trouble in this world.

'The current was more rapid now, the steamer seemed at her last gasp, the stern-wheel flopped languidly, and I caught myself listening on tiptoe for the next beat of the float,[18] for in sober truth I expected the wretched thing to give up every moment. It was like watching the last flickers of a life. But still we crawled. Sometimes I would pick out a tree a little way ahead to measure our progress towards Kurtz by, but I lost it invariably before we got abreast. To keep the eyes so long on one thing was too much for human patience. The manager displayed a beautiful resignation. I fretted and fumed and took to arguing with myself whether or no I would talk openly with Kurtz; but before I could come to any conclusion it occurred to me that my speech or my silence, indeed any action of mine, would be a mere futility. What did it matter what anyone knew or ignored? What did it matter who was manager? One gets sometimes such a flash of insight. The essentials of this affair lay deep under the surface, beyond my reach, and beyond my power of meddling.

'Towards the evening of the second day we judged ourselves about eight miles from Kurtz's station. I wanted to push on; but the manager looked grave, and told me the navigation up there was so dangerous that it would be advisable, the sun being very low already, to wait where we were till next morning. Moreover, he pointed out that if the warning to approach cautiously were to be followed, we must approach in daylight—not at dusk, or in the dark. This was sensible enough. Eight miles meant nearly three hours' steaming for us, and I could also see suspicious ripples at the upper end of the reach. Nevertheless, I was annoyed beyond expression at the delay, and most unreasonably, too, since one night more could not matter much after so many months. As we had plenty of wood, and caution was the word, I brought up in the middle of the stream. The reach was narrow, straight, with high sides like a railway cutting. The dusk came gliding into it long before the sun had set. The current ran smooth and swift, but a dumb immobility sat on the banks. The living trees, lashed together by the creepers and every living bush of the undergrowth, might have been changed into stone, even to the slenderest twig, to the lightest leaf. It was not sleep—it seemed unnatural, like a state of trance. Not the faintest sound of any kind could be heard. You looked on amazed, and began to suspect yourself of being deaf—then the night came suddenly, and struck you blind as well. About three in the morning some large fish leaped, and the loud splash made me jump as though a gun had been fired. When the sun rose there was a white fog, very warm and clammy, and more blinding than the night. It did not shift or driver; it was just there, standing all round you like something solid. At eight or nine, perhaps, it lifted as a shutter lifts. We had a glimpse of the towering multitude of trees, of the

---

[18]Individual blade of a paddle-wheel.

immense matted jungle, with the blazing little ball of the sun hanging over it—all perfectly still—and then the white shutter came down again, smoothly, as if sliding in greased grooves. I ordered the chain, which we had begun to heave in, to be paid out again. Before it stopped running with a muffled rattle, a cry, a very loud cry, as of infinite desolation, soared slowly in the opaque air. It ceased. A complaining clamour, modulated in savage discords, filled our ears. The sheer unexpectedness of it made my hair stir under my cap. I don't know how it struck the others: to me it seemed as though the mist itself had screamed, so suddenly, and apparently from all sides at once, did this tumultuous and mournful uproar arise. It culminated in a hurried outbreak of almost intolerably excessive shrieking, which stopped short, leaving us stiffened in a variety of silly attitudes, and obstinately listening to the nearly as appalling and excessive silence. "Good God! What is the meaning—" stammered at my elbow one of the pilgrims,—a little fat man, with sandy hair and red whiskers, who wore side-spring boots, and pink pyjamas tucked into his socks. Two others remained open-mouthed a whole minute, then dashed into the little cabin, to rush out incontinently and stand darting scared glances, with Winchesters at "ready" in their hands. What we could see was just the steamer we were on, her outlines blurred as though she had been on the point of dissolving, and a misty strip of water, perhaps two feet broad, around her— and that was all. The rest of the world was nowhere, as far as our eyes and ears were concerned. Just nowhere. Gone, disappeared; swept off without leaving a whisper or a shadow behind.

'I went forward, and ordered the chain to be hauled in short, so as to be ready to trip the anchor and move the steamboat at once if necessary. "Will they attack?" whispered an awed voice. "We will be all butchered in this fog," murmured another. The faces twitched with the strain, the hands trembled slightly, the eyes forgot to wink. It was very curious to see the contrast of expressions of the white men and of the black fellows of our crew, who were as much strangers to that part of the river as we, though their homes were only eight hundred miles away. The whites, of course greatly discomposed, had besides a curious look of being painfully shocked by such an outrageous row. The others had an alert, naturally interested expression; but their faces were essentially quiet, even those of the one or two who grinned as they hauled at the chain. Several exchanged short, grunting phrases, which seemed to settle the matter to their satisfaction. Their headman, a young, broad-chested black, severely draped in dark-blue fringed cloths, with fierce nostrils and his hair all done up artfully in oily ringlets, stood near me. "Aha!" I said, just for good fellowship's sake. "Catch 'im," he snapped, with a bloodshot widening of his eyes and a flash of sharp teeth—"catch 'im. Give 'im to us." "To you, eh?" I asked; "what would you do with them?" "Eat 'im!" he said, curtly, and, leaning his elbow on the rail, looked out into the fog in a dignified and profoundly pensive attitude. I would no doubt have been properly horrified, had it not occurred to me that he and his chaps must be very hungry: that they must have been growing increasingly hungry for at least this month past. They had been engaged for six months (I don't think a single one of them had any clear idea of time, as we at the end of countless ages have. They still belonged to the beginnings of time—had no inherited experience to teach them, as it were), and, of course, as long as there was a piece of paper written over in accordance with some farcical law or other made down the river, it didn't enter anybody's head to trouble how they would live. Certainly they had brought with them some rotten hippo-meat, which couldn't have lasted very long, anyway, even if the pilgrims hadn't, in the midst of a shocking hullabaloo, thrown a considerable quantity of it overboard. It looked like a high-handed proceeding; but it was really a case of legitimate self-defence. You can't breathe dead hippo waking, sleeping, and eating, and at the same time keep your precarious grip on existence. Besides that, they had given them every week three pieces of brass wire, each about nine inches long; and the theory was they were to buy their provisions with that currency in river-side villages. You can see how *that* worked. There were either no villages, or the people were hostile, or the director, who like the rest of us fed out of tins, with an occasional old he-goat thrown in, didn't want to stop the steamer for some more or less recondite reason. So, unless they swallowed the wire itself, or made loops of it to snare the fishes with, I don't see what good their extravagant salary could be to them. I must say it was paid with a regularity worthy of a large and honourable trading company. For the rest, the only thing to eat—though it didn't look eatable in the least—I saw in their possession was a few lumps of some stuff like half-cooked dough, of a dirty lavender colour, they kept wrapped in leaves, and now and then swallowed a piece of, but so small that it seemed done more for the looks of the thing than for any serious purpose of sustenance. Why in the name of all the gnawing devils of hunger they didn't go for us—they were thirty to five—and have a good tuck in for once, amazes me now when I think of it. They were big powerful men, with not much capacity to weigh the consequences, with courage, with strength, even yet, though their skins were no longer glossy and their muscles no longer hard. And I saw that something restraining, one of those human secrets that baffle probability, had come into play there. I looked at them with a swift quickening of interest— not because it occurred to me I might be eaten by them before very long, though I own to you that just then I perceived—in a new light, as it were— how unwholesome the pilgrims looked, and I hoped, yes, I positively hoped, that my aspect was not so—what shall I say?—so—unappetizing: a touch of fantastic vanity which fitted well with the dream-sensation that pervaded all my days at the time. Perhaps I had a little fever, too. One can't live with one's finger everlastingly on one's pulse. I had often "a little fever," or a little touch of other things—the playful paw-strokes of the wilderness, the preliminary trifling before the more serious onslaught which came in due course. Yes; I looked at them as you would on any human being, with a curiosity of their impulses, motives, capacities, weaknesses, when brought to the test of an inexorable physical necessity. Restraint! What possible restraint? Was it superstition, disgust, patience, fear—or some kind of primitive honour? No fear can stand up to hunger, no patience can wear it out, disgust simply does not exist where hunger is; and as to superstition, beliefs, and what you may call principles, they are less than chaff in a breeze. Don't you know the devilry of lingering starvation, its exasperating torment, its black thoughts, its sombre and brooding ferocity? Well, I do. It takes a man all his inborn strength to fight hunger properly. It's really easier to face bereavement, dishonour, and the perdition of one's soul—than this kind of prolonged hunger. Sad, but true. And these chaps, too, had no earthly reason for any kind of scruple. Restraint! I would just as soon have expected restraint from a hyena prowling amongst the corpses of a battlefield. But there was the fact facing me—the fact dazzling, to be seen, like the foam on the depths of the sea, like a ripple on an unfathomable enigma, a mystery greater—when I thought of it—than the curious, inexplicable note of desperate grief in this savage clamour that had swept by us on the river-bank, behind the blind whiteness of the fog.

'Two pilgrims were quarrelling in hurried whispers as to which bank. "Left." "No, no; how can you? Right, right, of course." "It is very serious," said the manager's voice behind me; "I would be desolated if anything should happen to Mr Kurtz before we came up." I looked at him, and had not the slightest doubt he was sincere. He was just the kind of man who would wish to preserve appearances. That was his restraint. But when he muttered something about going on at once, I did not even take the trouble to answer him. I knew, and he knew, that it was impossible. Were we to let go our hold of the bottom, we would be absolutely in the air—in space. We wouldn't be able to tell where we were going to—whether up or down stream, or across—till we fetched against one bank or the other—and then we wouldn't know at first which it was. Of course I made no move. I had no mind for a smash-up. You couldn't imagine a more deadly place for a shipwreck. Whether drowned at once or not, we were sure to perish speedily in one way or another. "I authorize you to take all the risks," he said, after a short silence. "I refuse to take any," I said, shortly; which was just the answer he expected, though its tone might have surprised him. "Well, I must defer to your judgement. You are captain," he said, with marked civility. I turned my shoulder to him in sign of my appreciation, and looked into the fog. How long would it last? It was the most hopeless look-out. The approach to this Kurtz grubbing for ivory in the wretched bush was beset by as many dangers as though he had been an enchanted princess sleeping in a fabulous castle. "Will they attack, do you think?" asked the manager, in a confidential tone.

'I did not think they would attack, for several obvious reasons. The thick fog was one. If they left the bank in their canoes they would get lost in it, as we would be if we attempted to move. Still, I had also judged the jungle of both banks quite impenetrable—and yet eyes were in it, eyes that had seen us. The river-side bushes were certainly very thick; but the undergrowth behind was evidently penetrable. However, during the short lift I had seen no canoes anywhere in the reach—certainly not abreast of the steamer. But what made the idea of attack inconceivable to me was the nature of the noise—of the cries we had heard. They had not the fierce character boding of immediate hostile intention. Unexpected, wild, and violent as they had been, they had given me an irresistible impression of sorrow. The glimpse of the steamboat had for some reason filled those savages with unrestrained grief. The danger, if any, I expounded, was from our proximity to a great human passion let loose. Even extreme grief may ultimately vent itself in violence—but more generally takes the form of apathy . . .

'You should have seen the pilgrims stare! They had no heart to grin, or even to revile me: but I believe they thought me gone mad—with fright, maybe. I delivered a regular lecture. My dear boys, it was no good bothering. Keep a look-out? Well, you may guess I watched the fog for the signs of lifting as a cat watches a mouse; but for anything else our eyes were of no more use to us than if we had been buried miles deep in a heap of cotton-wool. It felt like it, too—choking, warm, stifling. Besides, all I said, though it sounded extravagant, was absolutely true to fact. What we afterwards alluded to as an attack was really an attempt at repulse. The action was very far from being aggressive—it was not even defensive, in the usual sense: it was undertaken under the stress of desperation, and in its essence was purely protective.

'It developed itself, I should say, two hours after the fog lifted, and its commencement was at a spot, roughly speaking, about a mile and a half below Kurtz's station. We had just floundered and flopped round a bend, when I saw an islet, a mere grassy hummock of bright green, in the middle of the stream. It was the only thing of the kind; but as we opened the reach more, I perceived it was the head of a long sandbank, or rather of a chain of shallow patches stretching down the middle of the river. They were discoloured, just awash, and the whole lot was seen just under the water, exactly as a man's backbone is seen running down the middle of his back under the skin. Now, as far as I did see, I could go to the right or to the left of this. I didn't know either channel, of course. The banks looked pretty well alike, the depth appeared the same; but as I had been informed the station was on the west side, I naturally headed for the western passage.

'No sooner had we fairly entered it than I became aware it was much narrower than I had supposed. To the left of us there was the long uninterrupted shoal, and to the right a high, steep bank heavily overgrown with bushes. Above the bush the trees stood in serried ranks. The twigs overhung the current thickly, and from distance to distance a large limb of some tree projected rigidly over the stream. It was then well on in the afternoon, the face of the forest was gloomy, and a broad strip of shadow had already fallen on the water. In this shadow we steamed up—very slowly, as you may imagine. I steered her well inshore—the water being deepest near the bank, as the sounding-pole informed me.

'One of my hungry and forbearing friends was sounding in the bows just below me. This steamboat was exactly like a decked scow. On the deck, there were two little teak-wood houses, with doors and windows. The boiler was in the fore-end, and the machinery right astern. Over the whole there was a light roof, supported on stanchions. The funnel projected through that roof, and in front of the funnel a small cabin built of light planks served for a pilot-house. It contained a couch, two camp-stools, a loaded Martini-Henry leaning in one corner, a tiny table, and the steering-wheel. It had a wide door in front and a broad shutter at each side. All these were always thrown open, of course. I spent my days perched up there on the extreme fore-end of that roof, before the door. At night I slept, or tried to, on the couch. An athletic black belonging to some coast tribe, and educated by my poor predecessor, was the helmsman. He sported a pair of brass earrings, wore a blue cloth wrapper from the waist to the ankles, and thought all the world of himself. He was the most unstable kind of fool I had ever seen. He steered with no end of a swagger while you were by; but if he lost sight of you, he became instantly the prey of an abject funk, and would let that cripple of a steamboat get the upper hand of him in a minute.

'I was looking down at the sounding-pole, and feeling much annoyed to see at each try a little more of it stick out of that river, when I saw my poleman give up the business suddenly, and stretch himself flat on the deck, without even taking the trouble to haul his pole in. He kept hold on it though, and it trailed in the water. At the same time the fireman, whom I could also see below me, sat down abruptly before his furnace and ducked his head. I was amazed. Then I had to look at the river mighty quick, because there was a snag in the fairway. Sticks, little sticks, were flying about—thick: they were whizzing before my nose, dropping below me, striking behind me against my pilot-house. All this time the river, the shore, the woods, were very quiet—perfectly quiet. I could only hear the heavy splashing thump of the stern-wheel and the patter of these things. We cleared the snag clumsily. Arrows, by Jove! We were being shot at! I stepped in quickly to close the shutter on the land-side. That fool-helmsman, his hand on the spokes, was lifting his knees high, stamping his feet, champing his mouth, like a reined-in horse. Confound him! And we were staggering within ten feet of the bank. I had to lean right out to swing the heavy shutter, and I saw a face amongst the leaves on the level with my own, looking at me very fierce and steady and then suddenly, as though a veil had been removed from my eyes, I made out, deep in the tangled gloom, naked breasts, arms, legs, glaring eyes,—the bush was swarming with human limbs in movement, glistening, of bronze colour. The twigs shook, swayed, and rustled, the arrows flew out of them, and then the shutter came to. "Steer her straight," I said to the helmsman. He held his head rigid, face forward; but his eyes rolled, he kept on, lifting and setting down his feet gently, his mouth foamed a little. "Keep quiet!" I said in a fury. I might just as well have ordered a tree not to sway in the wind. I darted out. Below me there was a great scuf-fle of feet on the iron deck; confused exclamations; a voice screamed, "Can you turn back?" I caught sight of a V-shaped ripple on the water ahead. What? Another snag! A fusillade[19] burst out under my feet. The pilgrims had opened with their Winchesters,[20] and were simply squirting lead into that bush. A deuce of a lot of smoke came up and drove slowly forward. I swore at it. Now I couldn't see the ripple or the snag either. I stood in the doorway, peering, and the arrows came in swarms. They might have been poisoned, but they looked as though they wouldn't kill a cat. The bush began to howl. Our wood-cutters raised a warlike whoop; the report of a rifle just at my back deafened me. I glanced over my shoulder, and the pilot-house was yet full of noise and smoke when I made a dash at the wheel. The fool-nigger had dropped everything, to throw the shutter open and let off that Martini-Henry.[21] He stood before the wide opening, glaring, and I yelled at him to come back, while I straightened the sudden twist out of that steamboat. There was no room to turn even if I had wanted to, the snag was somewhere very near ahead in that confounded smoke, there was no time to lose, so I just crowded her into the bank—right into the bank, where I knew the water was deep.

'We tore slowly along the overhanging bushes in a whirl of broken twigs and flying leaves. The fusillade below stopped short, as I had foreseen it would when the squirts got empty. I threw my head back to a glinting whizz that traversed the pilot-house, in at one shutterhole and out at the other.

---

[19]Volley of rifle fire.

[20]An American-made lever-action rifle.

[21]A breech-action European military rifle.

Looking past that mad helmsman, who was shaking the empty rifle and yelling at the shore, I saw vague forms of men running bent double, leaping, gliding, indistinct, incomplete, evanescent. Something big appeared in the air before the shutter, the rifle went overboard, and the man stepped back swiftly, looked at me over his shoulder in an extraordinary, profound, familiar manner, and fell upon my feet. The side of his head hit the wheel twice, and the end of what appeared to be a long cane clattered round and knocked over a little camp-stool. It looked as though after wrenching that thing from somebody ashore he had lost his balance in the effort. The thin smoke had blown away, we were clear of the snag, and looking ahead I could see that in another hundred yards or so I would be free to sheer off, away from the bank; but my feet felt so very warm and wet that I had to look down. The man had rolled on his back and stared straight up at me; both his hands clutched that cane. It was the shaft of a spear that, either thrown or lunged through the opening, had caught him in the side just below the ribs; the blade had gone in out of sight, after making a frightful gash; my shoes were full; a pool of blood lay very still, gleaming dark-red under the wheel; his eyes shone with an amazing lustre. The fusillade burst out again. He looked at me anxiously, gripping the spear like something precious, with an air of being afraid I would try to take it away from him. I had to make an effort to free my eyes from his gaze and attend to the steering. With one hand I felt above my head for the line of the steam-whistle, and jerked out screech after screech hurriedly. The tumult of angry and warlike yells was checked instantly, and then from the depths of the woods went out such a tremulous and prolonged wail of mournful fear and utter despair as may be imagined to follow the flight of the last hope from the earth. There was a great commotion in the bush; the shower of arrows stopped, a few dropping shots rang out sharply—then silence, in which the languid beat of the stern-wheel came plainly to my ears. I put the helm hard a-starboard at the moment when the pilgrim in pink pyjamas, very hot and agitated, appeared in the doorway. "The manager sends me—" he began in an official tone, and stopped short. "Good God!" he said, glaring at the wounded man.

'We two whites stood over him, and his lustrous and inquiring glance enveloped us both. I declare it looked as though he would presently put to us some question in an understandable language; but he died without uttering a sound, without moving a limb, without twitching a muscle. Only in the very last moment, as though in response to some sign we could not see, to some whisper we could not hear, he frowned heavily, and that frown gave to his black death-mask an inconceivably sombre, brooding, and menacing expression. The lustre of the inquiring glance faded swiftly into vacant glassiness. "Can you steer?" I asked the agent eagerly. He looked very dubious; but I made a grab at his arm, and he understood at once I meant him to steer whether or no. To tell you the truth, I was morbidly anxious to change my shoes and socks. "He is dead," murmured the fellow, immensely impressed. "No doubt about it," said I, tugging like mad at the shoe-laces. "And by the way, I suppose Mr Kurtz is dead as well by this time."

'For the moment that was the dominate thought. There was a sense of extreme disappointment, as though I had found out I had been striving after something altogether without a substance. I couldn't have been more disgusted if I had travelled all this way for the sole purpose of talking with Mr Kurtz. Talking with . . . I flung one shoe overboard, and became aware that that was exactly what I had been looking forward to—a talk with Kurtz. I made the strange discovery that I had never imagined him as doing, you know, but as discoursing. I didn't say to myself, "Now I will never see him," or "Now I will never shake him by the hand," but, "Now I will never hear him." The man presented himself as a voice. Not of course that I did not connect him with some sort of action. Hadn't I been told in all the tones of jealousy and admiration that he had collected, bartered, swindled, or stolen more ivory than all the other agents together? That was not the point. The point was in his being a gifted creature, and that of all his gifts the one that stood out pre-eminently, that carried with it a sense of real presence, was his ability to talk, his words—the gift of expression, the bewildering, the illuminating, the most exalted and the most contemptible, the pulsating steam of light, or the deceitful flow from the heart of an impenetrable darkness.

'The other shoe went flying unto the devil-god of that river. I thought, By Jove! it's all over. We are too late; he has vanished—the gift has vanished, by means of some spear, arrow, or club. I will never hear that chap speak after all,—and my sorrow had a startling extravagance of emotion, even such as I had noticed in the howling sorrow of these savages in the bush. I couldn't have felt more of lonely desolation somehow, had I been robbed of a belief or had missed my destiny in life . . . Why do you sigh in this beastly way, somebody? Absurd? Well, absurd. Good Lord! mustn't a man ever—Here, give me some tobacco.' . . .

There was a pause of profound stillness, then a match flared, and Marlow's lean fact appeared, worn, hollow, with downward folds, and dropped eyelids, with an aspect of concentrated attention: and as he took vigorous draws at his pipe, it seemed to retreat and advance out of the night in the regular flicker of the tiny flame. The match went out.

'Absurd!' he cried. 'This is the worst of trying to tell . . . Here you all are, each moored with two good addresses, like a hulk with anchors, a butcher round one corner, a policeman round another, excellent appetites, and temperature normal—you hear—normal from year's end to year's end. And you say, Absurd! Absurd be—exploded! Absurd! My dear boys, what can you expect from a man who out of sheer nervousness had just flung overboard a pair of new shoes! Now I think of it, it is amazing I did not shed tears. I am, upon the whole, proud of my fortitude. I was cut to the quick at the idea of having lost the inestimable privilege of listening to the gifted Kurtz. Of course I was wrong. The privilege was waiting for me. Oh, yes, I heard more than enough. And I was right too. A voice. He was very little more than a voice. And I heard—him—it—this voice—other voices—all of them were so little more than voices—and the memory of that time itself lingers around me, impalpable, like a dying vibration of one immense jabber, silly, atrocious, sordid, savage, or simply mean, without any kind of sense. Voices, voices—even the girl herself—now—'

He was silent for a long time.

'I laid the ghost of his gifts at last with a lie,' he began, suddenly. 'Girl! What? Did I mention a girl? Oh, she is out of it—completely. They—the women I mean—are out of it—should be out of it. We must help them to stay in that beautiful world of their own, lest ours gets worse. Oh, she had to be out of it. You should have heard the disinterred body of Mr Kurtz saying. "My Intended." You would have perceived directly then how completely she was out of it. And the lofty frontal bone of Mr Kurtz! They say the hair goes on growing sometimes, but this—ah—specimen, was impressively bald. The wilderness had patted him on the head, and, behold, it was like a ball—an ivory ball; it had caressed him, and—lo!—he had withered; it had taken him, loved him, embraced him, got into his veins, consumed his flesh, and scaled his soul to its own by the inconceivable ceremonies of some devilish initiation. He was its spoiled and pampered favorite. Ivory? I should think so. Heaps of it, stacks of it. The old mud shanty was bursting with it. You would think there was not a single tusk left either above or below the ground in the whole country. "Mostly fossil," the manager had remarked, disparagingly. It was no more fossil than I am; but they call it fossil when it is dug up. It appears these niggers do bury the tusks sometimes—but evidently they couldn't bury this parcel deep enough to save the gifted Mr Kurtz from his fate. We filled the steamboat with it, and had to pile a lot on the deck. Thus he could see and enjoy as long as he could see, because the appreciation of this favour had remained with him to the last. You should have heard him say, "My ivory." Oh yes, I heard him. "My Intended, my ivory, my station, my river, my—" everything belonged to him. It made me hold my breath in expectation of hearing the wilderness burst into a prodigious peal of laughter that would shake the fixed stars in their places. Everything belonged to him—but that was a trifle. The thing was to know what he belonged to, how many powers of darkness claimed him for their own. That was the reflection that made you creepy all over. It was impossible—it was not good for one either—trying to imagine. He had taken a high seat amongst the devils of the land—I mean literally. You can't understand. How could you?—with solid pavement under your feet, surrounded by kind neighbours ready to cheer you or to fall on you, stepping delicately between the butcher and the policeman, in the holy terror of scandal and gallows and lunatic asylums—how can you imagine what particular region of the first ages a man's untrammelled feet may take him into by the way of solitude—utter solitude without a policeman—by the way of silence—utter silence, where no warning voice of a kind neighbour can be heard whispering of public opinion? These little things make all the great difference. When they are gone you must fall back upon your own innate strength, upon your own capacity for faithfulness. Of course you may be too much of a fool to go wrong—too dull even to know you are being assaulted by the powers of darkness. I take it, no fool ever made a bargain for his soul with the devil: the fool is too much of a fool, or the devil too much of a devil—I don't know which. Or you may be such a thunderingly exalted creature as to be altogether deaf and blind to anything but heavenly sights and sounds. Then the earth for you is only a standing place—and whether to be like this is your loss or your gain I won't pretend to say. But most of us are neither one nor the other. The earth for us is a place to live in, where we must put up with sights, with sounds, with smells, too, by Jove!—breathe dead hippo, so to speak, and not be contaminated. And there, don't you see? Your strength comes in, the faith in your ability for the digging of unostentatious holes to bury the stuff in—your power of devotion, not to yourself, but to an obscure, back-breaking business. And that's difficult enough. Mind, I am not trying to excuse or even explain—I am trying to account to myself for—for—Mr Kurtz—for the shade of Mr Kurtz. This initiated wraith from the back of Nowhere honoured me with its amazing confidence before it vanished altogether. This was because it could speak English to me. The original Kurtz had been educated partly in England, and—as he was good enough to say himself—his sympathies were in the right place. His mother was half-English, his father was half-French. All Europe contributed to the making of Kurtz; and by-and-by I learned that, most appropriately, the International Society for the Suppression of Savage Customs had entrusted him with the making of a report, for its future guidance. And he had written it, too. I've seen it. I've read it. It was eloquent, vibrating with eloquence, but too high-strung, I think. Seventeen pages of close writing he had found time for! But this must have been before his—let us say—nerves, went wrong, and caused him to preside at certain midnight dances ending with unspeakable rites, which—as far as I reluctantly gathered from what I heard at various times—were offered up to him—do you understand?—to Mr Kurtz himself. But it was a beautiful piece of writing. The opening paragraph, however, in the light of later information, strikes me now as ominous. He began with the argument that we whites, from the point of development we had arrived at, "must necessarily appear to them [savages] in the nature of supernatural beings—we approach them with the might as of a deity," and so on, and so on. "By the simple exercise of our will we can exert a power for good practically unbounded," etc., etc. From that point he soared and took me with him. The peroration was magnificent, though difficult to remember, you know. It gave me the notion of an exotic Immensity ruled by an august Benevolence. It made me tingle with enthusiasm. This was the unbounded power of eloquence—of words—of burning noble words. There were no practical hints to interrupt the magic current of phrases, unless a kind of note at the foot of the last page, scrawled evidently much later, in an unsteady hand, may be regarded as the exposition of a method. It was very simple, and at the end of that moving appeal to every altruistic sentiment it blazed at you, luminous and terrifying, like a flash of lightning in a serene sky: "Exterminate all the brutes!" The curious part was that he had apparently forgotten all about that valuable postscriptum, because, later on, when he in a sense came to himself, he repeatedly entreated me to take good care of "my pamphlet" (he called it), as it was sure to have in the future a good influence upon his career. I had full information about all these things, and, besides, as it turned out, I was to have the care of his memory. I've done enough for it to give me the indisputable right to lay it, if I choose, for an everlasting rest in the dust-bin of progress, amongst all the sweepings and, figuratively speaking, all the dead cats of civilization. But then, you see, I can't choose. He won't be forgotten. Whatever he was, he was not common. He had the power to charm or frighten rudimentary souls into an aggravated witch-dance in his honor; he could also fill the small souls of the pilgrims with bitter misgivings: he had one devoted friend at least, and he had conquered one soul in the world that was neither rudimentary nor tainted with self-seeking. No; I can't forget him, though I am not prepared to affirm the fellow was exactly worth the life we lost in getting to him. I missed my late helmsman awfully,—I missed him even while his body was still lying in the pilot-house. Perhaps you will think it passing strange, this regret for a savage who was of no more account than a grain of sand in a black Sahara. Well, don't you see, he had done something, he had steered; for months I had him at my back—a help— an instrument. It was a kind of partnership. He steered for me—I had to look after him, I worried about his deficiencies, and thus a subtle bond had been created, of which I only became aware when it was suddenly broken. And the intimate profundity of that look he gave me when he received his hurt remains to this day in my memory—like a claim of distant kinship affirmed in a supreme moment.

'Poor fool! If he had only left that shutter alone. He had no restraint, no restraint—just like Kurtz—a tree swayed by the wind. As soon as I had put on a dry pair of slippers, I dragged him out, after first jerking the spear out of his side, which operation I confess I performed with my eyes shut tight. His heels leaped together over the little doorstep; his shoulders were pressed to my breast; I hugged him from behind desperately. Oh! he was heavy, heavy; heavier than any man on earth, I should imagine. Then without more ado I tipped him overboard. The current snatched him as though he had been a wisp of grass, and I saw the body roll over twice before I lost sight of it for ever. All the pilgrims and the manager were then congregated on the awning-deck about the pilot-house, chattering at each other like a flock of excited magpies, and there was a scandalized murmur at my heartless promptitude. What they wanted to keep that body hanging about for I can't guess. Embalm it, maybe. But I had also heard another, and a very ominous, murmur on the deck below. My friends the wood-cutters were likewise scandalized, and with a better show of reason—though I admit that the reason itself was quite inadmissible. Oh, quite! I had made up my mind that if my late helmsman was to be eaten, the fishes alone should have him. He had been a very second-rate helmsman while alive, but now he was dead he might have become a first-class temptation, and possibly cause some startling trouble. Besides, I was anxious to take the wheel, the man in pink pyjamas showing himself a hopeless duffer at the business.

'This I did directly the simple funeral was over. We were going half-speed, keeping right in the middle of the stream, and I listened to the talk about me. They had given up Kurtz, they had given up the station; Kurtz was dead, and the station had been burnt—and so on—and so on. The red-haired pilgrim was beside himself with the thought that at least this poor Kurtz had been properly avenged. "Say! We must have made a glorious slaughter of them in the bush. Eh? What do you think? Say?" He positively danced, the bloodthirsty little gingery[22] beggar. And he had nearly fainted when he saw the wounded man! I could not help saying, "You made a glorious lot of smoke, anyhow." I had seen, from the way the tops of the bushes rustled and flew, that almost all the shots had gone too high. You can't hit anything unless you take aim and fire from the shoulder; but these chaps fired from the hip with their eyes shut. The retreat, I maintained—and I was right—was caused by the screeching of the steam-whistle. Upon this they forgot Kurtz, and began to howl at me with indignant protests.

'The manager stood by the wheel murmuring confidentially about the necessity of getting well away down the river before dark at all events, when I

---

[22]Red-headed.

saw in the distance a clearing on the river-side and the outlines of some sort of building. "What's this?" I asked. He clapped his hands in wonder. "The station!" he cried. I edged in at once; still going half-speed.

'Through my glasses I saw the slope of a hill interspersed with rare trees and perfectly free from undergrowth. A long decaying building on the summit was half buried in the high grass; the large holes in the peaked roof gaped black from afar; the jungle and the woods made a background. There was no enclosure or fence of any kind; but there had been one apparently, for near the house half-a-dozen slim posts remained in a row, roughly trimmed, and with their upper ends ornamented with round carved balls. The rails, or whatever there had been between, had disappeared. Of course the forest surrounded all that. The riverbank was clear, and on the water-side I saw a white man under a hat like a cart-wheel beckoning persistently with his whole arm. Examining the edge of the forest above and below, I was almost certain I could see movements—human forms gliding here and there. I steamed past prudently, then stopped the engines and let her drift down. The man on the shore began to shout, urging us to land. "We have been attacked," screamed the manager. "I know—I know. It's all right," yelled back the other, as cheerful as you please. "Come along. It's all right. I am glad."

'His aspect reminded me of something I had seen—something funny I had seen somewhere. As I manoeuvred to get alongside, I was asking myself, "What does this fellow look like?" Suddenly I got it. He looked like a harlequin. His clothes had been made of some stuff that was brown holland probably, but it was covered with patches all over, with bright patches, blue, red, and yellow,—patches on the back, patches on the front, patches on elbows, on knees; coloured binding around his jacket, scarlet edging at the bottom of his trousers; and the sunshine made him look extremely gay and wonderfully neat withal, because you could see how beautifully all this patching had been done. A beardless, boyish face, very fair, no feature to speak of, nose peeling, little blue eyes, smiles and frowns chasing each other over that open countenance like sunshine and shadow on a wind-swept plain. "Look out, captain!" he cried; "there's a snag lodged in here last night." What! Another snag? I confess I swore shamefully. I had nearly holed my cripple, to finish off that charming trip. The harlequin on the bank turned his little pug-nose up to me. "You English?" he asked, all smiles. "Are you?" I shouted from the wheel. The smiles vanished, and he shook his head as if sorry for my disappointment. Then he brightened up. "Never mind!" he cried, encouragingly. "Are we in time?" I asked. "He is up there," he replied, with a toss of the head up the hill, and becoming gloomy all of a sudden. His face was like the autumn sky, overcast one moment and bright the next.

'When the manager, escorted by the pilgrims, all of them armed to the teeth, had gone to the house this chap came on board. "I say, I don't like this.

These natives are in the bush," I said. He assured me earnestly it was all right. "They are simple people," he added; "well, I am glad you came. It took me all my time to keep them off." "But you said it was all right," I cried. "Oh, they meant no harm," he said; and as I stared he corrected himself, "Not exactly." Then vivaciously, "My faith, your pilot-house wants a clean-up!" In the next breath he advised me to keep enough steam on the boiler to blow the whistle in case of any trouble. "One good screech will do more for you than all your rifles. They are simple people," he repeated. He rattled away at such a rate he quite overwhelmed me. He seemed to be trying to make up for lots of silence, and actually hinted, laughing, that such was the case. "Don't you talk with Mr Kurtz?" I said. "You don't talk with that man—you listen to him," he exclaimed with severe exaltation. "But now—" He waved his arm, and in the twinkling of an eye was in the uttermost depths of despondency. In a moment he came up again with a jump, possessed himself of both hands, shook them continuously, while he gabbled: "Brother sailor . . . honour . . . pleasure . . . delight . . . introduce myself . . . Russian . . . son of an arch-priest . . . Government of Tambov . . . What? Tobacco! English tobacco; the excellent English tobacco! Now, that's brotherly. Smoke? Where's a sailor that does not smoke?"

'The pipe soothed him, and gradually I made out he had run away from school, had gone to sea in a Russian ship; ran away again; served some time in English ships; was now reconciled with the arch-priest. He made a point of that. "But when one is young one must see things, gather experience, ideas; enlarge the mind." "Here!" I interrupted. "You can never tell! Here I met Mr Kurtz," he said, youthfully solemn and reproachful. I held my tongue after that. It appears he had persuaded a Dutch trading-house on the coast to fit him out with stores and goods, and had started for the interior with a light heart, and no more idea of what would happen to him than a baby. He had been wandering about that river for nearly two years alone, cut off from everybody and everything. "I am not so young as I look. I am twenty-five," he said. "At first old Van Shuyten would tell me to go to the devil," he narrated with keen enjoyment; "but I stuck to him, and talked and talked, till at last he got afraid I would talk the hind-leg off his favorites dog, so he have me some cheap things and a few guns, and told me he hoped he would never see my face again. Good old Dutchman, Van Shuyten. I've sent him one small lot of ivory a year ago, so that he can't call me little thief when I get back. I hope he got it. And for the rest I don't care. I had some wood stacked for you. That was my old house. Did you see?"

'I gave him Towson's book. He made as though he would kiss me, but restrained himself. "The only book I had left, and I thought I had lost it," he said, looking at it ecstatically. "So many accidents happen to a man going about alone, you know. Canoes get upset sometimes—and sometimes you've got to clear out so quickly when the people get angry." He thumbed the pages. "You made notes in Russian?" I asked. He nodded. "I thought they were written in cipher," I said. He laughed, then became serious. "I had lots of trouble to keep these people off," he said. "Did they want to kill you?" I asked. "Oh no!" he cried, and checked himself. "Why did they attack us?" I pursued. He hesitated, then said shamefacedly, "They don't want him to go." "Don't they?" I said, curiously. He nodded a nod fully of mystery and wisdom. "I tell you," he cried, "this man has enlarged my mind." He opened his arms wide, starting at me with his little blue eyes that were perfectly round.'

3

'I looked at him, lost in astonishment. There he was before me, in motley, as though he had absconded from a troupe of mimes, enthusiastic, fabulous. His very existence was improbable, inexplicable, and altogether bewildering. He was an insoluble problem. It was inconceivable how he had existed, how he had succeeded in getting so far, how he had managed to remain—why he did not instantly disappear. "I went a little farther," he said, "then still a little farther— till I had gone so far that I don't know how I'll ever get back. Never mind. Plenty time. I can manage. You take Kurtz away quick—quick—I tell you." The glamour of youth enveloped his parti-coloured rags, his destitution, his loneliness, the essential desolation of his futile wanderings. For months—for years— his life hadn't been worth a day's purchase; and there he was gallantly, thoughtlessly alive, to all appearance indestructible solely by the virtue of his few years and of his unreflecting audacity. I was seduced into something like admiration—like envy. Glamour urged him on, glamour kept him unscathed. He surely wanted nothing from the wilderness but space to breathe in and to push on through. His need was to exist, and to move onwards at the greatest possible risk, and with a maximum of privation. If the absolutely pure, uncalculating, unpractical spirit of adventure had ever ruled a human being, it ruled this be-patched youth. I almost envied him the possession of this modest and clear flame. It seemed to have consumed all thought of self so completely, that even while he was talking to you, you forgot that it was he—the man before your eyes—who had gone through these things. I did not envy him his devotion to Kurtz, though. He had not meditated over it. It came to him, and he accepted it with a sort of eager fatalism. I must say that to me it appeared about the most dangerous thing in every way he had come upon so far.

'They had come together unavoidably, like two ships becalmed near each other, and lay rubbing sides at last. I suppose Kurtz wanted an audience, because on a certain occasion, when encamped in the forest, they had talked all night, or more probably Kurtz had talked. "We talked of everything," he said, quite transported at the recollection. "I forgot there was such a thing as sleep. The night did not seem to last an hour. Everything! Everything! . . . Of love, too." "Ah, he talked to you of love!" I said, much amused. "It isn't what you think," he cried, almost passionately. "It was in general. He made me see things—things."

'He threw his arms up. We were on deck at the time, and the headman of my wood-cutters, lounging near by, turned upon him his heavy and glittering eyes. I looked around, and I don't know why, but I assure you that never, never before, did this land, this river, this jungle, the very arch of this blazing sky, appear to me so hopeless and so dark, so impenetrable to human thought, so pitiless to human weakness. "And, ever since, you have been with him, of course?" I said.

'On the contrary. It appears their intercourse had been very much broken by various causes. He had, as he informed me proudly, managed to nurse Kurtz through two illnesses (he alluded to it as you would to some risky feat), but as a rule Kurtz wandered alone, far in the depths of the forest. "Very often coming to this station, I had to wait days and days before he would turn up," he said. "Ah, it was worth waiting for!—sometimes." "What was he doing? exploring or what?" I asked. "Oh, yes, of course"; he had discovered lots of villages, a lake, too—he did not know exactly in what direction; it was dangerous to inquire too much—but mostly his expeditions had been for ivory. "But he had no goods to trade with by that time," I objected. "There's a good lot of cartridges left even yet," he answered, looking away. "To speak plainly, he raided the country," I said. He nodded. "Not alone, surely!" He muttered something about the villages round that lake. "Kurtz got the tribe to follow him, did he?" I suggested. He fidgeted a little. "They adored him," he said. The tone of these words was so extraordinary that I looked at him searchingly. It was curious to see his mingled eagerness and reluctance to speak of Kurtz. The man filled his life, occupied his thoughts, swayed his emotions. "What can you expect?" he burst out; "he came to them with thunder and lightning, you know—and they had never seen anything like it—and very terrible. He could be very terrible. You can't judge Mr Kurtz as you would an ordinary man. No, no, no! Now—just to give you an idea—I don't mind telling you, he wanted to shoot me, too, one day— but I don't judge him." "Shoot you!" I cried. "What for?" "Well, I had a small lot of ivory the chief of that village near my house gave me. You see I used to shoot game for them. Well, he wanted it, and wouldn't hear reason. He declared he would shoot me unless I gave him the ivory and then cleared out of the country, because he could do so, and had a fancy for it, and there was nothing on earth to prevent him killing whom he jolly well pleased. And it was true, too. I gave him the ivory. What did I care! But I didn't clear out. No, no. I couldn't leave him. I had to be careful, of course, till we got friendly again for a time. He had his second illness then. Afterwards I had to keep out of the way; but I didn't mind. He was living for the most part in those villages on the lake. When he came down to the river, sometimes he would take to me, and sometimes it was better for me to be careful. This man suffered too much. He hated all this, and somehow he couldn't get away. When I had a chance I begged him to try and leave while there was time; I offered to go back with him. And he would say yes, and then he would remain; go off on another ivory hunt; disappear for weeks; forget himself amongst these people—forget himself—you know." "Why! he's mad," I said. He protested indignantly. Mr Kurtz couldn't be mad. If I had heard him talk, only two days ago, I wouldn't dare hint at such a thing . . . I had taken up my binoculars while we talked, and was looking at the shore, sweeping the limit of the forest at each side and at the back of the house. The consciousness of there being people in that bush, so silent, so quiet—as silent and quiet as the ruined house on the hill—made me uneasy. There was no sign on the face of nature of this amazing tale that was not so much told as suggested to me in desolate exclamations, completed by shrugs, in interrupted phrases, in hints ending in deep sighs. The woods were unmoved, like a mask—heavy, like the closed door of a prison—they looked with their air of hidden knowledge, of patient expectation, of unapproachable silence. The Russian was explaining to me that it was only lately that Mr Kurtz had come down to the river, bringing along with him all the fighting men of that lake tribe. He had been absent for several months—getting himself adored, I suppose—and had come down unexpectedly, with the intention to all appearance of making a raid either across the river or down stream. Evidently the appetite for more ivory had got the better of the—what shall I say?—less material aspirations. However he had got much worse suddenly. "I heard he was lying helpless, and so I came up— took my chance," said the Russian. "Oh, he is bad, very bad." I directed my glass to the house. There were no signs of life, but there was the ruined roof, the long mud wall peeping above the grass, with three little square window-holes, no two the same size: all this brought within reach of my hand, as it were. And then I made a brusque movement, and one the remaining posts of that vanished fence leaped up in the field of my glass. You remember I told you I had been struck at the distance by certain attempts at ornamentation, rather remarkable in the ruinous aspect of the place. Now I had suddenly a nearer view, and its first result was to make me throw my head back as if before a blow. Then I went carefully from post to post with my glass, and I saw my mistake. These round knobs were not ornamental but symbolic; they were expressive and puzzling, striking and disturbing—food for thought and also for the vultures if there had been any looking down from the sky; but at all events for such ants as were industrious enough to ascend the pole. They would have been even more impressive, those heads on the stakes, if their faces had not been turned to the house. Only one, the first I had made out, was facing my way. I was not so shocked as you may think. The start back I had given was really nothing but a movement of surprise. I had expected to see a knob of wood there, you know. I returned deliberately to the first I had seen—and there it was, black, dried, sunken, with closed eyelids—a head that seemed to sleep at the top of that pole, and, with the shrunken dry lips showing a narrow white line of teeth, was smiling, too, smiling continuously at some endless and jocose dream of that eternal slumber.

'I am not disclosing any trade secrets. In fact, the manager said afterwards that Mr Kurtz's methods had ruined the district. I have no opinion on that point, but I want you clearly to understand that there was nothing exactly profitable in these heads being there. They only showed that Mr Kurtz lacked restraint in the gratification of his various lusts, that there was something wanting in him—some small matter which, when the pressing need arose, could not be found under his magnificent eloquence. Whether he knew of this deficiency himself I can't say. I think the knowledge came to him at last—only at the very last. But the wilderness had found him out early, and had taken on him a terrible vengeance for the fantastic invasion. I think it had whispered to him things about himself which he did not know, things of which he had no conception till he took counsel with this great solitude—and the whisper had proved irresistibly fascinating. It echoed loudly within him because he was hollow at the core . . . I put down the glass, and the head that had appeared near enough to be spoken to seemed at once to have leaped away from me into inaccessible distance.

'The admirer of Mr Kurtz was a bit crestfallen. In a hurried, indistinct voice he began to assure me he had not dared to take these—say, symbols—down. He was not afraid of the natives; they would not stir till Mr Kurtz gave the word. His ascendancy was extraordinary. The camps of these people surrounded the place, and the chiefs came every day to see him. They would crawl . . . "I don't want to know anything of the ceremonies used when approaching Mr Kurtz," I shouted. Curious, this feeling that came over me that such details would be more intolerable than those heads drying on the stakes under Mr Kurtz's windows. After all, that was only a savage sight, while I seemed at one bound to have been transported into some lightless region of subtle horrors, where pure, uncomplicated savagery was a positive relief, being something that had a right to exist—obviously—in the sunshine. The young man looked at me with surprise. I suppose it did not occur to him that Mr Kurtz was no idol of mine. He forgot I hadn't heard any of these splendid monologues on, what was it? on love, justice, conduct of life—or what not. If it had come to crawling before Mr Kurtz, he crawled as much as the veriest savage of them all. I had no idea of the conditions, he said: these heads were the heads of rebels. I shocked him excessively by laughing. Rebels! What would be the next definition I was to hear? There had been enemies, criminals, workers—and these were rebels. Those rebellious heads looked very subdued to me on their sticks. "You don't know how such a life tries a man like Kurtz," cried Kurtz's last disciple. "Well, and you?" I said. "I! I! I am a simple man. I have no great thoughts. I want nothing from anybody. How can you compare me to? . . ." His feelings were too much for speech, and suddenly he broke down. "I don't understand," he groaned. "I've been doing my best to keep him alive, and that's enough. I had no hand in all this. I have no abilities. There hasn't been a drop of medicine or a mouthful of invalid food for months here. He was shamefully abandoned. A man like this, with such ideas. Shamefully! Shamefully! I—I—haven't slept for the last ten nights . . ."

'His voice lost itself in the calm of the evening. The long shadows of the forest had slipped down hill while we talked, had gone far beyond the ruined hovel, beyond the symbolic row of stakes. All this was in the gloom, while we down there were yet in the sunshine, and the stretch of the river abreast of the clearing glittered in a still and dazzling splendour, with a murky and over-shadowed bend above and below. Not a living soul was seen on the shore. The bushes did not rustle.

'Suddenly round the corner of the house a group of men appeared, as though they had come up from the ground. They waded waist-deep in the grass, in a compact body, bearing an improvised stretcher in their midst. Instantly, in the emptiness of the landscape, a cry arose whose shrillness pierced the still air like a sharp arrow flying straight to the very heart of the land; and, if by enchantment, streams of human beings—of naked human beings—with spears in their hands, with bows, with shields, with wild glances and savage movements, were poured into the clearing by the darkfaced and pensive forest. The bushes shook, the grass swayed for a time, and then everything stood still in attentive immobility.

' "Now, if he does not say the right thing to them we are all done for," said the Russian at my elbow. The knot of men with the stretcher had stopped, too, halfway to the steamer, as if petrified. I saw the man on the stretcher sit up, lank and with an uplifted arm, above the shoulders of the bearers. "Let us hope that the man who can talk so well of love in general will find some particular reason to spare us this time," I said. I resented bitterly the absurd danger of our situation, as if to be at the mercy of that atrocious phantom had been a dishonouring necessity. I could not hear a sound, but through my glasses I saw the thin arm extended commandingly, the lower jaw moving, the eyes of that apparition shining darkly far in its bony head that nodded with grotesque jerks. Kurtz—Kurtz—that means short in German—don't it? Well, the name was as true as everything else in his life—and death. He looked at least seven feet long. His covering had fallen off, and his body emerged from it pitiful and appalling as from a winding-sheet. I could see the cage of his ribs all astir, the bones of his arm waving. It was as though an animated image of death carved out of old ivory had been shaking its hand with menaces at a motionless crowd of men made of dark and glittering bronze. I saw him open his mouth wide—it gave him a weirdly voracious aspect, as though he had wanted to swallow all the air, all the earth, all the men before him. A deep voice reached me faintly. He must have been shouting. He fell back suddenly. The stretcher shook as the bearers staggered forward again, and almost at the same time I noticed that the crowd of savages was vanishing without any perceptible movement of retreat, as if the forest that had ejected these beings so suddenly had drawn them in again as the breath is drawn in a long aspiration.

'Some of the pilgrims behind the stretcher carried his arms—two shotguns, a heavy rifle, and a light revolver-carbine—the thunderbolts of that pitiful Jupiter. The manager bent over him murmuring as he walked beside his head. They laid him down in one of the little cabins—just a room for a bedplace and a campstool or two, you know. We had brought his belated correspondence, and a lot of torn envelopes and open letters littered his bed. His hand roamed feebly amongst these papers. I was struck by the fire of his eyes and the composed languor of his expression. It was not so much the exhaustion of disease. He did not seem in pain. This shadow looked satiated and calm, as though for the moment it had had its fill of all the emotions.

'He rustled one of the letters, and looking straight in my face said, "I am glad." Somebody had been writing to him about me. These special recommendations were turning up again. The volume of tone he emitted without effort, almost without the trouble of moving his lips, amazed me. A voice! a voice! It was grave, profound, vibrating, while the man did not seem capable of a whisper. However, he had enough strength in him—factitious no doubt—to very nearly make an end of us, as you shall hear directly.

'The manager appeared silently in the doorway; I stepped out at once and he drew the curtain after me. The Russian, eyed curiously by the pilgrims, was staring at the shore. I followed the direction of his glance.

'Dark human shapes could be made out in the distance, flitting indistinctly against the gloomy border of the forest, and near the river two bronze figures, leaning on tall spears, stood in the sunlight under fantastic headdresses of spotted skins, warlike and still in statuesque repose. And from right to left along the lighted shore moved a wild and gorgeous apparition of a woman.

'She walked with measured steps, draped in striped and fringed cloths, treading the earth proudly, with a slight jingle and flash of barbarous ornaments. She carried her head high; her hair was done in the shape of a helmet; she had brass leggings to the knees, brass wire gauntlets to the elbow, a crimson spot on her tawny cheek, innumerable necklaces of glass beads on her neck; bizarre things, charms, gifts of watch-men, that hung about her, glittered and trembled at every step. She must have had the value of several elephant tusks upon her. She was savage and superb, wild-eyed and magnificent; there was something ominous and stately in her deliberate progress. And in the hush that had fallen suddenly upon the whole sorrowful land, the immense wilderness, the colossal body of the fecund and mysterious life seemed to look at her, pensive, as though it had been looking at the image of its own tenebrous and passionate soul.

'She came abreast of the steamer, stood still, and faced us. Her long shadow fell to the water's edge. Her face had a tragic and fierce aspect of wild sorrow and of dumb pain mingled with the fear of some struggling, half-shaped resolve. She stood looking at us without a stir, and like the wilderness itself, with an air of brooding over an inscrutable purpose. A whole minute passed, and then she made a step forward. There was a low jingle, a glint of yellow metal, a sway of fringed draperies, and she stopped as if her heart had failed her. The young fellow by my side growled. The pilgrims murmured at my back. She looked at us all as if her life had depended upon the unswerving steadiness of her glance. Suddenly she opened her bared arms and threw them up rigid above her head, as though in an uncontrollable desire to touch the sky, and at the same time the swift shadows darted out on the earth, swept around on the river, gathering the steamer into a shadowy embrace. A formidable silence hung over the scene.

'She turned away slowly, walked on, following the bank, and passed into the bushes to the left. Once only her eyes gleamed back at us in the dusk of the thickets before she disappeared.

' "If she had offered to come aboard I really think I would have tried to shoot her," said the men of patches, nervously. "I had been risking my life every day for the last fortnight to keep her out of the house. She got in one day and kicked up a row about those miserable rags I picked up in the storeroom to mend my clothes with. I wasn't decent. At least it must have been that, for she talked like a fury to Kurtz for an hour, pointing at me now and then. I don't understand the dialect of this tribe. Luckily for me, I fancy Kurtz felt too ill that day to care, or there would have been mischief. I don't understand . . . No—it's too much for me. Ah, well, it's all over now."

'At this moment I heard Kurtz's deep voice behind the curtain: "Save me!—save the ivory, you mean. Don't tell me. Save *me*! Why, I've had to save you. You are interrupting my plans now. Sick! Sick! Not so sick as you would like to believe. Never mind. I'll carry my ideas out yet—I will return. I'll show you what can be done. You with your little peddling notions—you are interfering with me. I will return. I . . ."

'The manager came out. He did me the honour to take me under the arm and lead me aside. "He is very low, very low," he said. He considered it necessary to sigh, but neglected to be consistently sorrowful. "We have done all we could for him—haven't we? But there is no disguising the fact, Mr Kurtz has done more harm than good to the Company. He did not see the time was not ripe for vigorous action. Cautiously, cautiously—that's my principle. We must be cautious yet. The district is closed to us for a time. Deplorable! Upon the whole, the trade will suffer. I don't deny there is a remarkable quantity of ivory—mostly fossil. We must save it, at all events—but look how precarious the position is—and why? Because the method is unsound." "Do you," said I, looking at the shore, "call it 'unsound method'?" "Without doubt," he exclaimed, hotly. "Don't you?" . . .' "No method at all," I murmured after a while. "Exactly," he exulted. "I anticipated this. Shows a complete want of judgement. It is my duty to point it out in the proper quarter." "Oh," said I, "that fellow—what's his name?—the brickmaker, will make a readable report for you." He appeared confounded for a moment. It seemed to me I had never breathed an atmosphere so vile, and I turned mentally to Kurtz for relief— positively for relief. "Nevertheless I think Mr Kurtz is a remarkable man," I said with emphasis. He started, dropped on me a cold heavy glance, said very quietly, "He *was*," and turned his back on me. My hour of favour was over; I found myself lumped along with Kurtz as a partisan of methods for which the time was not ripe: I was unsound! Ah! but it was something to have at least a choice of nightmares.

'I had turned to the wilderness really, not to Mr Kurtz, who, I was ready to admit, was as good as buried. And for a moment it seemed to me as if I also were buried in a vast grave full of unspeakable secrets. I felt an intolerable weight oppressing my breast, the smell of the damp earth, the unseen presence of victorious corruption, the darkness of an impenetrable night . . . The Russian tapped me on the shoulder. I heard him mumbling and stammering something about "brother seaman—couldn't conceal—knowledge of matters that would affect Mr Kurtz's reputation." I waited. For him evidently Mr Kurtz was not in his grave; I suspect that for him Mr Kurtz was one of the immortals. "Well!" said I at last, "speak out. As it happens, I am Mr Kurtz's friend— in a way."

'He stated with a good deal of formality that had we not been "of the same profession," he would have kept the matter to himself without regard to consequences. "He suspected there was an active ill will towards him on the part of these white men that—" "You are right," I said, remembering a certain conversation I had overheard. "The manager thinks you ought to be hanged." He showed a concern at this intelligence which amused me at first. "I had better get out of the way quietly," he said, earnestly. "I can do no more for Kurtz now, and they would soon find some excuse. What's to stop them? There's a military post three hundred miles from here." "Well, upon my word," said I, "perhaps you had better go if you have any friends amongst the savages near by." "Plenty," he said. "They are simple people—and I want nothing, you know." He stood biting his lip, then: "I don't want any harm to happen to these whites here, but of course I was thinking of Mr Kurtz's reputation—but you are a brother seaman and—" "All right," said I, after a time. "Mr Kurtz's reputation is safe with me." I did not know how truly I spoke.

'He informed me, lowering his voice, that it was Kurtz who had ordered the attack to be made on the steamer. "He hated sometimes the idea of being taken away—and then again . . . But I don't understand these matters. I am a simple man. He thought it would scare you away—that you would give it up, thinking him dead. I could not stop him. Oh, I had an awful time of it this last month." "Very well," I said. "He is all right now." "Ye-e-es," he muttered, not very convinced apparently. "Thanks," said I; "I shall keep my eyes open." "But quiet—eh?" he urged, anxiously. "It would be awful for his reputation if anybody here—" I promised a complete discretion with great gravity. "I have a canoe and three black fellows waiting not very far. I am off. Could you give me a few Martini-Henry cartridges?" I could, and did, with proper secrecy. He helped himself, with a wink at me, to a handful of my tobacco. "Between sailors—you know—good English tobacco." At the door of the pilot-house he turned round—"I say, haven't you a pair of shoes you could spare?" He raised one leg. "Look." The soles were tied with knotted strings sandal-wise under his bare feet. I rooted out an old pair, at which he looked with admiration before tucking it under his left arm. One of his pockets (bright red) was bulging with cartridges, from the other (dark blue) peeped "Towson's Inquiry," etc., etc. He seemed to think himself excellently well equipped for a renewed encounter with the wilderness. 'Ah! I'll never, never meet such a man again. You ought to have heard him recite poetry—his own, too, it was, he told me. Poetry!" He rolled his eyes at the recollection of these delights. "Oh, he enlarged my mind!" "Good-bye," said I. He shook hands and vanished in the night. Sometimes I ask myself whether I had ever really seen him—whether it was possible to meet such a phenomenon! . . .

'When I woke up shortly after midnight his warning came to my mind with its hint of danger that seemed, in the starred darkness, real enough to make me get up for the purpose of having a look round. On the hill a big fire burned, illuminating fitfully a crooked corner of the station-house. One of the agents with a picket of a few of our blacks, armed for the purpose, was keeping guard over the ivory; but deep within the forest, red gleams that wavered, that seemed to sink and rise from the ground amongst confused columnar shapes of intense blackness, showed the exact position of the camp where Mr Kurtz's adorers were keeping their uneasy vigil. The monotonous beating of a big drum filled the air with muffled shocks and a lingering vibration. A steady droning sound of many men chanting each to himself some weird incantation came out from the black, flat wall of the woods as the humming of bees comes out of a hive, and had a strange narcotic effect upon my half-awake senses. I believe I dozed off leaning over the rail, till an abrupt burst of yells, an overwhelming outbreak of a pent-up and mysterious frenzy, woke me up in a bewildered wonder. It was cut short all at once, and the low droning went on with an effect of audible and soothing silence. I glanced casually into the little cabin. A light was burning within, but Mr Kurtz was not there.

'I think I would have raised an outcry if I had believed my eyes. But I didn't believe them at first—the thing seemed so impossible. The fact is I was completely unnerved by a sheer blank fright, pure abstract terror, unconnected with any distinct shape of physical danger. What made this emotion so overpowering was—how shall I define it?—the moral shock I received, as if something altogether monstrous, intolerable to thought and odious to the soul, had been thrust upon me unexpectedly. This lasted of course the merest fraction of a second, and then the usual sense of commonplace, deadly danger, the possibility of a sudden onslaught and massacre, or something of the kind, which I saw impending, was positively welcome and composing. It pacified me, in fact, so much, that I did not raise an alarm.

'There was an agent buttoned up inside an ulster and sleeping on a chair on deck within three feet of me. The yells had not awakened him; he snored very slightly; I left him to his slumbers and leaped ashore. I did not betray Mr Kurtz—it was ordered I should never betray him—it was written I should be loyal to the nightmare of my choice. I was anxious to deal with this shadow by myself alone,—and to this day I don't know why I was so jealous of sharing with anyone the peculiar blackness of that experience.

'As soon as I got on the bank I saw a trail—a broad trail through the grass. I remember the exultation with which I said to myself, "He can't walk—he is crawling on all-fours—I've got him." The grass was wet with dew. I strode rapidly with clenched fists. I fancy I had some vague notion of falling upon him and giving him a drubbing. I don't know. I had some imbecile thoughts. The knitting old woman with the cat obtruded herself upon my memory as a most improper person to be sitting at the other end of such an affair. I saw a row of pilgrims squirting lead in the air out of Winchesters held to the hip. I thought I would never get back to the steamer, and imagined myself living alone and unarmed in the woods to an advanced age. Such silly things—you know. And I remember I confounded the beat of the drum with the beating of my heart, and was pleased at its calm regularity.

'I kept to the track though—then stopped to listen. The night was very clear; a dark blue space, sparkling with dew and starlight, in which black things stood very still. I thought I could see a kind of motion ahead of me. I was strangely cocksure of everything that night. I actually left the track and ran in a wide semicircle (I verily believe chuckling to myself) so as to get in front of that stir, of that motion I had seen—if indeed I had seen anything. I was circumventing Kurtz as though it had been a boyish game.

'I came upon him, and, if he had not heard me coming, I would have fallen over him, too, but he got up in time. He rose, unsteady, long, pale indistinct, like a vapour exhaled by the earth, and swayed slightly, misty and silent before me; while at my back the fires loomed between the trees, and the murmur of many voices issued from the forest. I had cut him off cleverly; but when actually confronting him I seemed to come to my senses, I saw the danger in its right proportion. It was by no means over yet. Suppose he began to shout? Though he could hardly stand, there was still plenty of vigour in his voice. "Go away—hide yourself," he said, in that profound tone. It was very awful. I glanced back. We were within thirty yards from the nearest fire. A black figure stood up, strode on long black legs, waving long black arms, across the glow. It had horns—antelope horns, I think—on its head. Some sorcerer, some witch-man, no doubt: it looked fiend-like enough. "Do you know what you are doing?" I whispered. "Perfectly," he answered, raising his voice for that single word: it sounded to me far off and yet loud, like a hail through a speaking-trumpet. If he makes a row we are lost, I thought to myself. This clearly was not a case for fisticuffs, even apart from the very natural aversion I had to beat that Shadow—this wandering and tormented thing. "You will be lost," I said—"utterly lost." One gets sometimes such a flash of inspiration, you know. I did say the right thing, though indeed he could not have been more irretrievably lost than he was at this very moment, when the foundations of our intimacy were being laid—to endure—to endure—even to the end—even beyond.

' "I had immense plans," he muttered irresolutely. "Yes," said I; "but if you try to shout I'll smash your head with—" There was not a stick or a stone near. "I will throttle you for good," I corrected myself. "I was on the threshold of great things," he pleaded, in a voice of longing, with a wistfulness of tone that made my blood run cold. "And now for this stupid scoundrel—" "Your success in Europe is assured in any case," I affirmed, steadily. I did not want to have the throttling of him, you understand—and indeed it would have been very little use for any practical purpose. I tried to break the spell—the heavy, mute spell of the wilderness—that seemed to draw him to its pitiless breast by the awakening of forgotten and brutal instincts, by the memory of gratified and monstrous passions. This alone, I was convinced, had driven him out to the edge of the forest, to the bush, towards the gleam of fires, the throb of drums, the drone of weird incantations; this alone had beguiled his unlawful soul beyond the bounds of permitted aspirations. And, don't you see, the terror of the position was not in being knocked on the head—though I had a very lively sense of that danger, too—but in this, that I had to deal with a being to whom I could not appeal in the name of anything high or low. I had, even like the niggers, to invoke him—himself—his own exalted and incredible degradation. There was nothing either above or below him, and I knew it. He had kicked himself loose of the earth. Confound the man! he had kicked the very earth to pieces. He was alone, and I before him did not know whether I stood on the ground or floated in the air. I've been telling you what we said—repeating the phrases we pronounced—but what's the good? They were common everyday words—the familiar, vague sounds exchanged on every waking day of life. But what of that? They had behind them, to my mind, the terrific suggestiveness of words heard in dreams, of phrases spoken in nightmares. Soul! If anybody had ever struggled with a soul, I am the man. And I wasn't arguing with a lunatic either. Believe me or not, his intelligence was perfectly clear—concentrated, it is true, upon himself with horrible intensity, yet clear; and therein was my only chance—barring, of course, the killing him there and then, which wasn't so good, on account of unavoidable noise. But his soul was mad. Being alone in the wilderness, it had looked within itself, and, by heavens! I tell you, it had gone mad. I had—for my sins, I suppose—to go through the ordeal of looking into it myself. No eloquence could have been so withering to one's belief in mankind as his final burst of sincerity. He struggled with himself, too. I saw it,—I heard it. I saw the inconceivable mystery of a soul that knew no restraint, no faith, and no fear, yet struggling blindly with itself. I kept my head pretty well; but when I had him at last stretched on the couch, I wiped my forehead, while my legs shook under me as though I had carried half a ton on my back down that hill. And yet I had only supported him, his bony arm clasped round my neck—and he was not much heavier than a child.

'When next day we left at noon, the crowd, of whose presence behind the curtain of trees I had been acutely conscious all the time, flowed out of the woods again, filled the clearing, covered the slope with a mass of naked, breathing, quivering, bronze bodies. I steamed up a bit, then swung downstream, and two thousand eyes followed the evolutions of the splashing, thumping, fierce river-demon beating the water with its terrible tail and breathing black smoke into the air. In front of the first rank, along the river, three men, plastered with bright red earth from head to foot, strutted to and fro restlessly. When we came abreast again, they faced the river, stamped their feet, nodded their horned heads, swayed their scarlet bodies; they shook towards the fierce river-demon a bunch of black feathers, a mangy skin with a pendent tail—something that looked like a dried gourd; they shouted periodically together strings of amazing words that resembled no sounds of human language; and the deep murmurs of the crowd, interrupted suddenly, were like the responses of some satanic litany.

'We had carried Kurtz into the pilot-house: there was more air there. Lying on the couch, he stared through the open shutter. There was an eddy in the mass of human bodies, and the woman with helmeted head and tawny cheeks rushed out to the very brink of the stream. She put out her hands, shouted something, and all that wild mob took up the shout in a roaring chorus of articulated, rapid, breathless utterance.

' "Do you understand this?" I asked.

'He kept on looking out past me with fiery, longing eyes, with a mingled expression of wistfulness and hate. He made no answer, but I saw a smile, a smile of indefinable meaning, appear on his colourless lips that a moment after twitched convulsively. "Do I not?" he said slowly, gasping, as if the words had been torn out of him by a supernatural power.

'I pulled the string of the whistle, and I did this because I saw the pilgrims on deck getting out their rifles with an air of anticipating a jolly lark. At the sudden screech there was a movement of abject terror through that wedged mass of bodies. "Don't! don't you frighten them away," cried someone on deck disconsolately. I pulled the string time after time. They broke and ran, they leaped, they crouched, they swerved, they dodged the flying terror of the sound. The three red chaps had fallen flat, face down on the shore, as though they had been shot dead. Only the barbarous and superb woman did not so much as flinch and stretched tragically her bare arms after us over the sombre and glittering river.

'And then that imbecile crowd down on the deck started their little fun, and I could see nothing more for smoke.

'The brown current ran swiftly out of the heart of darkness, bearing us down towards the sea with twice the speed of our upward progress; and Kurtz's life was running swiftly, too, ebbing, ebbing out of his heart into the sea of inexorable time. The manager was very placid, he had no vital anxieties now, he took us both in with a comprehensive and satisfied glance: the "affair" had come off as well as could be wished. I saw the time approaching when I would be left alone of the party of "unsound method." The pilgrims looked upon me with disfavour. I was, so to speak, numbered with the dead. It is strange how I accepted this unforeseen partnership, this choice of nightmares forced upon me in the tenebrous land invaded by these mean and greedy phantoms.

'Kurtz discoursed. A voice! a voice! It rang deep to the very last. It survived his strength to hide in the magnificent folds of eloquence the barren darkness of his heart. Oh, he struggled! he struggled! The wastes of his weary brain were haunted by shadowy images now—images of wealth and fame revolving obsequiously round his unextinguishable gift of noble and lofty expression. My Intended, my station, my career, my ideas—these were the subjects for the occasional utterances of elevated sentiments. The shade of the original Kurtz frequented the bedside of the hollow sham, whose fate it was to be buried presently in the mould of primeval earth. But both the diabolic love and the unearthly hate of the mysteries it had penetrated fought for the possession of that soul satiated with primitive emotions, avid of lying fame, of sham distinction, of all the appearances of success and power.

'Sometimes he was contemptibly childish. He desired to have kings meet him at railway-stations on his return from some ghastly Nowhere, where he intended to accomplish great things. "You show them you have in you something that is really profitable, and then there will be no limits to the recognition of your ability," he would say. "Of course you must take care of the motives—right motives—always." The long reaches that were like one and the same reach, monotonous bends that were exactly alike, slipped past the steamer with their multitude of secular[23] trees looking patiently after this grimy fragment of another world, the forerunner of change, of conquest, of trade, of massacres, of blessings. I looked ahead—piloting. "Close the shutter," said Kurtz suddenly one day; "I can't bear to look at this." I did so. There was a silence. "Oh, but I will wring your heart yet!" he cried at the invisible wilderness.

'We broke down—as I had expected—and had to lie up for repairs at the head of an island. This delay was the first thing that shook Kurtz's confidence. One morning he gave me a packet of papers and a photograph—the lot tied together with a shoe-string. "Keep this for me," he said. "This noxious fool" (meaning the manager) "is capable of prying into my boxes when I am not looking." In the afternoon I saw him. He was lying on his back with closed eyes, and I withdrew quietly, but I heard him mutter, "Live rightly, die, die . . ." I listened. There was nothing more. Was he rehearsing some speech in his sleep, or was it a fragment of a phrase from some newspaper article? He had been writing for the papers and meant to do so again, "for the furthering of my ideas. It's a duty."

'His was an impenetrable darkness. I looked at him as you peer down at a man who is lying at the bottom of a precipice where the sun never shines. But I had not much time to give him, because I was helping the engine-driver to take to pieces the leaky cylinders, to straighten a bent connecting-rod, and in other such matters. I lived in an infernal mess of rust, filings, nuts, bolts, spanners, hammers, ratchet-drills—things I abominate, because I don't get on

---

[23]Aged, centuries old.

with them. I tended the little forge we fortunately had aboard; I toiled wearily in a wretched scrap-heap—unless I had the shakes too bad to stand.

'One evening coming in with a candle I was startled to hear him say a little tremulously, "I am lying here in the dark waiting for death." The light was within a foot of his eyes. I forced myself to murmur, "Oh, nonsense!" and stood over him as if transfixed.

'Anything approaching the change that came over his features I have never seen before, and hope never to see again. Oh, I wasn't touched. I was fascinated. It was as though a veil had been rent. I saw on that ivory face the expression of sombre pride, of ruthless power, of craven terror—of an intense and hopeless despair. Did he live life again in every detail of desire, temptation, and surrender during that supreme moment of complete knowledge? He cried in a whisper at some image, at some vision—he cried out twice, a cry that was no more than a breath—

' "The horror! The horror!"

'I blew the candle out and left the cabin. The pilgrims were dining in the mess-room, and I took my place opposite the manager, who lifted his eyes to give me a questioning glance, which I successfully ignored. He leaned back, serene, with that peculiar smile of his sealing the unexpressed depths of his meanness. A continuous shower of small flies streamed upon the lamp, upon the cloth, upon our hands and faces. Suddenly the manager's boy put his insolent black head in the doorway, and said in a tone of scathing contempt—

' "Mistah Kurtz—he dead."

'All the pilgrims rushed out to see. I remained, and went on with my dinner. I believe I was considered brutally callous. However, I did not eat much. There was a lamp in there—light, don't you know—and outside it was so beastly, beastly dark. I went no more near the remarkable man who had pronounced a judgement upon the adventures of his soul on this earth. The voice was gone. What else had been there? But I am of course aware that next day the pilgrims buried something in a muddy hole.

'And then they very nearly buried me.

'However, as you see, I did not go to join Kurtz there and then. I did not. I remained to dream the nightmare out to the end, and to show my loyalty to Kurtz once more. Destiny. My Destiny! Droll thing life is—that mysterious arrangement of merciless logic for a futile purpose. The most you can hope from it is some knowledge of yourself—that comes too late—a crop of unextinguishable regrets. I have wrestled with death. It is the most unexciting contest you can imagine. It takes place in an impalpable greyness, with nothing underfoot, with nothing around, without spectators, without clamour, without glory, without the great desire of victory, without the great fear of defeat, in a sickly atmosphere of tepid scepticism, without much belief in your own right, and still less in that of your adversary. If such is the form of ultimate wisdom, then life is a greater riddle than some of us think it to be. I was within a hair's-breadth of the last opportunity for pronouncement, and I found with humiliation that probably I would have nothing to say. This is the reason why I affirm that Kurtz was a remarkable man. He had something to say. He said it. Since I had peeped over the edge myself, I understand better the meaning of his stare, that could not see the flame of the candle, but was wide enough to embrace the whole universe, piercing enough to penetrate all the hearts that beat in the darkness. He had summed up—he had judged. "The horror!" He was a remarkable man. After all, this was the expression of some sort of belief; it had candour, it had conviction, it had a vibrating note of revolt in its whisper, it had the appalling face of a glimpsed truth—the strange commingling of desire and hate. And it is not my own extremity I remember best—a vision of greyness without form filled with physical pain, and a careless contempt for the evanescence of all things—even of this pain itself. No! It is his extremity that I seem to have lived through. True, he had made that last stride, he had stepped over the edge, while I had been permitted to draw back my hesitating foot. And perhaps in this is the whole difference; perhaps all the wisdom, and all truth, and all sincerity, are just compressed into that inappreciable moment of time in which we step over the threshold of the invisible. Perhaps! I like to think my summing-up would not have been a word of careless contempt. Better his cry—much better. It was an affirmation, a moral victory, paid for by innumerable defeats, by abominable terrors, by abominable satisfactions. But it was a victory! That is why I have remained loyal to Kurtz to the last, and even beyond, when a long time after I heard once more, not his own voice, but the echo of his magnificent eloquence thrown to me from a soul as translucently pure as a cliff of crystal.

'No, they did not bury me, though there is a period of time which I remember mistily, with a shuddering wonder, like a passage through some inconceivable world that had no hope in it and no desire. I found myself back in the sepulchral city resenting the sight of people hurrying through the streets to filch a little money from each other, to devour their infamous cookery, to gulp their unwholesome beer, to dream their insignificant and silly dreams. They trespassed upon my thoughts. They were intruders whose knowledge of life was to me an irritating pretence, because I felt so sure they could not possibly know the things I knew. Their bearing, which was simply the bearing of commonplace individuals going about their business in the assurance of perfect safety, was offensive to me like the outrageous flauntings of folly in the face of a danger it is unable to comprehend. I had no particular desire to enlighten them, but I had some difficulty in restraining myself from laughing in their faces, so full of stupid importance. I daresay I was not very well at that time. I tottered about the streets—there were various affairs to settle—grinning bitterly at perfectly respectable persons. I admit my behaviour was inexcusable, but then my temperature was seldom normal in these days. My dear aunt's endeavours to "nurse up my strength" seemed altogether beside the mark. It was not my strength that wanted nursing, it was my imagination that wanted soothing. I kept the bundle of papers given me by Kurtz, not knowing exactly what to do with it. His mother had died lately, watched over, as I was told, by his Intended. A clean-shaved man, with an official manner and wearing gold-rimmed spectacles, called on me one day and made inquiries, at first circuitous, afterwards suavely pressing, about what he was pleased to denominate certain "documents." I was not surprised, because I had had two rows with the manager on the subject out there. I had refused to give up the smallest scrap out of that package, and I took the same attitude with the spectacled man. He became darkly menacing at last, and with much heat argued that the Company had the right to every bit of information about its "territories." And said he, "Mr Kurtz's knowledge of unexplored regions must have been necessarily extensive and peculiar—owing to his great abilities and to the deplorable circumstances in which he had been placed: therefore—" I assured him Mr Kurtz's knowledge, however extensive, did not bear upon the problems of commerce or administration. He invoked then the name of science. "It would be an incalculable loss if," etc., etc. I offered him the report on the "Suppression of Savage Customs," with the post-scriptum torn off. He took it up eagerly, but ended by sniffing at it with an air of contempt. "This is not what we had a right to expect," he remarked. "Expect nothing else," I said. "There are only private letters." He withdrew upon some threat of legal proceedings, and I saw him no more; but another fellow, calling himself Kurtz's cousin, appeared two days later, and was anxious to hear all the details about his dear relative's last moments. Incidentally he gave me to understand that Kurtz had been essentially a great musician. "There was the making of an immense success," said the man, who was an organist, I believe, with lank grey hair flowing over a greasy coat-collar. I had no reason to doubt his statement; and to this day I am unable to say what was Kurtz's profession, whether he ever had any—which was the greatest of his talents. I had taken him for a painter who wrote for the papers, or else for a journalist who could paint—but even the cousin (who took snuff during the interview) could not tell me what he had been—exactly. He was a universal genius—on that point I agreed with the old chap, who thereupon blew his nose noisily into a large cotton handkerchief and withdrew in senile agitation, bearing off some family letters and memoranda without importance. Ultimately a journalist anxious to know something of the fate of his "dear colleague" turned up. This visitor informed me Kurtz's proper sphere ought to have been politics "on the popular side." He had furry straight eyebrows, bristly hair cropped short, an eye-glass on a broad ribbon, and, becoming expansive, confessed his opinion that Kurtz really couldn't write a bit—"but heavens! how that man could talk. He electrified large meetings. He had faith—don't you see?—he had the faith. He could get himself to believe anything—anything. He would have been a splendid leader of an extreme party." "What party?" I asked. "Any party," answered the other. "He was an—an—extremist." Did I not think so? I assented. Did I know, he asked, with a sudden flash of curiosity, "what it was that had induced him to go out there?" "Yes," said I, and forthwith handed him the famous Report for publication, if he thought fit. He glanced through it hurriedly, mumbling all the time, judged "it would do," and took himself off with this plunder.

'Thus I was left at last with a slim packet of letters and the girl's portrait. She struck me as beautiful—I mean she had a beautiful expression. I know that the sunlight can be made to lie, too, yet one felt that no manipulation of light and pose could have conveyed the delicate shade of truthfulness upon those features. She seemed ready to listen without mental reservation, without suspicion, without a thought for herself. I concluded I would go and give her back her portrait and those letters myself. Curiosity? Yes; and also some other feelings perhaps. All that had been Kurtz's had passed out of my hands: his soul, his body, his station, his plans, his ivory, his career. There remained only his memory and his Intended—and I wanted to give that up, too, to the past, in a way—to surrender personally all that remained of him with me to that oblivion which is the last word of our common fate. I don't defend myself. I had no clear perception of what it was I really wanted. Perhaps it was an impulse of unconscious loyalty, or the fulfilment of one of these ironic necessities that lurk in the facts of human existence. I don't know. I can't tell. But I went.

'I thought his memory was like the other memories of the dead that accumulate in every man's life—a vague impress on the brain of shadows that had fallen on it in their swift and final passage; but before the high and ponderous door, between the tall houses of a street as still and decorous as a well-kept alley in a cemetery, I had a vision of him on the stretcher, opening his mouth voraciously, as if to devour all the earth with all its mankind. He lived then before me; he lived as much as he had ever lived—a shadow insatiable of splendid appearances, of frightful realities, a shadow darker than the shadow of the night, and draped nobly in the folds of a gorgeous eloquence. The vision seemed to enter the house with me—the stretcher, the phantom-bearers, the wild crowd of obedient worshippers, the gloom of the forests, the glitter of the reach between the murky bends, the beat of the drum, regular and muffled like the beating of a heart—the heart of a conquering darkness. It was a moment of triumph for the wilderness, an invading and vengeful rush which, it seemed to me, I would have to keep back alone for the salvation of another soul. And the memory of what I had heard him say afar there, with the horned shapes stirring at my back, in the glow of fires, within the patient woods, those broken phrases came back to me, were heard again in their ominous and terrifying simplicity. I remembered his abject pleading, his abject threats, the colossal scale of his vile desires, the meanness, the torment, the tempestuous anguish of his soul. And later on I seemed to see his collected languid manner, when he said one day, "This lot of ivory now is really mine. The Company did not pay for it. I collected it myself at a very great personal risk. I am afraid they will try to claim it as theirs though. H'm. It is a difficult case. What do you think I ought to do—resist? Eh? I want no more than justice." . . . He wanted no more than justice—no more than justice. I rang the bell before a mahogany door on the first floor, and while I waited he seemed to stare at me out of the glassy panel—stare with that wide and immense stare embracing, condemning, loathing all the universe. I seemed to hear the whispered cry, "The horror! The horror!"

'The dusk was falling. I had to wait in a lofty drawing-room with three long windows from floor to ceiling that were like three luminous and bedraped columns. The bent gilt legs and backs of the furniture shone in indistinct curves. The tall marble fireplace had a cold and monumental whiteness. A grand piano stood massively in a corner; with dark gleams on the flat surfaces like a sombre and polished sarcophagus. A high door opened—closed. I rose.

'She came forward, all in black, with a pale head, floating towards me in the dusk. She was in mourning. It was more than a year since his death, more than a year since the news came; she seemed as though she would remember and mourn for ever. She took both my hands in hers and murmured, "I had heard you were coming." I noticed she was not very young—I mean not girlish. She had a mature capacity for fidelity, for belief, for suffering. The room seemed to have grown darker, as if all the sad light of the cloudy evening had taken refuge on her forehead. This fair hair, this pale visage, this pure brow, seemed surrounded by an ashy halo from which the dark eyes looked out at me. Their glance was guileless, profound, confident, and trustful. She carried her sorrowful head as though she were proud of that sorrow, as though she would say, I—I alone know how to mourn for him as he deserves. But while we were still shaking hands, such a look of awful desolation came upon her face that I perceived she was one of those creatures that are not the playthings of Time. For her he had died only yesterday. And, by Jove! the impression was so powerful that for me, too, he seemed to have died only yesterday—nay, this very minute, I saw her and him in the same instant of time—his death and her sorrow—I saw her sorrow in the very moment of his death. Do you understand? I saw them together—I heard them together. She had said, with a deep catch of the breath, "I have survived" while my strained ears seemed to hear distinctly, mingled with her tone of despairing regret, the summing-up whisper of his eternal condemnation. I asked myself what I was doing there, with a sensation of panic in my heart as though I had blundered into a place of cruel and absurd mysteries not fit for a human being to behold. She motioned me to a chair. We sat down. I laid the packet gently on the little table, and she put her hand over it . . . "You knew him well," she murmured, after a moment of mourning silence.

' "Intimacy grows quickly out there," I said. "I knew him as well as it is possible for one man to know another."

' "And you admired him," she said. "It was impossible to know him and not to admire him. Was it?"

' "He was a remarkable man," I said, unsteadily. Then before the appealing fixity of her gaze, that seemed to watch for more words on my lips, I went on. "It was impossible not to—"

' "Love him" she finished eagerly, silencing me into an appalled dumbness. "How true! how true! But when you think that no one knew him so well as I! I had all his noble confidence. I knew him best."

' "You knew him best," I repeated. And perhaps she did. But with every word spoken the room was growing darker, and only her forehead, smooth and white, remained illumined by the unextinguishable light of belief and love.

' "You were his friend," she went on. "His friend," she repeated, a little louder. "You must have been, if he had given you this, and sent you to me. I feel I can speak to you—and oh! I must speak. I want you—You who have heard his last words—to know I have been worthy of him . . . It is not pride . . . Yes! I am proud to know I understood him better than anyone on earth—he told me so himself. And since his mother died I have had no one— no one—to—to—"

'I listened. The darkness deepened. I was not even sure whether he had given me the right bundle. I rather suspect he wanted me to take care of another batch of his papers which, after his death, I saw the manager examining under the lamp. And the girl talked, easing her pain in the certitude of my sympathy; she talked as thirsty men drink. I had heard that her engagement with Kurtz had been disapproved by her people. He wasn't rich enough or something. And indeed I don't know whether he had not been a pauper all his life. He had given me some reason to infer that it was his impatience of comparative poverty that drove him out there.

' " . . . Who was not this friend who had heard him speak once?" she was saying. "He drew men towards him by what was best in them." She looked at me with intensity. "It is the gift of the great," she went on, and the sound of her low voice seemed to have the accompaniment of all the other sounds, full of mystery, desolation, and sorrow, I had ever heard—the ripple of the river, the soughing of the trees swayed by the wind, the murmurs of the crowds, the faint ring of incomprehensible words cried from afar, the whisper of a voice speaking from beyond the threshold of an eternal darkness. "But you have heard him! You know!" she cried.

' "Yes, I know," I said with something like despair in my heart, but bowing my head before the faith that was in her, before that great and saving illusion that shone with an unearthly glow in the darkness, in the triumphant darkness from which I could not have defended her—from which I could not even defend myself.

' "What a loss to me—to us!"—she corrected herself with beautiful generosity; then added in a murmur, "To the world." By the last gleams of twilight I could see the glitter of her eyes, full of tears—of tears that would not fall.

' "I have been very happy—very fortunate—very proud," she went on. "Too fortunate. Too happy for a little while. And now I am unhappy for—for life."

'She stood up; her fair hair seemed to catch all the remaining light in a glimmer of gold. I rose, too.

' "And of all this," she went on, mournfully, "of all his promise, and of all his greatness, of his generous mind, of his noble heart, nothing remains—nothing but a memory. You and I—"

' "We shall always remember him," I said, hastily.

' "No!" she cried. "It is impossible that all this should be lost—that such a life should be sacrificed to leave nothing—but sorrow. You know what vast plans he had. I knew of them, too—I could not perhaps understand—but others knew of them. Something must remain. His words, at least, have not died."

' "His words will remain," I said.

' "And his example," she whispered to herself. "Men looked up to him—his goodness shone in every act. His example—"

' "True," I said; "his example, too. Yes, his example. I forgot that."

' "But I do not. I cannot—I cannot believe—not yet. I cannot believe that I shall never seem him again, that nobody will see him again, never, never, never."

'She put out her arms as if after a retreating figure, stretching them black and with clasped pale hands across the fading and narrow sheen of the window. Never see him! I saw him clearly enough then. I shall see this eloquent phantom as long as I live, and I shall see her, too, a tragic and familiar Shade, resembling in this gesture another one, tragic also, and bedecked with powerless charms, stretching bare brown arms over the glitter of the infernal stream, the stream of darkness. She said suddenly very low, "He died as he lived."

' "His end," said I, with dull anger stirring in me, 'was in every way worthy of his life."

' "And I was not with him," she murmured. My anger subsided before a feeling of infinite pity.

' "Everything that could be done—" I mumbled.

' "Ah, but I believed in him more than anyone on earth—more than his own mother, more than—himself. He needed me! Me! I would have treasured every sigh, every word, every sign, every glance."

'I felt like a chill grip on my chest. "Don't," I said, in a muffled voice.

' "Forgive me. I—I—have mourned so long in silence—in silence . . . You were with him—to the last? I think of his loneliness. Nobody near to understand him as I would have understood. Perhaps no one to hear . . ."

' "To the very end," I said, shakily, "I heard his very last words . . ." I stopped in a fright.

' "Repeat them," she murmured in a heart-broken tone. "I want—I want—something—something—to—to live with."

'I was on the point of crying at her, "Don't you hear them?" The dusk was repeating them in a persistent whisper all around us, in a whisper that seemed to swell menacingly like the first whisper of a rising wind. "The horror! The horror!"

' "His last word—to live with," she insisted. "Don't you understand I loved him—I loved him—I loved him!"

'I pulled myself together and spoke slowly.

' "The last word the pronounced was—your name."

'I heard a light sigh and then my heart stood stiff, stopped dead short by an exulting and terrible cry, by the cry of inconceivable triumph and of unspeakable pain. "I knew it—I was sure!" . . . She knew. She was sure. I heard her weeping; she had hidden her face in her hands. It seemed to me that the house would collapse before I could escape, that the heavens would fall upon my head. But nothing happened. The heavens do not fall for such a trifle. Would they have fallen, I wonder, if I had rendered Kurtz that justice which was his due? Hadn't he said he wanted only justice? But I couldn't. I could not tell her. It would have been too dark—too dark altogether . . .'

Marlow ceased, and sat apart, indistinct and silent, in the pose of a meditating Buddha. Nobody moved for a time. 'We have lost the first of the ebb,' said the Director, suddenly. I raised my head. The offing was barred by a black bank of clouds, and the tranquil waterway leading to the uttermost ends of the earth flowed sombre under an overcast sky—seemed to lead into the heart of an immense darkness.

[1902]

e. e. cummings
[1894–1962]

Edward Estlin Cummings, or E. E. CUMMINGS *as he preferred his name to be styled, grew up in Cambridge, Massachusetts where his father taught at Harvard University and later was minister at the Unitarian church. cummings completed a bachelor's and a master's in English at Harvard where he became friends with novelist John Dos Passos. After moving to New York to become a writer, cummings volunteered for service in World War I as an ambulance driver. In France, cummings was wrongly jailed for spying for the Germans simply because he reported stories of the terrible conditions at the front in his letters home. cummings later wrote a fictionalized autobiography,* The Enormous Room, *of events during his stay in the French concentration camp.*

After release from prison in 1917, cummings returned to the United States and began to publish poetry in literary magazines. Unable, however, to find a publisher in the United States for a longer collection because of his frank treatment of sex, cummings left the United States to live in Paris. Realizing that his work would not be published if he pursued sexual themes, cummings sanitized and shortened them and finally saw publication in 1923. He soon published three other volumes of poetry. An avid pacifist, cummings was disturbed by the approach of World War II and produced X1, *a collection of disturbing yet insightful poems about the human condition.*

cummings's poetry is seen as dense and difficult to some, and overly simplistic and even childish to others. cummings's exploration of language and form force the reader to consider the purpose of conventions and their uses. For cummings, understanding the meaning of words and conventions was ultimately important; destroying their thoughtless application the goal. However, for all his experimentation with form and syntax, cummings can be thought of as a romantic and even pastoral poet.

i carry your heart with me(i carry it in
my heart)i am never without it(anywhere
i go you go, my dear; and whatever is done
by only me is your doing, my darling)
                    i fear
no fate(for you are my fate, my sweet)i want
no world(for beautiful you are my world, my true)
and it's you are whatever the moon has always
meant
and whatever a sun will always sing is you

here is the deepest secret nobody knows
here is the root of the root and the bud of the
bud
and the sky of the sky of a tree called life; which
grows
higher than soul can hope or mind can hide)
and this is the wonder that's keeping the stars
apart

i carry your heart(i carry it in my heart)

[l(a]

e. e. cummings

l(a

le
af
fa

ll   5

s)
one
l

iness

[1958]

Reprinted from *Complete Poems: 1904-1962,* by permission of Liveright Publishing Company. Copyright © 1958, 1986, 1991 by the Trustees for the E.E. Cummings Trust.

in Just -

e. e. cummings

in Just-
spring   when the world is mud-
luscious the little
lame balloonman

whistles   far   and wee   5

and eddieandbill come
running from marbles and
piracies and it's
spring

when the world is puddle-wonderful   10
the queer
old balloonman whistles
far   and   wee
and bettyandisbel come dancing

from hop-scotch and jump-rope and   15

it's
spring
and
     the
          goat-footed   20

balloonMan   whistles
far
and
wee

[1923]

Reprinted from *Complete Poems: 1904-1962,* by permission of Liveright Publishing Company. Copyright © 1958, 1986, 1991 by the Trustees for the E.E. Cummings Trust.

being to timelessness as it's to time,
love did no more begin than love will end;
where nothing is to breathe to sctroll to swim
love is the air the ocean and the land

(do lovers suffer? all divinities
proudly descending put on deathful flesh:
are lovers glad?only their smallest joy's
a universe emerging from a wish)

love is the voice under all silences,
the hope which has no opposite in fear;
the strength so strong mere force is feebleness:
the truth more first than sun more last than star

-do lovers love?why then to heaven with hell.
Whatever sages say and fools, all's well

Mark Doty
[1953–   ]

MARK DOTY *once described his approach to writing in this way: "I wait to be haunted, as it were, by an image. What happens is something I see registers on a deeper level than most experience does . . . Then I'll begin describing it to try to capture it. In the process of describing it I begin to understand what it is about the image that's compelling. It's not enough to describe it: The image is a vehicle for something I'm trying to understand. It's a metaphor-making process. My metaphors know more than I do: They know ahead of me." With this approach, Doty is able to find significance in even the most ordinary things, such as his dog chasing a stick in the park, and the sound of the dog's bark. This makes his poetry, in the attention it pays to things, meaningful. His poems remain, at the same time, accessible because of their descriptive quality and because of his obvious passion for the world around him.*

Doty is the author of six books of poetry. My Alexandria *(1993) was chosen for the National Poetry Series and also won the National Book Critics Circle Award. This collection was followed by* Atlantis *(1995);* Sweet Machine *(1998); and* Source *(2002). In 1996 Doty published a memoir,* Heaven's Coast, *which recounts the death from AIDS of his partner. It won the PEN Award for a first book of nonfiction. In 1999 he produced an autobiography, titled* Firebird. *He won fellowships from the Guggenheim, Merrill, Rockefeller, and Whiting foundations. He also received a grant from the National Endowment for the Arts. He lives in Provincetown, Massachusetts, and in Houston, Texas, where he teaches at the University of Houston.*

Golden Retrievals

MARK DOTY

Fetch? Balls and sticks capture my attention
seconds at a time. Catch? I don't think so.
Bunny, tumbling leaf, a squirrel who's—oh
joy—actually scared. Sniff the wind, then

I'm off again: muck, pond, ditch, residue   5
of any thrillingly dead thing. And you?
Either you're sunk in the past, half our walk,
thinking of what you never can bring back,

or else you're off in some fog concerning
—tomorrow, is that what you call it? My work: 10
to unsnare time's warp (and woof!), retrieving,
my haze-headed friend, you. This shining bark,

a Zen master's bronzy gong, calls you here,
entirely, now: bow-wow, bow-wow, bow-wow.

[1998]

Reprinted from *Sweet Machine,* by permission of HarperCollins Publishers, Inc. Copyright © 1998 by Mark Doty.

T. S. Eliot
[1888–1965]

T. S. ELIOT *was the seventh child of successful St. Louis merchant, Henry Ware Eliot, and school teacher, Charlotte Sterns Eliot. He showed such great intellectual abilities that he entered Harvard at age eighteen. There he studied English, Latin, Greek, German, and French literature. He also studied history, art, and philosophy, and wrote for the Harvard* Advocate. *After college he traveled in Europe and spent a year at the Sorbonne and wrote his first great poem, "The Love Song of J. Alfred Prufrock" at age twenty-three. He went home to America and studied for a doctorate at Harvard, returned to German to do doctoral research, but moved to London and Oxford at the beginning of World War I. In London he met Ezra Pound who championed Eliot's abilities as a poet and helped him publish "Prufrock" in* Poetry *in June 1915. Eliot also published "Preludes" and "Rhapsody on a Windy Night" in* Blast, *and "Portrait of a Lady" in* Others. *The following year he finished his doctorate but did not return to the United States to become a professor as his parents had expected. Instead he married Vivienne Haigh-Wood and took a job as a clerk in Lloyds Bank. During this era he wrote literary journalism for important newspapers and journals such as the* New Statesman, *the* Monist, *and the* Times Literary Supplement. *He became an assistant editor for the* Egoist *and wrote a short book on* Pound, Ezra Pound: His Metric and Poetry *(1918). His first book of poetry,* Prufrock and Other Observations *had appeared a year earlier. In 1920 he published* Poems *and a volume of essays,* The Sacred Wood.

In 1921, Eliot collapsed from over-work and spent a few months resting in Germany and traveling in France where he wrote The Waste Land *in consultation with Ezra Pound, (Pound mostly crossed out passages of a much longer draft; passages that were to become the starting points for later poems), that appeared in 1922. By 1925 Eliot was a literary celebrity, able to leave the bank and join the publishing house of Faber and Gwyer (later Faber and Faber). In 1927 he became a devout Anglican after years of meditation and study. In 1932, following years of Haigh-Wood's acute depressions, he and his first wife divorced. She died in a mental hospital in 1947. He published* The Hollow Men *and* Ash Wednesday *in 1930 and "Journey of the Magi" in 1931. His selected essays,* The Use of Poetry and The Use of Criticism, *were published in 1933. At that time also Eliot began to write drama, becoming a noted dramatist with* Murder in the Cathedral *in 1935 and* The Family Reunion *in 1939. His last great poems were "The Four Quartets: Burnt Norton" (1936), "East Coker" (1940), "The Dry Salvages" (1941), and "Little Gidding" (1942). He married Esme Valerie Fletcher in 1957 and lived as a celebrated writer until his death in 1965. He received the Nobel Prize for Literature and England's Order of Merit among many other honors.*

The Love Song of J. Alfred Prufrock

T. S. ELIOT

S'io credessi che mia risposta fosse
a persona che mai tornasse al mondo,
questa fiamma staria senza più scosse.
Ma per ciò che giammai di questo fondo
non tornò vivo alcun, s'i'odo il vero,
senza tema d'infamia ti rispondo.[1]

Let us go then, you and I,
When the evening is spread out against the sky
Like a patient etherised upon a table;
Let us go, through certain half-deserted streets,
The muttering retreats   5
Of restless nights in one-night cheap hotels
And sawdust restaurants with oyster-shells:
Streets that follow like a tedious argument
Of insidious intent
To lead you to an overwhelming question . . .   10
Oh, do not ask, 'What is it?'
Let us go and make our visit.

---

[1]"If I thought my answer were to one who would ever return to the world, this flame should stay without another movement; but since none ever returned alive from this depth, if what I hear is true, I answer thee without fear of infamy." Eliot's epigraph comes from Canto 27 of Dante's *Inferno*, in which Dante visits the eighth circle of hell, reserved for evil counselors. The words are uttered by Count Guido de Montefeltrano, also known in Dante's time as The Fox. Montefeltrano is condemned to burn in a prison of fire because of his destructive advice to Pope Boniface. A brilliant political and military tactician, Guido in his youth led troops against the Papacy and was excommunicated. He then repented his sins and retired to a monastery. The corrupt Pope Boniface, however, lured Guido out of retirement by offering him reinstatement in the church in exchange for his cunning services in suppressing the Pope's enemies. Seduced by the Pope's promises of a ticket to heaven, Guido aided the Pope's corrupt designs, only to find upon his death that he had been double-crossed and sent to hell for his efforts. Dante imagines Guido as a man "taken in by his own craftiness."

Published in *Prufrock and Other Observations* in 1917.

In the room the women come and go
Talking of Michelangelo,[2]

The yellow fog that rubs its back upon the window-panes,   *15*
The yellow smoke that rubs its muzzle on the window-panes,
Licked its tongue into the corners of the evening,
lingered upon the pools that stand in drains,
Let fall upon its back the soot that falls from chimneys,
Slipped by the terrace, made a sudden leap,   *20*
And seeing that it was a soft October night,
Curled once about the house, and fell asleep.

For indeed there will be time
For the yellow smoke that slides along the street
Rubbing its back upon the window-panes;   *25*
There will be time, there will be time
To prepare a face to meet the faces that you meet;
There will be time to murder and create,
And time for all the works and days of hands
That lift and drop a question on your plate;   *30*
Time for you and time for me,
And time yet for a hundred indecisions,
And for a hundred visions and revisions,
Before the taking of a toast and tea.

In the room the women come and go   *35*
Talking of Michelangelo.

And indeed there will be time
To wonder, 'Do I dare?' and, 'Do I dare?'
Time to turn back and descend the stair,
With a bald spot in the middle of my hair—   *40*
(They will say: 'How his hair is growing thin!')
My morning coat, my collar mounting firmly to the chin,
My necktie rich and modest, but asserted by a simple pin—
(They will say: 'But how his arms and legs are thin!')
Do I dare   *45*
Disturb the universe?

---

[2]Michelangelo (1475–1564), the revered Italian sculptor, painter, architect, and poet.

In a minute there is time
For decisions and revisions which a minute will reverse.
For I have known them all already, known them all—
Have known the evenings, mornings, afternoons,   *50*
I have measured out my life with coffee spoons;
I know the voices dying with a dying fall
Beneath the music from a farther room.
    So how should I presume?

And I have known the eyes already, known them all—   *55*
The eyes that fix you in a formulated phrase,
And when I am formulated, sprawling on a pin,
When I am pinned and wriggling on the wall,
Then how should I begin
to spit out all the butt-ends of my days and ways?   *60*
    And how should I presume?

And I have known the arms already, known them all—
Arms that are braceleted and white and bare
(But in the lamplight, downed with light brown hair!)
Is it perfume from a dress   *65*
That makes me so digress?
Arms that lie along a table, or wrap about a shawl.
    And should I then presume?
    And how should I begin?

   . . . . .

Shall I say, I have gone at dusk through narrow streets   *70*
And watched the smoke that rises from the pipes
Of lonely men in shirt-sleeves, leaning out of windows? . . .

I should have been a pair of ragged claws
Scuttling across the floors of silent seas.

   . . . . .

And the afternoon, the evening, sleeps so peacefully!   *75*
Smoothed by long fingers,
Asleep . . . tired . . . or it malingers,
Stretched on the floor, here beside you and me.
Should I, after tea and cakes and ices,
Have the strength to force the moment to its crisis?   *80*

But though I have wept and fasted, wept and prayed,
Though I have seen my head (grown slightly bald) brought in
    upon a platter,[3]
I am no prophet—and here's no great matter;
I have seen the moment of my greatness flicker,
And I have seen the eternal Footman hold my coat, and snicker,   *85*
And in short, I was afraid.

And would it have been worth it, after all,
After the cups, the marmalade, the tea,
Among the porcelain, among some talk of you and me,
Would it have been worth while,   *90*
To have bitten off the matter with a smile,
To have squeezed the universe into a ball
To roll it towards some overwhelming question,
To say: 'I am Lazarus,[4] come from the dead,
Come back to tell you all, I shall tell you all'—   *95*
If one, settling a pillow by her head,
    Should say: 'That is not what I meant at all.
    That is not it, at all.'

And would it have been worth it, after all,
Would it have been worth while,   *100*
After the sunsets and the dooryards and the sprinkled streets,
After the novels, after the teacups, after the skirts that trail along
    the floor—
And this, and so much more?—
It is impossible to say just what I mean!
But as if a magic lantern[5] threw the nerves in patterns on a   *105*
    screen:
Would it have been worth while

---

[3]In the Biblical story of Salome and John the Baptist (see Mark VI:17–28) Salome, the daughter of Queen Herodias hated John the Baptist. Herod, to please Herodias, imprisoned John. Salome danced before Herod and he promised to give anything she wished. Salome asked for the head of John the Baptist on a platter.

[4]Lazarus: Prufrock uses Jesus' parable of Lazarus and Dives told in Luke XVI:19–31. In the parable, Dives, a rich man, ignores the suffering of a poor man, Lazarus, who begs for crumbs from Dives's table. Lazarus dies and he goes to heaven. Dives goes to hell. Dives implores God to allow Lazarus to return from the dead to warn Dives's relatives to repent.

[5]An early form of optical projector.

If one, settling a pillow or throwing off a shawl,
And turning toward the window, should say:
    'That is not it at all,
    That is not what I meant, at all.'   *110*

   . . . . .

No! I am not Prince Hamlet,[6] nor was meant to be;
Am an attendant lord, one that will do
To swell a progress, start a scene or two,
Advise the prince; no doubt, an easy tool,
Deferential, glad to be of use,   *115*
Politic, cautious, and meticulous;
Full of high sentence, but a bit obtuse;
At times, indeed, almost ridiculous—
Almost, at times, the Fool[7]

I grow old . . . I grow old . . .   *120*
I shall wear the bottoms of my trousers rolled.

Shall I part my hair behind? Do I dare to eat a peach?
I shall wear white flannel trousers, and walk upon the beach.
I have heard the mermaids singing, each to each.

I do not think that they will sing to me.   *125*

I have seen them riding seaward on the waves
Combing the white hair of the waves blown back
When the wind blows the water white and black.

We have lingered in the chambers of the sea
By sea-girls wreathed with seaweed red and brown   *130*
Till human voices wake us, and we drown.

                   [1915]

---

[6]Prince Hamlet: the protagonist of William Shakespeare's tragedy, *Hamlet.*

[7]The Fool, or jester, was a stock character of Elizabethan drama.

Allen Ginsberg
[1926–1997]

"I saw the best minds of my generation destroyed by madness . . ." This opening line from the poem *"Howl"* perhaps most captures the significance of **ALLEN GINSBERG'S** presence as a twentieth century poet. A figure of great controversy during his life, Allen Ginsberg was a leader of the Beat Generation. *"Beat"* was originally street slang for being strung out or high on drugs, something that was not unknown to the Beat Generation. Fellow Beat writer Jack Kerouac redefined the term to include the idea that it was the beat of a extemporized jazz as well as the idea of beatitude—bliss and blessings. Ginsberg, like other Beat writers, preferred to define himself in his own terms and did not accept the commonplaces of his time. As an avid homosexual in a time when any deviance from culturally condoned sexuality was completely shunned and kept completely secret, and as a man who experimented with mind-altering drugs, Ginsberg strove to shake the world with his poetry—to slap American culture in the face with his words. Such a controversial stance, however, developed from years of struggle with his sexuality and his beliefs about social order.

Ginsberg was born in Newark, New Jersey. His father was a high school teacher and a poet; his mother was a political activist and member of the Communist Party who idealized Joseph Stalin. The influence of Ginsberg's parents is seen more in their occupations than in their desires for his career. Early on they pressured him to be a labor lawyer, a career that Ginsberg explored but ultimately dropped when he fled Patterson to end up in New York, on the street with his Beat compatriots. Struggling both financially and emotionally, Ginsberg began to experiment with poetry and explorations of himself. The poems quickly turned outward, however, as he saw the problems and discrimination rampant in American society. His first significant work, Howl and Other Poems appeared in 1956 to great underground acclaim. From this time forward, Ginsberg took on the mantle as leader of American counterculture. The deep alienation he felt from society and expressed through his work struck a cord with those living in the 1950s who did not feel a part of mainstream society or a part of the American Ideal. This alienation eventually led to the hippy movement of the sixties, a movement that Ginsberg whole-heartedly supported.

During the 1970s and 1980s, Ginsberg recorded and occasionally toured with Bob Dylan, John Hammond, Sr., and the Clash. In 1994, Rhino Records released Holy Soul Jelly Roll: Poems and Songs 1949–1993, a four-disk compilation of the poet's many spoken-word recordings. This multiset disk and its accompanying booklet serve as a kind of "selected works" of Ginsberg's spoken-word recordings. Other CD releases included The Lion For Real *(1989) and*

The Ballad of the Skeletons *(1996), as well as collaborative efforts with Philip Glass,* Hydrogen Jukebox *(1993), and the Kronos Quartet,* Howl U.S.A. *(1996).*

Ginsberg was a member of the American Institute of Arts and Letters. He also received a Guggenheim Fellowship, and was a Distinguished Professor at Brooklyn College in New York. Howl *has been translated into some twenty-three languages. His numerous other works include* Planet News, 1961–1967 *(1968);* The Fall of America: Poems of These States, 1965–1971 *(1972);* Collected Poems, 1947–1980 *(1984); and* Selected Poems, 1947–1995 *(1996).*

A Further Proposal

ALLEN GINSBERG

Come live with me and be my love,
And we will some old pleasures prove.
Men like me have paid in verse
This costly courtesy, or curse;

But I would bargain with my art   5
(As to the mind, now to the heart),
My symbols, images, and signs
Please me more outside these lines.

For your share and recompense,
You will be taught another sense: 10
The wisdom of the subtle worm
Will turn most perfect in your form.

Not that your soul need tutored be
By intellectual decree,
But graces that the mind can share   15
Will make you, as more wise, more fair,

Till all the world's devoted thought
Find all in you it ever sought,
And even I, of skeptic mind,
A Resurrection of a kind.   20

This compliment, in my own way,
For what I would receive, I pay;
Thus all the wise have writ thereof,
And all the fair have been their love.

[1947]

Copyright © 2002 by Allen Ginsberg. Reprinted by permission of The Wylie Agency, Inc.

A Supermarket in California

ALLEN GINSBERG

What thoughts I have of you tonight, Walt Whitman, for I
walked down the sidestreets under the trees with a headache self-
conscious looking at the full moon.
In my hungry fatigue, and shopping for images, I went into
the neon fruit supermarket, dreaming of your enumerations!
What peaches and what penumbras! Whole families
shopping at night! Aisles full of husbands! Wives in the avocados,
babies in the tomatoes!—and you, Garcia Lorca, what were you
doing down by the watermelons?

I saw you, Walt Whitman, childless, lonely old grubber, poking
among the meats in the refrigerator and eyeing the grocery boys.
I heard you asking questions of each: Who killed the pork   5
chops? What price bananas? Are you my Angel?
I wandered in and out of the brilliant stacks of cans following
you, and followed in my imagination by the store detective.
We strode down the open corridors together in our solitary
fancy tasting artichokes, possessing every frozen delicacy, and
never passing the cashier.

Where are we going, Walt Whitman? The doors close in an
hour. Which way does your beard point tonight?
(I touch your book and dream of our odyssey in the
supermarket and feel absurd.)
Will we walk all night through solitary streets? The trees add   10
shade to shade, lights out in the houses, we'll both be lonely.
Will we stroll dreaming of the lost America of love past blue
automobiles in driveways, home to our silent cottage?
Ah, dear father, graybeard, lonely old courage-teacher, what
America did you have when Charon quit poling his ferry and you

Reprinted from *Collected Poems 1947–1980*, by permission of HarperCollins Publishers,
Inc. Copyright © 1955 by Allen Ginsberg.

got out on a smoking bank and stood watching the boat
disappear on the black waters of Lethe?

[1956]

Arlo Guthrie
[1947–   ]

ARLO GUTHRIE, *originally from New York City, was born into show business. His father was the famous folk singer Woody Guthrie, and his mother was Marjorie Mazie, a professional dancer in New York. His father's friends, including such illustrious folk singers as Pete Seeger and Leadbelly, encouraged Arlo and helped him to begin performing publicly as a young teen. Guthrie was at the center of the great interest in folk singing and folk songs in New York City and Philadelphia, where he learned from both ballad singers and blues singers. He discovered himself as a singer in the company of such stars as Bob Dylan, Jim Croce, and Joan Baez. He wrote with the beat poet Allen Ginsberg and played guitar with nearly every famous folk musician of the era. In 1967, Guthrie became an international star with the album* Alice's Restaurant, *an album that led to the 1969 film* Alice's Restaurant. *Guthrie became even better know for his singing of the Steve Goodman song "City of New Orleans," a song still near and dear to people who came of age in the sixties.*

Guthrie has toured the world singing, telling stories, and entertaining people on all continents. He still performs most of each, often in the company of his children Abe and Sarah Lee. Guthrie has even entered the world of classical music with a symphonic arrangement of his music, An American Scrapbook. *He has performed with the Boston Pops symphony orchestra and has been a regular at concerts around the nation. Guthrie also has his own record label, Rising Son, and has been nominated for many awards, including a 1997 Grammy. Guthrie's music has been recorded widely including during his famous 2004 tour of Australia. His latest effort is a performance with the University of Kentucky Symphony Orchestra in 2006 that will be shown nationally in 2007. Guthrie has acted on ABC in "Byrds of Paradise" and in the USA Network series "Renegade." He writes and publishes* The Rolling Blunder Review, *and has published the award-winning children's book* Mooses Come Walking.

In 1991, Guthrie established The Guthrie Center, an interfaith church foundation aimed at many types of social service. He continues to work for social improvement nationally and internationally.

Alice's Restaurant

ARLO GUTHRIE

This song is called Alice's Restaurant, and it's about Alice, and the restaurant, but Alice's Restaurant is not the name of the restaurant, that's just the name of the song, and that's why I called the song Alice's Restaurant.

> You can get anything you want at Alice's Restaurant
> You can get anything you want at Alice's Restaurant
> Walk right in it's around the back
> Just a half a mile from the railroad track
> You can get anything you want at Alice's Restaurant

Now it all started two Thanksgivings ago, was on—two years ago on Thanksgiving, when my friend and I went up to visit Alice at the restaurant, but Alice doesn't live in the restaurant, she lives in the church nearby the restaurant, in the bell-tower, with her husband Ray and Fasha the dog. And livin' in the bell tower like that, they got a lot of room downstairs where the pews used to be in. Havin' all that room, seein' as how they took out all the pews, they decided that they didn't have to take out their garbage for a long time.

We got up there, we found all the garbage in there, and we decided it'd be a friendly gesture for us to take the garbage down to the city dump. So we took the half a ton of garbage, put it in the back of a red VW microbus, took shovels and rakes and implements of destruction and headed on toward the city dump.

Well we got there and there was a big sign and a chain across across the dump saying, "Closed on Thanksgiving." And we had never heard of a dump closed on Thanksgiving before, and with tears in our eyes we drove off into the sunset looking for another place to put the garbage.

We didn't find one. Until we came to a side road, and off the side of the side road there was another fifteen foot cliff and at the bottom of the cliff there was another pile of garbage. And we decided that one big pile is better than two little piles, and rather than bring that one up we decided to throw ours down.

That's what we did, and drove back to the church, had a Thanksgiving dinner that couldn't be beat, went to sleep and didn't get up until the next

Reprinted by permission of Appleseed Music, Inc., administered by The Royalty Network.
Copyright © 1967, 1966 by Appleseed Music, Inc.

morning, when we got a phone call from Officer Obie. He said, "Kid, we found your name on an envelope at the bottom of a half a ton of garbage, and just wanted to know if you had any information about it." And I said, "Yes, sir, Officer Obie, I cannot tell a lie, I put that envelope under that garbage."

After speaking to Obie for about forty-five minutes on the telephone we finally arrived at the truth of the matter and said that we had to go down and pick up the garbage, and also had to go down and speak to him at the police officer's station. So we got in the red VW microbus with the shovels and rakes and implements of destruction and headed on toward the police officer's station.

Now friends, there was only one or two things that Obie coulda done at the police station, and the first was he could have given us a medal for being so brave and honest on the telephone, which wasn't very likely, and we didn't expect it, and the other thing was he could have bawled us out and told us never to be seen driving garbage around the vicinity again, which is what we expected, but when we got to the police officer's station there was a third possibility that we hadn't even counted upon, and we was both immediately arrested. Handcuffed. And I said "Obie, I don't think I can pick up the garbage with these handcuffs on." He said, "Shut up, kid. Get in the back of the patrol car."

And that's what we did, sat in the back of the patrol car and drove to the-quote Scene of the Crime unquote. I want tell you about the town of Stockbridge, Massachusets, where this happened here, they got three stop signs, two police officers, and one police car, but when we got to the Scene of the Crime there was five police officers and three police cars, being the biggest crime of the last fifty years, and everybody wanted to get in the newspaper story about it. And they was using up all kinds of cop equipment that they had hanging around the police officer's station. They was taking plaster tire tracks, foot prints, dog smelling prints, and they took twenty-seven eight-by-ten color glossy photographs with circles and arrows and a paragraph on the back of each one explaining what each one was to be used as evidence against us. Took pictures of the approach, the getaway, the northwest corner, the southwest corner, and that's not to mention the aerial photography.

After the ordeal, we went back to the jail. Obie said he was going to put us in the cell. Said, "Kid, I'm going to put you in the cell, I want your wal-let and your belt." And I said, "Obie, I can understand you wanting my wal-let so I don't have any money to spend in the cell, but what do you want my belt for?" And he said, "Kid, we don't want any hangings." I said, "Obie, did you think I was going to hang myself for littering?" Obie said he was mak-ing sure, and friends Obie was, cause he took out the toilet seat so I could-n't hit myself over the head and drown, and he took out the toilet paper so I couldn't bend the bars roll out the—roll the toilet paper out the window, slide down the roll and have an escape. Obie was making sure, and it was about four or five hours later that Alice (remember Alice? It's a song about Alice), Alice came by and with a few nasty words to Obie on the side, bailed us out of jail, and we went back to the church, had another Thanksgiving dinner that couldn't be beat, and didn't get up until the next morning, when we all had to go to court.

We walked in, sat down, Obie came in with the twenty-seven eight-by-ten-color glossy pictures with circles and arrows and a paragraph on the back of each one, sat down. Man came in said, "All rise." We all stood up, and Obie stood up with the twenty-seven eight-by-ten color glossy pictures, and the judge walked in sat down with a seeing eye dog, and he sat down, we sat down. Obie looked at the seeing eye dog, and then at the twenty-seven eight-by-ten color glossy pictures with circles and arrows and a paragraph on the back of each one, and looked at the seeing eye dog. And then at twenty-seven eight-by-ten color glossy pictures with circles and arrows and a paragraph on the back of each one and began to cry, 'cause Obie came to the realization that it was a typical case of American blind justice, and there wasn't nothing he could do about it, and the judge wasn't going to look at the twenty-seven eight-by-ten color glossy pictures with the circles and arrows and a paragraph on the back of each one explaining what each one was to be used as evidence against us. And we was fined $50 and had to pick up the garbage in the snow, but that's not what I came to tell you about.

Came to talk about the draft.

They got a building down New York City, it's called Whitehall Street, where you walk in, you get injected, inspected, detected, infected, neglected and selected. I went down to get my physical examination one day, and I walked in, I sat down, got good and drunk the night before, so I looked and felt my best when I went in that morning. 'Cause I wanted to look like the all-American kid from New York City, man I wanted, I wanted to feel like the all, I wanted to be the all American kid from New York, and I walked in, sat down, I was hung down, brung down, hung up, and all kinds o' mean nasty ugly things. And I waked in and sat down and they gave me a piece of paper, said, "Kid, see the psychiatrist, room 604."

And I went up there, I said, "Shrink, I want to kill. I mean, I wanna, I wanna kill. Kill. I wanna, I wanna see, I wanna see blood and gore and guts and veins in my teeth. Eat dead burnt bodies. I mean kill, Kill, KILL, KILL." And I started jumpin' up and down yelling, "KILL, KILL," and he started jumpin' up and down with me and we was both jumpin' up and down yelling, "KILL, KILL." And the sergeant came over, pinned a medal on me, sent me down the hall, said, "You're our boy."

Didn't feel too good about it.

Proceeded on down the hall gettin, more injections, inspections, detections, neglections and all kinds of stuff that they was doin' to me at the thing there, and I was there for two hours, three hours, four hours, I was there for a long time going through all kinds of mean nasty ugly things and I was just having a tough time there, and they was inspecting, injecting every single part of me, and they was leaving no part untouched. Proceeded through, and when I finally came to the see the last man, I walked in, walked in sat down after a whole big thing there, and I walked up and said, "What do you want?" He said, "Kid, we only got one question. Have you ever been arrested?"

And I proceeded to tell him the story of the Alice's Restaurant Massacre, with full orchestration and five-part harmony and stuff like that and all the phenome—and he stopped me right there and said, "Kid, did you ever go to court?"

And I proceeded to tell him the story of the twenty-seven eight-by-ten color glossy pictures with the circles and arrows and the paragraph on the back of each one, and he stopped me right there and said, "Kid, I want you to go and sit down on that bench that says Group W . . . .NOW kid!!"

And I, I walked over to the, to the bench there, and there is, Group W's where they put you if you may not be moral enough to join the army after committing your special crime, and there was all kinds of mean nasty ugly looking people on the bench there. Mother rapers. Father stabbers. Father rapers! Father rapers sitting right there on the bench next to me! And they was mean and nasty and ugly and horrible crime-type guys sitting on the bench next to me. And the meanest, ugliest, nastiest one, the meanest father raper of them all, was coming over to me and he was mean 'n' ugly 'n' nasty 'n' horrible and all kind of things and he sat down next to me and said, "Kid, whad'ya get?" I said, "I didn't get nothing, I had to pay $50 and pick up the garbage." He said, "What were you arrested for, kid?" And I said, "Littering." And they all moved away from me on the bench there, and the hairy eyeball and all kinds of mean nasty things, till I said, "And creating a nuisance." And they all came back, shook my hand, and we had a great time on the bench, talkin about crime, mother stabbing, father raping, all kinds of groovy things that we was talking about on the bench. And everything was fine, we was smoking cigarettes and all kinds of things, until the Sergeant came over, had some paper in his hand, held it up and said:

"Kids, this-piece-of-paper's-got-47-words-37-sentences-58-words-we-wanna-know-details-of-the-crime-time-of-the-crime-and-any-other-kind-of-thing-you-gotta-say-pertaining-to-and-about-the-crime-I-want-to-know-arrest ing-officer's-name-and-any-other-kind-of-thing-you-gotta-say", and talked for forty-five minutes and nobody understood a word that he said, but we had fun filling out the forms and playing with the pencils on the bench there, and I filled out the massacre with the four-part harmony, and wrote it down there, just like it was, and everything was fine and I put down the pencil, and I turned over the piece of paper, and there, there on the other side, in the middle of the other side, away from everything else on the other side, in parentheses, capital letters, quoted, read the following words:

("KID, HAVE YOU REHABILITATED YOURSELF?")

I went over to the sergeant, said, "Sergeant, you got a lot a damn gall to ask me if I've rehabilitated myself, I mean, I mean, I mean that just, I'm sittin' here on the bench, I mean I'm sittin here on the Group W bench 'cause you want to know if I'm moral enough join the army, burn women, kids, houses and villages after bein' a litterbug." He looked at me and said, "Kid, we don't like your kind, and we're gonna send your fingerprints off to Washington."

And friends, somewhere in Washington enshrined in some little folder, is a study in black and white of my fingerprints. And the only reason I'm singing you this song now is cause you may know somebody in a similar situation, or you may be in a similar situation, and if you're in a situation like that there's only one thing you can do and that's walk into the shrink wherever you are, just walk in say "Shrink, You can get anything you want, at Alice's restaurant." And walk out. You know, if one person, just one person does it they may think he's really sick and they won't take him. And if two people, two people do it, in harmony, they may think they're both faggots and they won't take either of them. And three people do it, three, can you imagine, three people walking in singin' a bar of Alice's Restaurant and walking out. They may think it's an organization. And can you, can you imagine fifty people a day, I said fifty people a day walking in singin' a bar of Alice's Restaurant and walking out. And friends they may thinks it's a movement.

And that's what it is, the Alice's Restaurant Anti-Massacre Movement, and all you got to do to join is sing it the next time it comes around n the guitar. With feeling. So we'll wait for it to come around on the guitar here and sing it when it does. Here it comes.

> You can get anything you want, at Alice's Restaurant
> You can get anything you want, at Alice's Restaurant
> Walk right in it's around the back
> Just a half a mile from the railroad track
> You can get anything you want, at Alice's Restaurant

That was horrible. If you want to end war and stuff you got to sing loud. I've been singing this song now for twenty-five minutes. I could sing it for another twenty-five minutes. I'm not proud . . . .or tired.

So we'll wait till it comes around again, and this time with four-part harmony and feeling.

We're just waitin' for it to come around is what we're doing.

All right now.

You can get anything you want, at Alice's Restaurant
Excepting Alice
You can get anything you want, at Alice's Restaurant
Walk right in it's around the back
Just a half a mile from the railroad track
You can get anything you want, at Alice's Restaurant

Da da da da da da da dum
At Alice's Restaurant

Nathaniel Hawthorne
[1804–1864]

No writer's work has been more informed by the ghosts of the past than NATHANIEL HAWTHORNE'S. *He was born on Independence Day, 1804, in Salem, Massachusetts, to a family whose ancestors included a judge who persecuted Quakers, and another who played a key role in the Salem witchcraft trials. An acute awareness of his Puritan past would later lead to the complex explorations of sin and guilt found in his short stories and novels: As critic Alfred Kazin remarked, "Hawthorne's great subject was, indeed, the sense of guilt that is perhaps the most enduring theme in the moral history of the West—guilt that is the secret tie that binds us to others and to our own past."*

His position as a major literary figure was slow in coming, however. After graduating from Bowdoin College in Maine (where his classmates included poet Henry Wadsworth Longfellow and future U.S. President Franklin Pierce), he spent the next twelve years at his mother's house in Salem. During this time, he earned little income, lived in relative isolation, and immersed himself in literature and New England history. In 1828 he anonymously published the historical novel Fanshawe, *a work he would later go to great lengths to repudiate (always the harshest critic of his own work, he retrieved and destroyed as many copies of the novel as he could find). He struggled to find a publisher for a collection of his stories until 1836, when old friend Horatio Bridge helped him publish* Twice-told Tales. *Named after a line in Shakespeare's* King John, *the book featured several of Hawthorne's most enduring stories, including "The Maypole of Merry Mount" and "The Minister's Black Veil."*

Despite his success, Hawthorne still found it hard to make a living from writing. In order to support himself, and to earn money for his impending marriage (to Sophia Peabody in 1842), he spent the next couple of years working as a salt and coal measurer in the Boston Custom House. He also lived for a time at the experimental utopian community Brook Farm in West Roxbury, Massachusetts—an experience that provided the plot for his novel The Blithedale Romance *(1852). Hawthorne also published several more collections of short stories, including* Mosses from an Old Manse *in 1846. However, it was his novel* The Scarlet Letter *(1850) that secured his place in American letters. The story of Hester Prynne, a woman condemned by her community for bearing a child out of wedlock, the novel created a literary sensation in both the United States and England, and has since become one of the classics of literature.*

Hawthorne's other novels are The House of the Seven Gables *(1851), a work whose biographical elements include a family curse, and* The Marble Faun *(1860). He also penned the campaign biography* The Life of Franklin Pierce

(1852), an endeavor that his old Bowdoin classmate rewarded with a consulship at Liverpool, England. This position finally earned Hawthorne a measure of financial security for his later years in Concord, Massachusetts, when his creative abilities were on the decline. He died, most likely from a brain tumor, while visiting Pierce in Plymouth, New Hampshire, in 1864. He left behind a legacy of some of the most psychologically penetrating stories and novels in all of American fiction.

—Mark Lovely, *Merrimack College*

Young Goodman Brown

NATHANIEL HAWTHORNE

YOUNG GOODMAN BROWN CAME forth, at sunset, into the street of Salem village, but put his head back, after crossing the threshold, to exchange a parting kiss with his young wife.[1] And Faith, as the wife was aptly named, thrust her own pretty head into the street, letting the wind play with the pink ribbons of her cap, while she called to Goodman Brown.

"Dearest heart," whispered she, softly and rather sadly, when her lips were close to his ear, "pr'y thee, put off your journey until sunrise, and sleep in your own bed to-night. A lone woman is troubled with such dreams and such thoughts, that she's afeard of herself, sometimes. Pray, tarry with me this night, dear husband, of all nights in the year!"

"My love and my Faith," replied young Goodman Brown, "of all nights in the year, this one night must I tarry away from thee. My journey, as thou callest it, forth and back again, must needs be done 'twixt now and sunrise. What, my sweet, pretty wife, dost thou doubt me already, and we but three months married!"

"Then, God bless you!" said Faith, with the pink ribbons, "and may you find all well when you come back."

"Amen!" cried Goodman Brown. "Say thy prayers, dear Faith, and go to bed at dusk, and no harm will come to thee."

So they parted; and the young man pursued his way, until, being about to turn the corner by the meeting-house, he looked back, and saw the head of Faith still peeping after him, with a melancholy air, in spite of her pink ribbons.

"Poor little Faith!" thought he, for his heart smote him. "What a wretch am I, to leave her on such an errand! She talks of dreams, too. Methought, as she spoke, there was trouble in her face, as if a dream had warned her what work is to be done to-night. But, no, no! 'twould kill her to think it. Well; she's a blessed angel on earth; and after this one night, I'll cling to her skirts and follow her to Heaven."

---

[1]"Goodman" and "Goodwife" (short form "Goody") were typical forms of address for common people in colonial New England.

First published in the *New England Magazine* in April, 1835. Collected in *Mosses from an Old Manse* in 1846.

With this excellent resolve for the future, Goodman Brown felt himself justified in making more haste on his present evil purpose. He had taken a dreary road, darkened by all the gloomiest trees of the forest, which barely stood aside to let the narrow path creep through, and closed immediately behind. It was all as lonely as could be; and there is this peculiarity in such a solitude, that the traveller knows not who may be concealed by the innumerable trunks and the thick boughs overhead; so that, with lonely footsteps, he may yet be passing through an unseen multitude.

"There may be a devilish Indian behind every tree," said Goodman Brown, to himself; and he glanced fearfully behind him, as he added, "What if the devil himself should be at my very elbow!"

His head being turned back, he passed a crook of the road, and looking forward again, beheld the figure of a man, in grave and decent attire, seated at the foot of an old tree. He arose, at Goodman Brown's approach, and walked onward, side by side with him.

"You are late, Goodman Brown," said he. "The clock of the Old South[2] was striking as I came through Boston; and that is full fifteen minutes agone."

"Faith kept me back awhile," replied the young man, with a tremor in his voice, caused by the sudden appearance of his companion, though not wholly unexpected.

It was now deep dusk in the forest, and deepest in that part of it where these two were journeying. As nearly as could be discerned, the second traveller was about fifty years old, apparently in the same rank of life as Goodman Brown, and bearing a considerable resemblance to him, though perhaps more in expression than features. Still, they might have been taken for father and son. And yet, though the elder person was as simply clad as the younger, and as simple in manner too, he had an indescribable air of one who knew the world, and would not have felt abashed at the governor's dinner-table, or in King William's court, were it possible that his affairs should call him thither. But the only thing about him, that could be fixed upon as remarkable, was his staff, which bore the likeness of a great black snake, so curiously wrought, that it might almost be seen to twist and wriggle itself, like a living serpent. This, of course, must have been an ocular deception, assisted by the uncertain light.

"Come, Goodman Brown!" cried his fellow-traveller, "this is a dull pace for the beginning of a journey. Take my staff, if you are so soon weary."

"Friend," said the other, exchanging his slow pace for a full stop, "having kept covenant by meeting thee here, it is my purpose now to return whence I came. I have scruples, touching the matter thou wot'st[3] of.

---

[2]The Old South Church in Boston, near Salem village.

[3]Knowest

"Sayest thou so?" replied he of the serpent, smiling apart. "Let us walk on, nevertheless, reasoning as we go, and if I convince thee not, thou shalt turn back. We are but a little way in the forest, yet."

"Too far, too far!" exclaimed the goodman, unconsciously resuming his walk. "My father never went into the woods on such an errand, nor his father before him. We have been a race of honest men and good Christians, since the days of the martyrs.[4] And shall I be the first of the name of Brown, that ever took this path, and kept—"

"Such company, thou wouldst say," observed the elder person, interpreting his pause. "Well said, Goodman Brown! I have been as well acquainted with your family as with ever a one among the Puritans; and that's no trifle to say. I helped your grandfather, the constable, when he lashed the Quaker woman so smartly through the streets of Salem. And it was I that brought your father a pitch-pine knot, kindled at my own hearth, to set fire to an Indian village, in King Philip's war.[5] They were my good friends, both; and many a pleasant walk have we had along this path, and returned merrily after midnight. I would fain be friends with you, for their sake."

"If it be as thou sayest," replied Goodman Brown, "I marvel they never spoke of these matters. Or, verily, I marvel not, seeing that the least rumor of the sort would have driven them from New-England. We are a people of prayer, and good works, to boot, and abide no such wickedness."

"Wickedness or not," said the traveller with the twisted staff, "I have a very general acquaintance here in New-England. The deacons of many a church have drunk the communion wine with me; the selectmen, of divers towns, make me their chairman; and a majority of the Great and General Court[6] are firm supporters of my interest. The governor and I, too—but these are state-secrets."

"Can this be so!" cried Goodman Brown, with a stare of amazement at his undisturbed companion. "Howbeit, I have nothing to do with the governor and council; they have their own ways, and are no rule for a simple husbandman,[7] like me. But, were I to go on with thee, how should I meet the eye of that good old man, our minister, at Salem village? Oh, his voice would make me tremble, both Sabbath-day and lecture-day!"[8]

---

[4]Reference to the hundreds of Protestants executed between 1553 and 1558, during the reign of Roman Catholic Queen Mary I (1516–1558), who was known as Bloody Mary.

[5]Public whipping was a punishment for unrepentant Quakers, according to a 1661 Massachusetts law. Wampanoag chief Metacom, known as King Philip, led New England Indians in the King Philip's War against English colonists in 1675 and 1676,

[6]The legislative body of the Massachusetts Bay colony.

[7]Common man

[8]A mid-week day when attendance at a sermon was required.

Thus far, the elder traveller had listened with due gravity, but now burst into a fit of irrepressible mirth, shaking himself so violently, that his snake-like staff actually seemed to wriggle in sympathy.

"Ha! ha! ha!" shouted he, again and again; then composing himself, "Well, go on, Goodman Brown, go on; but pr'y thee, don't kill me with laughing!"

"Well, then, to end the matter at once," said Goodman Brown, considerably nettled, "there is my wife, Faith. It would break her dear little heart; and I'd rather break my own!"

"Nay, if that be the case," answered the other, "e'en go thy ways, Goodman Brown. I would not, for twenty old women like the one hobbling before us, that Faith should come to any harm."

As he spoke, he pointed his staff at a female figure on the path, in whom Goodman Brown recognized a very pious and exemplary dame, who had taught him his catechism, in youth, and was still his moral and spiritual adviser, jointly with the minister and Deacon Gookin.

"A marvel, truly, that Goody Cloyse[9] should be so far in the wilderness, at night-fall!" said he. "But, with your leave, friend, I shall take a cut through the woods, until we have left this Christian woman behind. Being a stranger to you, she might ask whom I was consorting with, and whither I was going."

"Be it so," said his fellow-traveller. "Betake you to the woods, and let me keep the path."

Accordingly, the young man turned aside, but took care to watch his companion, who advanced softly along the road, until he had come within a staff's length of the old dame. She, meanwhile, was making the best of her way, with singular speed for so aged a woman, and mumbling some indistinct words, a prayer, doubtless, as she went. The traveller put forth his staff, and touched her withered neck with what seemed the serpent's tail.

"The devil!" screamed the pious old lady.

"Then Goody Cloyse knows her old friend?" observed the traveller, confronting her, and leaning on his writhing stick.

"Ah, forsooth, and is it your worship, indeed?" cried the good dame. "Yea, truly is it, and in the very image of my old gossip, Goodman Brown, the grandfather of the silly fellow that now is. But—would your worship believe it?—my broomstick hath strangely disappeared, stolen, as I suspect, by that unhanged witch, Goody Cory,[10] and that, too, when I was all anointed with the juice of smallage and cinque-foil and wolf's-bane—"[11]

---

[9]Sarah Cloyse was one of the women sentence to death for witchcraft in 1692; she was not executed.

[10]Martha Corey was hanged as a witch in 1692.

[11]Plants thought to be used by witches.

"Mingled with fine wheat and the fat of a new-born babe," said the shape of old Goodman Brown.

"Ah, your worship knows the receipt," cried the old lady, cackling aloud. "So, as I was saying, being all ready for the meeting, and no horse to ride on, I made up my mind to foot it; for they tell me, there is a nice young man to be taken into communion to-night. But now your good worship will lend me your arm, and we shall be there in a twinkling."

"That can hardly be," answered her friend. "I may not spare you my arm, Goody Cloyse, but here is my staff, if you will."

So saying, he threw it down at her feet, where, perhaps, it assumed life, being one of the rods which its owner had formerly lent to the Egyptian Magi.[12] Of this fact, however, Goodman Brown could not take cognizance. He had cast up his eyes in astonishment, and looking down again, beheld neither Goody Cloyse nor the serpentine staff, but his fellow-traveller alone, who waited for him as calmly as if nothing had happened.

"That old woman taught me my catechism!" said the young man; and there was a world of meaning in this simple comment.

They continued to walk onward, while the elder traveller exhorted his companion to make good speed and persevere in the path, discoursing so aptly, that his arguments seemed rather to spring up in the bosom of his auditor, than to be suggested by himself. As they went, he plucked a branch of maple, to serve for a walking-stick, and began to strip it of the twigs and little boughs, which were wet with evening dew. The moment his fingers touched them, they became strangely withered and dried up, as with a week's sunshine. Thus the pair proceeded, at a good free pace, until suddenly, in a gloomy hollow of the road, Goodman Brown sat himself down on the stump of a tree, and refused to go any farther.

"Friend," said he, stubbornly, "my mind is made up. Not another step will I budge on this errand. What if a wretched old woman do choose to go to the devil, when I thought she was going to Heaven! Is that any reason why I should quit my dear Faith, and go after her?"

"You will think better of this, by-and-by," said his acquaintance, composedly. "Sit here and rest yourself awhile; and when you feel like moving again, there is my staff to help you along."

Without more words, he threw his companion the maple stick, and was as speedily out of sight, as if he had vanished into the deepening gloom. The young man sat a few moments, by the road-side, applauding himself greatly, and thinking with how clear a conscience he should meet the minister, in his morning-walk, nor shrink from the eye of good old Deacon Gookin. And

---

[12]In the Book of Exodus (7:9–12), Egyptian priests transform their rods into serpents.

what calm sleep would be his, that very night, which was to have been spent so wickedly, but purely and sweetly now, in the arms of Faith! Amidst these pleasant and praiseworthy meditations, Goodman Brown heard the tramp of horses along the road, and deemed it advisable to conceal himself within the verge of the forest, conscious of the guilty purpose that had brought him thither, though now so happily turned from it.

On came the hoof-tramps and the voices of the riders, two grave old voices, conversing soberly as they drew near. These mingled sounds appeared to pass along the road, within a few yards of the young man's hiding-place; but owing, doubtless, to the depth of the gloom, at that particular spot, neither the travellers nor their steeds were visible. Though their figures brushed the small boughs by the way-side, it could not be seen that they intercepted, even for a moment, the faint gleam from the strip of bright sky, athwart which they must have passed. Goodman Brown alternately crouched and stood on tip-toe, pulling aside the branches, and thrusting forth his head as far as he durst, without discerning so much as a shadow. It vexed him the more, because he could have sworn, were such a thing possible, that he recognized the voices of the minister and Deacon Gookin, jogging along quietly, as they were wont to do, when bound to some ordination or ecclesiastical council. While yet within hearing, one of the riders stopped to pluck a switch.

"Of the two, reverend Sir," said the voice like the deacon's, "I had rather miss an ordination-dinner than to-night's meeting. They tell me that some of our community are to be here from Falmouth and beyond, and others from Connecticut and Rhode-Island; besides several of the Indian powows,[13] who, after their fashion, know almost as much deviltry as the best of us. Moreover, there is a goodly young woman to be taken into communion."

"Mighty well, Deacon Gookin!" replied the solemn old tones of the minister. "Spur up, or we shall be late. Nothing can be done, you know, until I get on the ground."

The hoofs clattered again, and the voices, talking so strangely in the empty air, passed on through the forest, where no church had ever been gathered, nor solitary Christian prayed. Whither, then, could these holy men be journeying, so deep into the heathen wilderness? Young Goodman Brown caught hold of a tree, for support, being ready to sink down on the ground, faint and over-burthened with the heavy sickness of his heart. He looked up to the sky, doubting whether there really was a Heaven above him. Yet, there was the blue arch, and the stars brightening in it.

"With Heaven above, and Faith below, I will yet stand firm against the devil!" cried Goodman Brown.

---

[13]Medicine men

While he still gazed upward, into the deep arch of the firmament, and had lifted his hands to pray, a cloud, though no wind was stirring, hurried across the zenith, and hid the brightening stars. The blue sky was still visible, except directly overhead, where this black mass of cloud was sweeping swiftly northward. Aloft in the air, as if from the depths of the cloud, came a confused and doubtful sound of voices. Once, the listener fancied that he could distinguish the accents of town's-people of his own, men and women, both pious and ungodly, many of whom he had met at the communion-table, and had seen others rioting at the tavern. The next moment, so indistinct were the sounds, he doubted whether he had heard aught but the murmur of the old forest, whispering without a wind. Then came a stronger swell of those familiar tones, heard daily in the sunshine, at Salem village, but never, until now, from a cloud of night. There was one voice, of a young woman, uttering lamentations, yet with an uncertain sorrow, and entreating for some favor, which, perhaps, it would grieve her to obtain. And all the unseen multitude, both saints and sinners, seemed to encourage her onward.

"Faith!" shouted Goodman Brown, in a voice of agony and desperation; and the echoes of the forest mocked him, crying—"Faith! Faith!" as if bewildered wretches were seeking her, all through the wilderness.

The cry of grief, rage, and terror, was yet piercing the night, when the unhappy husband held his breath for a response. There was a scream, drowned immediately in a louder murmur of voices, fading into far-off laughter, as the dark cloud swept away, leaving the clear and silent sky above Goodman Brown. But something fluttered lightly down through the air, and caught on the branch of a tree. The young man seized it, and beheld a pink ribbon.

"My Faith is gone!" cried he, after one stupefied moment. "There is no good on earth; and sin is but a name. Come, devil! for to thee is this world given."

And maddened with despair, so that he laughed loud and long, did Goodman Brown grasp his staff and set forth again, at such a rate, that he seemed to fly along the forest-path, rather than to walk or run. The road grew wilder and drearier, and more faintly traced, and vanished at length, leaving him in the heart of the dark wilderness, still rushing onward, with the instinct that guides mortal man to evil. The whole forest was peopled with frightful sounds; the creaking of the trees, the howling of wild beasts, and the yell of Indians; while, sometimes, the wind tolled like a distant church-bell, and sometimes gave a broad roar around the traveller, as if all Nature were laughing him to scorn. But he was himself the chief horror of the scene, and shrank not from its other horrors.

"Ha! ha! ha!" roared Goodman Brown, when the wind laughed at him. "Let us hear which will laugh loudest! Think not to frighten me with your deviltry! Come witch, come wizard, come Indian powow, come devil himself! and here comes Goodman Brown. You may as well fear him as he fear you!"

In truth, all through the haunted forest, there could be nothing more frightful than the figure of Goodman Brown. On he flew, among the black pines, brandishing his staff with frenzied gestures, now giving vent to an inspiration of horrid blasphemy, and now shouting forth such laughter, as set all the echoes of the forest laughing like demons around him. The fiend in his own shape is less hideous, than when he rages in the breast of man. Thus sped the demoniac on his course, until, quivering among the trees, he saw a red light before him, as when the felled trunks and branches of a clearing have been set on fire, and throw up their lurid blaze against the sky, at the hour of midnight. He paused, in a lull of the tempest that had driven him onward, and heard the swell of what seemed a hymn, rolling solemnly from a distance, with the weight of many voices. He knew the tune; it was a familiar one in the choir of the village meeting-house. The verse died heavily away, and was lengthened by a chorus, not of human voices, but of all the sounds of the benighted wilderness, pealing in awful harmony together. Goodman Brown cried out; and his cry was lost to his own ear, by its unison with the cry of the desert.

In the interval of silence, he stole forward, until the light glared full upon his eyes. At one extremity of an open space, hemmed in by the dark wall of the forest, arose a rock, bearing some rude, natural resemblance either to an altar or a pulpit, and surrounded by four blazing pines, their tops aflame, their stems untouched, like candles at an evening meeting. The mass of foliage, that had overgrown the summit of the rock, was all on fire, blazing high into the night, and fitfully illuminating the whole field. Each pendent twig and leafy festoon was in a blaze. As the red light arose and fell, a numerous congregation alternately shone forth, then disappeared in shadow, and again grew, as it were, out of the darkness, peopling the heart of the solitary woods at once.

"A grave and dark-clad company!" quoth Goodman Brown.

In truth, they were such. Among them, quivering to-and-fro, between gloom and splendor, appeared faces that would be seen, next day, at the council-board of the province, and others which, Sabbath after Sabbath, looked devoutly heavenward, and benignantly over the crowded pews, from the holiest pulpits in the land. Some affirm, that the lady of the governor was there. At least, there were high dames well known to her, and wives of honored husbands, and widows, a great multitude, and ancient maidens, all of excellent repute, and fair young girls, who trembled, lest their mothers should espy them. Either the sudden gleams of light, flashing over the obscure field, bedazzled Goodman Brown, or he recognized a score of the churchmembers of Salem village, famous for their especial sanctity. Good old Deacon Gookin had arrived, and waited at the skirts of that venerable saint, his revered pastor.

But, irreverently consorting with these grave, reputable, and pious people, these elders of the church, these chaste dames and dewy virgins, there were men of dissolute lives and women of spotted fame, wretches given over to all mean and filthy vice, and suspected even of horrid crimes. It was strange to see, that the good shrank not from the wicked, nor were the sinners abashed by the saints. Scattered, also, among their palefaced enemies, were the Indian priests, or powows, who had often scared their native forest with more hideous incantations than any known to English witchcraft.

"But, where is Faith?" thought Goodman Brown; and, as hope came into his heart, he trembled.

Another verse of the hymn arose, a slow and mournful strain, such as the pious love, but joined to words which expressed all that our nature can conceive of sin, and darkly hinted at far more. Unfathomable to mere mortals is the lore of fiends. Verse after verse was sung, and still the chorus of the desert swelled between, like the deepest tone of a mighty organ. And, with the final peal of that dreadful anthem, there came a sound, as if the roaring wind, the rushing streams, the howling beasts, and every other voice of the unconverted wilderness, were mingling and according with the voice of guilty man, in homage to the prince of all. The four blazing pines threw up a loftier flame, and obscurely discovered shapes and visages of horror on the smokewreaths, above the impious assembly. At the same moment, the fire on the rock shot redly forth, and formed a glowing arch above its base, where now appeared a figure. With reverence be it spoken, the figure bore no slight similitude, both in garb and manner, to some grave divine of the New-England churches.

"Bring forth the converts!" cried a voice, that echoed through the field and rolled into the forest.

At the word, Goodman Brown stept forth from the shadow of the trees, and approached the congregation, with whom he felt a loathful brotherhood, by the sympathy of all that was wicked in his heart. He could have well nigh sworn, that the shape of his own dead father beckoned him to advance, looking downward from a smoke-wreath, while a woman, with dim features of despair, threw out her hand to warn him back. Was it his mother? But he had no power to retreat one step, nor to resist, even in thought, when the minister and good old Deacon Gookin seized his arms, and led him to the blazing rock. Thither came also the slender form of a veiled female, led between Goody Cloyse, that pious teacher of the catechism, and Martha Carrier,[14] who had received the devil's promise to be queen of hell. A rampant hag was she! And there stood the proselytes, beneath the canopy of fire.

---

[14]Hanged as a witch in 1692.

"Welcome, my children," said the dark figure, "to the communion of your race! Ye have found, thus young, your nature and your destiny. My children, look behind you!"

They turned; and flashing forth, as it were, in a sheet of flame, the fiend-worshippers were seen; the smile of welcome gleamed darkly on every visage.

"There," resumed the sable form, "are all whom ye have reverenced from youth. Ye deemed them holier than yourselves, and shrank from your own sin, contrasting it with their lives of righteousness, and prayerful aspirations heavenward. Yet, here are they all, in my worshipping assembly! This night it shall be granted you to know their secret deeds; how hoary-bearded elders of the church have whispered wanton words to the young maids of their households; how many a woman, eager for widow's weeds, has given her husband a drink at bedtime, and let him sleep his last sleep in her bosom; how beardless youths have made haste to inherit their fathers' wealth; and how fair damsels—blush not, sweet ones!—have dug little graves in the garden, and bidden me, the sole guest, to an infant's funeral. By the sympathy of your human hearts for sin, ye shall scent out all the places—whether in church, bed-chamber, street, field, or forest—where crime has been committed, and shall exult to behold the whole earth one stain of guilt, one mighty blood-spot. Far more than this! It shall be yours to penetrate, in every bosom, the deep mystery of sin, the fountain of all wicked arts, and which inexhaustibly supplies more evil impulses than human power—than my power, at its utmost!—can make manifest in deeds. And now, my children, look upon each other."

They did so; and, by the blaze of the hell-kindled torches, the wretched man beheld his Faith, and the wife her husband, trembling before that unhallowed altar.

"Lo! there ye stand, my children," said the figure, in a deep and solemn tone, almost sad, with its despairing awfulness, as if his once angelic nature could yet mourn for our miserable race. "Depending upon one another's hearts, ye had still hoped, that virtue were not all a dream. Now are ye undeceived! Evil is the nature of mankind. Evil must be your only happiness. Welcome, again, my children, to the communion of your race!"

"Welcome!" repeated the fiend-worshippers, in one cry of despair and triumph.

And there they stood, the only pair, as it seemed, who were yet hesitating on the verge of wickedness, in this dark world. A basin was hollowed, naturally, in the rock. Did it contain water, reddened by the lurid light? or was it blood? or, perchance, a liquid flame? Herein did the Shape of Evil dip his hand, and prepare to lay the mark of baptism upon their foreheads, that they might be partakers of the mystery of sin, more conscious of the secret guilt of others, both in deed and thought, than they could now be of their own. The husband cast one look at his pale wife, and Faith at him. What polluted wretches would the next glance shew them to each other, shuddering alike at what they disclosed and what they saw!

"Faith! Faith!" cried the husband. "Look up to Heaven, and resist the Wicked One!"

Whether Faith obeyed, he knew not. Hardly had he spoken, when he found himself amid calm night and solitude, listening to a roar of the wind, which died heavily away through the forest. He staggered against the rock and felt it chill and damp, while a hanging twig, that had been all on fire, besprinkled his cheek with the coldest dew.

The next morning, young Goodman Brown came slowly into the street of Salem village, staring around him like a bewildered man. The good old minister was taking a walk along the grave-yard, to get an appetite for breakfast and meditate his sermon, and bestowed a blessing, as he passed, on Goodman Brown. He shrank from the venerable saint, as if to avoid an anathema. Old Deacon Gookin was at domestic worship, and the holy words of his prayer were heard through the open window. "What God doth the wizard pray to?" quoth Goodman Brown. Goody Cloyse, that excellent old Christian, stood in the early sunshine, at her own lattice, catechising a little girl, who had brought her a pint of morning's milk. Goodman Brown snatched away the child, as from the grasp of the fiend himself. Turning the corner by the meeting-house, he spied the head of Faith, with the pink ribbons, gazing anxiously forth, and bursting into such joy at sight of him, that she skipt along the street, and almost kissed her husband before the whole village. But, Goodman Brown looked sternly and sadly into her face, and passed on without a greeting.

Had Goodman Brown fallen asleep in the forest, and only dreamed a wild dream of a witch-meeting?

Be it so, if you will. But, alas! it was a dream of evil omen for young Goodman Brown. A stern, a sad, a darkly meditative, a distrustful, if not a desperate man, did he become, from the night of that fearful dream. On the Sabbath-day, when the congregation were singing a holy psalm, he could not listen, because an anthem of sin rushed loudly upon his ear, and drowned all the blessed strain. When the minister spoke from the pulpit, with power and fervid eloquence, and, with his hand on the open Bible, of the sacred truths of our religion, and of saint-like lives and triumphant deaths, and of future bliss or misery unutterable, then did Goodman Brown turn pale, dreading, lest the roof should thunder down upon the gray blasphemer and his hearers. Often, awakening suddenly at midnight, he shrank from the bosom of Faith, and at morning or eventide, when the family knelt down at prayer, he scowled, and muttered to himself, and gazed sternly at his wife, and turned away. And when he had lived long, and was borne to his grave, a hoary corpse, followed by Faith, an aged woman, and children and grand-children, a goodly procession, besides neighbors, not a few, they carved no hopeful verse upon his tombstone; for his dying hour was gloom.

[1835]

Shirley Jackson

[1919–1965]

At once a doting mother who wrote humorous accounts of her family life and a self-described witch who penned incisive studies of psychologic aberration and unsettling tales of the supernatural, SHIRLEY JACKSON *explored the unstable boundary between domesticity and horror. Considered one of the finest American fiction writers of the 1950s and 1960s, Jackson is now best known for the widely anthologized short story "The Lottery" (1948).*

Jackson was born in 1919 in San Francisco, the first child of an affluent and conservative family. During childhood and adolescence and well into adulthood, this unruly and overweight daughter struggled against her mother Geraldine's firmly held standards of propriety and femininity. As she resisted the conventions of class and gender, Jackson developed her gift of seeing beneath the decorous surface of middle-class life into its vicious core. In the sunny and seemingly placid northern California suburb of Burlingame, where she attended high school and began writing poetry and short stories, Jackson discerned her neighbors' intolerance and cruelty—traits that later characterized the suburbanites of her fiction.

In 1933 Jackson's family moved to Rochester, New York. After attending the University of Rochester from 1934 to 1936, Jackson withdrew from school and spent a year at home, writing a thousand words a day. In 1937 she entered Syracuse University, where she edited the campus humor magazine, won second prize in a poetry contest, and founded the literary magazine Spectre. *She married the magazine's managing editor, Stanley Edgar Hyman, immediately after her graduation in 1940. The couple moved to New York City, where Jackson held a variety of unsatisfying jobs while continuing to write. In 1941 her experience selling books at Macy's formed the basis for "My Life with R. H. Macy," published in the* New Republic. *This success was followed by the birth of her first child and the publication of many stories in the New Yorker. Her reputation as a writer of short fiction grew, and in 1944 "Come Dance with Me in Ireland" was the first of her four stories chosen for* Best American Short Stories.

Jackson's family continued to grow, and her body of writing continued to expand after she moved to North Bennington, Vermont. She had three more children and published short stories, novels, family chronicles, a one-act play, a children's book, and a nonfictional account of witchcraft in Salem. Her works were made into plays, films, and television shows. "The Lottery" appeared as a short play, a television drama, a radio show, an opera, and a ballet. The family chronicles Life Among the Savages *(1953) and* Raising Demons *(1957) were bestsellers, and Jackson's popular success was matched by critical acclaim for her short fiction and novels alike. These latter include* The Road Through the Wall *(1948), a look at the dark side of suburban life inspired by Jackson's years in Burlingame;* Hangsaman *(1951) and* The Bird's Nest *(1954), two penetrating depictions of mental illness; and* The Sundial *(1958), a Gothic fantasy about the end of the world. Jackson's last two novels,* The Haunting of Hill House *(1959) and* We Have Always Lived in the Castle *(1962), are her best. At once chilling and tender, these haunted-house stories transcend their genre, portraying the often-strained relationship between mother and daughter with consummate sympathy and skill. Three years after* We Have Always Lived in the Castle *appeared on the bestseller list and was named one of the year's best novels by* Time *magazine, Shirley Jackson died of heart failure on August 8, 1965.*

—Jamil Musstafa, *Lewis University*

The Lottery

SHIRLEY JACKSON

THE MORNING OF JUNE 27TH was clear and sunny, with the fresh warmth of a full-summer day; the flowers were blossoming profusely and the grass was richly green. The people of the village began to gather in the square, between the post office and the bank, around ten o'clock; in some towns there were so many people that the lottery took two days and had to be started on June 26th, but in this village, where there were only about three hundred people, the whole lottery took less than two hours, so it could begin at ten o'clock in the morning and still be through in time to allow the villagers to get home for noon dinner.

The children assembled first, of course. School was recently over for the summer, and the feeling of liberty sat uneasily on most of them; they tended to gather together quietly for a while before they broke into boisterous play, and their talk was still of the classroom and the teacher, of books and reprimands. Bobby Martin had already stuffed his pockets full of stones, and the other boys soon followed his example, selecting the smoothest and roundest stones; Bobby and Harry Jones and Dickie Delacroix—the villagers pronounced this name "Dellacroy"—eventually made a great pile of stones in one corner of the square and guarded it against the raids of the other boys. The girls stood aside, talking among themselves, looking over their shoulders at the boys, and the very small children rolled in the dust or clung to the hands of their older brothers or sisters.

Soon the men began to gather, surveying their own children, speaking of planting and rain, tractors and taxes. They stood together, away from the pile of stones in the corner, and their jokes were quiet and they smiled rather than laughed. The women, wearing faded house dresses and sweaters, came shortly after their menfolk. They greeted one another and exchanged bits of gossip as they went to join their husbands. Soon the women, standing by their husbands, began to call to their children, and the children came reluctantly, having to be called four or five times. Bobby Martin ducked under his mother's grasping hand and ran, laughing, back to the pile of stones. His father spoke up sharply, and Bobby came quickly and took his place between his father and his oldest brother.

Reprinted from *The Lottery and Other Stories,* by permission of Farrar, Straus & Giroux, LLC. Copyright © 1976, 1977 by Laurence Hyman, Barry Hyman, Mrs. Sarah Webster and Mrs. Joanne Schnurer.

The lottery was conducted—as were the square dances, the teenage club, the Halloween program—by Mr. Summers, who had time and energy to devote to civic activities. He was a round-faced, jovial man and he ran the coal business, and people were sorry for him, because he had no children and his wife was a scold. When he arrived in the square, carrying the black wooden box, there was a murmur of conversation among the villagers, and he waved and called, "Little late today, folks." The postmaster, Mr. Graves, followed him, carrying a three-legged stool, and the stool was put in the center of the square and Mr. Summers set the black box down on it. The villagers kept their distance, leaving a space between themselves and the stool, and when Mr. Summers said, "Some of you fellows want to give me a hand?" there was a hesitation before two men, Mr. Martin and his oldest son, Baxter, came forward to hold the box steady on the stool while Mr. Summers stirred up the papers inside it.

The original paraphernalia for the lottery had been lost long ago, and the black box now resting on the stool had been put into use even before Old Man Warner, the oldest man in town, was born. Mr. Summers spoke frequently to the villagers about making a new box, but no one liked to upset even as much tradition as was represented by the black box. There was a story that the present box had been made with some pieces of the box that had preceded it, the one that had been constructed when the first people settled down to make a village here. Every year, after the lottery, Mr. Summers began talking again about a new box, but every year the subject was allowed to fade off without anything's being done. The black box grew shabbier each year; by now it was no longer completely black but splintered badly along one side to show the original wood color, and in some places faded or stained.

Mr. Martin and his oldest son, Baxter, held the black box securely on the stool until Mr. Summers had stirred the papers thoroughly with his hand. Because so much of the ritual had been forgotten or discarded, Mr. Summers had been successful in having slips of paper substituted for the chips of wood that had been used for generations. Chips of wood, Mr. Summers had argued, had been all very well when the village was tiny, but now that the population was more than three hundred and likely to keep on growing, it was necessary to use something that would fit more easily into the black box. The night before the lottery, Mr. Summers and Mr. Graves made up the slips of paper and put them in the box, and it was then taken to the safe of Mr. Summers' coal company and locked up until Mr. Summers was ready to take it to the square next morning. The rest of the year, the box was put away, sometimes one place, sometimes another; it had spent one year in Mr. Graves's barn and another year underfoot in the post office, and sometimes it was set on a shelf in the Martin grocery and left there.

There was a great deal of fussing to be done before Mr. Summers declared the lottery open. There were the lists to make up—of heads of families, heads of households in each family, members of each household in each family. There was the proper swearing-in of Mr. Summers by the postmaster, as the official of the lottery; at one time, some people remembered, there had been a recital of some sort, performed by the official of the lottery, a perfunctory, tuneless chant that had been rattled off duly each year; some people believed that the official of the lottery used to stand just so when he said or sang it, others believed that he was supposed to walk among the people, but years and years ago this part of the ritual had been allowed to lapse. There had been, also, a ritual salute, which the official of the lottery had had to use in addressing each person who came up to draw from the box, but this also had changed with time, until now it was felt necessary only for the official to speak to each person approaching. Mr. Summers was very good at all this; in his clean white shirt and blue jeans, with one hand resting carelessly on the black box, he seemed very proper and important as he talked interminably to Mr. Graves and the Martins.

Just as Mr. Summers finally left off talking and turned to the assembled villagers, Mrs. Hutchinson came hurriedly along the path to the square, her sweater thrown over her shoulders, and slid into place in the back of the crowd. "Clean forgot what day it was," she said to Mrs. Delacroix, who stood next to her, and they both laughed softly. "Thought my old man was out back stacking wood," Mrs. Hutchinson went on, "and then I looked out the window and the kids were gone, and then I remembered it was the twentyseventh and came a-running." She dried her hands on her apron, and Mrs. Delacroix said, "You're in time, though. They're still talking away up there."

Mrs. Hutchinson craned her neck to see through the crowd and found her husband and children standing near the front. She tapped Mrs. Delacroix on the arm as a farewell and began to make her way through the crowd. The people separated good-humoredly to let her through; two or three people said, in voices just loud enough to be heard across the crowd, "Here comes your Missus, Hutchinson," and "Bill, she made it after all." Mrs. Hutchinson reached her husband, and Mr. Summers, who had been waiting, said cheerfully, "Thought we were going to have to get on without you, Tessie." Mrs. Hutchinson said, grinning, "Wouldn't have me leave m'dishes in the sink, now, would you, Joe?" and soft laughter ran through the crowd as the people stirred back into position after Mrs. Hutchinson's arrival.

"Well, now," Mr. Summers said soberly, "guess we better get started, get this over with, so's we can go back to work. Anybody ain't here?"

"Dunbar," several people said. "Dunbar, Dunbar."

Mr. Summers consulted his list. "Clyde Dunbar," he said. "That's right. He's broke his leg, hasn't he? Who's drawing for him?"

"Me, I guess," a woman said, and Mr. Summers turned to look at her. "Wife draws for her husband," Mr. Summers said. "Don't you have a grown boy to do it for you, Janey?" Although Mr. Summers and everyone else in the village knew the answer perfectly well, it was the business of the official of the lottery to ask such questions formally. Mr. Summers waited with an expression of polite interest while Mrs. Dunbar answered.

"Horace's not but sixteen yet," Mrs. Dunbar said regretfully. "Guess I gotta fill in for the old man this year."

"Right," Mr. Summers said. He made a note on the list he was holding. Then he asked, "Watson boy drawing this year?"

A tall boy in the crowd raised his hand. "Here," he said. "I'm drawing for m'mother and me." He blinked his eyes nervously and ducked his head as several voices in the crowd said things like "Good fellow, Jack," and "Glad to see your mother's got a man to do it."

"Well," Mr. Summers said, "guess that's everyone. Old Man Warner make it?"

"Here," a voice said, and Mr. Summers nodded.

A sudden hush fell on the crowd as Mr. Summers cleared his throat and looked at the list. "All ready?" he called. "Now, I'll read the names—heads of families first—and the men come up and take a paper out of the box. Keep the paper folded in your hand without looking at it until everyone has had a turn. Everything clear?"

The people had done it so many times that they only half listened to the directions; most of them were quiet, wetting their lips, not looking around. Then Mr. Summers raised one hand high and said, "Adams." A man disengaged himself from the crowd and came forward. "Hi, Steve," Mr. Summers said, and Mr. Adams said, "Hi, Joe." They grinned at one another humorlessly and nervously. Then Mr. Adams reached into the black box and took out a folded paper. He held it firmly by one corner as he turned and went hastily back to his place in the crowd, where he stood a little apart from his family, not looking down at his hand.

"Allen," Mr. Summers said. "Anderson . . . Bentham."

"Seems like there's no time at all between lotteries any more," Mrs. Delacroix said to Mrs. Graves in the back row. "Seems like we got through with the last one only last week."

"Time sure goes fast," Mrs. Graves said.

"Clark . . . Delacroix."

"There goes my old man," Mrs. Delacroix said. She held her breath while her husband went forward.

"Dunbar," Mr. Summers said, and Mrs. Dunbar went steadily to the box while one of the women said, "Go on, Janey," and another said, "There she goes."

"We're next," Mrs. Graves said. She watched while Mr. Graves came around from the side of the box, greeted Mr. Summers gravely, and selected a slip of paper from the box. By now, all through the crowd there were men holding the small folded papers in their large hands, turning them over and over nervously. Mrs. Dunbar and her two sons stood together, Mrs. Dunbar holding the slip of paper.

"Harburt . . . Hutchinson."

"Get up there, Bill," Mrs. Hutchinson said, and the people near her laughed.

"Jones."

"They do say," Mr. Adams said to Old Man Warner, who stood next to him, "that over in the north village they're talking of giving up the lottery."

Old Man Warner snorted. "Pack of crazy fools," he said. "Listening to the young folks, nothing's good enough for *them*. Next thing you know, they'll be wanting to go back to living in caves, nobody work any more, live *that* way for a while. Used to be a saying about 'Lottery in June, corn be heavy soon.' First thing you know, we'd all be eating stewed chickweed and acorns. There's *always* been a lottery," he added petulantly. "Bad enough to see young Joe Summers up there joking with everybody."

"Some places have already quit lotteries," Mrs. Adams said.

"Nothing but trouble in *that*," Old Man Warner said stoutly. "Pack of young fools."

"Martin." And Bobby Martin watched his father go forward. "Overdyke . . . Percy."

"I wish they'd hurry," Mrs. Dunbar said to her older son. "I wish they'd hurry."

"They're almost through," her son said.

"You get ready to run tell Dad," Mrs. Dunbar said.

Mr. Summers called his own name and then stepped forward precisely and selected a slip from the box. Then he called, "Warner."

"Seventy-seventh year I been in the lottery," Old Man Warner said as he went through the crowd. "Seventy-seventh time."

"Watson." The tall boy came awkwardly through the crowd. Someone said, "Don't be nervous, Jack," and Mr. Summers said, "Take your time, son."

"Zanini."

After that, there was a long pause, a breathless pause, until Mr. Summers, holding his slip of paper in the air, said, "All right, fellows." For a minute, no one moved, and then all the slips of paper were opened. Suddenly, all the women began to speak at once, saying, "Who is it?" "Who's got it?" "Is it the Dunbars?" "Is it the Watsons?" Then the voices began to say, "It's Hutchinson. It's Bill," "Bill Hutchinson's got it."

"Go tell your father," Mrs. Dunbar said to her older son.

People began to look around to see the Hutchinsons. Bill Hutchinson was standing quiet, staring down at the paper in his hand. Suddenly, Tessie Hutchinson shouted to Mr. Summers, "You didn't give him time enough to take any paper he wanted. I saw you. It wasn't fair."

"Be a good sport, Tessie," Mrs. Delacroix called, and Mrs. Graves said, "All of us took the same chance."

"Shut up, Tessie," Bill Hutchinson said.

"Well, everyone," Mr. Summers said, "that was done pretty fast, and now we've got to be hurrying a little more to get done in time." He consulted his next list. "Bill," he said, "you draw for the Hutchinson family. You got any other households in the Hutchinsons?"

"There's Don and Eva," Mrs. Hutchinson yelled. "Make them take their chance!"

"Daughters draw with their husbands' families, Tessie," Mr. Summers said gently. "You know that as well as anyone else."

"It wasn't *fair*," Tessie said.

"I guess not, Joe," Bill Hutchinson said regretfully. "My daughter draws with her husband's family, that's only fair. And I've got no other family except the kids."

"Then, as far as drawing for families is concerned, it's you." Mr. Summers said in explanation, "and as far as drawing for households is concerned, that's you, too. Right?"

"Right," Bill Hutchinson said.

"How many kids, Bill?" Mr. Summers asked formally.

"Three," Bill Hutchinson said. "There's Bill, Jr., and Nancy, and little Dave. And Tessie and me."

"All right, then," Mr. Summers said. "Harry, you got their tickets back?"

Mr. Graves nodded and held up the slips of paper. "Put them in the box, then," Mr. Summers directed. "Take Bill's and put it in."

"I think we ought to start over," Mrs. Hutchinson said, as quietly as she could. "I tell you it wasn't *fair*. You didn't give him time enough to choose. *Every*body saw that."

Mr. Graves had selected the five slips and put them in the box, and he dropped all the papers but those onto the ground, where the breeze caught them and lifted them off.

"Listen, everybody," Mrs. Hutchinson was saying to the people around her.

"Ready, Bill?" Mr. Summers asked, and Bill Hutchinson, with one quick glance around at his wife and children, nodded.

"Remember," Mr. Summers said, "take the slips and keep them folded until each person has taken one. Harry, you help little Dave." Mr. Graves took the hand of the little boy, who came willingly with him up to the box. "Take a paper out of the box, Davy," Mr. Summers said. Davy put his hand into the box and laughed. "Take just *one* paper," Mr. Summers said. "Harry, you hold it for him." Mr. Graves took the child's hand and removed the folded paper from the tight fist and held it while little Dave stood next to him and looked up at him wonderingly.

"Nancy next," Mr. Summers said. Nancy was twelve, and her school friends breathed heavily as she went forward, switching her skirt, and took a slip daintily from the box. "Bill, Jr.," Mr. Summers said, and Billy, his face red and his feet over-large, nearly knocked the box over as he got a paper out. "Tessie," Mr. Summers said. She hesitated for a minute, looking around defiantly, and then set her lips and went up to the box. She snatched a paper out and held it behind her.

"Bill," Mr. Summers said, and Bill Hutchinson reached into the box and felt around, bringing his hand out at last with the slip of paper in it.

The crowd was quiet. A girl whispered, "I hope it's not Nancy," and the sound of the whisper reached the edges of the crowd.

"It's not the way it used to be," Old Man Warner said clearly. "People ain't the way they used to be."

"All right," Mr. Summers said. "Open the papers. Harry, you open little Dave's."

Mr. Graves opened the slip of paper and there was a general sigh through the crowd as he held it up and everyone could see that it was blank. Nancy and Bill, Jr., opened theirs at the same time, and both beamed and laughed, turning around to the crowd and holding their slips of paper above their heads.

"Tessie," Mr. Summers said. There was a pause, and then Mr. Summers looked at Bill Hutchinson, and Bill unfolded his paper and showed it. It was blank.

"It's Tessie," Mr. Summers said, and his voice was hushed. "Show us her paper, Bill."

Bill Hutchinson went over to his wife and forced the slip of paper out of her hand. It had a black spot on it, the black spot Mr. Summers had made the night before with the heavy pencil in the coal-company office. Bill Hutchinson held it up, and there was a stir in the crowd.

"All right, folks," Mr. Summers said. "Let's finish quickly."

Although the villagers had forgotten the ritual and lost the original black box, they still remembered to use stones. The pile of stones the boys had made earlier was ready; there were stones on the ground with the blowing scraps of paper that had come out of the box. Mrs. Delacroix selected a stone so large she had to pick it up with both hands and turned, to Mrs. Dunbar. "Come on," she said. "Hurry up."

Mrs. Dunbar had small stones in both hands, and she said, gasping for breath, "I can't run at all. You'll have to go ahead and I'll catch up with you."

The children had stones already, and someone gave little Davy Hutchinson a few pebbles.

Tessie Hutchinson was in the center of a cleared space by now, and she held her hands out desperately as the villagers moved in on her. "It isn't fair," she said. A stone hit her on the side of the head.

Old Man Warner was saying, "Come on, come on, everyone." Steve Adams was in the front of the crowd of villagers, with Mrs. Graves beside him.

"It isn't fair, it isn't right," Mrs. Hutchinson screamed, and then they were upon her.

[1949]

James Joyce
[1882–1941]

JAMES JOYCE *was born at Rathgar outside of Dublin, Ireland. Joyce's father was musical and charming but given to losing money, or at least not keeping it. Joyce's young life was spent watching the family fortunes dwindle. The combination of a charming but unreliable father and a strong and demanding mother may have set the scenes for much of his later writing. Joyce attended boarding school where he suffered the abuses of Jesuit discipline as it was practiced in the late 1800s. In his first novel,* A Portrait of the Artist as a Young Man, *he describes beatings and verbal abuse. Joyce joined the Faculty of Arts in University College, Dublin, but soon found that he was meant for the life in early twentieth century Paris. In Ireland Joyce spent time with such notable writers as William Butler Yeats and developed a strong interest in the Irish independence movement though he never actually participated in the rebellion. Joyce's collection of short stories,* Dubliners, *is a kind of farewell to Ireland, since the portraits that he draws in these tales all suggest a kind of moral and political paralysis in the Irish mind. Joyce sympathized with his countrymen but was unable to find interest or energy in joining their battles with the British.*

After his mother's death in 1902, Joyce and his lover Nora Barnacle departed for Paris and Europe permanently. They became the parents of a son and daughter and did eventually marry in 1931, despite Joyce's objections to formal marriage. Joyce taught in Switzerland, but the Paris appeal was always strong. The American poet Ezra Pound encouraged Joyce in his writing and acted as coach and editor as well as literary supporter. Joyce spent most of the rest of his life working on his two major works, Ulysses *and* Finnegans Wake. *The American courts fought over the pornographic nature of* Ulysses, *the case having elicited the famous quotation by a judge that he "knew pornography when he saw it."* Ulysses *would hardly be considered shocking by twenty-first century MTV standards, but in its day the novel was controversial.*

In the meantime, Joyce's eyesight deteriorated, but he continued to write, supported by patrons, or people who were willing to give money to important artists to encourage their writing. Harriet Weaver, a wealthy woman who supported the Joyces for most of Joyce's writing life, was willing to continue to offer patronage even when his works were threatened by American disapproval. Both wars caused the Joyces to move to neutral Switzerland. Joyce lived in Switzerland during World War I and went there again as World War II threatened. It was there that he died during the war. He is now thought of as one of the greatest writers of the twentieth century. His contributions to the changes in the way that novels and stories tell about life began what was to become a postmodern way of writing despite the modernist centrality of Joyce's attitudes and artistic temperament.

Araby

JAMES JOYCE

NORTH RICHMOND STREET, being blind, was a quiet street except at the hour when the Christian Brothers' School set the boys free. An uninhabited house of two storeys stood at the blind end, detached from its neighbours in a square ground. The other houses of the street, conscious of decent lives within them, gazed at one another with brown imperturbable faces.

The former tenant of our house, a priest, had died in the back drawing room. Air, musty from having long been enclosed, hung in all the rooms, and the waste room behind the kitchen was littered with old useless papers. Among these I found a few paper-covered books, the pages of which were curled and damp: *The Abbott*, by Walter Scott, *The Devout Communicant* and *The Memoirs of Vidocq*. I liked the last best because its leaves were yellow. The wild garden behind the house contained a central apple-tree and a few straggling bushes under one of which I found the late tenant's rusty bicycle-pump. He had been a very charitable priest; in his will he had left all his money to institutions and the furniture of his house to his sister.

When the short days of winter came dusk fell before we had well eaten our dinners. When we met in the street the houses had grown sombre. The space of sky above us was the colour of ever-changing violet and towards it the lamps of the street lifted their feeble lanterns. The cold air stung us and we played till our bodies glowed. Our shouts echoed in the silent street. The career of our play brought us through the dark muddy lanes behind the houses where we ran the gauntlet of the rough tribes from the cottages, to the back doors of the dark dripping gardens where odours arose from the ashpits, to the dark odorous stables where a coachman smoothed and combed the horse or shook music from the buckled harness. When we returned to the street light from the kitchen windows had filled the areas. If my uncle was seen turning the corner we hid in the shadow until we had seen him safely housed. Or if Mangan's sister came out on the doorstep to call her brother in to his tea we watched her from our shadow peer up and down the street. We waited to see whether she would remain or go in and, if she remained, we left our shadow and walked up to Mangan's steps resignedly. She was waiting for us, her figure defined by the light from the half-opened door. Her brother always teased her before he obeyed and I stood by the railings looking at her. Her dress swung as she moved her body and the soft rope of her hair tossed from side to side.

Every morning I lay on the floor in the front parlor watching her door. The blind was pulled down within an inch of the sash so that I could not be seen. When she came out on the doorstep my heart leaped. I ran to the hall, seized my books and followed her. I kept her brown figure always in my eye and, when we came near the point at which our ways diverged, I quickened my pace and passed her. This happened morning after morning. I had never spoken to her, except for a few casual words, and yet her name was like a summons to all my foolish blood.

Her image accompanied me even in places the most hostile to romance. On Saturday evenings when my aunt went marketing I had to go to carry some of the parcels. We walked through the flaring street, jostled by drunken men and bargaining women, amid the curses of labourers, the shrill litanies of shop-boys who stood on guard by the barrels of pigs' cheeks, the nasal chanting of street singers, who sang a *come-all-you* about O'Donovan Rossa, or a ballad about the troubles in our native land. These noises converged in a single sensation of life for me: I imagined that I bore my chalice safely through the throng of foes. Her name sprang to my lips at moments in strange prayers and praises which I myself did not understand. My eyes were often full of tears (I could not tell why) and at times a flood from my heart seemed to pour itself out into my bosom. I thought little of the future. I did not know whether I would ever speak to her or not or, if I spoke to her, how I could tell her of my confused adoration. But my body was like a harp and her words and gestures were like fingers running upon the wires.

One evening I went into the back drawing-room in which the priest had died. It was a dark rainy evening and there was no sound in the house. Through one of the broken panes I heard the rain impinge upon the earth, the fine incessant needles of water playing in the sodden beds. Some distant lamp or lighted window gleamed below me. I was thankful that I could see so little. All my senses seemed to desire to veil themselves and, feeling that I was about to slip from them, I pressed the palms of my hands together until they trembled, murmuring: "*O love! O love!*" many times.

At last she spoke to me. When she addressed the first words to me I was so confused that I did not know what to answer. She asked me was I going to *Araby*. I forget whether I answered yes or no. It would be a splendid bazaar, she said; she would love to go.

—And why can't you? I asked.

While she spoke she turned a silver bracelet round and round her wrist. She could not go, she said, because there would be a retreat that week in her convent. Her brother and two other boys were fighting for their caps and I was alone at the railings. She held one of the spikes, bowing her head towards me. The light from the lamp opposite our door caught the white curve of her neck, lit up her hair that rested there and, falling, lit up the hand upon the railing. It fell over one side of her dress and caught the white border of a petticoat, just visible as she stood at ease.

—It's well for you, she said.

—If I go, I said, I will bring you something.

What innumerable follies laid waste my waking and sleeping thoughts after that evening! I wished to annihilate the tedious intervening days. I chafed against the work of school. At night in my bedroom and by day in the classroom her image came between me and the page I strove to read. The syllables of the word *Araby* were called to me through the silence in which my soul luxuriated and cast an Eastern enchantment over me. I asked for leave to go to the bazaar on Saturday night. My aunt was surprised and hoped it was not some Freemason affair. I answered few questions in class. I watched my master's face pass from amiability to sternness; he hoped I was not beginning to idle. I could not call my wandering thoughts together. I had hardly any patience with the serious work of life which, now that it stood between me and my desire, seemed to me child's play, ugly monotonous child's play.

On Saturday morning I reminded my uncle that I wished to go to the bazaar in the evening. He was fussing at the hallstand, looking for the hatbrush, and answered me curtly:

—Yes, boy, I know.

As he was in the hall I could not go into the front parlour and lie at the window. I left the house in bad humour and walked slowly towards the school. The air was pitilessly raw and already my heart misgave me.

When I came home to dinner my uncle had not yet been home. Still, it was early. I sat staring at the clock for some time and, when its ticking began to irritate me, I left the room. I mounted the staircase and gained the upper part of the house. The high cold empty gloomy rooms liberated me and I went from room to room singing. From the front window I saw my companions playing below in the street. Their cries reached me weakened and indistinct and, leaning my forehead against the cool glass, I looked over at the dark house where she lived. I may have stood there for an hour, seeing nothing but the brown-clad figure cast by my imagination, touched discreetly by the lamplight at the curved neck, at the hand upon the railing and at the border below the dress.

When I came downstairs again I found Mrs. Mercer sitting at the fire. She was an old garrulous woman, a pawnbroker's widow, who collected used stamps for some pious purpose. I had to endure the gossip of the tea-table. The meal was prolonged beyond an hour and still my uncle did not come. Mrs. Mercer stood up to go: she was sorry she couldn't wait any longer, but it was after eight o'clock and she did not like to be out late, as the night air was bad for her. When she had gone I began to walk up and down the room, clenching my fists. My aunt said:

—I'm afraid you may put off your bazaar for this night of Our Lord.

At nine o'clock I heard my uncle's latchkey in the halldoor. I heard him talking to himself and heard the hallstand rocking when it had received the weight of his overcoat. I could interpret these signs. When he was midway through his dinner I asked him to give me the money to go to the bazaar. He had forgotten.

—The people are in bed and after their first sleep now, he said.

I did not smile. My aunt said to him energetically:

—Can't you give him the money and let him go? You've kept him late enough as it is.

My uncle said he was very sorry he had forgotten. He said he believed in the old saying: "All work and no play makes Jack a dull boy." He asked me where I was going and, when I had told him a second time he asked me did I know *The Arab's Farewell to his Steed*. When I left the kitchen he was about to recite the opening lines of the piece to my aunt.

I held a florin tightly in my hand as I strode down Buckingham Street towards the station. The sight of the streets thronged with buyers and glaring with gas recalled to me the purpose of my journey. I took my seat in a third-class carriage of a deserted train. After an intolerable delay the train moved out of the station slowly. It crept onward among ruinous houses and over the twinkling river. At Westland Row Station a crowd of people pressed to the carriage doors; but the porters moved them back, saying that it was a special train for the bazaar. I remained alone in the bare carriage. In a few minutes the train drew up beside an improvised wooden platform. I passed out on to the road and saw by the lighted dial of a clock that it was ten minutes to ten. In front of me was a large building which displayed the magical name.

I could not find any sixpenny entrance and, fearing that the bazaar would be closed, I passed in quickly through a turnstile, handing a shilling to a weary-looking man. I found myself in a big hall girdled at half its height by a gallery. Nearly all the stalls were closed and the greater part of the hall was in darkness. I recognized a silence like that which pervades a church after a service. I walked into the centre of the bazaar timidly. A few people were gathered about the stalls which were still open. Before a curtain, over which the words *Café Chantant* were written in coloured lamps, two men were counting money on a salver. I listened to the fall of the coins.

Remembering with difficulty why I had come I went over to one of the stalls and examined porcelain vases and flowered tea-sets. At the door of the stall a young lady was talking and laughing with two young gentlemen. I remarked their English accents and listened vaguely to their conversation.

—O, I never said such a thing!

—O, but you did!

—O, but I didn't!

—Didn't she say that?

—Yes I heard her.

—O, there's a . . . fib!

Observing me the young lady came over and asked me did I wish to buy anything. The tone in her voice was not encouraging; she seemed to have spoken to me out of a sense of duty. I looked humbly at the great jars that stood like eastern guards at either side of the dark entrance to the stall and murmured:

—No, thank you.

The young lady changed the position of one of the vases and went back to the two young men. They began to talk of the same subject. Once or twice the young lady glanced at me over her shoulder.

I lingered before her stall, though I knew my stay was useless, to make my interest in her wares seem the more real. Then I turned away slowly and walked down the middle of the bazaar. I allowed the two pennies to fall against the sixpence in my pocket. I heard a voice call from one end of the gallery that the light was out. The upper part of the hall was now completely dark.

Gazing up into the darkness I saw myself as a creature driven and derided by vanity; and my eyes burned with anguish and anger.

[1914]

Franz Kafka
[1883–1924]

FRANZ KAFKA *was born in Prague, which was then part of Austria. The term "Kafkaesque" reflects how the author has become emblematic of twentieth century dehumanization and totalitarianism. In the opening of one of his most famous stories, "The Metamorphosis" (1915), a man named Gregor Samsa awakes one morning to find himself "transformed in his bed into a gigantic insect. He was lying on his hard, as it were armor-plated, back and when he lifted his head a little he could see his dome-like brown belly divided into stiff arched segments on top . . ." At first, a reader might assume that Gregor is the in midst of a bad dream. He is not. Gregor, the reader quickly realizes, actually has been completely transformed, and this introduces a world in which strange fears are made rational and anxieties about modern life are made material.*

Kafka's worldview was likely shaped in part by the remoteness of his relationship with his domineering father. The household atmosphere was tense. He harbored intense feelings of alienation for being among the Jewish minority in Prague. Kafka earned a degree in law, worked as a claims investigator, and wrote at night—suffering frequently from intense insomnia. He never married and lived with his parents through most of his fairly brief life. He had many relationships with women, most significantly with Felice Bauer. He wrote her many letters in which he discussed his feelings of inadequacy. In 1913 Kafka entered a sanatorium due to health problems, where he continued his correspondence with Felice. Soon after it was determined that Kafka had tuberculosis. Kafka's disease only intensified his feeling of hopelessness, and this is reflected in his writing. In the novel In the Penal Colony *(1919), he sheds light on the horrors of capital punishment and on the relationship between justice and compassion. In the story "A Hunger Artist" (1924), the artist fasting in a circus cage is eventually ignored by the public, dies, and is replaced by a panther.* The Trial *(1925) relates the story of Joseph K., a respectable banker who is arrested for reasons unknown to him and must defend himself on charges never expressed. The book opens abruptly: "Someone must have been telling lies about Joseph K., for without having done anything wrong he was arrested one fine morning." In* The Castle *(1926), a man known only as K. is taken away at the end of the novel, executed, and is therefore denied access to "the castle." Much of his work expresses Kafka's sense of the arbitrary nature of authority, the law, and power. These two works, as well as* Amerika *(1927), with its image of the Statue of Liberty holding a sword, were published after Kafka's death. In fact, little of his work was published during his lifetime, mainly because of his meticulous approach to writing. He was typically dissatisfied with his writing so that he asked his friend Max Brod to burn all of his uncompleted works. Brod did not honor Kafka's wish. In 1924 Kafka moved to a sanatorium near Vienna where he died that same year. The nightmarish and absurdist situations he created in his work speak to universal aspects of alienation in the human condition.*

The Metamorphosis

FRANZ KAFKA
TRANSLATED BY EDWIN AND WILLA MUIR

I

As GREGOR SAMSA AWOKE one morning from uneasy dreams he found himself transformed in his bed into a gigantic insect. He was lying on his hard, as it were armor-plated, back and when he lifted his head a little he could see his dome-like brown belly divided into stiff arched segments on top of which the bed quilt could hardly keep in position and was about to slide off completely. His numerous legs, which were pitifully thin compared to the rest of his bulk, waved helplessly before his eyes.

What has happened to me? he thought. It was no dream. His room, a regular human bedroom, only rather too small, lay quiet between the four familiar walls. Above the table on which a collection of cloth samples was unpacked and spread out—Samsa was a commercial traveler—hung the picture which he had recently cut out of an illustrated magazine and put into a pretty gilt frame. It showed a lady, with a fur cap on and a fur stole, sitting upright and holding out to the spectator a huge fur muff into which the whole of her forearm had vanished!

Gregor's eyes turned next to the window, and the overcast sky—one could hear rain drops beating on the window gutter—made him quite melancholy. What about sleeping a little longer and forgetting all this nonsense, he thought, but it could not be done, for he was accustomed to sleep on his right side and in his present condition he could not turn himself over. However violently he forced himself towards his right side he always rolled on to his back again. He tried it at least a hundred times, shutting his eyes to keep from seeing his struggling legs, and only desisted when he began to feel in his side a faint dull ache he had never experienced before.

Oh God, he thought, what an exhausting job I've picked on! Traveling about day in, day out. It's much more irritating work than doing the actual business in the office, and on top of that there's the trouble of constant traveling, of worrying about train connections, the bed and irregular meals, casual

Reprinted by permission from *The Penal Colony*, translated by Edwin & Willa Muir. Copyright © 1948 and renewed 1976 by Schocken Books, a division of Random House, Inc.

acquaintances that are always new and never become intimate friends. The devil take it all! He felt a slight itching up on his belly; slowly pushed himself on his back nearer to the top of the bed so that he could lift his head more easily; identified the itching place which was surrounded by many small white spots the nature of which he could not understand and made to touch it with a leg, but drew the leg back immediately, for the contact made a cold shiver run through him.

He slid down again into his former position. This getting up early, he thought, makes one quite stupid. A man needs his sleep. Other commercials live like harem women. For instance, when I come back to the hotel of a morning to write up the orders I've got, these others are only sitting down to breakfast. Let me just try that with my chief; I'd be sacked on the spot. Anyhow, that might be quite a good thing for me, who can tell? If I didn't have to hold my hand because of my parents I'd have given notice long ago, I'd have gone to the chief and told him exactly what I think of him. That would knock him endways from his desk! It's a queer way of doing, too, this sitting on high at a desk and talking down to employees, especially when they have to come quite near because the chief is hard of hearing. Well, there's still hope; once I've saved enough money to pay back my parents' debts to him—that should take another five or six years—I'll do it without fail. I'll cut myself completely loose then. For the moment, though, I'd better get up, since my train goes at five.

He looked at the alarm clock ticking on the chest. Heavenly Father! he thought. It was half-past six o'clock and the hands were quietly moving on, it was even past the half-hour, it was getting on toward a quarter to seven. Had the alarm clock not gone off? From the bed one could see that it had been properly set for four o'clock; of course it must have gone off. Yes, but was it possible to sleep quietly through that ear-splitting noise? Well, he had not slept quietly, yet apparently all the more soundly for that. But what was he to do now? The next train went at seven o'clock; to catch that he would need to hurry like mad and his samples weren't even packed up, and he himself wasn't feeling particularly fresh and active. And even if he did catch the train he wouldn't avoid a row with the chief, since the firm's porter would have been waiting for the five o'clock train and would have long since reported his failure to turn up. The porter was a creature of the chief's, spineless and stupid. Well, supposing he were to say he was sick? But that would be most unpleasant and would look suspicious, since during his five years' employment he had not been ill once. The chief himself would be sure to come with the sick-insurance doctor, would reproach his parents with their son's laziness and would cut all excuses short by referring to the insurance doctor, who of course regarded all mankind as perfectly healthy malingerers. And would he be so far wrong on this occasion? Gregor really felt quite well, apart from a drowsiness that was utterly superfluous after such a long sleep, and he was even unusually hungry.

As all this was running through his mind at top speed without his being able to decide to leave his bed—the alarm clock had just struck a quarter to seven—there came a cautious tap at the door behind the head of his bed. "Gregor," said a voice—it was his mother's—"it's a quarter to seven. Hadn't you a train to catch?" That gentle voice! Gregor had a shock as he heard his own voice answering hers, unmistakably his own voice, it was true, but with a persistent horrible twittering squeak behind it like an undertone, that left the words in their clear shape only for the first moment and then rose up reverberating round them to destroy their sense, so that one could not be sure one had heard them rightly. Gregor wanted to answer at length and explain everything, but in the circumstances he confined himself to saying: "Yes, yes, thank you, Mother, I'm getting up now." The wooden door between them must have kept the change in his voice from being noticeable outside, for his mother contented herself with this statement and shuffled away. Yet this brief exchange of words had made the other members of the family aware that Gregor was still in the house, as they had not expected, and at one of the side doors his father was already knocking, gently, yet with his fist. "Gregor, Gregor," he called, "what's the matter with you?" And after a little while he called again in a deeper voice: "Gregor! Gregor!" At the other side door his sister was saying in a low, plaintive tone: "Gregor? Aren't you well? Are you needing anything?" He answered them both at once: "I'm just ready," and did his best to make his voice sound as normal as possible by enunciating the words very clearly and leaving long pauses between them. So his father went back to his breakfast, but his sister whispered: "Gregor, open the door, do." However, he was not thinking of opening the door, and felt thankful for the prudent habit he had acquired in traveling of locking all doors during the night, even at home.

His immediate intention was to get up quietly without being disturbed, to put on his clothes and above all eat his breakfast, and only then to consider what else was to be done, since in bed, he was well aware, his meditations would come to no sensible conclusion. He remembered that often enough in bed he had felt small aches and pains, probably caused by awkward postures, which had proved purely imaginary once he got up, and he looked forward eagerly to seeing this morning's delusions gradually fall away. That the change in his voice was nothing but the precursor of a severe chill, a standing ailment of commercial travelers, he had not the least possible doubt.

To get rid of the quilt was quite easy; he had only to inflate himself a little and it fell off by itself. But the next move was difficult, especially because he was so uncommonly broad. He would have needed arms and hands to hoist himself up; instead he had only the numerous little legs which never stopped waving in all directions and which he could not control in the least. When he tried to bend one of them it was the first to stretch itself straight; and did he succeed at last in making it do what he wanted, all the other legs meanwhile waved the more wildly in a high degree of unpleasant agitation. "But what's the use of lying idle in bed," said Gregor to himself.

He thought that he might get out of bed with the lower part of his body first, but this lower part, which he had not yet seen and of which he could form no clear conception, proved too difficult to move; it shifted so slowly; and when finally, almost wild with annoyance, he gathered his forces together and thrust out recklessly, he had miscalculated the direction and bumped heavily against the lower end of the bed, and the stinging pain he felt informed him that precisely this lower part of his body was at the moment probably the most sensitive.

So he tried to get the top part of himself out first, and cautiously moved his head towards the edge of the bed. That proved easy enough, and despite its breadth and mass the bulk of his body at last slowly followed the movement of his head. Still, when he finally got his head free over the edge of the bed he felt too scared to go on advancing, for after all if he let himself fall in this way it would take a miracle to keep his head from being injured. And at all costs he must not lose consciousness now, precisely now; he would rather stay in bed.

But when after a repetition of the same efforts he lay in his former position again, sighing, and watched his little legs struggling against each other more wildly than ever, if that were possible, and saw no way of bringing any order into this arbitrary confusion, he told himself again that it was impossible to stay in bed and that the most sensible course was to risk everything for the smallest hope of getting away from it. At the same time he did not forget meanwhile to remind himself that cool reflection, the coolest possible, was much better than desperate resolves. In such moments he focused his eyes as sharply as possible on the window, but, unfortunately, the prospect of the morning fog, which muffled even the other side of the narrow street, brought him little encouragement and comfort. "Seven o'clock already," he said to himself when the alarm clock chimed again, "seven o'clock already and still such a thick fog." And for a little while he lay quiet, breathing lightly, as if perhaps expecting such complete repose to restore all things to their real and normal condition.

But then he said to himself: "Before it strikes a quarter past seven I must be quite out of this bed, without fail. Anyhow, by that time someone will have come from the office to ask for me, since it opens before seven." And he set himself to rocking his whole body at once in a regular rhythm, with the idea of swinging it out of the bed. If he tipped himself out in that way he could keep his head from injury by lifting it at an acute angle when he fell. His back seemed to be hard and was not likely to suffer from a fall on the carpet. His biggest worry was the loud crash he would not be able to help making, which would probably cause anxiety, if not terror, behind all the doors. Still, he must take the risk.

When he was already half out of the bed—the new method was more a game than an effort, for he needed only to hitch himself across by rocking to and fro—it struck him how simple it would be if he could get help. Two strong people—he thought of his father and the servant girl—would be amply sufficient; they would only have to thrust their arms under his convex back, lever him out of the bed, bend down with their burden and then be patient enough to let him turn himself right over on to the floor, where it was to be hoped his legs would then find their proper function. Well, ignoring the fact that the doors were all locked, ought he really to call for help? In spite of his misery he could not suppress a smile at the very idea of it.

He had got so far that he could barely keep his equilibrium when he rocked himself strongly, and he would have to nerve himself very soon for the final decision since in five minutes' time it would be a quarter past seven—when the front door bell rang. "That's someone from the office," he said to himself, and grew almost rigid, while his little legs only jigged about all the faster. For a moment everything stayed quiet. "They're not going to open the door," said Gregor to himself, catching at some kind of irrational hope. But then of course the servant girl went as usual to the door with her heavy tread and opened it. Gregor needed only to hear the first good morning of the visitor to know immediately who it was—the chief clerk himself. What a fate, to be condemned to work for a firm where the smallest omission at once gave rise to the gravest suspicion! Were all employees in a body nothing but scoundrels, was there not among them one single loyal devoted man who, had he wasted only an hour or so of the firm's time in a morning, was so tormented by conscience as to be driven out of his mind and actually incapable of leaving his bed? Wouldn't it really have been sufficient to send an apprentice to inquire—if any inquiry were necessary at all—did the chief clerk himself have to come and thus indicate to the entire family, an innocent family, that this suspicious circumstance could be investigated by no one less versed in affairs than himself? And more through the agitation caused by these reflections than through any act of will Gregor swung himself out of bed with all his strength. There was a loud thump, but it was not really a crash. His fall was broken to some extent by the carpet, his back, too, was less stiff than he thought, and so there was merely a dull thud, not so very startling. Only he had not lifted his head carefully enough and had hit it; he turned it and rubbed it on the carpet in pain and irritation.

"That was something falling down in there," said the chief clerk in the next room to the left. Gregor tried to suppose to himself that something like what had happened to him today might some day happen to the chief clerk; one really could not deny that it was possible. But as if in brusque reply to this supposition the chief clerk took a couple of firm steps in the next-door room and his patent leather boots creaked. From the right-hand room his sister was whispering to inform him of the situation: "Gregor, the chief clerk's here." "I know," muttered Gregor to himself; but he didn't dare to make his voice loud enough for his sister to hear it.

"Gregor," said his father now from the left-hand room, "the chief clerk has come and wants to know why you didn't catch the early train. We don't know what to say to him. Besides, he wants to talk to you in person. So open the door, please. He will be good enough to excuse the untidiness of your room." "Good morning, Mr. Samsa," the chief clerk was calling amiably meanwhile. "He's not well," said his mother to the visitor, while his father was still speaking through the door, "he's not well, sir, believe me. What else would make him miss a train! The boy thinks about nothing but his work. It makes me almost cross the way he never goes out in the evenings; he's been here the last eight days and has stayed at home every single evening. He just sits there quietly at the table reading a newspaper or looking through railway timetables. The only amusement he gets is doing fretwork. For instance, he spent two or three evenings cutting out a little picture frame; you would be surprised to see how pretty it is; it's hanging in his room; you'll see it in a minute when Gregor opens the door. I must say I'm glad you've come, sir; we should never have got him to unlock the door by ourselves; he's so obstinate; and I'm sure he's unwell, though he wouldn't have it to be so this morning." "I'm just coming," said Gregor slowly and carefully, not moving an inch for fear of losing one word of the conversation. "I can't think of any other explanation, madam," said the chief clerk, "I hope it's nothing serious. Although on the other hand I must say that we men of business—fortunately or unfortunately—very often simply have to ignore any slight indisposition, since business must be attended to." "Well, can the chief clerk come in now?" asked Gregor's father impatiently, again knocking on the door. "No," said Gregor. In the left-hand room a painful silence followed this refusal, in the right-hand room his sister began to sob.

Why didn't his sister join the others? She was probably newly out of bed and hadn't even begun to put on her clothes yet. Well, why was she crying? Because he wouldn't get up and let the chief clerk in, because he was in danger of losing his job, and because the chief would begin dunning his parents again for the old debts? Surely these were things one didn't need to worry about for the present. Gregor was still at home and not in the least thinking of deserting his family. At the moment, true, he was lying on the carpet and no one who knew the condition he was in could seriously expect him to admit the chief clerk. But for such a small discourtesy, which could plausibly be explained away somehow later on, Gregor could hardly be dismissed on the spot. And it seemed to Gregor that it would be much more sensible to leave him in peace for the present than to trouble him with tears and entreaties. Still, of course, their uncertainty bewildered them all and excused their behavior.

"Mr. Samsa," the chief clerk called now in a louder voice, "what's the matter with you? Here you are, barricading yourself in your room, giving only 'yes' and 'no' for answers, causing your parents a lot of unnecessary trouble and neglecting—I mention this only in passing—neglecting your business duties in an incredible fashion. I am speaking here in the name of your parents and of your chief, and I beg you quite seriously to give me an immediate and precise explanation. You amaze me, you amaze me. I thought you were a quiet, dependable person, and now all at once you seem bent on making a disgraceful exhibition of yourself. The chief did hint to me early this morning a possible explanation for your disappearance—with reference to the cash payments that were entrusted to you recently—but I almost pledged my solemn word of honor that this could not be so. But not that I see how incredibly obstinate you are, I no longer have the slightest desire to take your part at all. And your position in the firm is not so unassailable. I came with the intention of telling you all this in private, but since you are wasting my time so needlessly I don't see why your parents shouldn't hear it too. For some time past your work has been most unsatisfactory; this is not the season of the year for a business boom, of course, we admit that, but a season of the year for doing no business at all, that does not exist, Mr. Samsa, must not exist."

"But, sir," cried Gregor, beside himself and in his agitation forgetting everything else, "I'm just going to open the door this very minute. A slight illness, an attack of giddiness, has kept me from getting up. I'm still lying in bed. But I feel all right again. I'm getting out of bed now. Just give me a moment or two longer! I'm not quite so well as I thought. But I'm all right, really. How a thing like that can suddenly strike one down! Only last night I was quite well, my parents can tell you, or rather I did have a slight presentiment. I must have showed some sign of it. Why didn't I report it at the office! But one always thinks that an indisposition can be got over without staying in the house. Oh sir, do spare my parents! All that you're reproaching me with now has no foundation; no one has ever said a word to me about it. Perhaps you haven't looked at the last orders I sent in. Anyhow, I can still catch the eight o'clock train, I'm much the better for my few hours' rest. Don't let me detain you here, sir; I'll be attending to business very soon, and do be good enough to tell the chief so and to make my excuses to him!"

And while all this was tumbling out pell-mell and Gregor hardly knew what he was saying, he had reached the chest quite easily, perhaps because of the practice he had had in bed, and was now trying to lever himself upright by means of it. He meant actually to open the door, actually to show himself and speak to the chief clerk; he was eager to find out what the others, after all their insistence, would say at the sight of him. If they were horrified then the responsibility was no longer his and he could stay quiet. But if they took it calmly, then he had no reason either to be upset, and could really get to the station for the eight o'clock train if he hurried. At first he slipped down a few times from the polished surface of the chest, but at length with a last heave he stood upright; he paid no more attention to the pains in the lower part of his body, however they smarted. Then he let himself fall against the back of a near-by chair, and clung with his little legs to the edges of it. That brought him into control of himself again and he stopped speaking, for now he could listen to what the chief clerk was saying.

"Did you understand a word of it?" the chief clerk was asking; "surely he can't be trying to make fools of us?" "Oh dear," cried his mother, in tears, "perhaps he's terribly ill and we're tormenting him. Grete! Grete!" she called out then. "Yes Mother?" called his sister from the other side. They were calling to each other across Gregor's room. "You must go this minute for the doctor. Gregor is ill. Go for the doctor, quick. Did you hear how he was speaking?" "That was no human voice," said the chief clerk in a voice noticeably low beside the shrillness of the mother's. "Anna! Anna!" his father was calling through the hall to the kitchen, clapping his hands, "get a locksmith at once!" And the two girls were already running through the hall with a swish of skirts—how could his sister have got dressed so quickly?—and were tearing the front door open. There was no sound of its closing again; they had evidently left it open, as one does in houses where some great misfortune has happened.

But Gregor was now much calmer. The words he uttered were no longer understandable, apparently, although they seemed clear enough to him, even clearer than before, perhaps because his ear had grown accustomed to the sound of them. Yet at any rate people now believed that something was wrong with him, and were ready to help him. The positive certainty with which these first measures had been taken comforted him. He felt himself drawn once more into the human circle and hoped for great and remarkable results from both the doctor and the locksmith, without really distinguishing precisely between them. To make his voice as clear as possible for the decisive conversation that was now imminent he coughed a little, as quietly as he could, of course, since this noise too might not sound like a human cough for all he was able to judge. In the next room meanwhile there was complete silence. Perhaps his parents were sitting at the table with the chief clerk, whispering, perhaps they were all leaning against the door and listening.

Slowly Gregor pushed the chair towards the door, then let go of it, caught hold of the door for support—the soles at the end of his little legs were somewhat sticky—and rested against it for a moment after his efforts. Then he set himself to tuning the key in the lock with his mouth. It seemed, unhappily, that he hadn't really any teeth—what could he grip the key with?—but on the other hand his jaws were certainly very strong; with their help he did manage to set the key in motion, heedless of the fact that he was undoubtedly damaging them somewhere, since a brown fluid issued from his mouth, flowed over the key and dripped on the floor. "Just listen to that," said the chief clerk next door; "he's turning the key." That was a great encouragement to Gregor; but they should all have shouted encouragement to him, his father and mother too: "Go on, Gregor," they should have called out, "keep going, hold on to that key!" And in the belief that they were all following his efforts intently, he clenched his jaws recklessly on the key with all the force at his command. As the turning of the key progressed he circled round the lock, holding on now only with his mouth, pushing on the key, as required, or pulling it down again with all the weight of his body. The louder click of the finally yielding lock literally quickened Gregor. With a deep breath of relief he said to himself: "So I didn't need the locksmith," and laid his head on the handle to open the door wide.

Since he had to pull the door towards him, he was still invisible when it was really wide open. He had to edge himself slowly round the near half of the double door, and to do it very carefully if he was not to fall plump upon his back just on the threshold. He was still carrying out this difficult manoeuvre, with no time to observe anything else, when he heard the chief clerk utter a loud "Oh!"—it sounded like a gust of wind—and now he could see the man, standing as he was nearest to the door, clapping one hand before his open mouth and slowly backing away as if driven by some invisible steady pressure. His mother—in spite of the chief clerk's being there her hair was still undone and sticking up in all directions—first clasped her hands and looked at his father, then took two steps towards Gregor and fell on the floor among her outspread skirts, her face quite hidden on her breast. His father knotted his fist with a fierce expression on his face as if he meant to knock Gregor back into his room, then looked uncertainly round the living room, covered his eyes with his hands and wept till his great chest heaved.

Gregor did not go now into the living room, but leaned against the inside of the firmly shut wing of the door, so that only half his body was visible and his head above it bending sideways to look at the others. The light had meanwhile strengthened; on the other side of the street one could see clearly a section of the endlessly long, dark gray building opposite—it was a hospital—abruptly punctuated by its row of regular windows; the rain was still falling, but only in large singly discernible and literally singly splashing drops. The breakfast dishes were set out on the table lavishly, for breakfast was the most important meal of the day to Gregor's father, who lingered it out for hours over various newspapers. Right opposite Gregor on the wall hung a photograph of himself on military service, as a lieutenant, hand on sword, a carefree smile on his face, inviting one to respect his uniform and military bearing. The door leading to the hall was open, and one could see that the front door stood open too, showing the landing beyond and the beginning of the stairs going down.

"Well," said Gregor, knowing perfectly that he was the only one who had retained any composure, "I'll put my clothes on at once, pack up my samples and start off. Will you only let me go? You see, sir, I'm not obstinate, and I'm willing to work; traveling is a hard life, but I couldn't live without it. Where are you going, sir? To the office? Yes? Will you give a true account of all this? One can be temporarily incapacitated, but that's just the moment for remembering former services and bearing in mind that later on, when the incapacity has been got over, one will certainly work with all the more industry and concentration. I'm loyally bound to serve the chief, you know that very well. Besides, I have to provide for my parents and my sister. I'm in great difficulties, but I'll get out of them again. Don't make things any worse for me than they are. Stand up for me in the firm. Travelers are not popular there, I know. People think they earn sacks of money and just have a good time. A prejudice there's no particular reason for revising. But you, sir, have a more comprehensive view of affairs than the rest of the staff, yes, let me tell you in confidence, a more comprehensive view than the chief himself, who, being the owner, lets his judgment easily be swayed against one of his employees. And you know very well that the traveler, who is never seen in the office almost the whole year round, can so easily fall a victim to gossip and ill luck and unfounded complaints, which he mostly knows nothing about, except when he comes back exhausted from his rounds, and only then suffers in person from their evil consequences, which he can no longer trace back to the original causes. Sir, sir, don't go away without a word to me to show that you think me in the right at least to some extent!"

But at Gregor's very first words the chief clerk had already backed away and only stared at him with parted lips over one twitching shoulder. And while Gregor was speaking he did not stand still one moment but stole away towards the door, without taking his eyes off Gregor, yet only an inch at a time, as if obeying some secret injunction to leave the room. He was already at the hall, and the suddenness with which he took his last step out of the living room would have made one believe he had burned the sole of his foot. Once in the hall he stretched his right arm before him towards the staircase, as if some supernatural power were waiting there to deliver him.

Gregor perceived that the chief clerk must on no account be allowed to go away in this frame of mind if his position in the firm were not to be endangered to the utmost. His parents did not understand this so well; they had convinced themselves in the course of years that Gregor was settled for life in this firm, and besides they were so preoccupied with their immediate troubles that all foresight had forsaken them. Yet Gregor had this foresight. The chief clerk must be detained, soothed, persuaded and finally won over; the whole future of Gregor and his family depended on it! If only his sister had been there! She was intelligent; she had begun to cry while Gregor was still lying quietly on his back. And no doubt the chief clerk, so partial to ladies, would have been guided by her; she would have shut the door of the flat and in the hall talked him out of his horror. But she was not there, and Gregor would have to handle the situation himself. And without remembering that he was still unaware what powers of movement he possessed, without even remembering that his words in all possibility, indeed in all likelihood, would again be unintelligible, he let go the wing of the door, pushed himself through the opening, started to walk towards the chief clerk, who was already ridiculously clinging with both hands to the railing on the landing; but immediately, as he was feeling for a support, he fell down with a little cry upon all his numerous legs. Hardly was he down when he experienced for the first time this morning a sense of physical comfort; his legs had firm ground under them; they were completely obedient, as he noted with joy; they even strove to carry him forward in whatever direction he chose; and he was inclined to believe that a final relief from all his sufferings was at hand. But in the same moment as he found himself on the floor, rocking with suppressed eagerness to move, not far from his mother, indeed just in front of her, she, who had seemed so completely crushed, sprang all at once to her feet, her arms and fingers outspread, cried: "Help, for God's sake, help!" bent her head down as if to see Gregor better, yet on the contrary kept backing senselessly away; had quite forgotten that the laden table stood behind her; sat upon it hastily, as if in absence of mind, when she bumped into it; and seemed altogether unaware that the big coffee pot beside her was upset and pouring coffee in a flood over the carpet.

"Mother, Mother," said Gregor in a low voice, and looked up at her. The chief clerk, for the moment, had quite slipped from his mind; instead, he could not resist snapping his jaws together at the sight of the streaming coffee. That made his mother scream again, she fled from the table and fell into the arms of his father, who hastened to catch her. But Gregor had now no time to spare for his parents; the chief clerk was already on the stairs; with his chin on the banisters he was taking one last backward look. Gregor made a spring, to be as sure as possible of overtaking him; the chief clerk must have divined his intention, for he leaped down several steps and vanished; he was still yelling "Ugh!" and it echoed through the whole staircase.

Unfortunately, the flight of the chief clerk seemed completely to upset Gregor's father, who had remained relatively calm until now, for instead of running after the man himself, or at least not hindering Gregor in his pursuit, he seized in his right hand the walking stick which the chief clerk had left behind on a chair, together with a hat and greatcoat, snatched in his left hand a large newspaper from the table and began stamping his feet and flourishing the stick and the newspaper to drive Gregor back into his room. No entreaty of Gregor's availed, indeed no entreaty was even understood, however humbly he bent his head his father only stamped on the floor the more loudly. Behind his father his mother had torn open a window, despite the cold weather, and was leaning far out of it with her face in her hands. A strong draught set in from the street to the staircase, the window curtains blew in, the newspapers on the table fluttered, stray pages whisked over the floor. Pitilessly Gregor's father drove him back, hissing and crying "Shoo!" like a savage. But Gregor was quite unpracticed in walking backwards, it really was a slow business. If he only had a chance to turn round he could get back to his room at once, but he was afraid of exasperating his father by the slowness of such a rotation and at any moment the stick in his father's hand might hit him a fatal blow on the back or on the head. In the end, however, nothing else was left for him to do since to his horror he observed that in moving backwards he could not even control the direction he took; and so, keeping an anxious eye on his father all the time over his shoulder, he began to turn round as quickly as he could, which was in reality very slowly. Perhaps his father noted his good intentions, for he did not interfere except every now and then to help him in the manoeuvre from a distance with the point of the stick. If only he would have stopped making that unbearable hissing noise! It made Gregor quite lose his head. He had turned almost completely round when the hissing noise so distracted him that he even turned a little the wrong way again. But when at last his head was fortunately right in front of the doorway, it appeared that his body was too broad simply to get through the opening. His father, of course, in his present mood was far from thinking of such a thing as opening the other half of the door, to let Gregor have enough space. He had merely the fixed idea of driving Gregor back into his room as quickly as possible. He would never have suffered Gregor to make the circumstantial preparations for standing up on end and perhaps slipping his way through the door. Maybe he was now making more noise than ever to urge Gregor forward, as if no obstacle impeded him; to Gregor, anyhow, the noise in his rear sounded no longer like the voice of one single father; this was really no joke, and Gregor thrust himself—come what might—into the doorway. One side of his body rose up, he was tilted at an angle in the doorway, his flank was quite bruised, horrid blotches stained the white door, soon he was stuck fast and, left to himself, could not have moved at all, his legs on one side fluttered trembling in the air, those on the other were crushed painfully to the floor—when from behind his father gave him a strong push which was literally a deliverance and he flew far into the room, bleeding freely. The door was slammed behind him with the stick, and then at last there was silence.

II

Not until it was twilight did Gregor awake out of a deep sleep, more like a swoon than a sleep. He would certainly have waked up on his own accord not much later, for he felt himself sufficiently rested and well-slept, but it seemed to him as if a fleeting step and a cautious shutting of the door leading into the hall had aroused him. The electric lights in the street cast a pale sheen here and there on the ceiling and the upper surfaces of the furniture, but down below, where he lay, it was dark. Slowly, awkwardly trying out his feelers, which he now first learned to appreciate, he pushed his way to the door to see what had been happening there. His left side felt like one single long, unpleasantly tense scar, and he had actually to limp on his two rows of legs. One little leg, moreover, had been severely damaged in the course of that morning's events—it was almost a miracle that only one had been damaged—and trailed uselessly behind him.

He had reached the door before he discovered what had really drawn him to it: the smell of food. For there stood a basin filled with fresh milk in which floated little sops of white bread. He could almost have laughed with joy, since he was now still hungrier than in the morning, and he dipped his head almost over the eyes straight into the milk. But soon in disappointment he withdrew it again; not only did he find it difficult to feed because of his tender left side—and he could only feed with the palpitating collaboration of his whole body—he did not like the milk either, although milk had been his favorite drink and that was certainly why his sister had set it there for him, indeed it was almost with repulsion that he turned away from the basin and crawled back to the middle of the room.

He could see through the crack of the door that the gas was turned on in the living room, but while usually at this time his father made a habit of reading the afternoon newspaper in a loud voice to his mother and occasionally to his sister as well, not a sound was now to be heard. Well, perhaps his father had recently given up this habit of reading aloud, which his sister had mentioned so often in conversation and in her letters. But there was the same silence all around, although the flat was certainly not empty of occupants. "What a quiet life our family has been leading," said Gregor to himself, and as he sat there motionless staring into the darkness he felt great pride in the fact that he had been able to provide such a life for his parents and sister in such a fine flat. But what if all the quiet, the comfort, the contentment were now to end in horror? To keep himself from being lost in such thoughts Gregor took refuge in movement and crawled up and down the room.

Once during the long evening one of the side doors was opened a little and quickly shut again, later the other side door too; someone had apparently wanted to come in and then thought better of it. Gregor now stationed himself immediately before the living room door, determined to persuade any hesitating visitor to come in or at least to discover who it might be; but the door was not opened again and he waited in vain. In the early morning, when the doors were locked, they had all wanted to come in, now that he had opened one door and the other had apparently been opened during the day, no one came in and even the keys were on the other side of the doors.

It was late at night before the gas went out in the living room, and Gregor could easily tell that his parents and his sister had all stayed awake until then, for he could clearly hear the three of them stealing away on tiptoe. No one was likely to visit him, not until the morning, that was certain; so he had plenty of time to meditate at his leisure on how he was to arrange his life afresh. But the lofty, empty room in which he had to lie flat on the floor filled him with an apprehension he could not account for, since it had been his very own room for the past five years—and with a half-unconscious action, not without a slight feeling of shame, he scuttled under the sofa, where he felt comfortable at once, although his back was a little cramped and he could not lift his head up, and his only regret was that his body was too broad to get the whole of it under the sofa.

He stayed there all night, spending the time partly in a light slumber, from which his hunger kept waking him up with a start, and partly in worrying and sketching vague hopes, which all led to the same conclusion, that he must lie low for the present and, by exercising patience and the utmost consideration, help the family to bear the inconvenience he was bound to cause them in his present condition.

Very early in the morning, it was still almost night, Gregor had the chance to test the strength of his new resolutions, for his sister, nearly fully dressed, opened the door from the hall and peered in. She did not see him at once, yet when she caught sight of him under the sofa—well, he had to be somewhere, he couldn't have flown away, could he?—she was so startled that without being able to help it she slammed the door shut again. But as if regretting her behavior she opened the door again immediately and came in on tiptoe, as if she were visiting an invalid or even a stranger. Gregor had pushed his head forward to the very edge of the sofa and watched her. Would she notice that he had left the milk standing, and not for lack of hunger, and would she bring in some other kind of food more to his taste? If she did not do it of her own accord, he would rather starve than draw her attention to the fact, although he felt a wild impulse to dart out from under the sofa, throw himself at her feet and beg her for something to eat. But his sister at once noticed, with surprise, that the basin was still full, except for a little milk that had been spilt all around it, she lifted it immediately, not with her bare hands, true, but with a cloth and carried it away. Gregor was wildly curious to know what she would bring instead, and made various speculations about it. Yet what she actually did next, in the goodness of her heart, he could never have guessed at. To find out what he liked she brought him a whole selection of food, all set out on an old newspaper. There were old, half-decayed vegetables, bones from last night's supper covered with a white sauce that had thickened; some raisins and almonds; a piece of cheese that Gregor would have called uneatable two days ago; a dry roll of bread, a buttered roll, and a roll both buttered and salted. Besides all that, she set down again the same basin, into which she had poured some water, and which was apparently to be reserved for his exclusive use. And with fine tact, knowing that Gregor would not eat in her presence, she withdrew quickly and even turned the key, to let him understand that he could take his ease as much as he liked. Gregor's legs all whizzed towards the food. His wounds must have healed completely, moreover, for he felt no disability, which amazed him and made him reflect how more than a month ago he had cut one finger a little with a knife and had still suffered pain from the wound only the day before yesterday. Am I less sensitive now? he thought, and sucked greedily at the cheese, which above all the other edibles attracted him at once and strongly. One after another and with tears of satisfaction in his eyes he quickly devoured the cheese, the vegetables and the sauce; the fresh food, on the other hand, had no charms for him, he could not even stand the smell of it and actually dragged away to some little distance the things he could eat. He had long finished his meal and was only lying lazily on the same spot when his sister turned the key slowly as a sign for him to retreat. That roused him at once, although he was nearly asleep, and he hurried under the sofa again. But it took considerable self-control for him to stay under the sofa, even for the short time his sister was in the room, since the large meal had swollen his body somewhat and he was so cramped he could hardly breathe. Slight attacks of breathlessness afflicted him and his eyes were starting a little out of his head as he watched his unsuspecting sister sweeping together with a broom not only the remains of what he had eaten but even the things he had not touched, as if these were now of no use to anyone, and hastily shoveling it all into a bucket, which she covered with a wooden lid and carried away. Hardly had she turned her back when Gregor came from under the sofa and stretched and puffed himself out.

In this manner Gregor was fed, once in the early morning while his parents and the servant girl were still asleep, and a second time after they had all had their midday dinner, for then his parents took a short nap and the servant girl could be sent out on some errand or other by his sister. Not that they would have wanted him to starve, of course, but perhaps they could not have borne to know more about his feeding than from hearsay, perhaps too his sister wanted to spare them such little anxieties wherever possible, since they had quite enough to bear as it was.

Under what pretext the doctor and the locksmith had been got rid of on that first morning Gregor could not discover, for since what he said was not understood by the others it never struck any of them, not even his sister, that he could understand what they said, and so whenever his sister came into his room he had to content himself with hearing her utter only a sigh now and then and an occasional appeal to the saints. Later on, when she had got a little used to the situation—of course she could never get completely used to it—she sometimes threw out a remark which was kindly meant or could be so interpreted. "Well, he liked his dinner today," she would say when Gregor had made a good clearance of his food; and when he had not eaten, which gradually happened more and more often, she would say almost sadly: "Everything's been left standing again."

But although Gregor could get no news directly, he overheard a lot from the neighboring rooms, and as soon as voices were audible, he would run to the door of the room concerned and press his whole body against it. In the first few days especially there was no conversation that did not refer to him somehow, even if only indirectly. For two whole days there were family consultations at every mealtime about what should be done; but also between meals the same subject was discussed, for there were always at least two members of the family at home, since no one wanted to be alone in the flat and to leave it quite empty was unthinkable. And on the very first of these days the household cook—it was not quite clear what and how much she knew of the situation—went down on her knees to his mother and begged leave to go, and when she departed, a quarter of an hour later, gave thanks for her dismissal with tears in her eyes as if for the greatest benefit that could have been conferred on her, and without any prompting swore a solemn oath that she would never say a single word to anyone about what had happened.

Now Gregor's sister had to cook too, helping her mother; true, the cooking did not amount to much, for they ate scarcely anything. Gregor was always hearing one of the family vainly urging another to eat and getting no answer but: "Thanks, I've had all I want," or something similar. Perhaps they drank nothing either. Time and again his sister kept asking his father if he wouldn't like some beer and offered kindly to go and fetch it herself, and when he made no answer suggested that she could ask the concierge to fetch it, so that he need feel no sense of obligation, but then a round "No" came from his father and no more was said about it.

In the course of that very first day Gregor's father explained the family's financial position and prospects to both his mother and his sister. Now and then he rose from the table to get some voucher or memorandum out of the small safe he had rescued from the collapse of his business five years earlier. One could hear him opening the complicated lock and rustling papers out and shutting it again. This statement made by his father was the first cheerful information Gregor had heard since his imprisonment. He had been of the opinion that nothing at all was left over from his father's business, at least his father had never said anything to the contrary, and of course he had not asked him directly. At that time Gregor's sole desire was to do his utmost to help the family to forget as soon as possible the catastrophe which had overwhelmed the business and thrown them all into a state of complete despair. And so he had set to work with unusual ardor and almost overnight had become a commercial traveler instead of a little clerk, with of course much greater chances of earning money, and his success was immediately translated into good round coin which he could lay on the table for his amazed and happy family. These had been fine times, and they had never recurred, at least not with the same sense of glory, although later on Gregor had earned so much money that he was able to meet the expenses of the whole household and did so. They had simply got used to it, both the family and Gregor; the money was gratefully accepted and gladly given, but there was no special uprush of warm feeling. With his sister alone had he remained intimate, and it was a secret plan of his that she, who loved music, unlike himself, and could play movingly on the violin, should be sent next year to study at the Conservatorium, despite the great expense that would entail, which must be made up in some other way. During his brief visits home the Conservatorium was often mentioned in the talks he had with his sister, but always merely as a beautiful dream which could never come true, and his parents discouraged even these innocent references to it; yet Gregor had made up his mind firmly about it and meant to announce the fact with due solemnity on Christmas Day.

Such were the thoughts, completely futile in his present condition, that went through his head as he stood clinging upright to the door and listening. Sometimes out of sheer weariness he had to give up listening and let his head fall negligently against the door, but he always had to pull himself together again at once, for even the slight sound his head made was audible next door and brought all conversation to a stop. "What can he be doing now?" his father would say after a while, obviously turning towards the door, and only then would the interrupted conversation gradually be set going again.

Gregor was now informed as amply as he could wish—for his father tended to repeat himself in his explanations, partly because it was a long time since he had handled such matters and partly because his mother could not always grasp things at once—that a certain amount of investments, a very small amount it was true, had survived the wreck of their fortunes and had even increased a little because the dividends had not been touched meanwhile. And besides that, the money Gregor brought home every month—he had kept only a few dollars for himself—had never been quite used up and now amounted to a small capital sum. Behind the door Gregor nodded his head eagerly, rejoiced at this evidence of unexpected thrift and foresight. True, he could really have paid off some more of his father's debts to the chief with this extra money, and so brought much nearer the day on which he could quit his job, but doubtless it was better the way his father had arranged it.

Yet this capital was by no means sufficient to let the family live on the interest of it; for one year, perhaps, or at the most two, they could live on the principal, that was all. It was simply a sum that ought not to be touched and should be kept for a rainy day; money for living expenses would have to be earned. Now his father was still hale enough but an old man, and he had done no work for the past five years and could not be expected to do much; during these five years, the first years of leisure in his laborious though unsuccessful life, he had grown rather fat and become sluggish. And Gregor's old mother, how was she to earn a living with her asthma, which troubled her even when she walked through the flat and kept her lying on a sofa every other day panting for breath beside an open window? And was his sister to earn her bread, she who was still a child of seventeen and whose life hitherto had been so pleasant, consisting as it did in dressing herself nicely, sleeping long, helping in the housekeeping, going out to a few modest entertainments and above all playing the violin? At first whenever the need for earning money was mentioned Gregor let go his hold on the door and threw himself down on the cool leather sofa beside it, he felt so hot with shame and grief.

Often he just lay there the long nights through without sleeping at all, scrabbling for hours on the leather. Or he nerved himself to the great effort of pushing an armchair to the window, then crawled up over the window sill and, braced against the chair, leaned against the window panes, obviously in some recollection of the sense of freedom that looking out of a window always used to give him. For in reality day by day things that were even a little way off were growing dimmer to his sight; the hospital across the street, which he used to execrate for being all too often before his eyes, was now quite beyond his range of vision, and if he had not known that he lived in Charlotte Street, a quiet street but still a city street, he might have believed that his window gave on a desert waste where gray sky and gray land blended indistinguishably into each other. His quick-witted sister only needed to observe twice that the armchair stood by the window; after that whenever she had tidied the room she always pushed the chair back to the same place at the window and even left the inner casements open.

If he could have spoken to her and thanked her for all she had to do for him, he could have borne her ministrations better; as it was, they oppressed him. She certainly tried to make as light as possible of whatever was disagreeable in her task, and as time went on she succeeded, of course, more and more, but time brought more enlightenment to Gregor too. The very way she came in distressed him. Hardly was she in the room when she rushed to the window, without even taking time to shut the door, careful as she was usually to shield the sight of Gregor's room from the others, and as if she were almost suffocating tore the casements open with hasty fingers, standing then in the open draught for a while even in the bitterest cold and drawing deep breaths. This noisy scurry of hers upset Gregor twice a day; he would crouch trembling under the sofa all the time, knowing quite well that she would certainly have spared him such a disturbance had she found it at all possible to stay in his presence without opening the window.

On one occasion, about a month after Gregor's metamorphosis, when there was surely no reason for her to be still startled at his appearance, she came a little earlier than usual and found him gazing out of the window, quite motionless, and thus well placed to look like a bogey. Gregor would not have been surprised had she not come in at all, for she could not immediately open the window while he was there, but no only did she retreat, she jumped back as if in alarm and banged the door shut; a stranger might well have thought that he had been lying in wait for her there meaning to bite her. Of course he hid himself under the sofa at once, but he had to wait until midday before she came again, and she seemed more ill at ease than usual. This made him realize how repulsive the sight of him still was to her, and that it was bound to go on being repulsive, and what an effort it must cost her not to run away even from the sight of the small portion of his body that stuck out from under the sofa. In order to spare her that, therefore, one day he carried a sheet on his back to the sofa—it cost him four hours' labor—and arranged it there in such a way as to hide him completely, so that even if she were to bend down she could not see him. Had she considered the sheet unnecessary, she would certainly have stripped it off the sofa again, for it was clear enough that this curtaining and confining of himself was not likely to conduce to Gregor's comfort, but she left it where it was, and Gregor even fancied that he caught a thankful glance from her eye when he lifted the sheet carefully a very little with his head to see how she was taking the new arrangement.

For the first fortnight his parents could not bring themselves to the point of entering his room, and he often heard them expressing their appreciation of his sister's activities, whereas formerly they had frequently scolded her for being as they thought a somewhat useless daughter. But now, both of them often waited outside the door, his father and his mother, while his sister tidied his room, and as soon as she came out she had to tell them exactly how things were in the room, what Gregor had eaten, how he had conducted himself this time and whether there was not perhaps some slight improvement in his condition. His mother, moreover, began relatively soon to want to visit him, but his father and sister dissuaded her at first with arguments which Gregor listened to very attentively and altogether approved. Later, however, she had to be held back by main force, and when she cried out: "Do let me in to Gregor, he is my unfortunate son! Can't you understand that I must go to him?" Gregor thought that it might be well to have her come in, not every day, of course, but perhaps once a week; she understood things, after all, much better than his sister, who was only a child despite the efforts she was making and had perhaps taken on so difficult a task merely out of childish thoughtlessness.

Gregor's desire to see his mother was soon fulfilled. During the daytime he did not want to show himself at the window, out of consideration for his parents, but he could not crawl very far around the few square yards of floor space he had, nor could he bear lying quietly at rest all during the night, while he was fast losing any interest he had ever taken in food, so that for mere recreation he had formed the habit of crawling crisscross over the walls and ceiling. He especially enjoyed hanging suspended from the ceiling; it was much better than lying on the floor; one could breathe more freely; one's body swung and rocked lightly; and in the almost blissful absorption induced by this suspension it could happen to his own surprise that he let go and fell plump on the floor. Yet he now had his body much better under control than formerly, and even such a big fall did him no harm. His sister at once remarked the new distraction Gregor had found for himself—he left traces behind him of the sticky stuff on his soles wherever he crawled—and she got the idea in her head of giving him as wide a field as possible to crawl in and of removing the pieces of furniture that hindered him, above all the chest of drawers and the writing desk. But that was more than she could manage all by herself; she did not dare ask her father to help her; and as for the servant girl, a young creature of sixteen who had had the courage to stay on after the cook's departure, she could not be asked to help, for she had begged as an especial favor that she might keep the kitchen door locked and open it only on a definite summons; so there was nothing left but to apply to her mother at an hour when her father was out. And the old lady did come, with exclamations of joyful eagerness, which, however, died away at the door of Gregor's room. Gregor's sister, of course, went in first, to see that everything was in order before letting his mother enter. In great haste Gregor pulled the sheet lower and tucked it more in folds so that it really looked as if it had been thrown accidentally over the sofa. And this time he did not peer out from under it; he renounced the pleasure of seeing his mother on this occasion and was only glad that she had come at all. "Come in, he's out of sight," said his sister, obviously leading her mother in by the hand. Gregor could now hear the two women struggling to shift the heavy old chest from its place, and his sister claiming the greater part of the labor for herself, without listening to the admonitions of her mother who feared she might overstrain herself. It took a long time. After at least a quarter of an hour's tugging his mother objected that the chest had better be left where it was, for in the first place it was too heavy and could never be got out before his father came home, and standing in the middle of the room like that it would only hamper Gregor's movements, while in the second place it was not at all certain that removing the furniture would be doing a service to Gregor. She was inclined to think to the contrary; the sight of the naked walls made her own heart heavy, and why shouldn't Gregor have the same feeling, considering that he had been used to his furniture for so long and might feel forlorn without it. "And doesn't it look," she concluded in a low voice—in fact she had been almost whispering all the time as if to avoid letting Gregor, whose exact whereabouts she did not know, hear even the tones of her voice, for she was convinced that he could not understand her words—"doesn't it look as if we were showing him, by taking away his furniture, that we have given up hope of his ever getting better and are just leaving him coldly to himself? I think it would be best to keep his room exactly as it has always been, so that when he comes back to us he will find everything unchanged and be able all the more easily to forget what has happened in between."

On hearing these words from his mother Gregor realized that the lack of all direct human speech for the past two months together with the monotony of family life must have confused his mind, otherwise he could not account for the fact that he had quite earnestly looked forward to having his room emptied of furnishing. Did he really want his warm room, so comfortably fitted with old family furniture, to be turned into a naked den in which he would certainly be able to crawl unhampered in all directions but at the price of shedding simultaneously all recollection of his human background? He had indeed been so near the brink of forgetfulness that only the voice of his mother, which he had not heard for so long, had drawn him back from it. Nothing should be taken out of his room, everything must stay as it was; he could not dispense with the good influence of the furniture on his state of mind; and even if the furniture did hamper him in his senseless crawling round and round, that was no drawback but a great advantage.

Unfortunately his sister was of the contrary opinion; she had grown accustomed, and not without reason, to consider herself an expert in Gregor's affairs as against her parents, and so her mother's advice was now enough to make her determined on the removal not only of the chest and the writing desk, which had been her first intention, but of all the furniture except the indispensable sofa. This determination was not, of course, merely the outcome of childish recalcitrance and of the self-confidence she had recently developed so unexpectedly and at such cost; she had in fact perceived that Gregor needed a lot of space to crawl about in, while on the other hand he never used the furniture at all, so far as could be seen. Another factor might have been also the enthusiastic temperament of an adolescent girl, which seeks to indulge itself on every opportunity and which now tempted Grete to exaggerate the horror of her brother's circumstances in order that she might do all the more for him. In a room where Gregor lorded it all alone over empty walls no one save herself was likely ever to set foot.

And so she was not to be moved from her resolve by her mother, who seemed moreover to be ill at ease in Gregor's room and therefore unsure of herself, was soon reduced to silence and helped her daughter as best she could to push the chest outside. Now, Gregor could do without the chest, if need be, but the writing desk he must retain. As soon as the two women had got the chest out of his room, groaning as they pushed it, Gregor stuck his head out from under the sofa to see how he might intervene as kindly and cautiously as possible. But as bad luck would have it, his mother was the first to return, leaving Grete clasping the chest in the room next door where she was trying to shift it all by herself, without of course moving it from the spot. His mother however was not accustomed to the sight of him, it might sicken her and so in alarm Gregor backed quickly to the other end of the sofa, yet could not prevent the sheet from swaying a little in front. That was enough to put her on the alert. She paused, stood still for a moment and then went back to Grete.

Although Gregor kept reassuring himself that nothing out of the way was happening, but only a few bits of furniture were being changed round, he soon had to admit that all this trotting to and fro of the two women, their little ejaculations and the scraping of furniture along the floor affected him like a vast disturbance coming from all sides at once, and however much he tucked in his head and legs and cowered to the very floor he was bound to confess that he would not be able to stand it for long. They were clearing his room out; taking away everything he loved; the chest in which he kept his fret saw and other tools was already dragged off; they were now loosening the writing desk which had almost sunk into the floor, the desk at which he had done all his homework when he was at the commercial academy, at the grammar school before that, and, yes, even the primary school—he had no more time to waste in weighing the good intentions of the two women, whose existence he had by now almost forgotten, for they were so exhausted that they were laboring in silence and nothing could be heard but the heavy scuffling of their feet.

And so he rushed out—the women were just leaning against the writing desk in the next room to give themselves a breather—and four times changed his direction, since he really did not know what to rescue first, then on the wall opposite, which was already otherwise cleared, he was struck by the picture of the lady muffled in so much fur and quickly crawled up to it and pressed himself to the glass, which was a good surface to hold on to and comforted his hot belly. This picture at least, which was entirely hidden beneath him, was going to be removed by nobody. He turned his head towards the door of the living room so as to observe the women when they came back.

They had not allowed themselves much of a rest and were already coming; Grete had twined her arm round her mother and was almost supporting her. "Well, what shall we take now?" said Grete, looking round. Her eyes met Gregor's from the wall. She kept her composure, presumably because of her mother, bent her head down to her mother, to keep her from looking up, and said, although in a fluttering, unpremeditated voice: "Come, hadn't we better go back to the living room for a moment?" Her intentions were clear enough to Gregor, she wanted to bestow her mother in safety and then chase him down from the wall. Well, just let her try it! He clung to his picture and would not give it up. He would rather fly in Grete's face.

But Grete's words had succeeded in disquieting her mother, who took a step to one side, caught sight of the huge brown mass on the flowered wallpaper, and before she was really conscious that what she saw was Gregor screamed in a loud, hoarse voice: "Oh God, oh God!" fell with outspread arms over the sofa as if giving up and did not move. "Gregor!" cried his sister, shaking her fist and glaring at him. This was the first time she had directly addressed him since his metamorphosis. She ran into the next room for some aromatic essence with which to rouse her mother from her fainting fit. Gregor wanted to help too—there was still time to rescue the picture—but he was stuck fast to the glass and had to tear himself loose; he then ran after his sister into the next room as if he could advise her, as he used to do; but then had to stand helplessly behind her; she meanwhile searched among various small bottles and when she turned round started in alarm at the sight of him; one bottle fell on the floor and broke; a splinter of glass cut Gregor's face and some kind of corrosive medicine splashed him; without pausing a moment longer Grete gathered up all the bottles she could carry and ran to her mother with them; she banged the door shut with her foot. Gregor was now cut off from his mother, who was perhaps nearly dying because of him; he dared not open the door for fear of frightening away his sister, who had to stay with her mother; there was nothing he could do but wait; and harassed by self-reproach and worry he began now to crawl to and fro, over everything, walls, furniture and ceiling, and finally in his despair, when the whole room seemed to be reeling round him, fell down on to the middle of the big table.

A little while elapsed, Gregor was still lying there feebly and all around was quiet, perhaps that was a good omen. Then the doorbell rang. The servant girl was of course locked in her kitchen, and Grete would have to open the door. It was his father. "What's been happening?" were his first words; Grete's face must have told him everything. Grete answered in a muffled voice, apparently hiding her head on his breast: "Mother has been fainting, but she's better now. Gregor's broken loose." "Just what I expected," said his father, "just what I've been telling you, but you women would never listen." It was clear to Gregor that his father had taken the worst interpretation of Grete's all too brief statement and was assuming that Gregor had been guilty of some violent act. Therefore Gregor must now try to propitiate his father, since he had neither time nor means for an explanation. And so he fled to the door of his own room and crouched against it, to let his father see as soon as he came in from the hall that his son had the good intention of getting back into his room immediately and that it was not necessary to drive him there, but that if only the door were opened he would disappear at once.

Yet his father was not in the mood to perceive such fine distinctions. "Ah!" he cried as soon as he appeared, in a tone which sounded at once angry and exultant. Gregor drew his head back from the door and lifted it to look at his father. Truly, this was not the father he had imagined to himself; admittedly he had been too absorbed of late in his new recreation of crawling over the ceiling to take the same interest as before in what was happening elsewhere in the flat, and he ought really to be prepared for some changes. And yet, and yet, could that be his father? The man who used to lie wearily sunk in bed whenever Gregor set out on a business journey; who welcomed him back of an evening lying in a long chair in a dressing gown; who could not really rise to his feet but only lifted his arms in greeting, and on the rare occasions when he did go out with his family, on one or two Sundays a year and on high holidays, walked between Gregor and his mother, who were slow walkers anyhow, even more slowly than they did, muffled in his old greatcoat, shuffling laboriously forward with the help of his crook-handled stick which he set down most cautiously at every step and, whenever he wanted to say anything, nearly always came to a full stop and gathered his escort around him? Now he was standing there in fine shape; dressed in a smart blue uniform with gold buttons, such as bank messengers wear; his strong double chin bulged over the stiff high collar of his jacket; from under his bushy eyebrows his black eyes darted fresh and penetrating glances; his onetime tangled white hair had been combed flat on either side of a shining and carefully exact parting. He pitched his cap, which bore a gold monogram, probably the badge of some bank, in a wide sweep across the whole room on to a sofa and with the tail ends of his jacket thrown back, his hands in his trouser pockets, advanced with a grim visage towards Gregor. Likely enough he did not himself know what he meant to do; at any rate he lifted his feet uncommonly high, and Gregor was dumbfounded at the enormous size of his shoe soles. But Gregor could not risk standing up to him, aware as he had been from the very first day of his new life that his father believed only the severest measures suitable for dealing with him. And so he ran before his father, stopping when he stopped and scuttling forward again when his father made any kind of move. In this way they circled the room several times without anything decisive happening, indeed the whole operation did not even look like a pursuit because it was carried out so slowly. And so Gregor did not leave the floor, for he feared that his father might take as a piece of peculiar wickedness any excursion of his over the walls or the ceiling. All the same, he could not stay this course much longer, for while his father took one step he had to carry out a whole series of movements. He was already beginning to feel breathless, just as in his former life his lungs had not been very dependable. As he was staggering along, trying to concentrate his energy on running, hardly keeping his eyes open; in his dazed state never even thinking of any other escape than simply going forward; and having almost forgotten that the walls were free to him, which in this room were well provided with finely carved pieces of furniture full of knobs and crevices—suddenly something lightly flung landed close behind him and rolled before him. It was an apple; a second apple followed immediately; Gregor came to a stop in alarm; there was no point in running on, for his father was determined to bombard him. He had filled his pockets with fruit from the dish on the sideboard and was now shying apple after apple, without taking particularly good aim for the moment. The small red apples rolled about the floor as if magnetized and cannoned into each other. An apple thrown without much force grazed Gregor's back and glanced off harmlessly. But another following immediately landed right on his back and sank in; Gregor wanted to drag himself forward, as if this startling, incredible pain could be left behind him; but he felt as if nailed to the spot and flattened himself out in a complete derangement of all his senses. With his last conscious look he saw the door of his room being torn open and his mother rushing out ahead of his screaming sister, in her underbodice, for her daughter had loosened her clothing to let her breathe more freely and recover from her swoon, he saw his mother rushing towards his father, leaving one after another behind her on the floor her loosened petticoats, stumbling over her petticoats straight to his father and embracing him, in complete union with him—but here Gregor's sight began to fail—with her hands clasped round his father's neck as she begged for her son's life.

III

The serious injury done to Gregor, which disabled him for more than a month—the apple went on sticking in his body as a visible reminder, since no one ventured to remove it—seemed to have made even his father recollect that Gregor was a member of the family, despite his present unfortunate and repulsive shape, and ought not to be treated as an enemy, that, on the contrary, family duty required the suppression of disgust and the exercise of patience, nothing but patience.

And although his injury had impaired, probably for ever, his powers of movement, and for the time being it took him long, long minutes to creep across his room like an old invalid—there was no question now of crawling up the wall—yet in his own opinion he was sufficiently compensated for this worsening of his condition by the fact that towards evening the living-room door, which he used to watch intently for an hour or two beforehand, was always thrown open, so that lying in the darkness of his room, invisible to the family, he could see them all at the lamp-lit table and listen to their talk, by general consent as it were, very different from his earlier eavesdropping.

True, their intercourse lacked the lively character of former times, which he had always called to mind with a certain wistfulness in the small hotel bedrooms where he had been wont to throw himself down, tired out, on damp bedding. They were now mostly very silent. Soon after supper his father would fall asleep in his armchair; his mother and sister would admonish each other to be silent; his mother, bending low over the lamp, stitched a fine sewing for an underwear firm; his sister, who had taken a job as a salesgirl, was learning shorthand and French in the evenings on the chance of bettering herself. Sometimes his father woke up, and as if quite unaware that he had been sleeping said to his mother: "What a lot of sewing you're doing today!" and at once fell asleep again, while the two women exchanged a tired smile.

With a kind of mulishness his father persisted in keeping his uniform on even in the house; his dressing gown hung uselessly on its peg and he slept fully dressed where he sat, as if he were ready for service at any moment and even here only at the beck and call of his superior. As a result, his uniform, which was not brand-new to start with, began to look dirty, despite all the loving care of the mother and sister to keep it clean, and Gregor often spent whole evenings gazing at the many greasy spots on the garment, gleaming with gold buttons always in a high state of polish, in which the old man sat sleeping in extreme discomfort and yet quite peacefully.

As soon as the clock struck ten his mother tried to rouse his father with gentle words and to persuade him after that to get into bed, for sitting there he could not have a proper sleep and that was what he needed most, since he had to go on duty at six. But with the mulishness that had obsessed him since he became a bank messenger he always insisted on staying longer at the table, although he regularly fell asleep again and in the end only with the greatest trouble could be got out of his armchair and in to his bed. However insistently Gregor's mother and sister kept urging him with gentle reminders, he would go on slowly shaking his head for a quarter of an hour, keeping his eyes shut, and refuse to get to his feet. The mother plucked at his sleeve, whispering endearments in his ear, the sister left her lessons to come to her mother's help, but Gregor's father was not to be caught. He would only sink down deeper in his chair. Not until the two women hoisted him up by the armpits did he open his eyes and look at them both, one after the other, usually with the remark: "This is a life. This is the peace and quiet of my old age." And leaning on the two of them he would heave himself up, with difficulty, as if he were a great burden to himself, suffer them to lead him as far as the door and then wave them off and go on alone, while the mother abandoned her needlework and the sister her pen in order to run after him and help him farther.

Who could find time, in this overworked and tired-out family, to bother about Gregor more than was absolutely needful? The household was reduced more and more; the servant girl was turned off; a gigantic bony charwoman with white hair flying round her head came in morning and evening to do the rough work; everything else was done by Gregor's mother, as well as great piles of sewing. Even various family ornaments, which his mother and sister used to wear with pride at parties and celebrations, had to be sold, as Gregor discovered of an evening from hearing them all discuss the prices obtained. But what they lamented most was the fact that they could not leave the flat which was much too big for their present circumstances, because they could not think of any way to shift Gregor. Yet Gregor saw well enough that consideration for him was not the main difficulty preventing the removal, for they could have easily shifted him in some suitable box with a few air holes in it; what really kept them from moving into another flat was rather their own complete hopelessness and the belief that they had been singled out for a misfortune such as had never happened to any of their relations or acquaintances. They fulfilled to the uttermost all that the world demands of poor people, the father fetched breakfast for the small clerks in the bank, the mother devoted her energy to making underwear for strangers, the sister trotted to and fro behind the counter at the behest of customers, but more than this they had not the strength to do. And the wound in Gregor's back began to nag at him afresh when his mother and sister, after getting his father into bed, came back again, left their work lying, drew close to each other and sat cheek by cheek; when his mother, pointing towards his room, said: "Shut that door now, Grete," and he was left again in darkness, while next door the women mingled their tears or perhaps sat dry-eyed staring at the table.

Gregor hardly slept at all by night or by day. He was often haunted by the idea that next time the door opened he would take the family's affairs in hand again just as he used to do; once more, after this long interval, there appeared in his thoughts the figures of the chief and the chief clerk, the commercial travelers and the apprentices, the porter who was so dull-witted, two or three friends in other firms, a chambermaid in one of the rural hotels, a sweet and fleeting memory, a cashier in a milliner's shop, whom he had wooed earnestly but too slowly—they all appeared, together with strangers or people he had quite forgotten, but instead of helping him and his family they were one and all unapproachable and he was glad when they vanished. At other times he would not be in the mood to bother about his family, he was only filled with rage at the way they were neglecting him, and although he had no clear idea of what he might care to eat he would make plans for getting into the larder to take the food that was after all his due, even if he were not hungry. His sister no longer took thought to bring him what might especially please him, but in the morning and at noon before she went to business hurriedly pushed into his room with her foot any food that was available, and in the evening cleared it out again with one sweep of the broom, heedless of whether it had been merely tasted, or—as most frequently happened—left untouched. The cleaning of his room, which she now did always in the evenings, could not have been more hastily done. Streaks of dirt stretched along the walls, here and there lay balls of dust and filth. At first Gregor used to station himself in some particularly filthy corner when his sister arrived, in order to reproach her with it, so to speak. But he could have sat there for weeks without getting her to make any improvement; she could see the dirt as well as he did, but she had simply made up her mind to leave it alone. And yet, with a touchiness that was new to her, which seemed anyhow to have infected the whole family, she jealously guarded her claim to be the sole caretaker of Gregor's room. His mother once subjected his room to a thorough cleaning, which was achieved only by means of several buckets of water—all this dampness of course upset Gregor too and he lay widespread, sulky and motionless on the sofa—but she was well punished for it. Hardly had his sister noticed the changed aspect of his room that evening than she rushed in high dudgeon into the living room and, despite the imploringly raised hands of her mother, burst into a storm of weeping, while her parents—her father had of course been startled out of his chair—looked on at first in helpless amazement; then they too began to go into action; the father reproached the mother on his right for not having left the cleaning of Gregor's room to his sister; shrieked at the sister on his left that never again was she to be allowed to clean Gregor's room; while the mother tried to pull the father into his bedroom, since he was beyond himself with agitation; the sister, shaken with sobs, then beat upon the table with her small fists; and Gregor hissed loudly with rage because not one of them thought of shutting the door to spare him such a spectacle and so much noise.

Still, even if the sister, exhausted by her daily work, had grown tired of looking after Gregor as she did formerly, there was no need for his mother's intervention or for Gregor's being neglected at all. The charwoman was there. This old widow, whose strong bony frame had enabled her to survive the worst a long life could offer, by no means recoiled from Gregor. Without being in the least curious she had once by chance opened the door of his room and at the sight of Gregor, who, taken by surprise, began to rush to and fro although no one was chasing him, merely stood there with her arms folded. From that time she never failed to open his door a little for a moment, morning and evening, to have a look at him. At first she even used to call him to her, with words which apparently she took to be friendly, such as: "Come along, then, you old dung beetle!" or "Look at the old dung beetle, then!" To such allocations Gregor made no answer, but stayed motionless where he was, as if the door had never been opened. Instead of being allowed to disturb him so senselessly whenever the whim took her, she should rather have been ordered to clean out his room daily, that charwoman! Once, early in the morning—heavy rain was lashing on the windowpanes, perhaps a sign that spring was on the way—Gregor was so exasperated when she began addressing him again that he ran at her, as if to attack her, although slowly and feebly enough. But the charwoman instead of showing fright merely lifted high a chair that happened to be beside the door, and as she stood there with her mouth wide open it was clear that she meant to shut it only when she brought the chair down on Gregor's back. "So you're not coming any nearer?" she asked, as Gregor turned away again, and quietly put the chair back into the corner.

Gregor was now eating hardly anything. Only when he happened to pass the food laid out for him did he take a bit of something in his mouth as a pastime, kept it there for an hour at a time and usually spat it out again. At first he thought it was chagrin over the state of his room that prevented him from eating, yet he soon got used to the various changes in his room. It had become a habit in the family to push into his room things there was no room for elsewhere, and there were plenty of these now, since one of the rooms had been let to three lodgers. These serious gentlemen—all three of them with full beards, as Gregor once observed through a crack in the door—had a passion for order, not only in their own room but, since they were now members of the household, in all its arrangements, especially in the kitchen. Superfluous, not to say dirty, objects they could not bear. Besides, they had brought with them most of the furnishings they needed. For this reason many things could be dispensed with that it was no use trying to sell but that should not be thrown away either. All of them found their way into Gregor's room. The ash can likewise and the kitchen garbage can. Anything that was not needed for the moment was simply flung into Gregor's room by the charwoman, who did everything in a hurry; fortunately Gregor usually saw only the object, whatever it was, and the hand that held it. Perhaps she intended to take the things away again as time and opportunity offered, or to collect them until she could throw them all out in a heap, but in fact they just lay wherever she happened to throw them, except when Gregor pushed his way through the junk heap and shifted it somewhat, at first out of necessity, because he had not room enough to crawl, but later with increasing enjoyment, although after such excursions, being sad and weary to death, he would lie motionless for hours. And since the lodgers often ate their supper at home in the common living room, the living-room door stayed shut many an evening, yet Gregor reconciled himself quite easily to the shutting of the door, for often enough on evenings when it was opened he had disregarded it entirely and lain in the darkest corner of his room, quite unnoticed by the family. But on one occasion the charwoman left the door open a little and it stayed ajar even when the lodgers came in for supper and the lamp was lit. They set themselves at the top end of the table where formerly Gregor and his father and mother had eaten their meals, unfolded their napkins and took knife and fork in hand. At once his mother appeared in the other doorway with a dish of meat and close behind her his sister with a dish of potatoes piled high. The food steamed with a thick vapor. The lodgers bent over the food set before them as if to scrutinize it before eating, in fact the man in the middle, who seemed to pass for an authority with the other two, cut a piece of meat as it lay on the dish, obviously to discover if it were tender or should be sent back to the kitchen. He showed satisfaction, and Gregor's mother and sister, who had been watching anxiously, breathed freely and began to smile.

The family itself took its meals in the kitchen. None the less, Gregor's father came into the living room before going into the kitchen and with one prolonged bow, cap in hand, made a round of the table. The lodgers all stood up and murmured something in their beards. When they were alone again they ate their food in almost complete silence. It seemed remarkable to Gregor that among the various noises coming from the table he could always distinguish the sound of their masticating teeth, as if this were a sign to Gregor that one needed teeth in order to eat, and that with toothless jaws even of the finest make one could do nothing. "I'm hungry enough," said Gregor sadly to himself, "but not for that kind of food. How these lodgers are stuffing themselves, and here am I dying of starvation!"

On that very evening—during the whole of his time there Gregor could not remember ever having heard the violin—the sound of violin-playing came from the kitchen. The lodgers had already finished their supper, the one in the middle had brought out a newspaper and given the other two a page apiece, and now they were leaning back at ease reading and smoking. When the violin began to play they pricked up their ears, got to their feet, and went on tiptoe to the hall door where they stood huddled together. Their movements must have been heard in the kitchen, for Gregor's father called out: "Is the violin-playing disturbing you, gentlemen? It can be stopped at once." "On the contrary," said the middle lodger, "could not Fräulein Samsa come and play in this room, beside us, where it is much more convenient and comfortable?" "Oh certainly," cried Gregor's father, as if he were the violin-player. The lodgers came back into the living room and waited. Presently Gregor's father arrived with the music stand, his mother carrying the music and his sister with the violin. His sister quietly made everything ready to start playing; his parents, who had never let rooms before and so had an exaggerated idea of the courtesy due to lodgers, did not venture to sit down on their own chairs; his father leaned against the door, the right hand thrust between two buttons of his livery coat, which was formally buttoned up; but his mother was offered a chair by one of the lodgers and, since she left the chair just where he had happened to put it, sat down in a corner to one side.

Gregor's sister began to play; the father and mother, from either side, intently watched the movements of her hands. Gregor, attracted by the playing, ventured to move forward a little until his head was actually inside the living room. He felt hardly any surprise at his growing lack of consideration for the others; there had been a time when he prided himself on being considerate. And yet just on this occasion he had more reason than ever to hide himself, since owing to the amount of dust which lay thick in his room and rose into the air at the slightest movement, he too was covered with dust; fluff and hair and remnants of food trailed with him, caught on his back and along his sides; his indifference to everything was much too great for him to turn on his back and scrape himself clean on the carpet, as once he had done several times a day. And in spite of his condition, no shame deterred him from advancing a little over the spotless floor of the living room.

To be sure, no one was aware of him. The family was entirely absorbed in the violin-playing; the lodgers, however, who first of all had stationed themselves, hands in pockets, much too close behind the music stand so that they could all have read the music, which must have bothered his sister, had soon retreated to the window, half-whispering with downbent heads, and stayed there while his father turned an anxious eye on them. Indeed, they were making it more than obvious that they had been disappointed in their expectation of hearing good or enjoyable violin-playing, that they had had more than enough of the performance and only out of courtesy suffered a continued disturbance of their peace. From the way they all kept blowing the smoke of their cigars high in the air through nose and mouth one could divine their irritation. And yet Gregor's sister was playing so beautifully. Her face leaned sideways, intently and sadly her eyes followed the notes of music. Gregor crawled a little farther forward and lowered his head to the ground so that it might be possible for his eyes to meet hers. Was he an animal, that music had such an effect upon him? He felt as if the way were opening before him to the unknown nourishment he craved. He was determined to push forward till he reached his sister, to pull at her skirt and so let her know that she was to come into his room with her violin, for no one here appreciated her playing as he would appreciate it. He would never let her out of his room, at least, not so long as he lived; his frightful appearance would become, for the first time, useful to him; he would watch all the doors of his room at once and spit at intruders; but his sister should need no constraint, she should stay with him of her own free will; she should sit beside him on the sofa, bend down her ear to him and hear him confide that he had had the firm intention of sending her to the Conservatorium, and that, but for his mishap, last Christmas—surely Christmas was long past?—he would have announced it to everybody without allowing a single objection. After this confession his sister would be so touched that she would burst into tears, and Gregor would then raise himself to her shoulder and kiss her on the neck, which, now that she went to business, she kept free of any ribbon or collar.

"Mr. Samsa!" cried the middle lodger, to Gregor's father, and pointed, without wasting any more words, at Gregor, now working himself slowly forwards. The violin fell silent, the middle lodger first smiled to his friends with a shake of the head and then looked at Gregor again. Instead of driving Gregor out, his father seemed to think it more needful to begin by soothing down the lodgers, although they were not at all agitated and apparently found Gregor more entertaining than the violin-playing. He hurried towards them and, spreading out his arms, tried to urge them back into their own room and at the same time to block their view of Gregor. They now began to be really a little angry, one could not tell whether because of the old man's behavior or because it had just dawned on them that all unwittingly they had such a neighbor as Gregor next door. They demanded explanations of his father, they waved their arms like him, tugged uneasily at their beards, and only with reluctance backed towards their room. Meanwhile Gregor's sister, who stood there as if lost when her playing was so abruptly broken off, came to life again, pulled herself together all at once after standing for a while holding violin and bow in nervelessly hanging hands and staring at her music, pushed her violin into the lap of her mother, who was still sitting in her chair fighting asthmatically for breath, and ran into the lodgers' room to which they were now being shepherded by her father rather more quickly than before. One could see the pillows and blankets on the beds flying under her accustomed fingers and being laid in order. Before the lodgers had actually reached their room she had finished making the beds and slipped out.

The old man seemed once more to be so possessed by his mulish self-assertiveness that he was forgetting all the respect he should show to his lodgers. He kept driving them on and driving them on until in the very door of the bedroom the middle lodger stamped his foot loudly on the floor and so brought him to a halt. "I beg to announce," said the lodger, lifting one hand and looking also at Gregor's mother and sister, "that because of the disgusting conditions prevailing in this household and family"—here he spat on the floor with emphatic brevity—"I give you notice on the spot. Naturally I won't pay you a penny for the days I have lived here, on the contrary I shall consider bringing an action for damages against you, based on claims—believe me—that will be easily susceptible of proof." He ceased and stared straight in front of him, as if he expected something. In fact his two friends at once rushed into the breach with these words: "And we too give notice on the spot." On that he seized the door-handle and shut the door with a slam.

Gregor's father, groping with his hands, staggered forward and fell into his chair; it looked as if he were stretching himself there for his ordinary evening nap, but the marked jerkings of his head, which was as if uncontrollable, showed that he was far from asleep. Gregor had simply stayed quietly all the time on the spot where the lodgers had espied him. Disappointment at the failure of his plan, perhaps also the weakness arising from extreme hunger, made it impossible for him to move. He feared, with a fair degree of certainty, that at any moment the general tension would discharge itself in a combined attack upon him, and he lay waiting. He did not react even to the noise made by the violin as it fell off his mother's lap from under her trembling fingers and gave out a resonant note.

"My dear parents," said his sister, slapping her hand on the table by way of introduction, "things can't go on like this. Perhaps you don't realize that, but I do. I won't utter my brother's name in the presence of this creature, and so all I say is: we must try to get rid of it. We've tried to look after it and to put up with it as far as is humanly possible, and I don't think anyone could reproach us in the slightest."

"She is more than right," said Gregor's father to himself. His mother, who was still choking for lack of breath, began to cough hollowly into her hand with a wild look in her eyes.

His sister rushed over to her and held her forehead. His father's thoughts seemed to have lost their vagueness at Grete's words, he sat more upright, fingering his service cap that lay among the plates still lying on the table from the lodgers' supper, and from time to time looked at the still form of Gregor.

"We must try to get rid of it," his sister now said explicitly to her father, since her mother was coughing too much to hear a word, "it will be the death of both of you, I can see that coming. When one has to work as hard as we do, all of us, one can't stand this continual torment at home on top of it. At least I can't stand it any longer." And she burst into such a passion of sobbing that her tears dropped on her mother's face, where she wiped them off mechanically.

"My dear," said the old man sympathetically, and with evident understanding, "but what can we do?"

Gregor's sister merely shrugged her shoulders to indicate the feeling of helplessness that had now overmastered her during her weeping fit, in contrast to her former confidence.

"If he could understand us," said his father, half questioningly; Grete, still sobbing, vehemently waved a hand to show how unthinkable that was.

"If he could understand us," repeated the old man, shutting his eyes to consider his daughter's conviction that understanding was impossible, "then perhaps we might come to some agreement with him. But as it is—"

"He must go," cried Gregor's sister, "that's the only solution, Father. You must just try to get rid of the idea that this is Gregor. The fact that we've believed it for so long is the root of all our trouble. But how can it be Gregor? If this were Gregor, he would have realized long ago that human beings can't live with such a creature, and he'd have gone away on his own accord. Then we wouldn't have any brother, but we'd be able to go on living and keep his memory in honor. As it is, this creature persecutes us, drives away our lodgers, obviously wants the whole apartment to himself and would have us all sleep in the gutter. Just look, Father," she shrieked all at once, "he's at it again!" And in an excess of panic that was quite incomprehensible to Gregor she even quitted her mother, literally thrusting the chair from her as if she would rather sacrifice her mother than stay so near to Gregor, and rushed behind her father, who also rose up, being simply upset by her agitation, and half-spread his arms out as if to protect her.

Yet Gregor had not the slightest intention of frightening anyone, far less his sister. He had only begun to turn round in order to crawl back to his room, but it was certainly a startling operation to watch, since because of his disabled condition he could not execute the difficult turning movements except by lifting his head and then bracing it against the floor over and over again. He paused and looked round. His good intentions seemed to have been recognized; the alarm had only been momentary. Now they were all watching him in melancholy silence. His mother lay in her chair, her legs stiffly outstretched and pressed together, her eyes almost closing for sheer weariness; his father and his sister were sitting beside each other, his sister's arm around the old man's neck.

Perhaps I can go on turning round now, thought Gregor, and began his labors again. He could not stop himself from panting with the effort, and had to pause now and then to take breath. Nor did anyone harass him, he was left entirely to himself. When he had completed the turn-round he began at once to crawl straight back. He was amazed at the distance separating him from his room and could not understand how in his weak state he had managed to accomplish the same journey so recently, almost without remarking it. Intent on crawling as fast as possible, he barely noticed that not a single word, not an ejaculation from his family, interfered with his progress. Only when he was already in the doorway did he turn his head round, not completely, for his neck muscles were getting stiff, but enough to see that nothing had changed behind him except that his sister had risen to her feet. His last glance fell on his mother, who was not quite overcome by sleep.

Hardly was he well inside his room when the door was hastily pushed shut, bolted and locked. The sudden noise in his rear startled him so much that his little legs gave beneath him. It was his sister who had shown such haste. She had been standing ready waiting and had made a light spring forward, Gregor had not even heard her coming, and she cried "At last!" to her parents as she turned the key in the lock.

"And what now?" said Gregor to himself, looking round in the darkness. Soon he made the discovery that he was now unable to stir a limb. This did not surprise him, rather it seemed unnatural that he should ever actually have been able to move on these feeble little legs. Otherwise he felt relatively comfortable. True, his whole body was aching, but it seemed that the pain was gradually growing less and would finally pass away. The rotting apple in his back and the inflamed area around it, all covered with soft dust, already hardly troubled him. He thought of his family with tenderness and love. The decision that he must disappear was one that he held to even more strongly than his sister, if that were possible. In this state of vacant and peaceful meditation he remained until the tower clock struck three in the morning. The first broadening of light in the world outside the window entered his consciousness once more. Then his head sank to the floor of its own accord and from his nostrils came the last faint flicker of his breath.

When the charwoman arrived early in the morning—what between her strength and her impatience she slammed all the doors so loudly, never mind how often she had been begged not to do so, that no one in the whole apartment could enjoy any quiet sleep after her arrival—she noticed nothing unusual as she took her customary peep into Gregor's room. She thought he was lying motionless on purpose, pretending to be in the sulks; she credited him with every kind of intelligence. Since she happened to have the long-handled broom in her hand she tried to tickle him up with it from the doorway. When that too produced no reaction she felt provoked and poked at him a little harder, and only when she had pushed him along the floor without meeting any resistance was her attention aroused. It did not take her long to establish the truth of the matter, and her eyes widened, she let out a whistle, yet did not waste much time over it but tore open the door of the Samsas' bedroom and yelled into the darkness at the top of her voice: "Just look at this, it's dead; it's lying here dead and done for!"

Mr. and Mrs. Samsa started up in their double bed and before they realized the nature of the charwoman's announcement had some difficulty in overcoming the shock of it. But then they got out of bed quickly, one on either side, Mr. Samsa throwing a blanket over his shoulders, Mrs. Samsa in nothing but her nightgown; in this array they entered Gregor's room. Meanwhile the door of the living room opened, too, where Grete had been sleeping since the advent of the lodgers; she was completely dressed as if she had not been to bed, which seemed to be confirmed also by the paleness of her face. "Dead?" said Mrs. Samsa, looking questioningly at the charwoman, although she could have investigated for herself, and the fact was obvious enough without investigation. "I should say so," said the charwoman, proving her words by pushing Gregor's corpse a long way to one side with her broomstick. Mrs. Samsa made a movement as if to stop her, but checked it. "Well," said Mr. Samsa, "now thanks be to God." He crossed himself, and the three women followed his example. Grete, whose eyes never left the corpse, said: "Just see how thin he was. It's such a long time since he's eaten anything. The food came out again just as it went in." Indeed, Gregor's body was completely flat and dry, as could only now be seen when it was no longer supported by the legs and nothing prevented one from looking closely at it.

"Come in beside us, Grete, for a little while," said Mrs. Samsa with a tremulous smile, and Grete, not without looking back at the corpse, followed her parents into their bedroom. The charwoman shut the door and opened the window wide. Although it was so early in the morning a certain softness was perceptible in the fresh air. After all, it was already the end of March.

The three lodgers emerged from their room and were surprised to see no breakfast; they had been forgotten. "Where's our breakfast?" said the middle lodger peevishly to the charwoman. But she put her finger to her lips and hastily, without a word, indicated by gestures that they should go into Gregor's room. They did so and stood, their hands in the pockets of their somewhat shabby coats, around Gregor's corpse in the room where it was now fully light.

At that the door of the Samsas' bedroom opened and Mr. Samsa appeared in his uniform, his wife on one arm, his daughter on the other. They all looked a little as if they had been crying; from time to time Grete hid her face on her father's arm.

"Leave my house at once!" said Mr. Samsa, and pointed to the door without disengaging himself from the women. "What do you mean by that?" said the middle lodger, taken somewhat aback, with a feeble smile. The two others put their hands behind them and kept rubbing them together, as if in gleeful expectation of a fine set-to in which they were bound to come off the winners. "I mean just what I say," answered Mr. Samsa, and advanced in a straight line with his two companions towards the lodger. He stood his ground at first quietly, looking at the floor as if his thoughts were taking a new pattern in his head. "Then let us go, by all means," he said, and looked up at Mr. Samsa as if in a sudden access of humility he were expecting some renewed sanction for this decision. Mr. Samsa merely nodded briefly once or twice with meaning eyes. Upon that the lodger really did go with long strides into the hall, his two friends had been listening and had quite stopped rubbing their hands for some moments and now went scuttling after him as if afraid that Mr. Samsa might get into the hall before them and cut them off from their leader. In the hall they all three took their hats from the rack, their sticks from the umbrella stand, bowed in silence and quitted the apartment. With a suspiciousness which proved quite unfounded Mr. Samsa and the two women followed them out to the landing; leaning over the banister they watched the three figures slowly but surely going down the long stairs, vanishing from sight at a certain turn of the staircase on every floor and coming into view again after a moment or so; the more they dwindled, the more the Samsa family's interest in them dwindled, and when a butcher's boy met them and passed them on the stairs coming up proudly with a tray on his head, Mr. Samsa and the two women soon left the landing and as if a burden had been lifted from them went back into their apartment.

They decided to spend this day in resting and going for a stroll; they had not only deserved such a respite from work, but absolutely needed it. And so they sat down at the table and wrote three notes of excuse, Mr. Samsa to his board of management, Mrs. Samsa to her employer and Grete to the head of her firm. While they were writing, the charwoman came in to say that she was going now, since her morning's work was finished. At first they only nodded without looking up, but as she kept hovering there they eyed her irritably. "Well?" said Mr. Samsa. The charwoman stood grinning in the doorway as if she had good news to impart to the family but meant not to say a word unless properly questioned. The small ostrich feather standing upright on her hat, which had annoyed Mr. Samsa ever since she was engaged, was waving gaily in all direction. "Well, what is it then?" asked Mrs. Samsa, who obtained more respect from the charwoman than the others. "Oh," said the charwoman, giggling so amiably that she could not at once continue, "just this, you don't need to bother about how to get rid of the thing next door. It's been seen to already." Mrs. Samsa and Grete bent over their letters again, as if preoccupied; Mr. Samsa, who perceived that she was eager to begin describing it all in detail, stopped her with a decisive hand. But since she was not allowed to tell her story, she remembered the great hurry she was in, being obviously deeply huffed: "Bye, everybody," she said, whirling off violently, and departed with a frightful slamming of doors.

"She'll be given notice tonight," said Mr. Samsa, but neither from his wife nor his daughter did he get any answer, for the charwoman seemed to have shattered again the composure they had barely achieved. They rose, went to the window and stayed there, clasping each other tight. Mr. Samsa turned in his chair to look at them and quietly observed them for a little. Then he called out: "Come along, now, do. Let bygones be bygones. And you might have some consideration for me." The two of them complied at once, hastened to him, caressed him and quickly finished their letters.

Then they all three left the apartment together, which was more than they had done for months, and went by tram into the open country outside the town. The tram, in which they were the only passengers, was filled with warm sunshine. Leaning comfortably back in their seats they canvassed their prospects for the future, and it appeared on closer inspection that these were not at all bad, for the jobs they had got, which so far they had never really discussed with each other, were all three admirable and likely to lead to better things later on. The greatest immediate improvement in their condition would of course arise from moving to another house; they wanted to take a smaller and cheaper but also better situated and more easily run apartment than the one they had, which Gregor had selected. While they were thus conversing, it struck both Mr. and Mrs. Samsa, almost at the same moment, as they became aware of their daughter's increasing vivacity, that in spite of all the sorrow of recent times, which had made her cheeks pale, she had bloomed into a pretty girl with a good figure. They grew quieter and half unconsciously exchanged glances of complete agreement, having come to the conclusion that it would soon be time to find a good husband for her. And it was like a confirmation of their new dreams and excellent intentions that at the end of their journey their daughter sprang to her feet first and stretched her young body.

[1912]

John Keats
[1795–1821]

JOHN KEATS'S *father kept a London livery stable—not a very auspicious begin-ning for the Romantic poet of the sublimely beautiful. His father died when he was nine, and when he was fifteen, he lost his mother to tuberculosis. His brother died of the same disease a few years later, and it took Keats, too, at age twenty-six. Tuberculosis was common in the early 1800s, and was especially prevelant among those who lived in London's smoggy interior. Despite these challenges, and his early death, Keats produced a large volume of memorable poetry.*

He attended school at Enfield, but in 1810 was apprenticed to a surgeon. The medical profession did not have the status that it has today, and this change was not a social improvement for the young Keats. Despite his removal from school, he read and fell in love with Edmund Spenser's Faerie Queen, *and even as he fin-ished his apprenticeship and began work in a London hospital, his heart and imagination were with Spenser's world of elves and knights. He met all the Romantic writers, including Percy Byssche Shelley and Samuel Taylor Coleridge, and became friends with Leigh Hunt, editor of* The Examiner, *which published some of his early sonnets. Keats dedicated his first volume of poems to Hunt in 1817. His first long poem,* Endymion, *appeared in 1818, but his friendship with Hunt, who was on the outs with the London critics, drew criticism of the poem. Keats was hurt, but continued to write, despite Shelley's later argument in* Adonais *that the critics had killed Keats with their reviews. At the same time he fell hopelessly in love with Fanny Brawne, whose social position would not allow her to marry a stable-boy-turned-physician, whatever poetic talents he possessed. These losses seemed to fuel his poetic passion. In 1819, he published* The Eve of St. Agnes, *arguably the signature poem of the sensuous and fanciful wing of the Romantic movement. This poem tells the story of a young knight who brings beautiful food to his lady's chamber, and appears to her as if in a dream to per-suade her to run away with him, which she does. His next two poems,* La Belle Dame sans Merci (The Beautiful Woman Without Mercy), *a poem about a witch, and* Lamia, *a poem about a woman who can become a snake, followed in 1820.* Isabella, or The Pot of Basil, *followed, a tale taken from Boccaccio's* Decameron *about a woman who plants her unfaithful lover's head in a pot of herbs. His last poem, the unfinished* Hyperion, *recounts a classical myth, and throughout the last years of his life, he wrote the sonnets that have become the jewels of the Romantic movement.*

Ode on a Grecian Urn

JOHN KEATS

I

Thou still unravished bride of quietness,
 Thou foster-child of silence and slow time,
Sylvan[1] historian, who canst thus express
 A flowery tale more sweetly than our rhyme:
What leaf-fringed legend haunts about thy shape   5
 Of deities or mortals, or of both,
  In Tempe or the dales of Arcady?
 What men or gods are these? What maidens loth?
What mad pursuit? What struggle to escape?
 What pipes and timbrels? What wild ecstasy?   10

II

Heard melodies are sweet, but those unheard
 Are sweeter; therefore, ye soft pipes, play on;
Not to the sensual ear, but, more endeared,
 Pipe to the spirit ditties of no tone:
Fair youth, beneath the trees, thou canst not leave   15
 Thy song, nor ever can those trees be bare;
  Bold Lover, never, never canst thou kiss,
Though winning near the goal—yet, do not grieve;
 She cannot fade, though thou hast not thy bliss,
 For ever wilt thou love, and she be fair!   20

---

[1] Of the woodland.

First published in *Annals of the Fine Arts,* December, 1819. Reprinted with minor changes in *John Keats, Lamia, Isabella, The Eve of St. Agnes, and Other Poems* in 1820.

III

Ah, happy, happy boughs! that cannot shed
  Your leaves, nor ever bid the Spring adieu;
And, happy melodist, unwearièd,
  For ever piping songs for ever new;
More happy love! more happy, happy love!   *25*
  For ever warm and still to be enjoyed,
    For ever panting, and for ever young—
All breathing human passion far above,
  That leaves a heart high-sorrowful and cloyed,
    A burning forehead, and a parching tongue.   *30*

IV

Who are these coming to the sacrifice?
  To what green altar, O mysterious priest,
Lead'st thou that heifer lowing at the skies,
  And all her silken flanks with garlands dressed?
What little town by river or sea shore,   *35*
  Or mountain-built with peaceful citadel,
    Is emptied of this folk, this pious morn?
And, little town, thy streets for evermore
  Will silent be; and not a soul to tell
    Why thou art desolate, can e'er return.   *40*

V

O Attic[2] shape! Fair attitude! with brede
  Of marble men and maidens overwrought,
With forest branches and the trodden weed;
  Thou, silent form, dost tease us out of thought
As doth eternity: Cold Pastoral!   *45*
  When old age shall this generation waste,
    Thou shalt remain, in midst of other woe
Than ours, a friend to man, to whom thou say'st,
  'Beauty is truth, truth beauty,—that is all
    Ye know on earth, and all ye need to know.'   *50*

[1819]

---

[2]Grecian

Andrew Marvell
[1621–1678]

ANDREW MARVELL *was born in England, in the region of Yorkshire, as the son of a reverend. He began his studies at Trinity College in Cambridge at the age of twelve, but eventually abandoned his formal studies after his father died in a drowning accident. By sixteen he had already published two poems, one written in Latin and the other in Greek, in a Cambridge anthology. While still in his twenties, he traveled throughout Europe—learning French, Spanish, Italian, and Dutch in the process. He worked as a tutor and was for a time the secretary to the poet John Milton. In 1660 he was elected to Parliament under Oliver Cromwell during a period of much political upheaval in England. Marvell turned out to be an astute politician, pamphleteer, and a severe critic of the English parliament and the court system. He wrote poems and satires, many of them related to the political topics of the period. Some of his best known of these poems include "Upon Appleton House," the* Mower *series, and "The Garden." No collection of Marvell's poetry was published until three years after his sudden death of a fever, although a few individual poems appeared during his lifetime. His more famous poems, however, were published after his death. Marvell is remembered for his sharp political satire and his poetic lyricism. He wrote in the neoclassical tradition, a period in which writers sought to imitate the lessons from the classical period—aesthetic discipline and perfection. "To His Coy Mistress" is perhaps his best-known poem. It is a supreme example of a* carpe diem *lyric, a poem that explores how time acts upon physical beauty and sexual desire.*

To His Coy Mistress

ANDREW MARVELL

Had we but world enough, and time,
This coyness, lady, were no crime.
We would sit down, and think which way
To walk, and pass our long love's day.
Thou by the Indian Ganges' side   5
Shouldst rubies find: I by the tide
Of Humber would complain. I would
Love you ten years before the Flood,
And you should if you please refuse
Till the conversion of the Jews.   10
My vegetable love should grow
Vaster than empires, and more slow;
An hundred years should go to praise
Thine eyes, and on thy forehead gaze;
Two hundred to adore each breast,   15
But thirty thousand to the rest.
An age at least to every part,
And the last age should show your heart.
For, lady, you deserve this state;
Nor would I love at lower rate.   20
    But at my back I always hear
Time's wingéd chariot hurrying near;
And yonder all before us lie
Deserts of vast eternity.
Thy beauty shall no more be found,   25
Nor, in thy marble vault, shall sound
My echoing song; then worms shall try
That long preserved virginity,
And your quaint honor turn to dust,
And into ashes all my lust: 30

First published in *Miscellaneous Poems* in 1681.

The grave's a fine and private place,
But none, I think, do there embrace.
   Now therefore, while the youthful hue
Sits on thy skin like morning dew,
And while thy willing soul transpires   *35*
At every pore with instant fires,
Now let us sport us while we may,
And now, like am'rous birds of prey,
Rather at once our time devour
Than languish in his slow-chapped pow'r.   *40*
Let us roll all our strength and all
Our sweetness up into one ball,
And tear our pleasures with rough strife
Thorough the iron gates of life.
Thus, though we cannot make our sun   *45*
Stand still, yet we will make him run.

[1681]

Edna St. Vincent Millay
[1892–1950]

EDNA ST. VINCENT MILLAY'S *life and career as a poet has undergone a great deal of telling and retelling in order to sanitize a woman of great poetic talent, who lead a trailblazing life exploring sexuality and the role of women in society. Millay's feminism had its roots in her mother's iconoclastic views—she divorced Millay's father and raised Edna independently—and her sexual politics were exposed early in her student career at Vassar. At Vassar, Millay participated in a radical theater group, where she wrote and acted in plays (theater being one of the few places a woman could share her thoughts and experiences in the early twentieth century.) After graduating from Vassar, Millay moved to New York where she hoped to forge a career in theater. In Greenwich Village she encountered the avant-garde theater group of Susan Glaspell, Eugene O'Neill, John Reed, and Jig Cook. Millay soon fell in with a bohemian crowd in which she would spend the next several years conducting affairs with men and women, while at the same time publishing poems in a variety of popular and literary magazines. She was proclaimed the "spokesman for the New Woman" and her poem "First Fig" became an anthem for rebellious youth of both genders.*

To the great surprise of her fans and friends in her bohemian circle, Millay married Eugen Boissevain 1923 and left New York to live a quiet life in the Berkshires. He gave up his own pursuits to manage her literary career, orchestrating her public appearances. Her relationship with her husband was in the bohemian tradition: they remained sexually open during their twenty-six-year marriage. Millay also continued to write and explore radical ideas. She was disturbed by the rise of fascism and wrote overtly political poems opposing it. Likewise she spoke out radically on the executions of Sacco and Vanzetti, who many believed were convicted of murder on the basis of their anarchist beliefs. It was, however, Millay's long narrative poem Fatal Interview *(1931) that drew far more attention—not for its poetic merit, but for its subject matter of an extramarital affair. Readers paid far less attention to the poems themselves than the identity of Millay's supposed lover. In 1921 she published a verse play titled* The Lamp and the Bell, *in which Millay dealt with the subject of love between women. For her fourth book of poetry,* The Harp Weaver *(1923), she was awarded the Pulitzer Prize. She published many dramas and poetry throughout her career. Her* Collected Poems *appeared in 1949 and again in 1956.*

What lips my lips have kissed, and where, and why

EDNA ST. VINCENT MILLAY

What lips my lips have kissed, and where, and why,
I have forgotten, and what arms have lain
Under my head till morning; but the rain
Is full of ghosts tonight, that tap and sigh
Upon the glass and listen for reply,   5
And in my heart there sits a quiet pain
For unremembered lads that not again
Will turn to me at midnight with a cry.
Thus in the winter stands the lonely tree,
Nor knows what birds have vanished one by one,   10
Yet knows its boughs more silent than before:
I cannot say what loves have come and gone,
I only know that summer sang in me
A little while, that in me sings no more.

[1923]

Composed in 1923.

Marianne Moore
[1887–1972]

When **MARIANNE MOORE** *was studying biology in college, she seriously considered becoming a doctor. She did, however, contribute "one or two little things" to the college's literary magazine, noting later that the precision required in laboratory work probably had a beneficial impact on her writing. Ultimately it was the dabbling in literary work rather than the intensive study of science that drew Moore to her life's work.*

Moore was born in the home of her maternal grandfather in Kirkwood, Missouri, in the same year that her father was committed to a mental institution. She never knew her father. She attended school there and in Carlisle, Pennsylvania, and graduated from Bryn Mawr College in 1909. In the years following her graduation, several of her poems were published in the Bryn Mawr alumnae magazine. Then, in 1915, sixteen of her poems appeared in three prestigious literary magazines, The Egoist, Others, *and* Poetry. *During the following year fifteen more poems appeared.*

Moore and her mother moved to Greenwich Village in 1918, where the young poet met other writers and critics, and continued to publish a few poems per year while working in clerical positions. Her first collection, Poems, *was published without her knowledge in London, to mixed reviews. In 1924 she published* Observations, *which included "An Octopus," an ode to the glacial Mount Ranier in Washington. In the poem, according to Elizabeth Phillips, Moore "creates an extraordinary visual sense of the flora and fauna, the delicate beauty, and the ecology of the park; but she is not the romantic poet looking into nature to find her own image everywhere. She is the self-effacing and invisible observer." This capacity to integrate the disinterested observer with the intensely involved poet characterizes much of Moore's work.*

The success of Observations *led to Moore's being selected as editor of the literary magazine* Dial, *a position she held until the magazine ceased publication in 1929. As editor, Moore published writers as T. S. Eliot, William Butler Yeats, Ezra Pound, e. e. cummings, and Archibald MacLeish, in addition to her own reviews and comments. In 1935 her third collection of poetry,* Selected Poems, *was published, with an introduction by T. S. Eliot and a dedication to her mother. She published a number of other brief collections in the 1930s and 1940s, and in 1951 compiled the comprehensive volume* Collected Poems, *dedicated to her mother, who had died four years earlier. An elegy to her mother, "By Disposition of Angels," was one of only nine new poems in the collection.*

The list of Moore's honors and awards is long: a Dial Award (1924); the Harriet Monroe Poetry Award (1944); a National Institute of Arts and Letters grant (1946); the National Book Award and the Pulitzer Prize (1952, for Collected Poems*); the Yale Bollingen Prize (1953); two Poetry Society of America gold medals (1960, 1967); and honorary degrees from Mount Holyoke College, Dickinson College, New York University, and Yale University, among others. In her lifetime she published over twenty volumes of poetry, as well as translations, criticism, and plays. As the critic Elizabeth Phillips said, "Writing, for her, was an act of intellectual self-preservation. She understood combat and rebellion. Otherwise, she would never have become a person to reckon with in modern poetry."*

Poetry (1919)

MARIANNE MOORE

I too, dislike it: there are things that are important beyond all this
        fiddle.
  Reading it, however, with a perfect contempt for it, one
        discovers that there is in
it after all, a place for the genuine.
        Hands that can grasp, eyes
    that can dilate, hair that can rise   5
      if it must, these things are important not because a

high sounding interpretation can be put upon them but because
        they are
  useful; when they become so derivative as to become
        unintelligible, the
same thing may be said for all of us—that we
    do not admire what   10
    we cannot understand. The bat,
      holding on upside down or in quest of something to

eat, elephants pushing, a wild horse taking a roll, a tireless wolf under
  a tree, the immovable critic twinkling his skin like a horse that
        feels a flea, the base-   15
ball fan, the statistician—case after case
    could be cited did
    one wish it; nor is it valid
      to discriminate against "business documents and

First published in *Others: A Magazine of Verse* in July, 1919. Later collected in *Moore's Observations* in 1924.

school-books"; all these phenomena are important. One must
        make a distinction
  however: when dragged into prominence by half poets, the
        result is not poetry,   *20*
  nor till the autocrats among us can be
    "literalists of
    the imagination"—above
        insolence and triviality and can present

for inspection, imaginary gardens with real toads in them, shall
        we have
  it. In the meantime, if you demand on one hand, in defiance of   *25*
        their opinion—
  the raw material of poetry in
    all its rawness and
    that which is on the other hand,
        genuine then you are interested in poetry.

                                        [1919]

Pablo Neruda
[1904–1973]

The poet who would gain international fame as **PABLO NERUDA** *was born Neftalí Ricardo Reyes Basoalto in Parral, Chile. Raised in a rural, working-class environment, he was forced to conceal his early literary aspirations from his family: At age sixteen, when he began contributing poems to the journal* Selva Austral, *he adopted the pseudonym Pablo Neruda, primarily as a means of deflecting his family's disapproval. In 1921, while attending the Instituto Pedagógico, a teachers' college in Santiago, Neruda won first prize in a prestigious poetry competition held during the city's annual Spring Festival. This encouraged him to leave his studies and devote himself entirely to writing poetry. Several years later, he published two books that seemed to validate his decision: the 1923 collection* Crepusculario, *and 1924's* Veinte poemas de amor y una cancion desesperada. *Both were well received.* Viente poemas *went on to become one of his most popular works, widely considered, in the words of one critic, "one of the finest books of verse in the Spanish language."*

Neruda's literary success was rewarded with a number of consulships in Europe and Asia between 1927 and 1935. This marked the beginning of a political involvement he would maintain throughout his life, but it was the outbreak of the Spanish Civil War the following year that was to affect Neruda most deeply. The war also had a significant impact on his work: Whereas his earlier poems centered on traditional subjects such as love and death, and stylistically bore the influence of Surrealism, Modernism, and the French poetry that he had studied in his teens, Neruda's poetry now became increasingly political, presented in much more straightforward language. His 1937 book España en el Corazon, printed on the front lines of the war by Spanish Republican soldiers, documented the violence witnessed, including the execution of his friend, the poet Federico García Lorca.

The following years saw an intensification of both Neruda's political activity and his literary output. Recalled from Madrid because of his Loyalist sympathies, he became active in the cause to relocate Spanish refugees to Chile. In 1945 he was elected to the senate as a member of the Communist Party, but was forced to flee the country several years later, when his outspoken criticisms of President Gonzalez Videla resulted in a treason indictment. Even in exile, however, Neruda continued to write. In 1950 he produced Canto General, a work of 340 poems chronicling the history of Latin America from a Marxist point of view. While critical assessment of his later work is mixed, many regard Canto General as his masterpiece.

After the defeat of the Gonzalez Videla regime, Neruda returned home to Chile. In 1958 he published the collection Estravagario, *a critical self-assessment of his youthful experiences and Marxist philosophy that many feel is his last major work. In 1971 came the culmination of Neruda's literary career, when he was awarded the Nobel Prize for Literature. He died of cancer two years later in Santiago, having produced over forty volumes of poetry, plays, and translations.*

—Mark Lovely, *Merrimack College*

We Are Many

PABLO NERUDA
TRANSLATED BY ALASTAIR REID

Of the many men who I am, who we are,
I can't find a single one;
they disappear among my clothes,
they've left for another city.

When everything seems to be set   5
to show me off as intelligent,
the fool I always keep hidden
takes over all that I say.

At other times, I'm asleep
among distinguished people,   10
and when I look for my brave self,
a coward unknown to me
rushes to cover my skeleton
with a thousand fine excuses.

When a decent house catches fire,   15
instead of the fireman I summon,
an arsonist bursts on the scene,
and that's me. What can I do?
What can I do to distinguish myself?
How can I pull myself together?   20

All the books I read
are full of dazzling heroes,
always sure of themselves.
I die with envy of them;
and in films full of wind and bullets,   25

Reprinted from *Extravagaria,* translated by Alastair Reid, by permission from Farrar, Straus and Giroux, LLC. Copyright © 1974 by Alistair Reid.

I goggle at the cowboys,
I even admire the horses.

But when I call for a hero,
out comes my lazy old self;
so I never know who I am,   *30*
nor how many I am or will be.
I'd love to be able to touch a bell
and summon the real me,
because if I really need myself,
I mustn't disappear.   *35*

While I am writing, I'm far away;
and when I come back, I've gone.
I would like to know if others
go through the same things that I do,
have as many selves as I have,   *40*
and see themselves similarly;
and when I've exhausted this problem,
I'm going to study so hard
that when I explain myself,
I'll be talking geography.   *45*

[1958]

Tim O'Brien
[1946–   ]

TIM O'BRIEN *grew up in Worthington, Minnesota. A month after graduating from Macalester College in St. Paul, he received his draft notice. O'Brien, who received his degree in political science, had been very involved in anti-war demonstrations prior to being drafted, and he later remembered the period after receiving his induction notice as "a horrid, confused, traumatic period— the trauma of deciding whether or not to go to Canada." O'Brien did not go to Canada, but instead served in Vietnam with the U.S. infantry from January 1969 to March 1970. When he returned to the United States with a Purple Heart, he began graduate study in Harvard University's government program, but instead found himself with many stories from the war that needed to be told. During graduate school, O'Brien also worked for a brief time as a reporter for* The Washington Post, *honing his writing skills and his writerly discipline. During this same period, O'Brien wrote and published his first book,* If I Die in a Combat Zone, Box Me Up and Ship Me Home *(1973), a semi-fictional-ized memoir of an infantryman's year in Vietnam. This book was widely praised by reviewers, who called it "powerfully written," and described it as "a beautiful, painful book, arousing pity and fear for the daily realities of modern disaster."*

O'Brien followed this memoir with two novels, Northern Lights *(1975), which tells the story of a soldier's homecoming from Vietnam, and* Going After Cacciato *(1978), for which O'Brien received the National Book Award.* Cacciato *is the story of an escape from the war, rendered with dream-like vividness, begin-ning with a soldier's decision to abandon his platoon in Vietnam and walk to Paris. His next book,* The Nuclear Age *(1981), tells the story of a former anti-war radical's paranoia in the face of possible nuclear annihilation.*

Throughout the 1980s, O'Brien published a series of short stories that fol-low a platoon through its experiences in Vietnam; these stories laid the ground-work for the volume The Things They Carried *(1990), a cycle of interconnected stories narrated by "Tim O'Brien," a character bearing similarities to, but not identical with, the author. These stories play, as did O'Brien's memoir, with the line between fiction and fact, suggesting in one of the tales, "How to Tell a True War Story," that more truth about war might be created from fiction than from strictly factual accounts of events. Since this celebrated volume, which was a finalist for both the National Book Critics Circle Award and the Pulitzer Prize, O'Brien has published several more novels, including* In the Lake of the Woods *(1994),* Tomcat in Love *(1998), and* July July *(2002). Though most of O'Brien's* work revolves around his experiences of Vietnam, he should not be dismissed as a "Vietnam writer." Rather, his writing explores the unresolvable moral complexities of contemporary life, of which the war was only one small, if exceedingly painful, part.

How to Tell a True War Story

TIM O'BRIEN

THIS IS TRUE.

I had a buddy in Vietnam. His name was Bob Kiley, but everybody called him Rat.

A friend of his gets killed, so about a week later Rat sits down and writes a letter to the guy's sister. Rat tells her what a great brother she had, how together the guy was, a number one pal and comrade. A real soldier's soldier, Rat says. Then he tells a few stories to make the point, how her brother would always volunteer for stuff nobody else would volunteer for in a million years, dangerous stuff, like doing recon or going out on these really badass night patrols. Stainless steel balls, Rat tells her. The guy was a little crazy, for sure, but crazy in a good way, a real daredevil, because he liked the challenge of it, he liked testing himself, just man against gook. A great, great guy, Rat says.

Anyway, it's a terrific letter, very personal and touching. Rat almost bawls writing it. He gets all teary telling about the good times they had together, how her brother made the war seem almost fun, always raising hell and lighting up villes and bringing smoke to bear every which way. A great sense of humor, too. Like the time at this river when he went fishing with a whole damn crate of hand grenades. Probably the funniest thing in world history, Rat says, all that gore, about twenty zillion dead gook fish. Her brother, he had the right attitude. He knew how to have a good time. On Halloween, this real hot spooky night, the dude paints up his body all different colors and puts on this weird mask and hikes over to a ville and goes trick-or-treating almost stark naked, just boots and balls and an M-16. A tremendous human being, Rat says. Pretty nutso sometimes, but you could trust him with your life.

And then the letter gets very sad and serious. Rat pours his heart out. He says he loved the guy. He says the guy was his best friend in the world. They were like soul mates, he says, like twins or something, they had a whole lot in common. He tells the guy's sister he'll look her up when the war's over.

So what happens?

Rat mails the letter. He waits two months. The dumb cooze never writes back.

A true war story is never moral. It does not instruct, nor encourage virtue, nor suggest models of proper human behavior, nor restrain men from doing the things

Reprinted from *The Things They Carried*, by permission of Houghton Mifflin Company. Copyright © 1990 by Tim O'Brien.

men have always done. If a story seems moral, do not believe it. If at the end of a war story you feel uplifted, or if you feel that some small bit of rectitude has been salvaged from the larger waste, then you have been made the victim of a very old and terrible lie. There is no rectitude whatsoever. There is no virtue. As a first rule of thumb, therefore, you can tell a true war story by its absolute and uncompromising allegiance to obscenity and evil. Listen to Rat Kiley. Cooze, he says. He does not say bitch. He certainly does not say woman, or girl. He says cooze. Then he spits and stares. He's nineteen years old—it's too much for him—so he looks at you with those big sad gentle killer eyes and says *cooze*, because his friend is dead, and because it's so incredibly sad and true: she never wrote back.

You can tell a true war story if it embarrasses you. If you don't care for obscenity, you don't care for the truth; if you don't care for the truth, watch how you vote. Send guys to war, they come home talking dirty.

Listen to Rat: "Jesus Christ, man, I write this beautiful fuckin' letter, I slave over it, and what happens? The dumb cooze never writes back."

The dead guy's name was Curt Lemon. What happened was, we crossed a muddy river and marched west into the mountains, and on the third day we took a break along a trail junction in deep jungle. Right away, Lemon and Rat Kiley started goofing. They didn't understand about the spookiness. They were kids; they just didn't know. A nature hike, they thought, not even a war, so they went off into the shade of some giant trees—quadruple canopy, no sunlight at all— and they were giggling and calling each other yellow mother and playing a silly game they'd invented. The game involved smoke grenades, which were harmless unless you did stupid things, and what they did was pull out the pin and stand a few feet apart and play catch under the shade of those huge trees. Whoever chickened out was a yellow mother. And if nobody chickened out, the grenade would make a light popping sound and they'd be covered with smoke and they'd laugh and dance around and then do it again.

It's all exactly true.

It happened, to *me*, nearly twenty years ago, and I still remember that trail junction and those giant trees and a soft dripping sound somewhere beyond the trees. I remember the smell of moss. Up in the canopy there were tiny white blossoms, but no sunlight at all, and I remember the shadows spreading out under the trees where Curt Lemon and Rat Kiley were playing catch with smoke grenades. Mitchell Sanders sat flipping his yo-yo. Norman Bowker and Kiowa and Dave Jensen were dozing, or half dozing, and all around us were those ragged green mountains.

Except for the laughter things were quiet.

At one point, I remember, Mitchell Sanders turned and looked at me, not quite nodding, as if to warn me about something, as if he already *knew,* then after a while he rolled up his yo-yo and moved away.

It's hard to tell you what happened next.

They were just goofing. There was a noise, I suppose, which must've been the detonator, so I glanced behind me and watched Lemon step from the shade into bright sunlight. His face was suddenly brown and shining. A handsome kid, really. Sharp gray eyes, lean and narrow-waisted, and when he died it was almost beautiful, the way the sunlight came around him and lifted him up and sucked him high into a tree full of moss and vines and white blossoms.

In any war story, but especially a true one, it's difficult to separate what happened from what seemed to happen. What seems to happen becomes its own happening and has to be told that way. The angles of vision are skewed. When a booby trap explodes, you close your eyes and duck and float outside yourself. When a guy dies, like Curt Lemon, you look away and then look back for a moment and then look away again. The pictures get jumbled; you tend to miss a lot. And then afterward, when you go to tell about it, there is always that surreal seemingness, which makes the story seem untrue, but which in fact represents the hard and exact truth as it *seemed*.

*   *   *

In many cases a true war story cannot be believed. If you believe it, be skeptical. It's a question of credibility. Often the crazy stuff is true and the normal stuff isn't, because the normal stuff is necessary to make you believe the truly incredible craziness.

In other cases you can't even tell a true war story. Sometimes it's just beyond telling.

I heard this one, for example, from Mitchell Sanders. It was near dusk and we were sitting at my foxhole along a wide muddy river north of Quang Ngai. I remember how peaceful the twilight was. A deep pinkish red spilled out on the river, which moved without sound, and in the morning we would cross the river and march west into the mountains. The occasion was right for a good story.

"God's truth," Mitchell Sanders said. "A six-man patrol goes up into the mountains on a basic listening-post operation. The idea's to spend a week up there, just lie low and listen for enemy movement. They've got a radio along, so if they hear anything suspicious—anything—they're supposed to call in artillery or gunships, whatever it takes. Otherwise they keep strict field discipline. Absolute silence. They just listen."

Sanders glanced at me to make sure I had the scenario. He was playing with his yo-yo, dancing it with short, tight little strokes of the wrist.

His face was blank in the dusk.

---

[1] LP: listening post

"We're talking regulation, by-the-book LP.[1] These six guys, they don't say boo for a solid week. They don't got tongues. *All* ears."

"Right," I said.

"Understand me?"

"Invisible."

Sanders nodded.

"Affirm," he said. "Invisible. So what happens is, these guys get themselves deep in the bush, all camouflaged up, and they lie down and wait and that's all they do, nothing else, they lie there for seven straight days and just listen. And man, I'll tell you—it's spooky. This is mountains. You don't *know* spooky till you been there. Jungle, sort of, except it's way up in the clouds and there's always this fog—like rain, except it's not raining—everything's all wet and swirly and tangled up and you can't see jack, you can't find your own pecker to piss with. Like you don't even have a body. Serious spooky. You just go with the vapors—the fog sort of takes you in . . . And the sounds, man. The sounds carry forever. You hear stuff nobody should *ever* hear."

Sanders was quiet for a second, just working the yo-yo, then he smiled at me.

"So after a couple days the guys start hearing this real soft, kind of wacked-out music. Weird echoes and stuff. Like a radio or something, but it's not a radio, it's this strange gook music that comes right out of the rocks. Faraway, sort of, but right up close, too. They try to ignore it. But it's a listening post, right? So they listen. And every night they keep hearing that crazyass gook concert. All kinds of chimes and xylophones. I mean, this is wilderness—no way, it can't be real—but there it *is*, like the mountains are tuned in to Radio fucking Hanoi. Naturally they get nervous. One guy sticks Juicy Fruit in his ears. Another guy almost flips. Thing is, though, they can't report music. They can't get on the horn and call back to base and say, 'Hey, listen, we need some firepower, we got to blow away this weirdo gook rock band.' They can't do that. It wouldn't go down. So they lie there in the fog and keep their mouths shut. And what makes it extra bad, see, is the poor dudes can't horse around like normal. Can't joke it away. Can't even talk to each other except maybe in whispers, all hush-hush, and that just revs up the willies. All they do is listen."

Again there was some silence as Mitchell Sanders looked out on the river. The dark was coming on hard now, and off to the west I could see the mountains rising in silhouette, all the mysteries and unknowns.

"This next part," Sanders said quietly, "you won't believe."

"Probably not," I said.

"You won't. And you know why?" He gave me a long, tired smile. "Because it happened. Because every word is absolutely dead-on true."

Sanders made a sound in his throat, like a sigh, as if to say he didn't care if I believed him or not. But he did care. He wanted me to feel the truth, to believe by the raw force of feeling. He seemed sad, in a way.

"These six guys," he said, "they're pretty fried out by now, and one night they start hearing voices. Like at a cocktail party. That's what it sounds like, this big swank gook cocktail party somewhere out there in the fog. Music and chitchat and stuff. It's crazy, I know, but they hear the champagne corks. They hear the actual martini glasses. Real hoity-toity, all very civilized, except this isn't civilization. This is Nam.

"Anyway, the guys try to be cool. They just lie there and groove, but after a while they start hearing—you won't believe this—they hear chamber music. They hear violins and cellos. They hear this terrific mama-san soprano. Then after a while they hear gook opera and a glee club and the Haiphong Boys Choir and a barbershop quartet and all kinds of weird chanting and Buddha-Buddha stuff. And the whole time, in the background, there's still that cocktail party going on. All these different voices. Not human voices, though. Because it's the mountains. Follow me? The rock—it's *talking*. And the fog, too, and the grass and the goddamn mongooses. Everything talks. The trees talk politics, the monkeys talk religion. The whole country. Vietnam. The place talks. It talks. Understand? Nam—it truly *talks*.

"The guys can't cope. They lose it. They get on the radio and report enemy movement—a whole army, they say—and they order up the firepower. They get arty and gunships. They call in air strikes. And I'll tell you, they fuckin' crash that cocktail party. All night long, they just smoke those mountains. They make jungle juice. They blow away trees and glee clubs and whatever else there is to blow away. Scorch time. They walk napalm up and down the ridges. They bring in the Cobras and F-4s, they use Willie Peter and HE and incendiaries. It's all fire. They make those mountains burn.

"Around dawn things finally get quiet. Like you never even *heard* quiet before. One of those real thick, real misty days—just clouds and fog, they're off in this special zone—and the mountains are absolutely dead-flat silent. Like Brigadoon[2]—pure vapor, you know? Everything's all sucked up inside the fog. Not a single sound, except they still *hear* it.

"So they pack up and start humping. They head down the mountain, back to base camp, and when they get there they don't say diddly. They don't talk. Not a word, like they're deaf and dumb. Later on this fat bird colonel comes up and asks what the hell happened out there. What'd they hear? Why all the ordnance? The man's ragged out, he gets down tight on their case. I mean, they spent six trillion dollars on firepower, and this fatass colonel wants answers, he wants to know what the fuckin' story is.

"But the guys don't say zip. They just look at him for a while, sort of funny like, sort of amazed, and the whole war is right there in that stare. It says

---

[2] Brigadoon: mythical Scottish village that is shrouded in mist

everything you can't ever say. It says, man, you got *wax* in your ears. It says, poor bastard, you'll never know—wrong frequency—you don't *even* want to hear this. Then they salute the fucker and walk away, because certain stories you don't ever tell."

You can tell a true war story by the way it never seems to end. Not then, not ever. Not when Mitchell Sanders stood up and moved off into the dark.

It all happened.

Even now, at this instant, I remember that yo-yo. In a way, I suppose, you had to be there, you had to hear it, but I could tell how desperately Sanders wanted me to believe him, his frustration at not quite getting the details right, not quite pinning down the final and definitive truth.

And I remember sitting at my foxhole that night, watching the shadows of Quang Ngai, thinking about the coming day and how we would cross the river and march west into the mountains, all the ways I might die, all the things I did not understand.

Late in the night Mitchell Sanders touched my shoulder.

"Just came to me," he whispered. "The moral, I mean. Nobody listens. Nobody hears nothin'. Like that fatass colonel. The politicians, all the civilian types. Your girlfriend. My girlfriend. Everybody's sweet little virgin girlfriend. What they need is to go out on LP. The vapors, man. Trees and rocks—you got to *listen* to your enemy."

And then again, in the morning, Sanders came up to me. The platoon was preparing to move out, checking weapons, going through all the little rituals that preceded a day's march. Already the lead squad had crossed the river and was filing off toward the west.

"I got a confession to make," Sanders said. "Last night, man, I had to make up a few things."

"I know that."

"The glee club. There wasn't any glee club."

"Right."

"No opera."

"Forget it, I understand."

"Yeah, but listen, it's still true. Those six guys, they heard wicked sound out there. They heard sound you just plain won't believe."

Sanders pulled on his rucksack, closed his eyes for a moment, then almost smiled at me. I knew what was coming.

"All right," I said, "what's the moral?"

"Forget it."

"No, go ahead."

For a long while he was quiet, looking away, and the silence kept stretching out until it was almost embarrassing. Then he shrugged and gave me a stare that lasted all day.

"Hear that quiet, man?" he said. "That quiet—just listen. There's your moral."

In a true war story, if there's a moral at all, it's like the thread that makes the cloth. You can't tease it out. You can't extract the meaning without unraveling the deeper meaning. And in the end, really, there's nothing much to say about a true war story, except maybe "Oh."

True war stories do not generalize. They do not indulge in abstraction or analysis.

For example: War is hell. As a moral declaration the old truism seems perfectly true, and yet because it abstracts, because it generalizes, I can't believe it with my stomach. Nothing turns inside.

It comes down to gut instinct. A true war story, if truly told, makes the stomach believe.

This one does it for me. I've told it before—many times, many versions—but here's what actually happened.

We crossed that river and marched west into the mountains. On the third day, Curt Lemon stepped on a booby-trapped 105 round. He was playing catch with Rat Kiley, laughing, and then he was dead. The trees were thick; it took nearly an hour to cut an LZ for the dustoff.[3]

Later, higher in the mountains, we came across a baby VC[4] water buffalo. What it was doing there I don't know—no farms or paddies—but we chased it down and got a rope around it and led it along to a deserted village where we set up for the night. After supper Rat Kiley went over and stroked its nose.

He opened up a can of C rations, pork and beans, but the baby buffalo wasn't interested.

Rat shrugged.

He stepped back and shot it through the right front knee. The animal did not make a sound. It went down hard, then got up again, and Rat took careful aim and shot off an ear. He shot it in the hindquarters and in the little hump at its back. He shot it twice in the flanks. It wasn't to kill; it was to hurt. He put the rifle muzzle up against the mouth and shot the mouth away. Nobody said much. The whole platoon stood there watching, feeling all kinds of things, but there wasn't a great deal of pity for the baby water buffalo. Curt Lemon was

---

[3] LZ for the dustoff: landing zone for the Medivac helicopter
[4] VC: Viet Cong, North Vietnamese armed forces

dead. Rat Kiley had lost his best friend in the world. Later in the week he would write a long personal letter to the guy's sister, who would not write back, but for now it was a question of pain. He shot off the tail. He shot away chunks of meat below the ribs. All around us there was the smell of smoke and filth and deep greenery, and the evening was humid and very hot. Rat went to automatic. He shot randomly, almost casually, quick little spurts in the belly and butt. Then he reloaded, squatted down, and shot it in the left front knee. Again the animal fell hard and tried to get up, but this time it couldn't quite make it. It wobbled and went down sideways. Rat shot it in the nose. He bent forward and whispered something, as if talking to a pet, then he shot it in the throat. All the while the baby buffalo was silent, or almost silent, just a light bubbling sound where the nose had been. It lay very still. Nothing moved except the eyes, which were enormous, the pupils shiny black and dumb.

Rat Kiley was crying. He tried to say something, but then cradled his rifle and went off by himself.

The rest of us stood in a ragged circle around the baby buffalo. For a time no one spoke. We had witnessed something essential, something brand-new and profound, a piece of the world so startling there was not yet a name for it.

Somebody kicked the baby buffalo.

It was still alive, though just barely, just in the eyes.

"Amazing," Dave Jensen said. "My whole life, I never seen anything like it."

"Never?"

"Not hardly. Not once."

Kiowa and Mitchell Sanders picked up the baby buffalo. They hauled it across the open square, hoisted it up, and dumped it in the village well.

Afterward, we sat waiting for Rat to get himself together.

"Amazing," Dave Jensen kept saying. "A new wrinkle. I never seen it before."

Mitchell Sanders took out his yo-yo. "Well, that's Nam," he said. "Garden of Evil. Over here, man, every sin's real fresh and original."

How do you generalize?

War is hell, but that's not the half of it, because war is also mystery and terror and adventure and courage and discovery and holiness and pity and despair and longing and love. War is nasty; war is fun. War is thrilling; war is drudgery. War makes you a man; war makes you dead.

The truths are contradictory. It can be argued, for instance, that war is grotesque. But in truth war is also beauty. For all its horror, you can't help but gape at the awful majesty of combat. You stare out at tracer rounds unwinding through the dark like brilliant red ribbons. You crouch in ambush as a cool, impassive moon rises over the nighttime paddies. You admire the fluid symmetries of troops on the move, the harmonies of sound and shape and proportion, the great sheets of metal-fire streaming down from a gunship, the illumination rounds, the white phosphorus, the purply orange glow of napalm, the rocket's red glare. It's not pretty, exactly. It's astonishing. It fills the eye. It commands you. You hate it, yes, but your eyes do not. Like a killer forest fire, like cancer under a microscope, any battle or bombing raid or artillery barrage has the aesthetic purity of absolute moral indifference—a powerful, implacable beauty—and a true war story will tell the truth about this, though the truth is ugly.

To generalize about war is like generalizing about peace. Almost everything is true. Almost nothing is true. At its core, perhaps, war is just another name for death, and yet any soldier will tell you, if he tells the truth, that proximity to death brings with it a corresponding proximity to life. After a firefight, there is always the immense pleasure of aliveness. The trees are alive. The grass, the soil—everything. All around you things are purely living, and you among them, and the aliveness makes you tremble. You feel an intense, out-of-the-skin awareness of your living self—your truest self, the human being you want to be and then become by the force of wanting it. In the midst of evil you want to be a good man. You want decency. You want justice and courtesy and human concord, things you never knew you wanted. There is a kind of largeness to it, a kind of godliness. Though it's odd, you're never more alive than when you're almost dead. You recognize what's valuable. Freshly, as if for the first time, you love what's best in yourself and in the world, all that might be lost. At the hour of dusk you sit at your foxhole and look out on a wide river turning pinkish red, and at the mountains beyond, and although in the morning you must cross the river and go into the mountains and do terrible things and maybe die, even so, you find yourself studying the fine colors on the river, you feel wonder and awe at the setting of the sun, and you are filled with a hard, aching love for how the world could be and always should be, but now is not.

Mitchell Sanders was right. For the common soldier, at least, war has the feel—the spiritual texture—of a great ghostly fog, thick and permanent. There is no clarity. Everything swirls. The old rules are no longer binding, the old truths no longer true. Right spills over into wrong. Order blends into chaos, love into hate, ugliness into beauty, law into anarchy, civility into savagery. The vapors suck you in. You can't tell where you are, or why you're there, and the only certainty is overwhelming ambiguity.

In war you lose your sense of the definite, hence your sense of truth itself, and therefore it's safe to say that in a true war story nothing is ever absolutely true.

Often in a true war story there is not even a point, or else the point doesn't hit you until twenty years later, in your sleep, and you wake up and shake your wife and start telling the story to her, except when you get to the end you've forgotten the point again. And then for a long time you lie there watching the story happen in your head. You listen to your wife's breathing. The war's over. You close your eyes. You smile and think, Christ, what's the *point?*

This one wakes me up.

In the mountains that day, I watched Lemon turn sideways. He laughed and said something to Rat Kiley. Then he took a peculiar half step, moving from shade into bright sunlight, and the booby-trapped 105 round blew him into a tree. The parts were just hanging there, so Dave Jensen and I were ordered to shinny up and peel him off. I remember the white bone of an arm. I remember pieces of skin and something wet and yellow that must've been the intestines. The gore was horrible, and stays with me. But what wakes me up twenty years later is Dave Jensen singing "Lemon Tree"[5] as we threw down the parts.

You can tell a true war story by the questions you ask. Somebody tells a story, let's say, and afterward you ask, "Is it true?" and if the answer matters, you've got your answer.

For example, we've all heard this one. Four guys go down a trail. A grenade sails out. One guy jumps on it and takes the blast and saves his three buddies.

Is it true?

The answer matters.

You'd feel cheated if it never happened. Without the grounding reality, it's just a trite bit of puffery, pure Hollywood, untrue in the way all such stories are untrue. Yet even if it did happen—and maybe it did, anything's possible—even then you know it can't be true, because a true war story does not depend upon that kind of truth. Absolute occurrence is irrelevant. A thing may happen and be a total lie; another thing may not happen and be truer than the truth. For example: Four guys go down a trail. A grenade sails out. One guy jumps on it and takes the blast, but it's a killer grenade and everybody dies anyway. Before they die, though, one of the dead guys says, "The fuck you do *that* for?" and the jumper says, "Story of my life, man," and the other guy starts to smile but he's dead.

That's a true story that never happened.

Twenty years later, I can still see the sunlight on Lemon's face. I can see him turning, looking back at Rat Kiley, then he laughed and took that curious half step from shade into sunlight, his face suddenly brown and shining, and when his foot touched down, in that instant, he must've thought it was the sunlight that was killing him. It was not the sunlight. It was a rigged 105 round. But if I could ever get the story right, how the sun seemed to gather around him

---

[5] "Lemon Tree": popular folk song of the 1960s

and pick him up and lift him high into a tree, if I could somehow recreate the fatal whiteness of that light, the quick glare, the obvious cause and effect, then you would believe the last thing Curt Lemon believed, which for him must've been the final truth.

Now and then, when I tell this story, someone will come up to me afterward and say she liked it. It's always a woman. Usually it's an older woman of kindly temperament and humane politics. She'll explain that as a rule she hates war stories; she can't understand why people want to wallow in all the blood and gore. But this one she liked. The poor baby buffalo, it made her sad. Sometimes, even, there are little tears. What I should do, she'll say, is put it all behind me. Find new stories to tell.

I won't say it but I'll think it.

I'll picture Rat Kiley's face, his grief, and I'll think, *You dumb cooze*.

Because she wasn't listening.

It *wasn't* a war story. It was a *love* story.

But you can't say that. All you can do is tell it one more time, patiently, adding and subtracting, making up a few things to get at the real truth. No Mitchell Sanders, you tell her. No Lemon, no Rat Kiley. No trail junction. No baby buffalo. No vines or moss or white blossoms. Beginning to end, you tell her, it's all made up. Every goddamn detail—the mountains and the river and especially that poor dumb baby buffalo. None of it happened. *None* of it. And even if it did happen, it didn't happen in the mountains, it happened in this little village on the Batangan Peninsula, and it was raining like crazy, and one night a guy named Stink Harris woke up screaming with a leech on his tongue. You can tell a true war story if you just keep on telling it.

And in the end, of course, a true war story is never about war. It's about sunlight. It's about the special way that dawn spreads out on a river when you know you must cross the river and march into the mountains and do things you are afraid to do. It's about love and memory. It's about sorrow. It's about sisters who never write back and people who never listen.

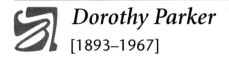

Dorothy Parker
[1893–1967]

DOROTHY PARKER, *born Dorothy Rothschild, is best remembered for her sharp-tongued satiric wit, conveyed through her poems, short stories, and acerbic theater and book reviews. Parker was the youngest of four children in a comfortable Jewish family living in New York; after her mother's death, when Dorothy was five, she was sent first to a convent school run by Catholic nuns, and then later to a private school in New Jersey. Parker first became a staff writer for* Vogue *magazine, and in 1915 moved to* Vanity Fair, *where she worked with fellow writers Robert E. Sherwood and Robert Benchley, and later succeeded P. G. Wodehouse as* Vanity Fair's *chief drama critic. In 1917, Parker married a Wall Street broker, who soon left for Europe to serve as a volunteer ambulance driver in World War I. During this period, Parker had regular lunches at the Algonquin Hotel with Sherwood and Benchley and other literary figures, including* New York Times *drama critic Alexander Woollcott and the founder of* The New Yorker *magazine, Harold Ross. This cluster of luminaries came to be known as the Algonquin Round Table, known for their sharp, often vicious wit. Parker's wit, however, resulted in her termination by* Vanity Fair *in 1920, after her criticisms of theatrical productions by several of the magazine's major advertisers became too caustic for the publishers' taste. Parker went on to write for several other publications, continuing her review and essay writing, but also producing extremely popular, often viciously humorous poetry. Parker also experimented during this period with the monologue as the basis for a style of short fiction.*

Parker's marriage did not long survive after her husband returned from the war, and as her depression over the failure of that relationship and other aspects of her personal life grew, she increasingly turned to alcohol for comfort. This addiction was a contributing factor in her first suicide attempt, in 1923, and Parker's writing around this time often displayed a somewhat wistful consideration of suicide's appeal. This was, however, the most productive period of her life; between 1926 and 1939, Parker published seven volumes of poetry and fiction, including Enough Rope *(1926),* Sunset Gun *(1927),* Death and Taxes *(1931),* After Such Pleasures *(1933), and* Here Lies *(1939). During the 1930s and 1940s, Parker turned her attention toward Hollywood, working on the screenplays for numerous films, including* A Star Is Born *(1937), which was nominated for an Academy Award for best screenplay. She also became increasingly involved in political causes, helping to found the Anti-Nazi League in 1936 and later declaring herself a Communist. This affiliation, however, resulted in her blacklisting by the California State Senate Committee on Un-American Activities in 1949.*

Parker died of a heart attack in 1967. Her continued alcoholism profoundly affected the last years of her career, which never regained the luster of her Round Table and Hollywood years. Her literary reputation has also suffered somewhat due to the apparent simplicity of her caustic one-liners, but her sharp wit made her one of the foremost observers, and critics, of the sentimental ideals of early twentieth-century culture.

Big Blonde

DOROTHY PARKER

I

HAZEL MORSE WAS a large, fair woman of the type that incites some men when they use the word "blonde" to click their tongues and wag their heads roguishly. She prided herself upon her small feet and suffered for her vanity, boxing them in snub-toed, high-heeled slippers of the shortest bearable size. The curious things about her were her hands, strange terminations to the flabby white arms splattered with pale tan spots—long, quivering hands with deep and convex nails. She should not have disfigured them with little jewels.

She was not a woman given to recollections. At her middle thirties, her old days were a blurred and flickering sequence, an imperfect film, dealing with the actions of strangers.

In her twenties, after the deferred death of a hazy widowed mother, she had been employed as a model in a wholesale dress establishment—it was still the day of the big woman, and she was then prettily colored and erect and high-breasted. Her job was not onerous, and she met numbers of men and spent numbers of evenings with them, laughing at their jokes and telling them she loved their neckties. Men liked her, and she took it for granted that the liking of many men was a desirable thing. Popularity seemed to her to be worth all the work that had to be put into its achievement. Men liked you because you were fun, and when they liked you they took you out, and there you were. So, and successfully, she was fun. She was a good sport. Men like a good sport.

No other form of diversion, simpler or more complicated, drew her attention. She never pondered if she might not be better occupied doing something else. Her ideas, or, better, her acceptances, ran right along with those of the other substantially built blondes in whom she found her friends.

When she had been working in the dress establishment some years she met Herbie Morse. He was thin, quick, attractive, with shifting lines about his shiny, brown eyes and a habit of fiercely biting at the skin around his finger nails.

Reprinted from *The Portable Dorothy Parker*, edited by Marion Meade, by permission of Viking Penguin, a division of Penguin Group (USA) Inc. Copyright © 1957, 1956, 1929, 1928 by Dorothy Parker.

He drank largely; she found that entertaining. Her habitual greeting to him was an allusion to his state of the previous night.

"Oh, what a peach you had," she used to say, through her easy laugh. "I thought I'd die, the way you kept asking the waiter to dance with you."

She liked him immediately upon their meeting. She was enormously amused at his fast, slurred sentences, his interpolations of apt phrases from vaudeville acts and comic strips; she thrilled at the feel of his lean arm tucked firm beneath the sleeve of her coat; she wanted to touch the wet, flat surface of his hair. He was as promptly drawn to her. They were married six weeks after they had met.

She was delighted at the idea of being a bride; coquetted with it, played upon it. Other offers of marriage she had had, and not a few of them, but it happened that they were all from stout, serious men who had visited the dress establishment as buyers; men from Des Moines and Houston and Chicago and, in her phrase, even funnier places. There was always something immensely comic to her in the thought of living elsewhere than New York. She could not regard as serious proposals that she share a western residence.

She wanted to be married. She was nearing thirty now, and she did not take the years well. She spread and softened, and her darkening hair turned her to inexpert dabblings with peroxide. There were times when she had little flashes of fear about her job. And she had had a couple of thousand evenings of being a good sport among her male acquaintances. She had come to be more conscientious than spontaneous about it.

Herbie earned enough, and they took a little apartment far uptown. There was a Mission-furnished dining-room with a hanging central light globed in liver-colored glass; in the living-room were an "over-stuffed suite," a Boston fern, and a reproduction of the Henner "Magdalene" with the red hair and the blue draperies; the bedroom was in gray enamel and old rose, with Herbie's photograph on Hazel's dressing-table and Hazel's likeness on Herbie's chest of drawers.

She cooked—and she was a good cook—and marketed and chatted with the delivery boys and the colored laundress. She loved the flat, she loved her life, she loved Herbie. In the first months of their marriage she gave him all the passion she was ever to know.

She had not realized how tired she was. It was a delight, a new game, a holiday, to give up being a good sport. If her head ached or her arches throbbed, she complained piteously, babyishly. If her mood was quiet she did not talk. If tears came to her eyes, she let them fall.

She fell readily into the habit of tears during the first year of her marriage. Even in her good sport days, she had been known to weep lavishly and disinterestedly on occasion. Her behavior at the theater was a standing joke. She could weep at anything in a play—tiny garments, love both unrequited and mutual, seduction, purity, faithful servitors, wedlock, the triangle.

"There goes Haze," her friends would say, watching her. "She's off again."

Wedded and relaxed, she poured her tears freely. To her who had laughed so much, crying was delicious. All sorrows became her sorrows; she was Tenderness. She would cry long and softly over newspaper accounts of kidnaped babies, deserted wives, unemployed men, strayed cats, heroic dogs. Even when the paper was no longer before her, her mind revolved upon these things and the drops slipped rhythmically over her plump cheeks.

"Honestly," she would say to Herbie, "all the sadness there is in the world when you stop to think about it!"

"Yeah," Herbie would say.

She missed nobody. The old crowd, the people who had brought her and Herbie together, dropped from their lives, lingeringly at first. When she thought of this at all, it was only to consider it fitting. This was marriage. This was peace.

But the thing was that Herbie was not amused.

For a time, he had enjoyed being alone with her. He found the voluntary isolation novel and sweet. Then it palled with a ferocious suddenness. It was as if one night, sitting with her in the steam-heated living-room, he would ask no more; and the next night he was through and done with the whole thing.

He became annoyed by her misty melancholies. At first, when he came home to find her softly tired and moody, he kissed her neck and patted her shoulder and begged her to tell her Herbie what was wrong. She loved that. But time slid by, and he found that there was never anything really, personally, the matter.

"Ah, for God's sake," he would say. "Crabbing again. All right, sit here and crab your head off. I'm going out."

And he would slam out of the flat and come back late and drunk.

She was completely bewildered by what happened to their marriage. First they were lovers; and then, it seemed without transition, they were enemies. She never understood it.

There were longer and longer intervals between his leaving his office and his arrival at the apartment. She went through agonies of picturing him run over and bleeding, dead and covered with a sheet. Then she lost her fears for his safety and grew sullen and wounded. When a person wanted to be with a person, he came as soon as possible. She desperately wanted him to want to be with her; her own hours only marked the time till he would come. It was often nearly nine o'clock before he came home to dinner. Always he had had many drinks, and their effect would die in him, leaving him loud and querulous and bristling for affronts.

He was too nervous, he said, to sit and do nothing for an evening. He boasted, probably not in all truth, that he had never read a book in his life.

"What am I expected to do—sit around this dump on my tail all night?" he would ask, rhetorically. And again he would slam out.

She did not know what to do. She could not manage him. She could not meet him.

She fought him furiously. A terrific domesticity had come upon her, and she would bite and scratch to guard it. She wanted what she called "a nice home." She wanted a sober, tender husband, prompt at dinner, punctual at work. She wanted sweet, comforting evenings. The idea of intimacy with other men was terrible to her; the thought that Herbie might be seeking entertainment in other women set her frantic.

It seemed to her that almost everything she read—novels from the drug-store lending library, magazine stories, women's pages in the papers—dealt with wives who lost their husbands' love. She could bear those, at that, better than accounts of neat, companionable marriage and living happily ever after.

She was frightened. Several times when Herbie came home in the evening, he found her determinedly dressed—she had had to alter those of her clothes that were not new, to make them fasten—and rouged.

"Let's go wild tonight, what do you say?" she would hail him. "A person's got lots of time to hang around and do nothing when they're dead."

So they would go out, to chop houses and the less expensive cabarets. But it turned out badly. She could no longer find amusement in watching Herbie drink. She could not laugh at his whimsicalities, she was so tensely counting his indulgences. And she was unable to keep back her remonstrances—"Ah, come on, Herb, you've had enough, haven't you? You'll feel something terrible in the morning."

He would be immediately enraged. All right, crab; crab, crab, crab, crab, that was all she ever did. What a lousy sport *she* was! There would be scenes, and one or the other of them would rise and stalk out in fury.

She could not recall the definite day that she started drinking, herself. There was nothing separate about her days. Like drops upon a window-pane, they ran together and trickled away. She had been married six months; then a year; then three years.

She had never needed to drink, formerly. She could sit for most of a night at a table where the others were imbibing earnestly and never droop in looks or spirits, nor be bored by the doings of those about her. If she took a cocktail, it was so unusual as to cause twenty minutes or so of jocular comment. But now anguish was in her. Frequently, after a quarrel, Herbie would stay out for the night, and she could not learn from him where the time had been spent. Her heart felt tight and sore in her breast, and her mind turned like an electric fan.

She hated the taste of liquor. Gin, plain or in mixtures, made her promptly sick. After experiment, she found that Scotch whisky was best for her. She took it without water, because that was the quickest way to its effect.

Herbie pressed it on her. He was glad to see her drink. They both felt it might restore her high spirits, and their good times together might again be possible.

"'Atta girl," he would approve her. "Let's see you get boiled, baby."

But it brought them no nearer. When she drank with him, there would be a little while of gaiety and then, strangely without beginning, they would be in a wild quarrel. They would wake in the morning not sure what it had all been about, foggy as to what had been said and done, but each deeply injured and bitterly resentful. There would be days of vengeful silence.

There had been a time when they had made up their quarrels, usually in bed. There would be kisses and little names and assurances of fresh starts. . . . "Oh, it's going to be great now, Herb. We'll have swell times. I was a crab. I guess I must have been tired. But everything's going to be swell. You'll see."

Now there were no gentle reconciliations. They resumed friendly relations only in the brief magnanimity caused by liquor, before more liquor drew them into new battles. The scenes became more violent. There were shouted invectives and pushes, and sometimes sharp slaps. Once she had a black eye. Herbie was horrified next day at sight of it. He did not go to work; he followed her about, suggesting remedies and heaping dark blame on himself. But after they had had a few drinks—"to pull themselves together"—she made so many wistful references to her bruise that he shouted at her and rushed out and was gone for two days.

Each time he left the place in a rage, he threatened never to come back. She did not believe him, nor did she consider separation. Somewhere in her head or her heart was the lazy, nebulous hope that things would change and she and Herbie settle suddenly into soothing married life. Here were her home, her furniture, her husband, her station. She summoned no alternatives.

She could no longer bustle and potter. She had no more vicarious tears; the hot drops she shed were for herself. She walked ceaselessly about the rooms, her thoughts running mechanically round and round Herbie. In those days began the hatred of being alone that she was never to overcome. You could be by yourself when things were all right, but when you were blue you got the howling horrors.

She commenced drinking alone, little, short drinks all through the day. It was only with Herbie that alcohol made her nervous and quick in offense. Alone, it blurred sharp things for her. She lived in a haze of it. Her life took on a dreamlike quality. Nothing was astonishing.

A Mrs. Martin moved into the flat across the hall. She was a great blonde woman of forty, a promise in looks of what Mrs. Morse was to be. They made acquaintance, quickly became inseparable. Mrs. Morse spent her days in the opposite apartment. They drank together, to brace themselves after the drinks of the nights before.

She never confided her troubles about Herbie to Mrs. Martin. The subject was too bewildering to her to find comfort in talk. She let it be assumed that her husband's business kept him much away. It was not regarded as important; husbands, as such, played but shadowy parts in Mrs. Martin's circle.

Mrs. Martin had no visible spouse; you were left to decide for yourself whether he was or was not dead. She had an admirer, Joe, who came to see her almost nightly. Often he brought several friends with him—"The Boys," they were called. The Boys were big, red, good-humored men, perhaps forty-five, perhaps fifty. Mrs. Morse was glad of invitations to join the parties—Herbie was scarcely ever at home at night now. If he did come home, she did not visit Mrs. Martin. An evening alone with Herbie meant inevitably a quarrel, yet she would stay with him. There was always her thin and wordless idea that, maybe, this night, things would begin to be all right.

The Boys brought plenty of liquor along with them whenever they came to Mrs. Martin's. Drinking with them, Mrs. Morse became lively and good-natured and audacious. She was quickly popular. When she had drunk enough to cloud her most recent battle with Herbie, she was excited by their approbation. Crab, was she? Rotten sport, was she? Well, there were some that thought different.

Ed was one of The Boys. He lived in Utica—had "his own business" there was the awed report—but he came to New York almost every week. He was married. He showed Mrs. Morse the then current photographs of Junior and Sister, and she praised them abundantly and sincerely. Soon it was accepted by the others that Ed was her particular friend.

He staked her when they all played poker; sat next her and occasionally rubbed his knee against hers during the game. She was rather lucky. Frequently she went home with a twenty-dollar bill or a ten-dollar bill or a handful of crumpled dollars. She was glad of them. Herbie was getting, in her words, something awful about money. To ask him for it brought an instant row.

"What the hell do you do with it?" he would say. "Shoot it all on Scotch?"

"I try to run this house half-way decent," she would retort. "Never thought of that, did you? Oh, no, his lordship couldn't be bothered with that."

Again, she could not find a definite day, to fix the beginning of Ed's proprietorship. It became his custom to kiss her on the mouth when he came in, as well as for farewell, and he gave her little quick kisses of approval all through the evening. She liked this rather more than she disliked it. She never thought of his kisses when she was not with him.

He would run his hand lingeringly over her back and shoulders.

"Some dizzy blonde, eh?" he would say. "Some doll."

One afternoon she came home from Mrs. Martin's to find Herbie in the bedroom. He had been away for several nights, evidently on a prolonged drinking bout. His face was gray, his hands jerked as if they were on wires. On the bed were two old suitcases, packed high. Only her photograph remained on his bureau, and the wide doors of his closet disclosed nothing but coat-hangers.

"I'm blowing," he said. "I'm through with the whole works. I got a job in Detroit."

She sat down on the edge of the bed. She had drunk much the night before, and the four Scotches she had had with Mrs. Martin had only increased her fogginess.

"Good job?" she said.

"Oh, yeah," he said. "Looks all right."

He closed a suitcase with difficulty, swearing at it in whispers.

"There's some dough in the bank," he said. "The bank book's in your top drawer. You can have the furniture and stuff."

He looked at her, and his forehead twitched.

"God damn it, I'm through, I'm telling you," he cried. "I'm through."

"All right, all right," she said. "I heard you, didn't I?"

She saw him as if he were at one end of a cannon and she at the other. Her head was beginning to ache bumpingly, and her voice had a dreary, tiresome tone. She could not have raised it.

"Like a drink before you go?" she asked.

Again he looked at her, and a corner of his mouth jerked up.

"Cockeyed again for a change, aren't you?" he said. "That's nice. Sure, get a couple of shots, will you?"

She went to the pantry, mixed him a stiff highball, poured herself a couple of inches of whisky and drank it. Then she gave herself another portion and brought the glasses into the bedroom. He had strapped both suitcases and had put on his hat and overcoat.

He took his highball.

"Well," he said, and he gave a sudden, uncertain laugh. "Here's mud in your eye."

"Mud in your eye," she said.

They drank. He put down his glass and took up the heavy suitcases.

"Got to get a train around six," he said.

She followed him down the hall. There was a song, a song that Mrs. Martin played doggedly on the phonograph, running loudly through her mind. She had never liked the thing.

"Night and daytime,
Always playtime.
Ain't we got fun?"

At the door he put down the bags and faced her.

"Well," he said. "Well, take care of yourself. You'll be all right, will you?"

"Oh, sure," she said.

He opened the door, then came back to her, holding out his hand.

"'By, Haze," he said. "Good luck to you."

She took his hand and shook it.

"Pardon my wet glove," she said.

When the door had closed behind him, she went back to the pantry.

She was flushed and lively when she went in to Mrs. Martin's that evening. The Boys were there, Ed among them. He was glad to be in town, frisky and loud and full of jokes. But she spoke quietly to him for a minute.

"Herbie blew today," she said. "Going to live out west."

"That so?" he said. He looked at her and played with the fountain pen clipped to his waistcoat pocket.

"Think he's gone for good, do you?" he asked.

"Yeah," she said. "I know he is. I know. Yeah."

"You going to live on across the hall just the same?" he said. "Know what you're going to do?"

"Gee, I don't know," she said. "I don't give much of a damn."

"Oh, come on, that's no way to talk," he told her. "What you need—you need a little snifter. How about it?"

"Yeah," she said. "Just straight."

She won forty-three dollars at poker. When the game broke up, Ed took her back to her apartment.

"Got a little kiss for me?" he asked.

He wrapped her in his big arms and kissed her violently. She was entirely passive. He held her away and looked at her.

"Little tight, honey?" he asked, anxiously. "Not going to be sick, are you?"

"Me?" she said. "I'm swell."

II

When Ed left in the morning, he took her photograph with him. He said he wanted her picture to look at, up in Utica. "You can have that one on the bureau," she said.

She put Herbie's picture in a drawer, out of her sight. When she could look at it, she meant to tear it up. She was fairly successful in keeping her mind from racing around him. Whisky slowed it for her. She was almost peaceful, in her mist.

She accepted her relationship with Ed without question or enthusiasm. When he was away, she seldom thought definitely of him. He was good to her; he gave her frequent presents and a regular allowance. She was even able to save. She did not plan ahead of any day, but her wants were few, and you might as well put money in the bank as have it lying around.

When the lease of her apartment neared its end, it was Ed who suggested moving. His friendship with Mrs. Martin and Joe had become strained over a dispute at poker; a feud was impending.

"Let's get the hell out of here," Ed said. "What I want you to have is a place near the Grand Central. Make it easier for me."

So she took a little flat in the Forties. A colored maid came in every day to clean and to make coffee for her—she was "through with that housekeeping stuff," she said, and Ed, twenty years married to a passionately domestic woman, admired this romantic uselessness and felt doubly a man of the world in abetting it.

The coffee was all she had until she went out to dinner, but alcohol kept her fat. Prohibition she regarded only as a basis for jokes. You could always get all you wanted. She was never noticeably drunk and seldom nearly sober. It required a larger daily allowance to keep her misty-minded. Too little, and she was achingly melancholy.

Ed brought her to Jimmy's. He was proud, with the pride of the transient who would be mistaken for a native, in his knowledge of small, recent restaurants occupying the lower floors of shabby brownstone houses; places where, upon mentioning the name of an habitué friend, might be obtained strange whisky and fresh gin in many of their ramifications. Jimmy's place was the favorite of his acquaintances.

There, through Ed, Mrs. Morse met many men and women, formed quick friendships. The men often took her out when Ed was in Utica. He was proud of her popularity.

She fell into the habit of going to Jimmy's alone when she had no engagement. She was certain to meet some people she knew, and join them. It was a club for her friends, both men and women.

The women at Jimmy's looked remarkably alike, and this was curious, for, through feuds, removals, and opportunities of more profitable contacts, the personnel of the group changed constantly. Yet always the newcomers resembled those whom they replaced. They were all big women and stout, broad of shoulder and abundantly breasted, with faces thickly clothed in soft, high-colored flesh. They laughed loud and often, showing opaque and lusterless teeth like squares of crockery. There was about them the health of the big, yet a slight, unwholesome suggestion of stubborn preservation. They might have been thirty-six or forty-five or anywhere between.

They composed their titles of their own first names with their husbands' surnames—Mrs. Florence Miller, Mrs. Vera Riley, Mrs. Lilian Block. This gave at the same time the solidity of marriage and the glamour of freedom. Yet only one or two were actually divorced. Most of them never referred to their dimmed spouses; some, a shorter time separated, described them in terms of great biological interest. Several were mothers, each of an only child—a boy at school somewhere, or a girl being cared for by a grandmother. Often, well on towards morning, there would be displays of kodak portraits and of tears.

They were comfortable women, cordial and friendly and irrepressibly matronly. Theirs was the quality of ease. Become fatalistic, especially about money matters, they were unworried. Whenever their funds dropped alarmingly, a new donor appeared; this had always happened. The aim of each was to have one man, permanently, to pay all her bills, in return for which she would have immediately given up other admirers and probably would have become exceedingly fond of him; for the affections of all of them were, by now, unexacting, tranquil, and easily arranged. This end, however, grew increasingly difficult yearly. Mrs. Morse was regarded as fortunate.

Ed had a good year, increased her allowance and gave her a sealskin coat. But she had to be careful of her moods with him. He insisted upon gaiety. He would not listen to admissions of aches or weariness.

"Hey, listen," he would say, "I got worries of my own, and plenty. Nobody wants to hear other people's troubles, sweetie. What you got to do, you got to be a sport and forget it. See? Well, slip us a little smile, then. That's my girl."

She never had enough interest to quarrel with him as she had with Herbie, but she wanted the privilege of occasional admitted sadness. It was strange. The other women she saw did not have to fight their moods. There was Mrs. Florence Miller who got regular crying jags, and the men sought only to cheer and comfort her. The others spent whole evenings in grieved recitals of worries and ills; their escorts paid them deep sympathy. But she was instantly undesirable when she was low in spirits. Once, at Jimmy's, when she could not make herself lively, Ed had walked out and left her.

"Why the hell don't you stay home and not go spoiling everybody's evening?" he had roared.

Even her slightest acquaintances seemed irritated if she were not conspicuously light-hearted.

"What's the matter with you, anyway?" they would say. "Be your age, why don't you? Have a little drink and snap out of it."

When her relationship with Ed had continued nearly three years, he moved to Florida to live. He hated leaving her; he gave her a large check and some shares of a sound stock, and his pale eyes were wet when he said good-by. She did not miss him. He came to New York infrequently, perhaps two or three times a year, and hurried directly from the train to see her. She was always pleased to have him come and never sorry to see him go.

Charley, an acquaintance of Ed's that she had met at Jimmy's, had long admired her. He had always made opportunities of touching her and leaning close to talk to her. He asked repeatedly of all their friends if they had ever heard such a fine laugh as she had. After Ed left, Charley became the main figure in her life. She classified him and spoke of him as "not so bad." There was nearly a year of Charley; then she divided her time between him and Sydney, another frequenter of Jimmy's; then Charley slipped away altogether.

Sydney was a little, brightly dressed, clever Jew. She was perhaps nearest contentment with him. He amused her always; her laughter was not forced.

He admired her completely. Her softness and size delighted him. And he thought she was great, he often told her, because she kept gay and lively when she was drunk.

"Once I had a gal," he said, "used to try and throw herself out of the window every time she got a can on. Jee-*zuss*," he added, feelingly.

Then Sydney married a rich and watchful bride, and then there was Billy. No—after Sydney came Ferd, then Billy. In her haze, she never recalled how men entered her life and left it. There were no surprises. She had no thrill at their advent, nor woe at their departure. She seemed to be always able to attract men. There was never another as rich as Ed, but they were all generous to her, in their means.

Once she had news of Herbie. She met Mrs. Martin dining at Jimmy's, and the old friendship was vigorously renewed. The still admiring Joe, while on a business trip, had seen Herbie. He had settled in Chicago, he looked fine, he was living with some woman—seemed to be crazy about her. Mrs. Morse had been drinking vastly that day. She took the news with mild interest, as one hearing of the sex peccadilloes of somebody whose name is, after a moment's groping, familiar.

"Must be damn near seven years since I saw him," she commented. "Gee. Seven years."

More and more, her days lost their individuality. She never knew dates, nor was sure of the day of the week.

"My God, was that a year ago!" she would exclaim, when an event was recalled in conversation.

She was tired so much of the time. Tired and blue. Almost everything could give her the blues. Those old horses she saw on Sixth Avenue—struggling and slipping along the car-tracks, or standing at the curb, their heads dropped level with their worn knees. The tightly stored tears would squeeze from her eyes as she teetered past on her aching feet in the stubby, champagne-colored slippers.

The thought of death came and stayed with her and lent her a sort of drowsy cheer. It would be nice, nice and restful, to be dead.

There was no settled, shocked moment when she first thought of killing herself; it seemed to her as if the idea had always been with her. She pounced upon all the accounts of suicides in the newspapers. There was an epidemic of self-killings—or maybe it was just that she searched for the stories of them so eagerly that she found many. To read of them roused reassurance in her; she felt a cozy solidarity with the big company of the voluntary dead.

She slept, aided by whisky, till deep into the afternoons, then lay abed, a bottle and glass at her hand, until it was time to dress to go out for dinner. She was beginning to feel towards alcohol a little puzzled distrust, as toward an old friend who has refused a simple favor. Whisky could still soothe her for most of the time, but there were sudden, inexplicable moments when the cloud fell treacherously away from her, and she was sawed by the sorrow and bewilderment and nuisance of all living. She played voluptuously with the thought of cool, sleepy retreat. She had never been troubled by religious belief and no vision of an after-life intimidated her. She dreamed by day of never again putting on tight shoes, of never having to laugh and listen and admire, of never more being a good sport. Never.

But how would you do it? It made her sick to think of jumping from heights. She could not stand a gun. At the theater, if one of the actors drew a revolver, she crammed her fingers into her ears and could not even look at the stage until after the shot had been fired. There was no gas in her flat. She looked long at the bright blue veins in her slim wrists—a cut with a razor blade, and there you'd be. But it would hurt, hurt like hell, and there would be blood to see. Poison—something tasteless and quick and painless—was the thing. But they wouldn't sell it to you in drugstores, because of the law.

She had few other thoughts.

There was a new man now—Art. He was short and fat and exacting and hard on her patience when he was drunk. But there had been only occasionals for some time before him, and she was glad of a little stability. Too, Art must be away for weeks at a stretch, selling silks, and that was restful. She was convincingly gay with him, though the effort shook her.

"The best sport in the world," he would murmur, deep in her neck. "The best sport in the world."

One night, when he had taken her to Jimmy's, she went into the dressing-room with Mrs. Florence Miller. There, while designing curly mouths on their faces with lip-rouge, they compared experiences of insomnia.

"Honestly," Mrs. Morse said, "I wouldn't close an eye if I didn't go to bed full of Scotch. I lie there and toss and turn and toss and turn. Blue! Does a person get blue lying awake that way!"

"Say, listen Hazel," Mrs. Miller said, impressively, "I'm telling you I'd be awake for a year if I didn't take veronal. That stuff makes you sleep like a fool."

"Isn't it poison, or something?" Mrs. Morse asked.

"Oh, you take too much and you're out for the count," said Mrs. Miller. "I just take five grains—they come in tablets. I'd be scared to fool around with it. But five grains, and you cork off pretty."

"Can you get it anywhere?" Mrs. Morse felt superbly Machiavellian.

"Get all you want in Jersey," said Mrs. Miller. "They won't give it to you here without you have a doctor's prescription. Finished? We'd better go back and see what the boys are doing."

That night, Art left Mrs. Morse at the door of her apartment; his mother was in town. Mrs. Morse was still sober, and it happened that there was no whisky left in her cupboard. She lay in bed, looking up at the black ceiling.

She rose early, for her, and went to New Jersey. She had never taken the tube, and did not understand it. So she went to the Pennsylvania Station and bought a railroad ticket to Newark. She thought of nothing in particular on the trip out. She looked at the uninspired hats of the women about her and gazed through the smeared window at the flat, gritty scene.

In Newark, in the first drug-store she came to, she asked for a tin of talcum powder, a nailbrush, and a box of veronal tablets. The powder and the brush were to make the hypnotic seem also a casual need. The clerk was entirely unconcerned. "We only keep them in bottles," he said, and wrapped up for her a little glass vial containing ten white tablets, stacked one on another.

She went to another drug-store and bought a face-cloth, an orange-wood stick, and a bottle of veronal tablets. The clerk was also uninterested.

"Well, I guess I got enough to kill an ox," she thought, and went back to the station.

At home, she put the little vials in the drawer of her dressing-table and stood looking at them with a dreamy tenderness.

"There they are, God bless them," she said, and she kissed her fingertip and touched each bottle.

The colored maid was busy in the living-room.

"Hey, Nettie," Mrs. Morse called. "Be an angel, will you? Run around to Jimmy's and get me a quart of Scotch."

She hummed while she awaited the girl's return.

During the next few days, whisky ministered to her as tenderly as it had done when she first turned to its aid. Alone, she was soothed and vague, at Jimmy's she was the gayest of the groups. Art was delighted with her.

Then, one night, she had an appointment to meet Art at Jimmy's for an early dinner. He was to leave afterward on a business excursion, to be away for a week. Mrs. Morse had been drinking all the afternoon; while she dressed to go out, she felt herself rising pleasurably from drowsiness to high spirits. But as she came out into the street the effects of the whisky deserted her completely, and she was filled with a slow, grinding wretchedness so horrible that she stood swaying on the pavement, unable for a moment to move forward. It was a gray night with spurts of mean, thin snow, and the streets shone with dark ice. As she slowly crossed Sixth Avenue, consciously dragging one foot past the other, a big, scarred horse pulling a rickety express-wagon crashed to his knees before her. The driver swore and screamed and lashed the beast insanely, bringing the whip back over his shoulder for every blow, while the horse struggled to get a footing on the slippery asphalt. A group gathered and watched with interest.

Art was waiting, when Mrs. Morse reached Jimmy's.

"What's the matter with you, for God's sake?" was his greeting to her.

"I saw a horse," she said. "Gee, I—a person feels sorry for horses. I—it isn't just horses. Everything's kind of terrible, isn't it? I can't help getting sunk."

"Ah, sunk, me eye," he said. "What's the idea of all the bellyaching? What have you got to be sunk about?"

"I can't help it," she said.

"Ah, help it, me eye," he said. "Pull yourself together, will you? Come on and sit down, and take that face off you."

She drank industriously and she tried hard, but she could not overcome her melancholy. Others joined them and commented on her gloom, and she could do no more for them than smile weakly. She made little dabs at her eyes with her handkerchief, trying to time her movements so they would be unnoticed, but several times Art caught her and scowled and shifted impatiently in his chair.

When it was time for him to go to his train, she said she would leave, too and go home.

"And not a bad idea, either," he said. "See if you can't sleep yourself out of it. I'll see you Thursday. For God's sake, try and cheer up by then, will you?"

"Yeah," she said. "I will."

In her bedroom, she undressed with a tense speed wholly unlike her usual slow uncertainty. She put on her nightgown, took off her hair-net and passed the comb quickly through her dry, vari-colored hair. Then she took the two little vials from the drawer and carried them into the bathroom. The splintering misery had gone from her, and she felt the quick excitement of one who is about to receive an anticipated gift.

She uncorked the vials, filled a glass with water and stood before the mirror, a tablet between her fingers. Suddenly she bowed graciously to her reflection, and raised the glass to it.

"Well, here's mud in your eye," she said.

The tablets were unpleasant to take, dry and powdery and sticking obstinately half-way down her throat. It took her a long time to swallow all twenty of them. She stood watching her reflection with deep, impersonal interest, studying the movements of the gulping throat. Once more she spoke aloud.

"For God's sake, try and cheer up by Thursday, will you?" she said. "Well, you know what he can do. He and the whole lot of them."

She had no idea how quickly to expect effect from the veronal. When she had taken the last tablet, she stood uncertainly, wondering, still with a courteous, vicarious interest, if death would strike her down then and there. She felt in no way strange, save for a slight stirring of sickness from the effort of swallowing the tablets, nor did her reflected face look at all different. It would not be immediate, then; it might even take an hour or so.

She stretched her arms high and gave a vast yawn.

"Guess I'll go to bed," she said. "Gee, I'm nearly dead."

That struck her as comic, and she turned out the bathroom light and went in and laid herself down in her bed, chuckling softly all the time.

"Gee, I'm nearly dead," she quoted. "That's a hot one!"

III

Nettie, the colored maid, came in late the next afternoon to clean the apartment, and found Mrs. Morse in her bed. But then, that was not unusual. Usually, though, the sounds of cleaning waked her, and she did not like to wake up. Nettie, an agreeable girl, had learned to move softly about her work.

But when she had done the living-room and stolen in to tidy the little square bedroom, she could not avoid a tiny clatter as she arranged the objects on the dressing-table. Instinctively, she glanced over her shoulder at the sleeper, and without warning a sickly uneasiness crept over her. She came to the bed and stared down at the woman lying there.

Mrs. Morse lay on her back, one flabby, white arm flung up, the wrist against her forehead. Her stiff hair hung untenderly along her face. The bed covers were pushed down, exposing a deep square of soft neck and a pink nightgown, its fabric worn uneven by many launderings; her great breasts, freed from their tight confiner, sagged beneath her armpits. Now and then she made knotted, snoring sounds, and from the corner of her opened mouth to the blurred turn of her jaw ran a lane of crusted spittle.

"Mis' Morse," Nettie called. "Oh, Mis' Morse! It's terrible late."

Mrs. Morse made no move.

"Mis' Morse," said Nettie. "Look, Mis' Morse. How'm I goin' get this bed made?"

Panic sprang upon the girl. She shook the woman's hot shoulder.

"Ah, wake up, will yuh?" she whined. "Ah, please wake up."

Suddenly the girl turned and ran out in the hall to the elevator door, keeping her thumb firm on the black, shiny button until the elderly car and its Negro attendant stood before her. She poured a jumble of words over the boy, and led him back to the apartment. He tiptoed creakingly in to the bedside; first gingerly, then so lustily that he left marks in the soft flesh, he prodded the unconscious woman.

"Hey, there!" he cried, and listened intently, as for an echo.

"Jeez. Out like a light," he commented.

At his interest in the spectacle, Nettie's panic left her. Importance was big in both of them. They talked in quick, unfinished whispers, and it was the boy's suggestion that he fetch the young doctor who lived on the ground floor. Nettie hurried along with him. They looked forward to the limelit moment of breaking their news of something untoward, something pleasurably unpleasant. Mrs. Morse had become the medium of drama. With no ill wish to her, they hoped that her state was serious, that she would not let them down by being awake and normal on their return. A little fear of this determined them to make the most, to the doctor of her present condition. "Matter of life and death," returned to Nettie from her thin store of reading. She considered startling the doctor with the phrase.

The doctor was in and none too pleased at interruption. He wore a yellow and blue striped dressing-gown, and he was lying on his sofa, laughing with a dark girl, her face scaly with inexpensive powder, who perched on the arm. Half-emptied highball glasses stood beside them and her coat and hat were neatly hung up with the comfortable implication of a long stay.

Always something, the doctor grumbled. Couldn't let anybody alone after a hard day. But he put some bottles and instruments into a case, changed his dressing-gown for his coat and started out with the Negroes.

"Snap it up there, big boy," the girl called after him. "Don't be all night."

The doctor strode loudly into Mrs. Morse's flat and on to the bedroom, Nettie and the boy right behind him. Mrs. Morse had not moved; her sleep was as deep, but soundless, now. The doctor looked sharply at her, then plunged his thumbs into the lidded pits above her eyeballs and threw his weight upon them. A high, sickened cry broke from Nettie.

"Look like he tryin' to push her right on th'ough the bed," said the boy. He chuckled.

Mrs. Morse gave no sign under the pressure. Abruptly the doctor abandoned it, and with one quick movement swept the covers down to the foot of the bed. With another he flung her nightgown back and lifted the thick, white legs, cross-hatched with blocks of tiny, iris colored veins. He pinched them repeatedly, with long, cruel nips, back of the knees. She did not awaken.

"What's she been drinking?" he asked Nettie, over his shoulder.

With the certain celerity of one who knows just where to lay hands on a thing, Nettie went into the bathroom, bound for the cupboard where Mrs. Morse kept her whisky. But she stopped at the sight of the two vials, with their red and white labels, lying before the mirror. She brought them to the doctor.

"Oh, for the Lord Almighty's sweet sake!" he said. He dropped Mrs. Morse's legs, and pushed them impatiently across the bed. "What did she want to go taking that tripe for? Rotten yellow trick, that's what a thing like that is. Now we'll have to pump her out, and all that stuff. Nuisance, a thing like that is; that's what it amounts to. Here, George, take me down in the elevator. You wait here, maid. She won't do anything."

"She won't die on me, will she?" cried Nettie.

"No," said the doctor. "God, no. You couldn't kill her with an ax."

IV

After two days, Mrs. Morse came back to consciousness, dazed at first then with a comprehension that brought with it the slow, saturating wretchedness.

"Oh, Lord, oh, Lord," she moaned, and tears for herself and for life striped her cheeks.

Nettie came in at the sound. For two days she had done the ugly, incessant tasks in the nursing of the unconscious, for two nights she had caught broken bits of sleep on the living-room couch. She looked coldly at the big, blown woman in the bed.

"What you been tryin' to do, Mis' Morse?" she said. "What kine o' work is that, takin' all that stuff?"

"Oh, Lord," moaned Mrs. Morse, again, and she tried to cover her eyes with her arms. But the joints felt stiff and brittle, and she cried out at their ache.

"Tha's no way to ack, takin' them pills," said Nettie. "You can thank you' stars you heah at all. How you feel now?"

"Oh, I feel great," said Mrs. Morse. "Swell, I feel."

Her hot, painful tears fell as if they would never stop.

"Tha's no way to take on, cryin' like that," Nettie said. "After what you done. The doctor, he says he could have you arrested, doin' a thing like that. He was fit to be tied, here."

"Why couldn't he let me alone?" wailed Mrs. Morse. "Why the hell couldn't he have?"

"Tha's terr'ble, Mis' Morse, swearin' an' talkin' like that," said Nettie, "after what people done for you. Here I ain' had no sleep at all for two nights, an' had to give up goin' out to my other ladies!"

"Oh, I'm sorry, Nettie," she said. "You're a peach. I'm sorry I've given you so much trouble. I couldn't help it. I just got sunk. Didn't you ever feel like doing it? When everything looks just lousy to you?"

"I wouldn' think o' no such thing," declared Nettie. "You got to cheer up. Tha's what you got to do. Everybody's got their troubles."

"Yeah," said Mrs. Morse. "I know."

"Come a pretty picture card for you," Nettie said. "Maybe that will cheer you up."

She handed Mrs. Morse a post-card. Mrs. Morse had to cover one eye with her hand, in order to read the message; her eyes were not yet focusing correctly.

It was from Art. On the back of a view of the Detroit Athletic Club he had written: "Greeting and salutations. Hope you have lost that gloom. Cheer up and don't take any rubber nickles. See you on Thursday."

She dropped the card to the floor. Misery crushed her as if she were between great smooth stones. There passed before her a slow, slow pageant of days spent lying in her flat, of evenings at Jimmy's being a good sport, making herself laugh and coo at Art and other Arts; she saw a long parade of weary horses and shivering beggars and all beaten, driven, stumbling things. Her feet throbbed as if she had crammed them into the stubby champagne-colored slippers. Her heart seemed to swell and harden.

"Nettie," she cried, "for heaven's sake pour me a drink, will you?"

The maid looked doubtful.

"Now you know, Mis' Morse," she said, "you been near daid. I don' know if the doctor he let you drink nothin' yet."

"Oh, never mind him," she said. "You get me one, and bring in the bottle. Take one yourself."

"Well," said Nettie.

She poured them each a drink, deferentially leaving hers in the bathroom to be taken in solitude, and brought Mrs. Morse's glass in to her.

Mrs. Morse looked into the liquor and shuddered back from its odor. Maybe it would help. Maybe, when you had been knocked cold for a few days, your very first drink would give you a lift. Maybe whisky would be her friend again. She prayed without addressing a God, without knowing a God. Oh, please, please, let her be able to get drunk, please keep her always drunk.

She lifted the glass.

"Thanks, Nettie," she said. "Here's mud in your eye."

The maid giggled. "Tha's the way, Mis' Morse," she said. "You cheer up, now."

"Yeah," said Mrs. Morse. "Sure."

[1929]

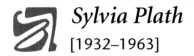

Sylvia Plath
[1932–1963]

SYLVIA PLATH *was born in Boston to academic parents. Her father, Otto, was a professor of entomology at Boston College while her mother taught high school German and English. Plath's father became ill in 1936 with diabetes and died in 1940 from complications after surgery. Plath's mother supported the family by teaching, but Plath herself suffered at her father's loss and began cycles of depression early in life. The cycles were eventually to lead to her own much-publicized suicide as a young mother. While still in high school she published poems in* The Boston Globe, Seventeen, *and* The Christian Science Monitor. *In 1950 she began school at Smith College where she earned prizes in poetry and fiction, becoming an intern in the summer of 1953 for* Mademoiselle. *She wrote a feature called "Poets on Campus" in which she interviewed important poets such as Elizabeth Bowen and Richard Wilbur. This hard work contributed to her first collapse, sending her to a hospital for treatments, which at the time meant electro-shock therapy. She healed and returned to Smith where she graduated with honors in 1955. In the meantime, Plath published poems in* Harpers, Atlantic Monthly, Mademoiselle, *and* The Nation. *After graduation, she moved to England to study literature at Newnham College, Cambridge. There she met Ted Hughes, the poet, and married within four months. She took a teaching job at Smith back in the United States to support Hughes while his career was on the rise. By the summer of 1958, she was publishing poems regularly in* New Yorker, The Nation, *and the* Sewanee Review. *In the summer of 1959 Plath and Hughes moved to the artist colony at Yaddo where she was able to write, collect, and publish her first book of poems,* The Colossus and Other Poems *(1960).*

At this point the poets moved to London where difficulties followed. Plath worked on her autobiography The Bell Jar *(1961) and Hughes also continued to write. The tale of her life described her early struggles with her father's death and her desperate efforts to adjust to a world where talented women were expected to live the housewife life of the 1950s. The book, like Plath's poems, spoke to intellectual and educated women of the time, being read by the sixties women's advocates as a cry for change. Plath gave birth to a daughter in 1960 and a son in 1962. The marriage, however, crumbled as Hughes became interested in another woman and Plath spiraled into anger and despair. Out of this despair grew some of her most powerful poetry, including "Daddy" and "Lady Lazarus." These poems speak about women's feelings in a world where talented women stay at home with dishes and children while men make their ways in the wider world. Alone in a small London flat with two toddlers, she committed suicide in the winter of 1963. Hughes collected her poems into* Ariel, *published in 1968. In 1982, after her works sold over 120,000 copies, she was awarded a posthumous Pulitzer Prize.*

Daddy

SYLVIA PLATH

You do not do, you do not do
Any more, black shoe
In which I have lived like a foot
For thirty years, poor and white,
Barely daring to breathe or Achoo.   5

Daddy, I have had to kill you.
You died before I had time——
Marble-heavy, a bag full of God,
Ghastly statue with one grey toe
Big as a Frisco seal   10
And a head in the freakish Atlantic
Where it pours bean green over blue
In the waters off beautiful Nauset.
I used to pray to recover you.
Ach, du.   15

In the German tongue, in the Polish town
Scraped flat by the roller
Of wars, wars, wars.
But the name of the town is common.
My Polack friend   20

Says there are a dozen or two.
So I never could tell where you
Put your foot, your root,
I never could talk to you.
The tongue stuck in my jaw.   25

Reprinted from *Ariel*, by permission of HarperCollins Publishers, Inc. Copyright © 1963 by
Ted Hughes.

It stuck in a barb wire snare.
Ich, ich, ich, ich,
I could hardly speak.
I thought every German was you.
And the language obscene   *30*

An engine, an engine
Chuffing me off like a Jew.
A Jew to Dachau, Auschwitz, Belsen.
I began to talk like a Jew.
I think I may well be a Jew.   *35*

The snows of the Tyrol, the clear beer of Vienna
Are not very pure or true.
With my gypsy ancestress and my weird luck
And my Taroc pack and my Taroc pack
I may be a bit of a Jew.   *40*

I have always been scared of *you*,
With your Luftwaffe, your gobbledygoo.
And your neat moustache
And your Aryan eye, bright blue.
Panzer-man, panzer-man, O You——   *45*

Not God but a swastika
So black no sky could squeak through.
Every woman adores a Fascist,
The boot in the face, the brute
Brute heart of a brute like you.   *50*

You stand at the blackboard, daddy,
In the picture I have of you,
A cleft in your chin instead of your foot
But no less a devil for that, no not
Any less the black man who   *55*

Bit my pretty red heart in two.
I was ten when they buried you.
At twenty I tried to die
And get back, back, back to you.
I thought even the bones would do   *60*

But they pulled me out of the sack,
And they stuck me together with glue.
And then I knew what to do.
I made a model of you,
A man in black with a Meinkampf look   65

And a love of the rack and the screw.
And I said I do, I do.
So daddy, I'm finally through.
The black telephone's off at the root,
The voices just can't worm through.   70

If I've killed one man, I've killed two——
The vampire who said he was you
And drank my blood for a year,
Seven years, if you want to know.
Daddy, you can lie back now.   75

There's a stake in your fat black heart
And the villagers never liked you.
They are dancing and stamping on you.
They always *knew* it was you.
Daddy, daddy, you bastard, I'm through.   80

[1962]

Lady Lazarus[1]

SYLVIA PLATH

I have done it again.
One year in every ten
I manage it—

A sort of walking miracle, my skin
Bright as a Nazi lampshade,   5
My right foot

A paperweight,
My face a featureless, fine
Jew linen.

Peel off the napkin   10
O my enemy.
Do I terrify?—

The nose, the eye pits, the full set of teeth?
The sour breath
Will vanish in a day.   15

Soon, soon the flesh
The grave cave ate will be
At home on me

And I a smiling woman.
I am only thirty.   20
And like the cat I have nine times to die.

---

[1]Lazarus was the friend of Jesus who died and was raised to life by him.

Reprinted from *Ariel,* by permission of HarperCollins Publishers, Inc. Copyright © 1963 by Ted Hughes.

This is Number Three.
What a trash
To annihilate each decade.

What a million filaments.   *25*
The peanut-crunching crowd
Shoves in to see

Them unwrap me hand and foot—
The big strip tease.
Gentlemen, ladies   *30*

These are my hands
My knees.
I may be skin and bone,

Nevertheless, I am the same, identical woman.
The first time it happened I was ten.   *35*
It was an accident.

The second time I meant
To last it out and not come back at all.
I rocked shut

As a seashell.   *40*
They had to call and call
And pick the worms off me like sticky pearls.

Dying
Is an art, like everything else.
I do it exceptionally well.   *45*

I do it so it feels like hell.
I do it so it feels real.
I guess you could say I've a call.

It's easy enough to do it in a cell.
It's easy enough to do it and stay put.   *50*
It's the theatrical

Comeback in broad day
to the same place, the same face, the same brute
Amused shout:

"A miracle!"   *55*
That knocks me out.
There is a charge

For the eyeing of my scars, there is a charge
For the hearing of my heart—
It really goes.   *60*

And there is a charge, a very large charge
For a word or a touch
Or a bit of blood

Or a piece of my hair or my clothes.
So, so, Herr Doktor.   *65*
So, Herr Enemy.

I am your opus,
I am your valuable,
The pure gold baby

That melts to a shriek.   *70*
I turn and burn.
Do not think I underestimate your great concern.

Ash, ash—
You poke and stir.
Flesh, bone, there is nothing there—   *75*

A cake of soap,
A wedding ring,
A gold filling.

Herr God, Herr Lucifer
Beware   *80*
Beware.

Out of the ash
I rise with my red hair
And I eat men like air.

[1962]

Metaphors

SYLVIA PLATH

I'm a riddle in nine syllables,
An elephant, a ponderous house,
A melon strolling on two tendrils.
O red fruit, ivory, fine timbers!
This loaf's big with its yeasty rising.   5
Money's new-minted in this fat purse.
I'm a means, a stage, a cow in calf.
I've eaten a bag of green apples,
Boarded the train there's no getting off.

[1960]

Reprinted from *Crossing the Water*, by permission of HarperCollins Publishers, Inc.
Copyright © 1960 by Ted Hughes.

Mirror

SYLVIA PLATH

I am silver and exact. I have no preconceptions.
Whatever I see I swallow immediately
Just as it is, unmisted by love or dislike.
I am not cruel, only truthful—
The eye of a little god, four-cornered.   5
Most of the time I meditate on the opposite wall.
It is pink, with speckles. I have looked at it so long
I think it is a part of my heart. But it flickers.
Faces and darkness separate us over and over.

Now I am a lake. A woman bends over me,   10
Searching my reaches for what she really is.
Then she turns to those liars, the candles or the moon.
I see her back, and reflect it faithfully.
She rewards me with tears and an agitation of hands.
I am important to her. She comes and goes.   15
Each morning it is her face that replaces the darkness.
In me she has drowned a young girl, and in me an old woman
Rises toward her day after day, like a terrible fish.

[1963]

Reprinted from *Crossing the Water,* by permission of HarperCollins Publishers, Inc.
Copyright © 1963 by Ted Hughes.

Morning Song

SYLVIA PLATH

Love set you going like a fat gold watch.
The midwife slapped your footsoles, and your bald cry
Took its place among the elements.

Our voices echo, magnifying your arrival. New statue.
In a drafty museum, your nakedness   5
Shadows our safety. We stand round blankly as walls.

I'm no more your mother
Than the cloud that distils a mirror to reflect its own slow
Effacement at the wind's hand.

All night your moth-breath   10
Flickers among the flat pink roses. I wake to listen:
A far sea moves in my ear.

One cry, and I stumble from bed, cow-heavy and floral
In my Victorian nightgown.   15
Your mouth opens clean as a cat's. The window square

Whitens and swallows its dull stars. And now you try
Your handful of notes;
The clear vowels rise like balloons.

[1961]

Reprinted from *Ariel,* by permission of HarperCollins Publishers, Inc. Copyright © 1961 by Ted Hughes.

Edgar Allan Poe
[1809–1849]

The son of traveling actors, **EDGAR ALLAN POE** was probably abandoned by his father shortly after his birth. In any case, his father died in 1810, and his mother continued to act, moving frequently with her children until 1811, when she too died, leaving Poe and his siblings destitute. Poe was adopted by the family of John and Frances Allan, and at his baptism assumed his benefactor's name. Despite this early gesture of connectedness, Poe's relationship with the Allans was fractious, especially after Poe began attending the University of Virginia in 1836. Here Poe was known both for his writing and also for his gambling and drinking. His repeated, abusive pleas for money caused John Allan to cut him off periodically. After one such incident Poe left the university and joined the army. During his service he published his first book of poetry, Tamerlane and Other Poems (1827). His second, Al Aaraaf, was published in 1829. In 1830, through Allan's influence, Poe was awarded an appointment to West Point, but he was soon expelled. Among cadets the legend still circulates that he forced this himself by showing up naked for morning formation, but it is more likely that drinking and gambling lay at the heart of the matter. In any event, this disgrace seems to have been fortuitous, because at this time Poe began to devote himself to writing, publishing several stories and winning a fiction contest in 1832.

In 1833 he became editor of the Southern Literary Messenger, one of several important literary posts he would fill in his life. In 1839 he became editor of Burton's Gentleman's Magazine; in 1840 editor of Graham's; and in 1845 editor of the Broadway Journal. He published a great deal of his own poetry and fiction in these journals, as well as numerous reviews (many of them quite strident), and in this way had a significant impact on literary trends and tastes. However, despite the fact that he continued to be awarded editorial positions, the same kind of behavior that resulted in his dismissal from West Point—drinking, gambling, and a disinclination to bow to authority—led him regularly into conflict with his employers. And although he published his work regularly, he was never far from poverty. He also had a tendency to pick literary fights, and was most famously dismissive of the New England transcendentalists. Some speculate that this kind of controversy may have been a ploy to sell magazines.

Although his writing career was relatively brief and his habits were self-destructive, Poe managed to amass an impressive canon before his death in 1849. In addition to such works as "Ligeia" (1838); "The Fall of the House of Usher" (1839); Tales of the Grotesque and Arabesque (1840); and the popular "The Raven" (1844); Poe is credited with the invention of the detective story. His character C. Auguste Dupin from "The Murders in the Rue Morgue"; "The Mystery *of Marie Roget"; and "The Purloined Letter" served as type for Sherlock Holmes and countless other detectives. In these and other stories Poe demonstrates an obsession with the dark side of human psychology. Many of his tales explore a concept he labeled "the spirit of perverseness . . . the unfathomable longing of the soul to vex itself." This phenomenon can be seen in stories such as "The Black Cat" and "The Tell-Tale Heart," in which seemingly rational characters are drawn to commit ghastly crimes for reasons they cannot explain. While his last years were clouded by the death of his wife from tuberculosis in 1846, he seemed on the road to recovery when, in 1849, he stopped in Baltimore on his way to Philadelphia and was found on the street four days later, unconscious and near death. The exact cause of his death on October 7 remains a mystery.*

—David L. G. Arnold, *University of Wisconsin, Stevens Point*

The Tell-Tale Heart

EDGAR ALLAN POE

TRUE!—NERVOUS—VERY, VERY dreadfully nervous I had been and am; but why *will* you say that I am mad? The disease had sharpened my senses—not destroyed—not dulled them. Above all was the sense of hearing acute. I heard all things in the heaven and in the earth. I heard many things in hell. How, then, am I mad? Hearken! and observe how healthily—how calmly I can tell you the whole story.

It is impossible to say how first the idea entered my brain; but once conceived, it haunted me day and night. Object there was none. Passion there was none. I loved the old man. He had never wronged me. He had never given me insult. For his gold I had no desire. I think it was his eye! yes, it was this! He had the eye of a vulture—a pale blue eye, with a film over it. Whenever it fell upon me, my blood ran cold; and so by degrees—very gradually—I made up my mind to take the life of the old man, and thus rid myself of the eye forever.

Now this is the point. You fancy me mad. Madmen know nothing. But you should have seen *me*. You should have seen how wisely I proceeded—with what caution—with what foresight—with what dissimulation[1] I went to work! I was never kinder to the old man than during the whole week before I killed him. And every night, about midnight, I turned the latch of his door and opened it—oh so gently! And then, when I had made an opening sufficient for my head, I put in a dark lantern,[2] all closed, closed, so that no light shone out, and then I thrust in my head. Oh, you would have laughed to see how cunningly I thrust it in! I moved it slowly—very, very slowly, so that I might not disturb the old man's sleep. It took me an hour to place my whole head within the opening so far that I could see him he lay upon his bed. Ha!—would a madman have been so wise as this? And then, when my head was well in the room, I undid the lantern cautiously—oh, so cautiously—cautiously (for the hinges creaked)—I undid it just so much that a single thin ray fell upon the vulture eye. And this I did for seven long nights—every night just at

---

[1]Deception

[2]A lantern with a sliding or perforated cover that limits the beam of light.

First published in *The Pioneer* in January, 1843.

midnight—but I found the eye always closed; and so it was impossible to do the work; for it was not the old man who vexed me, but his Evil Eye. And every morning, when the day broke, I went boldly into the chamber, and spoke courageously to him, calling him by name in a hearty tone and inquiring how he had passed the night. So you see he would have been a very profound old man, indeed, to suspect that every night, just at twelve, I looked in upon him while he slept.

Upon the eighth night I was more than usually cautious in opening the door. A watch's minute hand moves more quickly than did mine. Never, before that night, had I *felt* the extent of my own powers—of my sagacity. I could scarcely contain my feelings of triumph. To think that there I was, opening the door, little by little, and he not even to dream of my secret deeds or thoughts. I fairly chuckled at the idea; and perhaps he heard me; for he moved on the bed suddenly, as if startled. Now you may think that I drew back—but no. His room was as black as pitch with the thick darkness, (for the shutters were close fastened, through fear of robbers,) and so I knew that he could not see the opening of the door, and I kept pushing it on steadily, steadily.

I had my head in, and was about to open the lantern, when my thumb slipped upon the tin fastening, and the old man sprang up in bed, crying out—"Who's there?"

I kept quite still and said nothing. For a whole hour I did not move a muscle, and in the meantime I did not hear him lie down. He was still sitting up in the bed listening;—just as I have done, night after night, hearkening to the death watches[3] in the wall.

Presently I heard a slight groan, and I knew it was the groan of mortal terror. It was not a groan of pain or of grief—oh, no!—it was the low stifled sound that arises from the bottom of the soul when overcharged with awe. I knew the sound well. Many a night, just at midnight, when all the world slept, it had welled up from my own bosom, deepening, with its dreadful echo, the terrors that distracted me. I say I knew it well. I knew what the old man felt, and pitied him, although I chuckled at heart. I knew that he had been lying awake ever since the first slight noise, when he had turned in the bed. His fears had been ever since growing upon him. He had been trying to fancy them causeless, but could not. He had been saying to himself—"It is nothing but the wind in the chimney—it is only a mouse crossing the floor," or "it is merely a cricket which has made a single chirp." Yes, he had been trying to comfort himself with these suppositions: but he had found all in vain. *All in vain*; because Death, in approaching him, had stalked with his black shadow before him, and enveloped the victim. And it was the mournful influence of the perceived

---

[3]Small wood-beetles whose ticking noises were thought to predict a death.

shadow that caused him to feel—although he neither saw nor heard—to *feel* the presence of my head within the room.

When I had waited a long time, very patiently, without hearing him lie down, I resolved to open a little—a very, very little crevice in the lantern. So I opened it—you cannot imagine how stealthily, stealthily—until, at length, a single dim ray, like the thread of the spider, shot from out the crevice and fell full upon the vulture eye.

It was open—wide, wide open—and I grew furious as I gazed upon it. I saw it with perfect distinctness—all a dull blue, with a hideous veil over it that chilled the very marrow in my bones; but I could see nothing else of the old man's face or person: for I had directed the ray as if by instinct, precisely upon the damned spot.

And have I not told you that what you mistake for madness is but over acuteness of the senses?—now, I say, there came to my ears a low, dull quick sound, such as a watch makes when enveloped in cotton. I knew *that* sound well, too. It was the beating of the old man's heart. It increased my fury, as the beating of a drum stimulates the soldier into courage.

But even yet I refrained and kept still. I scarcely breathed. I held the lantern motionless. I tried how steadily I could maintain the ray upon the eye. Meantime the hellish tattoo[4] of the heart increased. It grew quicker and quicker, and louder and louder every instant. The old man's terror *must* have been extreme! It grew louder, I say, louder every moment!—do you mark me well? I have told you that I am nervous: so I am. And now at the dead hour of the night, amid the dreadful silence of that old house, so strange a noise as this excited me to uncontrollable terror. Yet, for some minutes longer I refrained and stood still. But the beating grew louder, louder! I thought the he heart must burst. And now a new anxiety seized me—the sound would be heard by a neighbour! The old man's hour had come! With a loud yell, I threw open the lantern and leaped into the room. He shrieked once—once only. In an instant I dragged him to the floor, and pulled the heavy bed[5] over him. I then smiled gaily, to find the deed so far done. But, for many minutes, the heart beat on with a muffled sound. This, however, did not vex me; it would not be heard through the wall. At length it ceased. The old man was dead. I removed the bed and examined the corpse. Yes, he was stone, stone dead. I placed my hand upon the heart and held it there many minutes. There was no pulsation. He was stone dead. His eye would trouble me no more.

If still you think me mad, you will think so no longer when I describe the wise precautions I took for the concealment of the body. The night waned,

---

[4]In this sense, a "tattoo" is a rhythmic beat.

[5]Down comforter sometimes used as a mattress.

and I worked hastily, but in silence. First of all I dismembered the corpse. I cut off the head and the arms and the legs.

I then took up three planks from the flooring of the chamber, and deposited all between the scantlings.[6] I then replaced the boards so cleverly, so cunningly, that no human eye—not even *his*—could have detected anything wrong. There was nothing to wash out—no stain of any kind—no blood-spot whatever. I had been too wary for that. A tub had caught all—ha! ha!

When I had made an end of these labors, it was four o'clock—still dark as midnight. As the bell sounded the hour, there came a knocking at the street door. I went down to open it with a light heart,—for what had I *now* to fear? There entered three men, who introduced themselves, with perfect suavity, as officers of the police. A shriek had been heard by a neighbour during the night; suspicion of foul play had been aroused; information had been lodged at the police office, and they (the officers) had been deputed to search the premises.

I smiled,—for *what* had I to fear? I bade the gentlemen welcome. The shriek, I said, was my own in a dream. The old man, I mentioned, was absent in the country. I took my visitors all over the house. I bade them search— search *well*. I led them, at length, to *his* chamber. I showed them his treasures, secure, undisturbed. In the enthusiasm of my confidence, I brought chairs into the room and desired them *here* to rest from their fatigues, while I myself, in the wild audacity of my perfect triumph, placed my own seat upon the very spot beneath which reposed the corpse of the victim.

The officers were satisfied. My *manner* had convinced them. I was singularly at ease. They sat, and while I answered cheerily, they chatted of familiar things. But, ere long, I felt myself getting pale and wished them gone. My head ached, and I fancied a ringing in my ears: but still they sat and still chatted. The ringing became more distinct:—it continued and became more distinct: I talked more freely to get rid of the feeling: but it continued and gained definiteness—until, at length, I found that the noise was *not* within my ears.

No doubt I now grew *very* pale;—but I talked more fluently, and with a heightened voice. Yet the sound increased—and what could I do? It was *a low, dull, quick sound—much such a sound as a watch makes when enveloped in cotton.* I gasped for breath—and yet the officers heard it not. I talked more quickly— more vehemently; but the noise steadily increased. I arose and argued about trifles, in a high key and with violent gesticulations; but the noise steadily increased. Why *would* they not be gone? I paced the floor to and fro with heavy strides, as if excited to fury by the observations of the men—but the noise steadily increased. Oh God! what *could* I do? I foamed—I raved—I swore! I

[6]Beams

swung the chair upon which I had been sitting, and grated it upon the boards, but the noise arose over all and continually increased. It grew louder—louder—*louder!* And still the men chatted pleasantly, and smiled. Was it possible they heard not? Almighty God!—no, no! They heard!—they suspected!—they *knew!*—they were making a mockery of my horror!—this I thought, and this I think. But anything was better than this agony! Anything was more tolerable than this derision! I could bear those hypocritical smiles no longer! I felt that I must scream or die! and now—again!—hark! louder! louder! louder! *louder!*

"Villains!" I shrieked, "dissemble no more! I admit the deed!—tear up the planks! here, here!—it is the beating of his hideous heart!"

[1843]

Edward Said
[1935–2003]

EDWARD SAID *has been described as one of the United States's few genuine "public intellectuals," a writer whose ideas and opinions resonate inside the academy, and in the world beyond. His writing draws connections between literary representations and cultural politics, between language and power. Said was born in Palestine and educated in Western schools in Jerusalem, Cairo, and the United States; he was throughout his life a highly active and public proponent of Palestinian rights and a respected commentator on Middle Eastern affairs. In his critical work, Said was interested in the tension between individual self-expression in writing and the larger cultural forces that attempt to regulate what the individual is able to say. In his most influential text,* Orientalism *(1978), he argues that two centuries of Western scholarship on and literary representations of the Orient—or the system of discourse that he refers to collectively as Orientalism— determined what can and cannot be known about the region by creating indelible and stereotypical preconceptions that have influenced all further writing. For Said, Orientalism is grounded in a cluster of principles: that the Orient is less rational, less developed, and less civilized than the West. Such discourse inevitably has imperial effects, but Orientalism, for Said, has been given birth and legitimacy not by politicians or military officials but by scholars, whose ostensible "objectivity" allowed such assumptions to become "fact." In* Orientalism, *Said calls attention to the inevitable conjunction of knowledge and power; he continues this project in subsequent books, including* The Question of Palestine *(1979),* Covering Islam *(1981), and* Culture and Imperialism *(1994).*

from *Orientalism*

EDWARD SAID

Knowing the Oriental

ON JUNE 13, 1910, Arthur James Balfour lectured the House of Commons on "the problems with which we have to deal in Egypt." These, he said, "belong to a wholly different category" than those "affecting the Isle of Wight or the West Riding of Yorkshire." He spoke with the authority of a long-time member of Parliament, former private secretary to Lord Salisbury, former chief secretary for Ireland, former secretary for Scotland, former prime minister, veteran of numerous overseas crises, achievements, and changes. During his involvement in imperial affairs Balfour served a monarch who in 1876 had been declared Empress of India; he had been especially well placed in positions of uncommon influence to follow the Afghan and Zulu wars, the British occupation of Egypt in 1882, the death of General Gordon in the Sudan, the Fashoda Incident, the battle of Omdurman, the Boer War, the Russo-Japanese War. In addition his remarkable social eminence, the breadth of his learning and wit—he could write on such varied subjects as Bergson, Handel, theism, and golf—his education at Eton and Trinity College, Cambridge, and his apparent command over imperial affairs all gave considerable authority to what he told the Commons in June 1910. But there was still more to Balfour's speech, or at least to his need for giving it so didactically and moralistically. Some members were questioning the necessity for "England in Egypt," the subject of Alfred Milner's enthusiastic book of 1892, but here designating a once-profitable occupation that had become a source of trouble now that Egyptian nationalism was on the rise and the continuing British presence in Egypt no longer so easy to defend. Balfour, then, to inform and explain.

Recalling the challenge of J. M. Robertson, the member of Tyneside, Balfour himself put Robertson's question again: "What right have you to take up these airs of superiority with regard to people whom you choose to call Oriental?" The choice of "Oriental" was canonical; it had been employed by Chaucer and Mandeville, by Shakespeare, Dryden, Pope, and Byron. It designated Asia or the East, geographically, morally, culturally. One could speak in Europe of an Oriental personality, an Oriental atmosphere, an Oriental tale,

Reprinted from *Orientalism* by permission of Pantheon Books, a division of Random House, Inc. Copyright © 1978 by Edward W. Said.

Oriental despotism, or an Oriental mode of production, and be understood. Marx had used the word, and now Balfour was using it; his choice was understandable and called for no comment whatever.

> I take up no attitude of superiority. But I ask [Robertson and anyone else] . . . who has even the most superficial knowledge of history, if they will look in the face the facts with which a British statesman has to deal when he is put in a position of supremacy over great races like the inhabitants of Egypt and countries in the East. We know the civilization of Egypt better than we know the civilization of any other country. We know it further back; we know it more intimately; we know more about it. It goes far beyond the petty span of the history of our race, which is lost in the prehistoric period at a time when the Egyptian civilisation had already passed its prime. Look at all the Oriental countries. Do not talk about superiority or inferiority.

Two great themes dominate his remarks here and in what will follow: knowledge and power, the Baconian themes.[1] As Balfour justifies the necessity for British occupation of Egypt, supremacy in his mind is associated with "our" knowledge of Egypt and not principally with military or economic power. Knowledge to Balfour means surveying a civilization from its origins to its prime to its decline—and of course, it means *being able to do that*. Knowledge means rising above immediacy, beyond self, into the foreign and distant. The object of such knowledge is inherently vulnerable to scrutiny; this object is a "fact" which, if it develops, changes, or otherwise transforms itself in the way that civilizations frequently do, nevertheless is fundamentally, even ontologically stable. To have such knowledge of such a thing is to dominate it, to have authority over it. And authority here means for "us" to deny autonomy to "it"—the Oriental country—since we know it and it exists, in a sense, *as* we know it. British knowledge of Egypt *is* Egypt for Balfour, and the burdens of knowledge make such questions as inferiority and superiority seem petty ones. Balfour nowhere denies British superiority and Egyptian inferiority; he takes them for granted as he describes the consequences of knowledge.

> First of all, look at the facts of the case. Western nations as soon as they emerge into history show the beginnings of those capacities for self-government . . . having merits of their own. . . . You may look through the whole history of the Orientals in what is called, broadly speaking, the East, and you never find traces of self-government. All their great centuries—and they have been very great—have been passed under despotisms, under absolute government. All their great contributions to civilisation—and they have been great—have been made under that form of government. Conqueror has succeeded conqueror; one domination has followed another;

---

[1]The reference is to Sir Francis Bacon (1561–1626), English philosopher and scientist, and originator of the expression "Knowledge is power." [Ed. note.]

436

but never in all the revolutions of fate and fortune have you seen one of those nations of its own motion establish what we, from a Western point of view, call self-government. That is the fact. It is not a question of superiority and inferiority. I suppose a true Eastern sage would say that the working government which we have taken upon ourselves in Egypt and elsewhere is not a work worthy of a philosopher—that it is the dirty work, the inferior work, of carrying on the necessary labour.

Since these facts are facts, Balfour must then go on to the next part of his argument.

Is it a good thing for these great nations—I admit their greatness—that this absolute government should be exercised by us? I think it is a good thing. I think that experience shows that they have got under it far better government than in the whole history of the world they ever had before, and which not only is a benefit to them, but is undoubtedly a benefit to the whole of the civilised West. . . . We are in Egypt not merely for the sake of the Egyptians, though we are there for their sake; we are there also for the sake of Europe at large.

Balfour produces no evidence that Egyptians and "the races with whom we deal" appreciate or even understand the good that is being done them by colonial occupation. It does not occur to Balfour, however, to let the Egyptian speak for himself, since presumably any Egyptian who would speak out is more likely to be "the agitator [who] wishes to raise difficulties" than the good native who overlooks the "difficulties" of foreign domination. And so, having settled the ethical problems, Balfour turns at last to the practical ones. "If it is our business to govern, with or without gratitude, with or without the real and genuine memory of all the loss of which we have relieved the population [Balfour by no means implies, as part of that loss, the loss or at least the indefinite postponement of Egyptian independence] and no vivid imagination of all the benefits which we have given to them; if that is our duty, how is it to be performed?" England exports "our very best to these countries." These selfless administrators do their work "amidst tens of thousands of persons belonging to a different creed, a different race, a different discipline, different conditions of life." What makes their work of governing possible is their sense of being supported at home by a government that endorses what they do. Yet

directly the native populations have that instinctive feeling that those with whom they have got to deal have not behind them the might, the authority, the sympathy, the full and ungrudging support of the country which sent them there, those populations lose all that sense of order which is the very basis of their civilisation, just as our officers lose all that sense of power and authority, which is the very basis of everything they can do for the benefit of those among whom they have been sent.

Balfour's logic here is interesting, not least for being completely consistent with the premises of his entire speech. England knows Egypt; Egypt is what England knows; England knows that Egypt cannot have self-government; England confirms that by occupying Egypt; for the Egyptians, Egypt is what England has occupied and now governs; foreign occupation therefore becomes "the very basis" of contemporary Egyptian civilization; Egypt requires, indeed insists upon, British occupation. But if the special intimacy between governor and governed in Egypt is disturbed by Parliament's doubts at home, then "the authority of what . . . is the dominant race—and as I think ought to remain the dominant race—has been undermined." Not only does English prestige suffer; "it is vain for a handful of British officials—endow them how you like, give them all the qualities of character and genius you can imagine—it is impossible for them to carry out the great task which in Egypt, not we only, but the civilised world have imposed upon them."[2]

As a rhetorical performance Balfour's speech is significant for the way in which he plays the part of, and represents, a variety of characters. There are of course "the English," for whom the pronoun "we" is used with the full weight of a distinguished, powerful man who feels himself to be representative of all that is best in his nation's history. Balfour can also speak for the civilized world, the West, and the relatively small corps of colonial officials in Egypt. If he does not speak directly for the Orientals, it is because they after all speak another language; yet he knows how they feel since he knows their history, their reliance upon such as he, and their expectations. Still, he does speak for them in the sense that what they might have to say, were they to be asked and might they be able to answer, would somewhat uselessly confirm what is already evident: that they are a subject race, dominated by a race that knows them and what is good for them better than they could possibly know themselves. Their great moments were in the past; they are useful in the modern world only because the powerful and up-to-date empires have effectively brought them out of the wretchedness of their decline and turned them into rehabilitated residents of productive colonies.

Egypt in particular was an excellent case in point, and Balfour was perfectly aware of how much right he had to speak as a member of his country's parliament on behalf of England, the West, Western civilization, about modern Egypt. For Egypt was not just another colony: it was the vindication of

---

[2]This and the preceding quotations from Arthur James Balfour's speech to the House of Commons are from Great Britain, *Parliamentary Debates* (Commons), 5th ser., 17 (1910): 1140–46. See also A. P. Thornton, *The Imperial Idea and Its Enemies: A Study in British Power* (London: MacMillan & Co., 1959), pp. 357–60. Balfour's speech was a defense of Eldon Gorst's policy in Egypt; for a discussion of that see Peter John Dreyfus Mellini, "Sir Eldon Gorst and British Imperial Policy in Egypt," unpublished Ph.D. dissertation, Stanford University, 1971.

Western imperialism; it was, until its annexation by England, an almost academic example of Oriental backwardness; it was to become the triumph of English knowledge and power. Between 1882, the year in which England occupied Egypt and put an end to the nationalist rebellion of Colonel Arabi, and 1907, England's representative in Egypt, Egypt's master, was Evelyn Baring (also known as "Over-baring"), Lord Cromer. On July 30, 1907, it was Balfour in the Commons who had supported the project to give Cromer a retirement prize of fifty thousand pounds as a reward for what he had done in Egypt. Cromer *made* Egypt, said Balfour:

> Everything he has touched he has succeeded in.... Lord Cromer's services during the past quarter of a century have raised Egypt from the lowest pitch of social and economic degradation until it now stands among Oriental nations, I believe, absolutely alone in its prosperity, financial and moral.[3]

How Egypt's moral prosperity was measured, Balfour did not venture to say. British exports to Egypt equaled those to the whole of Africa; that certainly indicated a sort of financial prosperity, for Egypt and England (somewhat unevenly) together. But what really mattered was the unbroken, all-embracing Western tutelage of an Oriental country, from the scholars, missionaries, businessmen, soldiers, and teachers who prepared and then implemented the occupation to the high functionaries like Cromer and Balfour who saw themselves as providing for, directing, and sometimes even forcing Egypt's rise from Oriental neglect to its present lonely eminence.

If British success in Egypt was as exceptional as Balfour said, it was by no means an inexplicable or irrational success. Egyptian affairs had been controlled according to a general theory expressed both by Balfour in his notions about Oriental civilization and by Cromer in his management of everyday business in Egypt. The most important thing about the theory during the first decade of the twentieth century was that it worked, and worked staggeringly well. The argument, when reduced to its simplest form, was clear, it was precise, it was easy to grasp. There are Westerners, and there are Orientals. The former dominate; the latter must be dominated, which usually means having their land occupied, their internal affairs rigidly controlled, their blood and treasure put at the disposal of one or another Western power. That Balfour and Cromer, as we shall soon see, could strip humanity down to such ruthless cultural and racial essences was not at all an indication of their particular

---

[3]Denis Judd, *Balfour and the British Empire: A Study in Imperial Evolution*, 1874–1932 (London: MacMillan & Co., 1968), p. 286. See also p. 292: as late as 1926 Balfour spoke—without irony—of Egypt as an "independent nation."

viciousness. Rather it was an indication of how streamlined a general doctrine had become by the time they put it to use—how streamlined and effective.

Unlike Balfour, whose theses on Orientals pretended to objective universality, Cromer spoke about Orientals specifically as what he had ruled or had to deal with, first in India, then for the twenty-five years in Egypt during which he emerged as the paramount consul-general in England's empire. Balfour's "Orientals" are Cromer's "subject races," which he made the topic of a long essay published in the *Edinburgh Review* in January 1908. Once again, knowledge of subject races or Orientals is what makes their management easy and profitable; knowledge gives power, more power requires more knowledge, and so on in an increasingly profitable dialectic of information and control. Cromer's notion is that England's empire will not dissolve if such things as militarism and commercial egotism at home and "free institutions" in the colony (as opposed to British government "according to the Code of Christian morality") are kept in check. For if, according to Cromer, logic is something "the existence of which the Oriental is disposed altogether to ignore," the proper method of ruling is not to impose ultrascientific measures upon him or to force him bodily to accept logic. It is rather to understand his limitations and "endeavor to find, in the contentment of the subject race, a more worthy and, it may be hoped, a stronger bond of union between the rulers and the ruled." Lurking everywhere behind the pacification of the subject race is imperial might, more effective for its refined understanding and infrequent use than for its soldiers, brutal tax gatherers, and incontinent force. In a word, the Empire must be wise; it must temper its cupidity with selflessness, and its impatience with flexible discipline.

To be more explicit, what is meant when it is said that the commercial spirit should be under some control is this—that in dealing with Indians or Egyptians, or Shilluks, or Zulus, the first question is to consider what these people, who are all, nationally speaking, more or less *in statu pupillari*, themselves think is best in their own interests, although this is a point which deserves serious consideration. But it is essential that each special issue should be decided mainly with reference to what, by the light of Western knowledge and experience tempered by local considerations, we conscientiously think is best for the subject race, without reference to any real or supposed advantage which may accrue to England as a nation, or—as is more frequently the case—to the special interests represented by some one or more influential classes of Englishmen. If the British nation as a whole persistently bears this principle in mind, and insists sternly on its application, though we can never create a patriotism akin to that based on affinity of race or community of language, we may perhaps foster some sort of cosmopolitan allegiance grounded on the respect always accorded to superior talents and unselfish conduct, and on the gratitude derived both from favours conferred and from those to come. There may then at all events be some hope that the Egyptian will hesitate before he throws in his lot with any future Arabi. . . . Even the Central African savage may eventually learn to chant a hymn in honour of Astraea Redux, as represented by the British official who denies him gin but gives him justice. More than this, commerce will gain.[4]

How much "serious consideration" the ruler ought to give proposals from the subject race was illustrated in Cromer's total opposition to Egyptian nationalism. Free native institutions, the absence of foreign occupation, a self-sustaining national sovereignty: these unsurprising demands were consistently rejected by Cromer, who asserted unambiguously that "the real future of Egypt . . . lies not in the direction of a narrow nationalism, which will only embrace native Egyptians . . . but rather in that of an enlarged cosmopolitanism."[5] Subject races did not have it in them to know what was good for them. Most of them were Orientals, of whose characteristics Cromer was very knowledgeable since he had had experience with them both in India and Egypt. One of the convenient things about Orientals for Cromer was that managing them, although circumstances might differ slightly here and there, was almost everywhere nearly the same.[6] This was, of course, because Orientals were almost everywhere nearly the same.

Now at last we approach the long-developing core of essential knowledge, knowledge both academic and practical, which Cromer and Balfour inherited from a century of modern Western Orientalism: knowledge about and knowledge of Orientals, their race, character, culture, history, traditions, society, and possibilities. This knowledge was effective: Cromer believed he had put it to use in governing Egypt. Moreover, it was tested and unchanging knowledge, since "Orientals" for all practical purposes were a Platonic essence, which any Orientalist (or ruler of Orientals) might examine, understand, and expose. Thus in the thirty-fourth chapter of his two-volume work *Modern Egypt*, the magisterial record of his experience and achievement, Cromer puts down a sort of personal canon of Orientalist wisdom:

> Sir Alfred Lyall once said to me: "Accuracy is abhorrent to the Oriental mind. Every Anglo-Indian should always remember that maxim." Want of accuracy, which easily degenerates into untruthfulness, is in fact the main characteristic of the Oriental mind.

---

[4]Evelyn Baring, Lord Cromer, *Political and Literary Essays*, 1908–1913 (1913; reprint ed., Freeport, N. Y.: Books for Libraries Press, 1969), pp. 40, 53, 12–14.

[5]Ibid., p. 171.

[6]Roger Owen, "The Influence of Lord Cromer's Indian Experience on British Policy in Egypt 1883–1907," in *Middle Eastern Affairs, Number Four: St. Antony's Papers Number 17*, ed. Albert Hourani (London: Oxford University Press, 1965), pp. 109–39.

The European is a close reasoner; his statements of fact are devoid of any ambiguity; he is a natural logician, albeit he may not have studied logic; he is by nature sceptical and requires proof before he can accept the truth of any proposition; his trained intelligence works like a piece of mechanism. The mind of the Oriental, on the other hand, like his picturesque streets, is eminently wanting in symmetry. His reasoning is of the most slipshod description. Although the ancient Arabs acquired in a somewhat higher degree the science of dialectics, their descendants are singularly deficient in the logical faculty. They are often incapable of drawing the most obvious conclusions from any simple premises of which they may admit the truth. Endeavor to elicit a plain statement of facts from any ordinary Egyptian. His explanation will generally be lengthy, and wanting in lucidity. He will probably contradict himself half-a-dozen times before he has finished his story. He will often break down under the mildest process of cross-examination.

Orientals or Arabs are thereafter shown to be gullible, "devoid of energy and initiative," much given to "fulsome flattery," intrigue, cunning, and unkindness to animals; Orientals cannot walk on either a road or a pavement (their disordered minds fail to understand what the clever European grasps immediately, that roads and pavements are made for walking); Orientals are inveterate liars, they are "lethargic and suspicious," and in everything oppose the clarity, directness, and nobility of the Anglo-Saxon race.[7]

Cromer makes no effort to conceal that Orientals for him were always and only the human material he governed in British colonies. "As I am only a diplomatist and an administrator, whose proper study is also man, but from the point of view of governing him," Cromer says, ". . . I content myself with noting the fact that somehow or other the Oriental generally acts, speaks, and thinks in a manner exactly opposite to the European."[8] Cromer's descriptions are of course based partly on direct observation, yet here and there he refers to orthodox Orientalist authorities (in particular Ernest Renan and Constantin de Volney[9]) to support his views. To these authorities he also defers when it comes to explaining why Orientals are the way they are. He has no doubt that *any* knowledge of the Oriental will confirm his views, which, to judge from his description of the Egyptian breaking under cross-examination,

---

[7]Evelyn Baring, Lord Cromer, *Modern Egypt* (New York: Macmillan Co., 1908), 2: 146–67. For a British view of British policy in Egypt that runs totally counter to Cromer's, see Wilfrid Scawen Blunt, *Secret History of the English Occupation of Egypt: Being a Personal Narrative of Events* (New York: Alfred A. Knopf, 1922). There is a valuable discussion of Egyptian opposition to British rule in Mounah A. Khouri, *Poetry and the Making of Modern Egypt, 1882–1922* (Leiden: E. J. Brill, 1971).

[8]Cromer, *Modern Egypt*, 2: 164.

[9]Ernest Renan (1823–1892), French philosopher and scholar of the Hebrew language and culture; Constantin de Volney (1757–1820), French scholar and author of *Voyage en Syrie at en Egypte* (1787). [Ed. note.]

find the Oriental to be guilty. The crime was that the Oriental was an Oriental, and it is an accurate sign of how commonly acceptable such a tautology was that it could be written without even an appeal to European logic or symmetry of mind. Thus any deviation from what were considered the norms of Oriental behavior was believed to be unnatural; Cromer's last annual report from Egypt consequently proclaimed Egyptian nationalism to be an "entirely novel idea" and "a plant of exotic rather than of indigenous growth."[10]

We would be wrong, I think, to underestimate the reservoir of accredited knowledge, the codes of Orientalist orthodoxy, to which Cromer and Balfour refer everywhere in their writing and in their public policy. To say simply that Orientalism was a rationalization of colonial rule is to ignore the extent to which colonial rule was justified in advance by Orientalism, rather than after the fact. Men have always divided the world up into regions having either real or imagined distinction from each other. The absolute demarcation between East and West, which Balfour and Cromer accept with such complacency, had been years, even centuries, in the making. There were of course innumerable voyages of discovery; there were contacts through trade and war. But more than this, since the middle of the eighteenth century there had been two principal elements in the relation between East and West. One was a growing systematic knowledge in Europe about the Orient, knowledge reinforced by the colonial encounter as well as by the widespread interest in the alien and unusual, exploited by the developing sciences of ethnology, comparative anatomy, philology, and history; furthermore, to this systematic knowledge was added a sizable body of literature produced by novelists, poets, translators, and gifted travelers. The other feature of Oriental-European relations was that Europe was always in a position of strength, not to say domination. There is no way of putting this euphemistically. True, the relationship of strong to weak could be disguised or mitigated, as when Balfour acknowledged the "greatness" of Oriental civilizations. But the essential relationship, on political, cultural, and even religious grounds, was seen—in the West, which is what concerns us here—to be one between a strong and a weak partner.

Many terms were used to express the relation: Balfour and Cromer, typically, used several. The Oriental is irrational, depraved (fallen), childlike, "different"; thus the European is rational, virtuous, mature, "normal." But the way of enlivening the relationship was everywhere to stress the fact that the Oriental lived in a different but thoroughly organized world of his own, a world with its own national, cultural, and epistemological boundaries and principles of internal coherence. Yet what gave the Oriental's world its intelligibility and identity was not the result of his own efforts but rather the whole

---

[10]Cited in John Marlowe, *Cromer in Egypt* (London: Elek Books, 1970), p. 271.

complex series of knowledgeable manipulations by which the Orient was identified by the West. Thus the two features of cultural relationship I have been discussing come together. Knowledge of the Orient, because generated out of strength, in a sense *creates* the Orient, the Oriental, and his world. In Cromer's and Balfour's language the Oriental is depicted as something one judges (as in a court of law), something one studies and depicts (as in a curriculum), something one disciplines (as in a school or prison), something one illustrates (as in a zoological manual). The point is that in each of these cases the Oriental is *contained* and *represented* by dominating frameworks. Where do these come from?

Cultural strength is not something we can discuss very easily—and one of the purposes of the present work is to illustrate, analyze, and reflect upon Orientalism as an exercise of cultural strength. In other words, it is better not to risk generalizations about so vague and yet so important a notion as cultural strength until a good deal of material has been analyzed first. But at the outset one can say that so far as the West was concerned during the nineteenth and twentieth centuries, an assumption had been made that the Orient and everything in it was, if not patently inferior to, then in need of corrective study by the West. The Orient was viewed as if framed by the classroom, the criminal court, the prison, the illustrated manual. Orientalism, then, is knowledge of the Orient that places things Oriental in class, court, prison, or manual for scrutiny, study, judgment, discipline, or governing.

During the early years of the twentieth century, men like Balfour and Cromer could say what they said, in the way they did, because a still earlier tradition of Orientalism than the nineteenth-century one provided them with a vocabulary, imagery, rhetoric, and figures with which to say it. Yet Orientalism reinforced, and was reinforced by, the certain knowledge that Europe or the West literally commanded the vastly greater part of the earth's surface. The period of immense advance in the institutions and content of Orientalism coincides exactly with the period of unparalleled European expansion; from 1815 to 1914 European direct colonial dominion expanded from about 35 percent of the earth's surface to about 85 percent of it.[11] Every continent was affected, none more so than Africa and Asia. The two greatest empires were the British and the French; allies and partners in some things, in others they were hostile rivals. In the Orient, from the eastern shores of the Mediterranean to Indochina and Malaya, their colonial possessions and imperial spheres of influence were adjacent, frequently overlapped, often were fought over. But it was in

---

[11]Harry Magdoff, "Colonialism (1763–c. 1970)," *Encyclopaedia Britannica*, 15th ed. (1974), pp. 893–4. See also D. K. Fieldhouse, *The Colonial Empires: A Comparative Survey from the Eighteenth Century* (New York: Delacorte Press, 1967), p. 178.

the Near Orient, the lands of the Arab Near East, where Islam was supposed to define cultural and racial characteristics, that the British and the French encountered each other and "the Orient" with the greatest intensity, familiarity, and complexity. For much of the nineteenth century, as Lord Salisbury put it in 1881, their common view of the Orient was intricately problematic: "When you have got a . . . faithful ally who is bent on meddling in a country in which you are deeply interested—you have three courses open to you. You may renounce—or monopolize—or share. Renouncing would have been to place the French across our road to India. Monopolizing would have been very near the risk of war. So we resolved to share."[12]

And share they did, in ways that we shall investigate presently. What they shared, however, was not only land or profit or rule; it was the kind of intellectual power I have been calling Orientalism. In a sense Orientalism was a library or archive of information commonly and, in some of its aspects, unanimously held. What bound the archive together was a family of ideas[13] and a unifying set of values proven in various ways to be effective. These ideas explained the behavior of Orientals; they supplied Orientals with a mentality, a genealogy, an atmosphere; most important, they allowed Europeans to deal with and even to see Orientals as a phenomenon possessing regular characteristics. But like any set of durable ideas, Orientalist notions influenced the people who were called Orientals as well as those called Occidental, European, or Western; in short, Orientalism is better grasped as a set of constraints upon and limitations of thought than it is simply as a positive doctrine. If the essence of Orientalism is the ineradicable distinction between Western superiority and Oriental inferiority, then we must be prepared to note how in its development and subsequent history Orientalism deepened and even hardened the distinction. When it became common practice during the nineteenth century for Britain to retire its administrators from India and elsewhere once they had reached the age of fifty-five, then a further refinement in Orientalism had been achieved; no Oriental was ever allowed to see a Westerner as he aged and degenerated, just as no Westerner needed ever to see himself, mirrored in the eyes of the subject race, as anything but a vigorous, rational, ever-alert young Raj.[14]

---

[12]Quoted in Afaf Lutfi al-Sayyid, *Egypt and Cromer: A Study in Anglo-Egyptian Relations* (New York: Frederick A. Praeger, 1969), p. 3.

[13]The phrase is to be found in Ian Hacking, *The Emergence of Probability: A Philosophical Study of Early Ideas About Probability, Induction and Statistical Inference* (London: Cambridge University Press, 1975), p. 17.

[14]V. G. Kiernan, *The Lords of Human Kind: Black Man, Yellow Man, and White Man in an Age of Empire* (Boston: Little, Brown & Co., 1969), p. 55.

Orientalist ideas took a number of different forms during the nineteenth and twentieth centuries. First of all, in Europe there was a vast literature about the Orient inherited from the European past. What is distinctive about the late eighteenth and early nineteenth centuries, which is where this study assumes modern Orientalism to have begun, is that an Oriental renaissance took place, as Edgar Quinet phrased it.[15] Suddenly it seemed to a wide variety of thinkers, politicians, and artists that a new awareness of the Orient, which extended from China to the Mediterranean, had arisen. This awareness was partly the result of newly discovered and translated Oriental texts in languages like Sanskrit, Zend, and Arabic; it was also the result of a newly perceived relationship between the Orient and the West. For my purposes here, the keynote of the relationship was set for the Near East and Europe by the Napoleonic invasion of Egypt in 1798, an invasion which was in many ways the very model of a truly scientific appropriation of one culture by another, apparently stronger one. For with Napoleon's occupation of Egypt processes were set in motion between East and West that still dominate our contemporary cultural and political perspectives. And the Napoleonic expedition, with its great collective monument of erudition, the *Description de l'Egypte*, provided a scene or setting for Orientalism, since Egypt and subsequently the other Islamic lands were viewed as the live province, the laboratory, the theater of effective Western knowledge about the Orient. I shall return to the Napoleonic adventure a little later.

With such experiences as Napoleon's the Orient as a body of knowledge in the West was modernized, and this is a second form in which nineteenth- and twentieth-century Orientalism existed. From the outset of the period I shall be examining there was everywhere amongst Orientalists the ambition to formulate their discoveries, experiences, and insights suitably in modern terms, to put ideas about the Orient in very close touch with modern realities. Renan's linguistic investigations of Semitic in 1848, for example, were couched in a style that drew heavily for its authority upon contemporary comparative grammar, comparative anatomy, and racial theory; these lent his Orientalism prestige and—the other side of the coin—made Orientalism vulnerable, as it has been ever since, to modish as well as seriously influential currents of thought in the West. Orientalism has been subjected to imperialism, positivism, utopianism, historicism, Darwinism, racism, Freudianism, Marxism, Spenglerism. But Orientalism, like many of the natural and social sciences, has had "paradigms" of research, its own learned societies, its own Establishment. During the nineteenth century the field increased enormously in prestige, as did also the reputation and influence of

---

[15]Edgar Quinet, *Le Génie des religions*, in *Oeuvres complètes* (Paris: Paguerre, 1857), pp. 55–74.

such institutions as the Société asiatique,[16] the Royal Asiatic Society, the Deutsche Morgenländische Gesellschaft,[17] and the American Oriental Society. With the growth of these societies went also an increase, all across Europe, in the number of professorships in Oriental studies; consequently there was an expansion in the available means for disseminating Orientalism. Orientalist periodicals, beginning with the *Fundgraben des Orients* (1809),[18] multiplied the quantity of knowledge as well as the number of specialties.

Yet little of this activity and very few of these institutions existed and flourished freely, for in a third form in which it existed, Orientalism imposed limits upon thought about the Orient. Even the most imaginative writers of an age, men like Flaubert, Nerval, or Scott,[19] were constrained in what they could either experience of or say about the Orient. For Orientalism was ultimately a political vision of reality whose structure promoted the difference between the familiar (Europe, the West, "us") and the strange (the Orient, the East, "them"). This vision in a sense created and then served the two worlds thus conceived. Orientals lived in their world, "we" lived in ours. The vision and material reality propped each other up, kept each other going. A certain freedom of intercourse was always the Westerner's privilege; because his was the stronger culture, he could penetrate, he could wrestle with, he could give shape and meaning to the great Asiatic mystery, as Disraeli[20] once called it. Yet what has, I think, been previously overlooked is the constricted vocabulary of such a privilege, and the comparative limitations of such a vision. My argument takes it that the Orientalist reality is both antihuman and persistent. Its scope, as much as its institutions and all-pervasive influence, lasts up to the present.

But how did and does Orientalism work? How can one describe it all together as a historical phenomenon, a way of thought, a contemporary problem, and a material reality? Consider Cromer again, an accomplished technician of empire but also a beneficiary of Orientalism. He can furnish us with a rudimentary answer. In "The Government of Subject Races" he wrestles with the problem of how Britain, a nation of individuals, is to administer a wide-flung empire according to a number of central principles. He contrasts the

---

[16]French: Asiatic Society. [Ed. note.]

[17]German: German Oriental Society. [Ed. note.]

[18]The periodical's title is actually *Fundgruben des Orients*, or *Storehouses of the Orient*, founded by German Orientalist scholar Joseph von Hammer-Purgstall. [Ed. note.]

[19]Gustave Flaubert (1821–1880), French novelist; Gérard de Nerval (1808–1855), French poet; Sir Walter Scott (1771–1832), Scottish novelist and poet.

[20]Benjamin Disraeli (1804–1881), British novelist and Prime Minister of England.

"local agent," who has both a specialist's knowledge of the native and an Anglo-Saxon individuality, with the central authority at home in London. The former may "treat subjects of local interest in a manner calculated to damage, or even to jeopardize, Imperial interests. The central authority is in a position to obviate any danger arising from this cause." Why? Because this authority can "ensure the harmonious working of the different parts of the machine" and "should endeavour, so far as is possible, to realise the circumstances attendant on the government of the dependency."[21] The language is vague and unattractive, but the point is not hard to grasp. Cromer envisions a seat of power in the West, and radiating out from it towards the East a great embracing machine, sustaining the central authority yet commanded by it. What the machine's branches feed into it in the East—human material, material wealth, knowledge, what have you—is processed by the machine, then converted into more power. The specialist does the immediate translation of mere Oriental matter into useful substance: the Oriental becomes, for example, a subject race, an example of an "Oriental" mentality, all for the enhancement of the "authority" at home. "Local interests" are Orientalist special interests, the "central authority" is the general interest of the imperial society as a whole. What Cromer quite accurately sees is the management of knowledge by society, the fact that knowledge—no matter how special—is regulated first by the local concerns of a specialist, later by the general concerns of a social system of authority. The interplay between local and central interests is intricate, but by no means indiscriminate.

In Cromer's own case as an imperial administrator the "proper study is also man," he says. When Pope[22] proclaimed the proper study of mankind to be man, he meant all men, including "the poor Indian"; whereas Cromer's "also" reminds us that certain men, such as Orientals, can be singled out as the subject for *proper* study. The proper study—in this sense—of Orientals is Orientalism, properly separate from other forms of knowledge, but finally useful (because finite) for the material and social reality enclosing all knowledge at any time, supporting knowledge, providing it with uses. An order of sovereignty is set up from East to West, a mock chain of being whose clearest form was given once by Kipling:[23]

Mule, horse, elephant, or bullock, he obeys his driver, and the driver his sergeant, and the sergeant his lieutenant, and the lieutenant his captain, and the captain his

---

[21]Cromer, *Political and Literary Essays*, p. 35.

[22]Alexander Pope (1688–1744), English poet; the quote is from his *Essay on Man* (1733).

[23]Rudyard Kipling (1865–1936), English novelist and poet, primarily remembered for his glorification of the British Empire. The quote is from his *The Jungle Book* (1894).

major, and the major his colonel, and the colonel his brigadier commanding three regiments, and the brigadier his general, who obeys the Viceroy, who is the servant of the Empress.[24]

As deeply forged as is this monstrous chain of command, as strongly managed as is Cromer's "harmonious working," Orientalism can also express the strength of the West and the Orient's weakness—as seen by the West. Such strength and such weakness are as intrinsic to Orientalism as they are to any view that divides the world into large general divisions, entities that coexist in a state of tension produced by what is believed to be radical difference.

For that is the main intellectual issue raised by Orientalism. Can one divide human reality, as indeed human reality seems to be genuinely divided, into clearly different cultures, histories, traditions, societies, even races, and survive the consequences humanly? By surviving the consequences humanly, I mean to ask whether there is any way of avoiding the hostility expressed by the division, say, of men into "us" (Westerners) and "they" (Orientals). For such divisions are generalities whose use historically and actually has been to press the importance of the distinction between some men and some other men, usually towards not especially admirable ends. When one uses categories like Oriental and Western as both the starting and the end points of analysis, research, public policy (as the categories were used by Balfour and Cromer), the result is usually to polarize the distinction—the Oriental becomes more Oriental, the Westerner more Western—and limit the human encounter between different cultures, traditions, and societies. In short, from its earliest modern history to the present, Orientalism as a form of thought for dealing with the foreign has typically shown the altogether regrettable tendency of any knowledge based on such hard-and-fast distinctions as "East" and "West": to channel thought into a West or an East compartment. Because this tendency is right at the center of Orientalist theory, practice, and values found in the West, the sense of Western power over the Orient is taken for granted as having the status of scientific truth.

A contemporary illustration or two should clarify this observation perfectly. It is natural for men in power to survey from time to time the world with which they must deal. Balfour did it frequently. Our contemporary Henry Kissinger[25] does it also, rarely with more express frankness than in his essay "Domestic Structure and Foreign Policy." The drama he depicts is a real one, in which the United States must manage its behavior in the world under

---

[24]See Jonah Raskin, *The Mythology of Imperialism* (New York: Random House, 1971), p. 40.

[25]Henry Kissinger (1923–), Secretary of State of the United States, 1973–1977; Assitant to the President for National Security Affairs, 1969–1975; winner of the Nobel Peace Prize, 1973.

the pressures of domestic forces on the one hand and of foreign realities on the other. Kissinger's discourse must for that reason alone establish a polarity between the United States and the world; in addition, of course, he speaks consciously as an authoritative voice for the major Western power, whose recent history and present reality have placed it before a world that does not easily accept its power and dominance. Kissinger feels that the United States can deal less problematically with the industrial, developed West than it can with the developing world. Again, the contemporary actuality of relations between the United States and the so-called Third World (which includes China, Indochina, the Near East, Africa, and Latin America) is manifestly a thorny set of problems, which even Kissinger cannot hide.

Kissinger's method in the essay proceeds according to what linguists call binary opposition: that is, he shows that there are two styles in foreign policy (the prophetic and the political), two types of technique, two periods, and so forth. When at the end of the historical part of his argument he is brought face to face with the contemporary world, he divides it accordingly into two halves, the developed and the developing countries. The first half, which is the West, "is deeply committed to the notion that the real world is external to the observer, that knowledge consists of recording and classifying data—the more accurately the better." Kissinger's proof for this is the Newtonian revolution, which has not taken place in the developing world: "Cultures which escaped the early impact of Newtonian thinking have retained the essentially pre-Newtonian view that the real world is almost completely *internal* to the observer." Consequently, he adds, "empirical reality has a much different significance for many of the new countries than for the West because in a certain sense they never went through the process of discovering it."[26]

Unlike Cromer, Kissinger does not need to quote Sir Alfred Lyall on the Oriental's inability to be accurate; the point he makes is sufficiently unarguable to require no special validation. We had our Newtonian revolution; they didn't. As thinkers we are better off than they are. Good: the lines are drawn in much the same way, finally, as Balfour and Cromer drew them. Yet sixty or more years have intervened between Kissinger and the British imperialists. Numerous wars and revolutions have proved conclusively that the pre-Newtonian prophetic style, which Kissinger associates both with "inaccurate" developing countries and with Europe before the Congress of Vienna, is not entirely without its successes. Again unlike Balfour and Cromer, Kissinger therefore feels obliged to respect this pre-Newtonian perspective, since "it offers great flexibility with respect to the contemporary revolutionary turmoil."

---

[26]Henry A. Kissinger, *American Foreign Policy* (New York: W. W. Norton & Co., 1974), pp. 48–9.

Thus the duty of men in the post-Newtonian (real) world is to "construct an international order *before* a crisis imposes it as a necessity": in other words, *we* must still find a way by which the developing world can be contained. Is this not similar to Cromer's vision of a harmoniously working machine designed ultimately to benefit some central authority, which opposes the developing world?

Kissinger may not have known on what fund of pedigreed knowledge he was drawing when he cut the world up into pre-Newtonian and post-Newtonian conceptions of reality. But his distinction is identical with the orthodox one made by Orientalists, who separate Orientals from Westerners. And like Orientalism's distinction Kissinger's is not value-free, despite the apparent neutrality of his tone. Thus such words as "prophetic," "accuracy," "internal," "empirical reality," and "order" are scattered throughout his description, and they characterize either attractive, familiar, desirable virtues or menacing, peculiar, disorderly defects. Both the traditional Orientalist, as we shall see, and Kissinger conceive of the difference between cultures, first, as creating a battlefront that separates them, and second, as inviting the West to control, contain, and otherwise govern (through superior knowledge and accommodating power) the Other. With what effect and at what considerable expense such militant divisions have been maintained, no one at present needs to be reminded.

Another illustration dovetails neatly—perhaps too neatly—with Kissinger's analysis. In its February 1972 issue, the *American Journal of Psychiatry* printed an essay by Harold W. Glidden, who is identified as a retired member of the Bureau of Intelligence and Research, United States Department of State; the essay's title ("The Arab World"), its tone, and its content argue a highly characteristic Orientalist bent of mind. Thus for his four-page, double-columned psychological portrait of over 100 million people, considered for a period of 1,300 years, Glidden cites exactly four sources for his views: a recent book on Tripoli, one issue of the Egyptian newspaper *Al-Ahram*, the periodical *Oriente Moderno*, and a book by Majid Khadduri, a well-known Orientalist. The article itself purports to uncover "the inner workings of Arab behavior," which from *our* point of view is "aberrant" but for Arabs is "normal." After this auspicious start, we are told that Arabs stress conformity; that Arabs inhabit a shame culture whose "prestige system" involves the ability to attract followers and clients (as an aside we are told that "Arab society is and always has been based on a system of client-patron relationships"); that Arabs can function only in conflict situations; that prestige is based solely on the ability to dominate others; that a shame culture—and therefore Islam itself—makes a virtue of revenge (here Glidden triumphantly cites the June 29, 1970 *Ahram* to show that "in 1969 [in Egypt] in 1070 cases of murder where the perpetrators were apprehended, it was found that 20 percent of the murders were based on a desire to wipe out shame, 30 percent on a desire to satisfy real or imaginary wrongs, and 31 percent on a desire for blood revenge"); that if from a Western point of view "the only rational thing for the Arabs to do is to make peace . . . for the Arabs the situation is not governed by this kind of logic, for objectivity is not a value in the Arab system."

Glidden continues, now more enthusiastically: "it is a notable fact that while the Arab value system demands absolute solidarity within the group, it at the same time encourages among its members a kind of rivalry that is destructive of that very solidarity"; in Arab society only "success counts" and "the end justifies the means"; Arabs live "naturally" in a world "characterized by anxiety expressed in generalized suspicion and distrust, which has been labelled free-floating hostility"; "the art of subterfuge is highly developed in Arab life, as well as in Islam itself"; the Arab need for vengeance overrides everything, otherwise the Arab would feel "ego-destroying" shame. Therefore, if "Westerners consider peace to be high on the scale of values" and if "we have a highly developed consciousness of the value of time," this is not true of Arabs. "In fact," we are told, "in Arab tribal society (where Arab values originated), strife, not peace, was the normal state of affairs because raiding was one of the two main supports of the economy." The purpose of this learned disquisition is merely to show how on the Western and Oriental scale of values "the relative position of the elements is quite different." QED.[27]

This is the apogee of Orientalist confidence. No merely asserted generality is denied the dignity of truth; no theoretical list of Oriental attributes is without application to the behavior of Orientals in the real world. On the one hand there are Westerners, and on the other there are Arab-Orientals; the former are (in no particular order) rational, peaceful, liberal, logical, capable of holding real values, without natural suspicion; the latter are none of these things. Out of what collective and yet particularized view of the Orient do these statements emerge? What specialized skills, what imaginative pressures, what institutions and traditions, what cultural forces produce such similarity in the descriptions of the Orient to be found in Cromer, Balfour, and our contemporary statesmen?

[1978]

---

[27]Harold W. Glidden, "The Arab World," *American Journal of Psychiatry* 128, no. 8 (February 1972): 984–8.

William Shakespeare
[1564–1616]

WILLIAM SHAKESPEARE *was born in Stratford-upon-Avon, the son of a glove-maker and wool dealer. Though his father, John, held some status in the city, at some point the family lost its position and thus, though his eldest son William attended Stratford Grammar School and may have had hopes of attending university, he did not. When Shakespeare was eighteen years old, he married Anne Hathaway and had three children before his twenty-first birthday. By the early 1590s he was established in London as an actor and a playwright, as well as the part-owner and manager of a theater company. He was a prolific writer, having written (or, in a couple of cases, co-written) at the time of his death thirty-eight plays and several volumes of poetry—*The Sonnets *(1609),* Venus and Adonis *(1593), and* The Rape of Lucrece *(1593).*

Perhaps the most pored-over of all authors, Shakespeare fascinates in part because of the lack of detail known about his life. However, a good deal is discernable about the social milieu surrounding his life and work. By the time Shakespeare emerged as an actor and a playwright in the theater scene in London of the early 1590s, he must have spent some time as an apprentice actor, and tried his hand at playwriting. Theater-going at that time spanned all social classes. His earliest plays draw heavily on classical sources and models, suggesting something about his early education. Playwriting at that time was probably considered more a professional skill than an art. When theaters were shut down because of the plague (1592–1593), he wrote his narrative poems, probably dedicated to the Earl of Southampton, a patron. When Shakespeare retired to Stratford-upon-Avon, he had seen to the publication of the poems, though not his plays. Plays at that time were written for a fee, with the rights retained by production companies. Shakespeare owned a share of the theater company, which had Lord Chamberlain as its patron and was under the royal sponsorship of King James. The company built the Globe Theater, where many of the plays were produced. He was buried in the same parish church where he was baptized. Not until seven years after his death were most of the plays collected and published by two of his partners.

The sonnets have a special place in the Shakespeare oeuvre. They are still considered models of the form, and are part of a vibrant sonnet-writing tradition in the Renaissance. The kind of sonnet Shakespeare—and other Renaissance writers such as Sir Thomas Wyatt, Henry Howard, Earl of Surrey, Edmund Spenser, and Sir Philip Sidney—wrote is often called the Elizabethan or Shakespearean sonnet. Differing from the Italian or Petrarchan sonnet, the

Elizabethan sonnet was organized in quatrains, with a concluding couplet. (The Petrarchan sonnet had an octave and a sestet.) Typically, the quatrains created an argument of examples, with each set of four lines offering an instance or amplification of the poem's central idea.

Othello, the Moor of Venice

WILLIAM SHAKESPEARE

THE NAMES OF THE ACTORS

OTHELLO,	the Moor
BRABANTIO,	(a senator,) father to Desdemona
CASSIO,	an honorable lieutenant (to Othello)
IAGO,	(Othello's ancient,) a villain
RODERIGO,	a gulled gentleman
DUKE OF VENICE	
SENATORS	(*of Venice*)
MONTANO,	Governor of Cyprus
GENTLEMEN	of Cyprus
LODOVICO *and* GRATIANO,	(kinsmen to Brabantio,) two noble Venetians
SAILORS	
CLOWN	
DESDEMONA,	(daughter to Brabantio and) wife to Othello
EMILIA,	wife to Iago
BIANCA,	a courtesan (and mistress to Cassio)
A MESSENGER	
A HERALD	
A MUSICIAN	

SERVANTS, ATTENDANTS, OFFICERS, SENATORS, MUSICIANS, GENTLEMEN

SCENE

Venice; a seaport in Cyprus

1.1

Enter Roderigo and Iago.

1.1 **Location: Venice. A street.**

Reprinted by permission from *The Complete Works of Shakespeare,* edited by David Bevington. Copyright © 1997 Pearson Education.

RODERIGO. Tush, never tell me! I take it much unkindly   *1*
   That thou, Iago, who hast had my purse
   As if the strings were thine, shouldst know of this.   *3*
IAGO. 'Sblood, but you'll not hear me.   *4*
   If ever I did dream of such a matter,
   Abhor me.
RODERIGO. Thou toldst me thou didst hold him in thy hate.   *6*
IAGO. Despise me
   If I do not. Three great ones of the city,
   In personal suit to make me his lieutenant,
   Off-capped to him; and by the faith of man,
   I know my price, I am worth no worse a place.
   But he, as loving his own pride and purposes,
   Evades them with a bombast circumstance   *14*
   Horribly stuffed with epithets of war,   *15*
   And, in conclusion,
   Nonsuits my mediators. For, "Certes," says he,   *17*
   "I have already chose my officer."
   And what was he?
   Forsooth, a great arithmetician,   *20*
   One Michael Cassio, a Florentine,
   A fellow almost damned in a fair wife,   *22*
   That never set a squadron in the field
   Nor the division of a battle knows   *24*
   More than a spinster—unless the bookish theoric,   *25*
   Wherein the togaed consuls can propose   *26*
   As masterly as he. Mere prattle without practice
   Is all his soldiership. But he, sir, had th'election;
   And I, of whom his eyes had seen the proof   *29*
   At Rhodes, at Cyprus, and on other grounds
   Christened and heathen, must be beleed and calmed   *31*

---

1 never tell me (An expression of incredulity, like "tell me another one.")   **3 this** i.e., Desdemona's elopement.   **4 'Sblood** By His (Christ's) blood   **6 him** Othello   **14 bombast circumstance** wordy evasion. (*Bombast* is cotton padding.)   **15 epithets of war** military expressions   **17 Nonsuits** rejects the petition of.   **Certes** Certainly   **20 arithmetician** i.e., a man whose military knowledge is merely theoretical, based on books of tactics   **22 A . . . wife** (Cassio does not seem to be married, but his counter-part in Shakespeare's source does have a woman in his house. See also 4.1.131.)   **24 division of a battle** disposition of a military unit   **25 a spinster** i.e., a housewife, one whose regular occupation is spinning.   **theoric** theory   **26 togaed consuls** toga-wearing counselors or senators. **propose** discuss   **29 his** Othello's   **31 beleed and calmed** left to leeward without wind, becalmed. (A sailing metaphor.)

By debitor and creditor. This countercaster, 32
He, in good time, must his lieutenant be, 33
And I—God bless the mark!—His Moorship's ancient. 34
RODERIGO. By heaven, I rather would have been his hangman. 35
IAGO. Why, there's no remedy. 'Tis the curse of service;
Preferment goes by letter and affection, 37
And not by old gradation, where each second 38
Stood heir to th' first. Now, sir, be judge yourself
Whether I in any just term am affined 40
To love the Moor.
RODERIGO. I would not follow him then.
IAGO. Oh, sir, content you. 43
I follow him to serve my turn upon him.
We cannot all be masters, nor all masters
Cannot be truly followed. You shall mark 46
Many a duteous and knee-crooking knave
That, doting on his own obsequious bondage,
Wears out his time, much like his master's ass,
For naught but provender, and when he's old, cashiered. 50
Whip me such honest knaves. Others there are 51
Who, trimmed in forms and visages of duty, 52
Keep yet their hearts attending on themselves,
And, throwing but shows of service on their lords,
Do well thrive by them, and when they have lined their
   coats, 55
Do themselves homage. These fellows have some soul, 56
And such a one do I profess myself. For, sir,
It is as sure as you are Roderigo,
Were I the Moor I would not be Iago. 59
In following him, I follow but myself—
Heaven is my judge, not I for love and duty,

---

32 debitor and creditor (A name for a system of bookkeeping, here used as a contemptuous nickname for Cassio.) **countercaster** i.e., bookkeeper, one who tallies with *counters*, or "metal disks." (Said contemptuously.) **33 in good time** opportunely, i.e., forsooth **34 God bless the mark** (Perhaps originally a formula to ward off evil; here an expression of impatience.) **ancient** standard-bearer, ensign. **35 his hangman** the executioner of him. **37 Preferment** promotion. **letter and affection** personal influence and favoritism **38 old gradation** step-by-step seniority, the traditional way **40 term** respect. **affined** bound **43 content you** don't you worry about that. **46 truly** faithfully **50 cashiered** dismissed from service. **51 Whip me** Whip, as far as I'm concerned **52 trimmed . . . duty** dressed up in the mere form and show of dutifulness **55 lined their coats** i.e., stuffed their purses **56 Do themselves homage** i.e., attend to self-interest solely. **59 Were . . . Iago** i.e., if I were able to assume command, I certainly would not choose to remain a subordinate, or, I would keep a suspicious eye on a flattering subordinate.

But seeming so for my peculiar end.   *62*
For when my outward action doth demonstrate
The native act and figure of my heart   *64*
In compliment extern, 'tis not long after   *65*
But I will wear my heart upon my sleeve
For daws to peck at. I am not what I am.   *67*
RODERIGO. What a full fortune does the thick-lips owe   *68*
   If he can carry't thus!
IAGO.   Call up her father.   *69*
   Rouse him, make after him, poison his delight,
   Proclaim him in the streets; incense her kinsmen,
   And, though he in a fertile climate dwell,   *72*
   Plague him with flies. Though that his joy be joy,   *73*
   Yet throw such changes of vexation on't   *74*
   As it may lose some color.   *75*
RODERIGO. Here is her father's house. I'll call aloud.
IAGO. Do, with like timorous accent and dire yell   *77*
   As when, by night and negligence, the fire   *78*
   Is spied in populous cities.
RODERIGO. What ho, Brabantio! Signor Brabantio, ho!
IAGO. Awake! What ho, Brabantio! Thieves, thieves, thieves!
   Look to your house, your daughter, and your bags!
   Thieves, thieves!   *83*

(*Brabantio* [*enters*] *above* [*at a window*].)

BRABANTIO. What is the reason of this terrible summons?
   What is the matter there?
RODERIGO. Signor, is all your family within?
IAGO. Are your doors locked?
BRABANTIO.   Why, wherefore ask you this?
IAGO. Zounds, sir, you're robbed. For shame, put on your
   gown!   *88*

---

62 peculiar particular, personal   **64 native** innate. **figure** shape, intent   **65 compliment extern** outward show (conforming in this case to the inner workings and intention of the heart)   **67 daws** small crowlike birds, proverbially stupid and avaricious.   **I am not what I am** i.e., I am not one who wears his heart on his sleeve.   **68 full** swelling. **thick-lips** (Elizabethans often applied the term "Moor" to Negroes.) **owe** own   **69 carry't thus** carry this off.   **72–3 though ... flies** though he seems prosperous and happy now, vex him with misery.   **73 Though ... be joy** Although he seems fortunate and happy. (Repeats the idea of line 72.)   **74 changes of vexation** vexing changes **75 As ... color** that may cause it to lose some of its first gloss.   **77 timorous** frightening **78 As ... fire** as when a fire, having gained hold by negligence at night   **83.1 at a window** (This stage direction, from the Quarto, probably calls for an appearance on the gallery above and rearstage.)   **88 Zounds** By His (Christ's) wounds

Your heart is burst; you have lost half your soul.
Even now, now, very now, an old black ram
Is tupping your white ewe. Arise, arise!   91
Awake the snorting citizens with the bell,   92
Or else the devil will make a grandsire of you.   93
Arise, I say!

BRABANTIO. What, have you lost your wits?

RODERIGO. Most reverend signor, do you know my voice?

BRABANTIO. Not I. What are you?

RODERIGO. My name is Roderigo.

BRABANTIO. The worser welcome.
I have charged thee not to haunt about my doors.
In honest plainness thou hast heard me say
My daughter is not for thee; and now, in madness,
Being full of supper and distemp'ring drafts,   102
Upon malicious bravery dost thou come   103
To start my quiet.   104

RODERIGO. Sir, sir, sir—

BRABANTIO.   But thou must needs be sure
My spirits and my place have in their power
To make this bitter to thee.

RODERIGO.   Patience, good sir.

BRABANTIO. What tell'st thou me of robbing? This is Venice;
My house is not a grange.

RODERIGO.   Most grave Brabantio,   109
In simple and pure soul I come to you.   110

IAGO. Zounds, sir, you are one of those that will not
serve God if the devil bid you. Because we come to do
you service and you think we are ruffians, you'll have
your daughter covered with a Barbary horse; you'll   114
have your nephews neigh to you; you'll have coursers   115
for cousins and jennets for germans.   116

BRABANTIO. What profane wretch art thou?

---

91 tupping covering, copulating with. (Said of sheep.)   **92 snorting** snoring   **93 the devil** (The devil was conventionally pictured as black.)   **102 distemp'ring** intoxicating   **103 Upon malicious bravery** with hostile intent to defy me   **104 start** startle, disrupt   **106 My ... power** my temperament and my authority of office have it in their power   **109 grange** isolated country house. **110 simple** sincere   **114 Barbary** from northern Africa (and hence associated with Othello) **115 nephews** i.e., grandsons   **115–16 you'll ... germans** you'll consent to have powerful horses for kinfolks and small Spanish horses for near relatives.

IAGO. I am one, sir, that comes to tell you your daughter
    and the Moor are now making the beast with two backs.
BRABANTIO. Thou art a villain.
IAGO.   You are—a senator.   *121*
BRABANTIO. This thou shalt answer. I know thee, Roderigo.   *122*
RODERIGO. Sir, I will answer anything. But I beseech you,
    If't be your pleasure and most wise consent—   *124*
    As partly I find it is—that your fair daughter,
    At this odd-even and dull watch o'th' night,   *126*
    Transported with no worse nor better guard   *127*
    But with a knave of common hire, a gondolier,   *128*
    To the gross clasps of a lascivious Moor—
    If this be known to you and your allowance   *130*
    We then have done you bold and saucy wrongs.   *131*
    But if you know not this, my manners tell me
    We have your wrong rebuke. Do not believe
    That, from the sense of all civility,   *134*
    I thus would play and trifle with your reverence.   *135*
    Your daughter, if you have not given her leave,
    I say again, hath made a gross revolt,
    Tying her duty, beauty, wit, and fortunes   *138*
    In an extravagant and wheeling stranger   *139*
    Of here and everywhere. Straight satisfy yourself.   *140*
    If she be in her chamber or your house,
    Let loose on me the justice of the state
    For thus deluding you.
BRABANTIO (*calling*). Strike on the tinder, ho!   *144*
    Give me a taper! Call up all my people!
    This accident is not unlike my dream.   *146*
    Belief of it oppresses me already.
    Light, I say, light!   (*Exit [above].*)
IAGO.   Farewell, for I must leave you.
    It seems not meet nor wholesome to my place   *149*

---

121 **a senator** (Said with mock politeness, as though the word itself were an insult.)   122 **answer** be held accountable for.   124 **wise** well-informed   126 **At ... night** at this hour that is between day and night, neither the one nor the other   127 **with** by   128 **But with a knave** than by a low fellow, a servant   130 **and your allowance** and has your permission   131 **saucy** insolent 134 **from** contrary to.   **civility** good manners, decency   135 **your reverence** (1) the respect due to you (2) Your Reverence.   138 **wit** intelligence   139–40 **In ... everywhere** to a wandering and vagabond foreigner of uncertain origins.   140 **Straight** Straightway   144 **tinder** charred linen ignited by a spark from flint and steel, used to light torches or *tapers* (lines 145, 170)   146 **accident** occurrence, event   149 **meet** fitting.   **place** position (as ensign)

To be produced—as, if I stay, I shall— 150
Against the Moor. For I do know the state,
However this may gall him with some check, 152
Cannot with safety cast him, for he's embarked 153
With such loud reason to the Cyprus wars, 154
Which even now stands in act, that, for their souls, 155
Another of his fathom they have none 156
To lead their business; in which regard, 157
Though I do hate him as I do hell pains,
Yet for necessity of present life 159
I must show out a flag and sign of love,
Which is indeed but sign. That you shall surely find
    him,
Lead to the Sagittary the raisèd search, 162
And there will I be with him. So farewell.   (*Exit.*) 163

(*Enter [below] Brabantio [in his nightgown] with
servants and torches.*)

BRABANTIO. It is too true an evil. Gone she is;
   And what's to come of my despisèd time 165
   Is naught but bitterness. Now, Roderigo,
   Where didst thou see her?—Oh, unhappy girl!—
   With the Moor, say'st thou?—Who would be a father!—
   How didst thou know 'twas she?—Oh, she deceives me
   Past thought!—What said she to you?—Get more tapers.
   Raise all my kindred.—Are they married, think you?
RODERIGO. Truly, I think they are.
BRABANTIO. Oh, heaven! How got she out? Oh, treason of the
    blood!
   Fathers, from hence trust not your daughters' minds
   By what you see them act. Is there not charms 175
   By which the property of youth and maidhood 176
   May be abused? Have you not read, Roderigo, 177
   Of some such thing?

---

150 produced produced (as a witness)   **152 gall** rub; oppress.   **check** rebuke
153 cast dismiss.   **embarked** engaged   **154 loud** urgent   **155 stands in act** have started.   **for their
souls** to save their souls   **156 fathom** i.e., ability, depth of experience   **157 in which regard** out of
regard for which   **159 life** livelihood   **162 Sagittary** (An inn or house where Othello and
Desdemona are staying, named for its sign of Sagittarius, or Centaur.)   **raisèd search** search party
roused out of sleep   **163.1 nightgown** dressing gown. (This costuming is specified in the Quarto
text.)   **165 time** i.e., remainder of life   **175 charms** spells   **176 property** special quality, nature
177 abused deceived.

RODERIGO. Yes, sir, I have indeed.

BRABANTIO. Call up my brother.—Oh, would you had had
    her!—
    Some one way, some another.—Do you know
    Where we may apprehend her and the Moor?

RODERIGO. I think I can discover him, if you please   *182*
    To get good guard and go along with me.

BRABANTIO. Pray you, lead on. At every house I'll call;
    I may command at most.—Get weapons, ho!   *185*
    And raise some special officers of night.—
    On, good Roderigo. I will deserve your pains.   *187*

(Exeunt.)

1.2

Enter Othello, Iago, attendants with torches.

IAGO. Though in the trade of war I have slain men,
    Yet do I hold it very stuff o'th' conscience   *2*
    To do no contrived murder. I lack iniquity   *3*
    Sometimes to do me service. Nine or ten times
    I had thought t'have yerked him here under the ribs.   *5*

OTHELLO. 'Tis better as it is.

IAGO.   Nay, but he prated,
    And spoke such scurvy and provoking terms
    Against your honor
    That, with the little godliness I have,
    I did full hard forbear him. But, I pray you, sir,   *10*
    Are you fast married? Be assured of this,
    That the magnifico is much beloved,   *12*
    And hath in his effect a voice potential   *13*
    As double as the Duke's. He will divorce you,
    Or put upon you what restraint or grievance
    The law, with all his might to enforce it on,
    Will give him cable.

OTHELLO.   Let him do his spite.   *17*

---

182 discover reveal, uncover   **185 command** demand assistance   **187 deserve** show gratitude for
1.2. Location: Venice. Another street, before Othello's lodgings.
2 very stuff essence, basic material. (Continuing the metaphor of *trade* from line 1.)   **3 contrived**
premeditated   **5 yerked** stabbed. **him** i.e., Roderigo   **10 I . . . him** I restrained myself with great
difficulty from assaulting him.   **12 magnifico** Venetian grandee, i.e., Brabantio   **13 in his effect** at
his command. **potential** powerful   **17 cable** i.e., scope.

My services which I have done the seigniory   18
Shall out-tongue his complaints. 'Tis yet to know—   19
Which, when I know that boasting is an honor,
I shall promulgate—I fetch my life and being
From men of royal siege, and my demerits   22
May speak unbonneted to as proud a fortune   23
As this that I have reached. For know, Iago,
But that I love the gentle Desdemona,
I would not my unhousèd free condition   26
Put into circumscription and confine   27
For the sea's worth. But look, what lights come yond?   28

(*Enter Cassio [and officers] with torches.*)

IAGO. Those are the raisèd father and his friends.
     You were best go in.
OTHELLO.   Not I. I must be found.
     My parts, my title, and my perfect soul   31
     Shall manifest me rightly. Is it they?
IAGO. By Janus, I think no.   33
OTHELLO. The servants of the Duke? And my lieutenant?
     The goodness of the night upon you, friends!
     What is the news?
CASSIO.   The Duke does greet you, General,
     And he requires your haste-post-haste appearance
     Even on the instant.
OTHELLO.   What is the matter, think you?
CASSIO. Something from Cyprus, as I may divine.   39
     It is a business of some heat. The galleys   40
     Have sent a dozen sequent messengers   41
     This very night at one another's heels,
     And many of the consuls, raised and met,   43
     Are at the Duke's already. You have been hotly called for;
     When, being not at your lodging to be found,
     The Senate hath sent about three several quests   46

---

18 seigniory Venetian government   **19 yet to know** not yet widely known   **22 siege** i.e., rank.
(Literally, a seat used by a person of distinction.)   **demerits** deserts   **23 unbonneted** without removing the hat, i.e., on equal terms (? Or "with hat off," "in all due modesty.")   **26 unhousèd** unconfined,
undomesticated   **27 circumscription and confine** restriction and confinement   **28 the sea's worth**
all the riches at the bottom of the sea.   **28.1 officers** (The Quarto text specifies, "*Enter* Cassio *with
lights, Officers, and torches.*")   **31 My . . . soul** My natural gifts, my position or reputation, and my
unflawed conscience   **33 Janus** Roman two-faced god of beginnings   **39 divine** guess.   **40 heat**
urgency.   **41 sequent** successive   **43 consuls** senators   **46 about** all over the city.   **several** separate

To search you out.

OTHELLO.   'Tis well I am found by you.
   I will but spend a word here in the house
   And go with you.   (*Exit.*)

CASSIO.   Ancient, what makes he here?   *49*

IAGO. Faith, he tonight hath boarded a land carrack.   *50*
   If it prove lawful prize, he's made forever."   *51*

CASSIO. I do not understand.

IAGO.   He's married.

CASSIO.   To who?

(*Enter Othello.*)

IAGO. Marry, to—Come, Captain, will you go?   *53*

OTHELLO. Have with you.   *54*

CASSIO. Here comes another troop to seek for you.   *55*

(*Enter Brabantio, Roderigo, with officers and torches.*)

IAGO. It is Brabantio. General, be advised.   *56*
   He comes to bad intent.

OTHELLO.   Holla! Stand there!

RODERIGO. Signor, it is the Moor.

BRABANTIO.   Down with him, thief!

(*They draw on both sides.*)

IAGO. You, Roderigo! Come, sir, I am for you.

OTHELLO. Keep up your bright swords, for the dew will rust
     them.   *60*
   Good signor, you shall more command with years
   Than with your weapons.

BRABANTIO. O thou foul thief, where hast thou stowed my
     daughter?
   Damned as thou art, thou hast enchanted her!
   For I'll refer me to all things of sense,   *65*
   If she in chains of magic were not bound
   Whether a maid so tender, fair, and happy,
   So opposite to marriage that she shunned

---

49 makes does   **50 boarded** gone aboard and seized as an act of piracy. (With sexual suggestion.)
carrack large merchant ship   **51 prize** booty   **53 Marry** (An oath, originally "by the Virgin Mary";
here used with wordplay on *married*.)   **54 Have with you** i.e., Let's go.   **55.1 *officers and torches***
(The Quarto text calls for "*others with lights and weapons.*")   **56 be advised** be on your guard.
60 Keep up Keep in the sheath   **65 I'll . . . sense** I'll submit my case to one and all

The wealthy curlèd darlings of our nation,
Would ever have, t'incur a general mock,
Run from her guardage to the sooty bosom   71
Of such a thing as thou—to fear, not to delight.
Judge me the world if 'tis not gross in sense   73
That thou hast practiced on her with foul charms,
Abused her delicate youth with drugs or minerals   75
That weakens motion. I'll have't disputed on;   76
'Tis probable and palpable to thinking.
I therefore apprehend and do attach thee   78
For an abuser of the world, a practicer   79
Of arts inhibited and out of warrant.—   80
Lay hold upon him! If he do resist,
Subdue him at his peril.
OTHELLO.   Hold your hands,
Both you of my inclining and the rest.   83
Were it my cue to fight, I should have known it
Without a prompter.—Whither will you that I go
To answer this your charge?
BRABANTIO. To prison, till fit time
Of law and course of direct session   88
Call thee to answer.
OTHELLO.   What if I do obey?
How may the Duke be therewith satisfied,
Whose messengers are here about my side
Upon some present business of the state
To bring me to him?
OFFICER.   'Tis true, most worthy signor.
The Duke's in council, and your noble self,
I am sure, is sent for.
BRABANTIO.   How? The Duke in council?
In this time of the night? Bring him away.   96
Mine's not an idle cause. The Duke himself,   97
Or any of my brothers of the state,
Cannot but feel this wrong as 'twere their own;

---

71 **guardage** guardianship   73 **gross in sense** obvious   75 **minerals** i.e., poisons   76 **weakens motion** impair the vital faculties.   **disputed on** argued in court by professional counsel, debated by experts   78 **attach** arrest   79 **abuser** deceiver   80 **arts inhibited** prohibited arts, black magic.   **out of warrant** illegal.   83 **inclining** following, party   88 **course of direct session** regular or specially convened legal proceedings   96 **away** right along.   97 **idle** trifling

For if such actions may have passage free,   *100*
Bondslaves and pagans shall our statesmen be.

(Exeunt.)

<u>**1.3**</u>

Enter Duke (and) Senators (and sit at a table, with lights),
and Officers. (The Duke and Senators are reading
dispatches.)

DUKE. There is no composition in these news   *1*
    That gives them credit.
FIRST SENATOR. Indeed, they are disproportioned.   *3*
    My letters say a hundred and seven galleys.
DUKE. And mine, a hundred forty.
SECOND SENATOR.   And mine, two hundred.
    But though they jump not on a just account—   *6*
    As in these cases, where the aim reports   *7*
    'Tis oft with difference—yet do they all confirm
    A Turkish fleet, and bearing up to Cyprus.
DUKE. Nay, it is possible enough to judgment.
    I do not so secure me in the error   *11*
    But the main article I do approve   *12*
    In fearful sense.
SAILOR *(within)*. What ho, what ho, what ho!

(Enter Sailor.)

OFFICER. A messenger from the galleys.
DUKE. Now, what's the business?
SAILOR. The Turkish preparation makes for Rhodes.   *16*
    So was I bid report here to the state
    By Signor Angelo.
DUKE. How say you by this change?
FIRST SENATOR.   This cannot be   *19*
    By no assay of reason. 'Tis a pageant   *20*

---

100 may ... free are allowed to go unchecked
1.3. Location: Venice. A council chamber.
0.1–2 Enter ... Officers (The Quarto text calls for the Duke and senators to "*set at a Table with lights and Attendants.*") **1 composition** consistency **3 disproportioned** inconsistent. **6 jump** agree.
just exact **7 the aim** conjecture **11–12 I do not ... approve** I do not take such (false) comfort in the discrepancies that I fail to perceive the main point, i.e., that the Turkish fleet is threatening **16 preparation** fleet prepared for battle **19 by** about **20 assay** test. **pageant** mere show

To keep us in false gaze. When we consider 21
Th'importancy of Cyprus to the Turk,
And let ourselves again but understand
That, as it more concerns the Turk than Rhodes,
So may he with more facile question bear it, 25
For that it stands not in such warlike brace, 26
But altogether lacks th'abilities 27
That Rhodes is dressed in—if we make thought of this, 28
We must not think the Turk is so unskillful 29
To leave that latest which concerns him first, 30
Neglecting an attempt of ease and gain
To wake and wage a danger profitless. 32

DUKE. Nay, in all confidence, he's not for Rhodes.
OFFICER. Here is more news.

(*Enter a Messenger.*)

MESSENGER. The Ottomites, reverend and gracious,
Steering with due course toward the isle of Rhodes,
Have there injointed them with an after fleet. 37

FIRST SENATOR. Ay, so I thought. How many, as you guess?
MESSENGER. Of thirty sail; and now they do restem 39
Their backward course, bearing with frank appearance 40
Their purposes toward Cyprus. Signor Montano,
Your trusty and most valiant servitor, 42
With his free duty recommends you thus, 43
And prays you to believe him.

DUKE. 'Tis certain then for Cyprus.
Marcus Luccicos, is not he in town?

FIRST SENATOR. He's now in Florence.
DUKE. Write from us to him, post-post-haste. Dispatch.
FIRST SENATOR. Here comes Brabantio and the valiant Moor.

(*Enter Brabantio, Othello, Cassio, Iago, Roderigo, and officers.*)

DUKE. Valiant Othello, we must straight employ you 50

---

21 in false gaze looking the wrong way.   **25 So may ... it** so also he (the Turk) can more easily
capture it (Cyprus)   **26 For that** since.   **brace** state of defense   **27 th'abilities** the means of self-
defense   **28 dressed in** equipped with   **29 unskillful** deficient in judgment   **30 latest** last
32 wake and wage stir up and risk   **37 injointed them** joined themselves.   **after** second, following
39–40 restem ... course retrace their original course   **40 frank appearance** undisguised intent
42 servitor officer under your command   **43 free duty** freely given and loyal service.   **recommends**
commends himself and reports to   **50 straight** straightway

Against the general enemy Ottoman. 51

(*To Brabantio*) I did not see you; welcome, gentle signor. 52

We lacked your counsel and your help tonight.

BRABANTIO. So did I yours. Good Your Grace, pardon me;

Neither my place nor aught I heard of business 55

Hath raised me from my bed, nor doth the general care

Take hold on me, for my particular grief 57

Is of so floodgate and o'erbearing nature 58

That it engluts and swallows other sorrows 59

And it is still itself.

DUKE.   Why, what's the matter? 60

BRABANTIO. My daughter! Oh, my daughter!

DUKE AND SENATORS.   Dead?

BRABANTIO.   Ay, to me.

She is abused, stol'n from me, and corrupted 62

By spells and medicines bought of mountebanks;

For nature so preposterously to err,

Being not deficient, blind, or lame of sense, 65

Sans witchcraft could not. 66

DUKE. Whoe'er he be that in this foul proceeding

Hath thus beguiled your daughter of herself,

And you of her, the bloody book of law

You shall yourself read in the bitter letter

After your own sense—yea, though our proper son 71

Stood in your action.

BRABANTIO.   Humbly I thank Your Grace. 72

Here is the man, this Moor, whom now it seems

Your special mandate for the state affairs

Hath hither brought.

ALL.   We are very sorry for't.

DUKE (*to Othello*). What, in your own part, can you say to
     this?

BRABANTIO. Nothing, but this is so.

OTHELLO. Most potent, grave, and reverend signors,

My very noble and approved good masters: 79

---

51 general enemy universal enemy to all Christendom   **52 gentle** noble   **55 place** official position
57 particular personal   **58 floodgate** i.e., overwhelming (as when floodgates are opened)   **59 eng-**
luts engulfs   **60 is still itself** remains undiminished.   **62 abused** deceived   **65 deficient** defective.
lame of sense deficient in sensory perception   **66 Sans** without   **71 After . . . sense** according to
your own interpretation.   **our proper** my own   **72 Stood . . . action** were under your accusation.
79 approved proved, esteemed

That I have ta'en away this old man's daughter,
It is most true; true, I have married her.
The very head and front of my offending   *82*
Hath this extent, no more. Rude am I in my speech,   *83*
And little blessed with the soft phrase of peace;
For since these arms of mine had seven years' pith,   *85*
Till now some nine moons wasted, they have used   *86*
Their dearest action in the tented field;   *87*
And little of this great world can I speak
More than pertains to feats of broils and battle,
And therefore little shall I grace my cause
In speaking for myself. Yet, by your gracious patience,
I will a round unvarnished tale deliver   *92*
Of my whole course of love—what drugs, what charms,
What conjuration, and what mighty magic,
For such proceeding I am charged withal,   *95*
I won his daughter.
BRABANTIO.   A maiden never bold;
Of spirit so still and quiet that her motion   *97*
Blushed at herself; and she, in spite of nature,   *98*
Of years, of country, credit, everything,   *99*
To fall in love with what she feared to look on!
It is a judgment maimed and most imperfect
That will confess perfection so could err   *102*
Against all rules of nature, and must be driven
To find out practices of cunning hell   *104*
Why this should be. I therefore vouch again   *105*
That with some mixtures powerful o'er the blood,   *106*
Or with some dram conjured to this effect,   *107*
He wrought upon her.
DUKE.   To vouch this is no proof,
Without more wider and more overt test   *109*
Than these thin habits and poor likelihoods   *110*

---

82 head and front height and breadth, entire extent   **83 Rude** Unpolished   **85 since . . . pith** i.e.,
since I was seven. (*Pith* means "strength, vigor.")   **86 Till . . . wasted** until some nine months ago
(since when Othello has evidently not been on active duty, but in Venice)   **87 dearest** most valuable
92 round plain   **95 withal** with   **97–8 her . . . herself** i.e., she blushed easily at herself. (*Motion* can
suggest the impulse of the soul or of the emotions, or physical movement.)   **99 years** i.e., difference
in age.   **credit** virtuous reputation   **102 confess** concede (that)   **104 practices** plots   **105 vouch**
assert   **106 blood** passions   **107 dram . . . effect** dose made by magical spells to have this effect
109 more wider fuller.   **test** testimony   **110 habits** garments, i.e., appearances.   **poor likelihoods**
weak inferences

Of modern seeming do prefer against him.   *111*

FIRST SENATOR. But Othello, speak.

Did you by indirect and forcèd courses   *113*
Subdue and poison this young maid's affections?
Or came it by request and such fair question   *115*
As soul to soul affordeth?

OTHELLO.   I do beseech you,
Send for the lady to the Sagittary
And let her speak of me before her father.
If you do find me foul in her report,
The trust, the office I do hold of you
Not only take away, but let your sentence
Even fall upon my life.

DUKE.   Fetch Desdemona hither.

OTHELLO (*to Iago*). Ancient, conduct them. You best know
    the place.

(Exeunt Iago and attendants.)

And, till she come, as truly as to heaven
I do confess the vices of my blood,   *125*
So justly to your grave ears I'll present   *126*
How I did thrive in this fair lady's love,
And she in mine.

DUKE. Say it, Othello.

OTHELLO. Her father loved me, oft invited me,
Still questioned me the story of my life   *131*
From year to year—the battles, sieges, fortunes
That I have passed.
I ran it through, even from my boyish days
To th' very moment that he bade me tell it,
Wherein I spoke of most disastrous chances,
Of moving accidents by flood and field,   *137*
Of hairbreadth scapes i'th'imminent deadly breach,   *138*
Of being taken by the insolent foe
And sold to slavery, of my redemption thence,
And portance in my travels' history,   *141*

---

111 **modern seeming** commonplace assumption.   **prefer** bring forth   113 **forcèd courses** means used against her will   115 **question** conversation   125 **blood** passions, human nature   126 **justly** truthfully, accurately   131 **Still** continually   137 **moving accidents** stirring happenings 138 **i'th'imminent ... breach** in death-threatening gaps made in a fortification   141 **portance** conduct

Wherein of antres vast and deserts idle,   142
Rough quarries, rocks, and hills whose heads touch heaven,   143
It was my hint to speak—such was my process—   144
And of the Cannibals that each other eat,
The Anthropophagi, and men whose heads   146
Do grow beneath their shoulders. These things to hear
Would Desdemona seriously incline;
But still the house affairs would draw her thence,
Which ever as she could with haste dispatch
She'd come again, and with a greedy ear
Devour up my discourse. Which I, observing,
Took once a pliant hour, and found good means   153
To draw from her a prayer of earnest heart
That I would all my pilgrimage dilate,   155
Whereof by parcels she had something heard,   156
But not intentively. I did consent,   157
And often did beguile her of her tears,
When I did speak of some distressful stroke
That my youth suffered. My story being done,
She gave me for my pains a world of sighs.
She swore, in faith, 'twas strange, 'twas passing strange,   162
'Twas pitiful, 'twas wondrous pitiful.
She wished she had not heard it, yet she wished
That heaven had made her such a man. She thanked me,   165
And bade me, if I had a friend that loved her,
I should but teach him how to tell my story,
And that would woo her. Upon this hint I spake.   168
She loved me for the dangers I had passed,
And I loved her that she did pity them.
This only is the witchcraft I have used.
Here comes the lady. Let her witness it.

(*Enter Desdemona, Iago, [and] attendants.*)

DUKE. I think this tale would win my daughter too.
　　Good Brabantio,
　　Take up this mangled matter at the best.   175

---

142 **antres** caverns.　**idle** barren, desolate　143 **Rough quarries** rugged rock formations　144 **hint**
occasion, opportunity　146 **Anthropophagi** man-eaters. (A term from Pliny's *Natural History*.)
153 **pliant** well-suiting　155 **dilate** relate in detail　156 **by parcels** piecemeal　157 **intentively** with
full attention, continuously.　162 **passing** exceedingly　165 **made her** (1) created her to be (2)
made for her　168 **hint** opportunity. (Othello does not mean that she was dropping hints.)
175 **Take . . . best** make the best of a bad bargain.

Men do their broken weapons rather use
Than their bare hands.

BRABANTIO.   I pray you, hear her speak.
If she confess that she was half the wooer,
Destruction on my head if my bad blame
Light on the man!—Come hither, gentle mistress.
Do you perceive in all this noble company
Where most you owe obedience?

DESDEMONA.   My noble father,
I do perceive here a divided duty.
To you I am bound for life and education;   *184*
My life and education both do learn me   *185*
How to respect you. You are the lord of duty;   *186*
I am hitherto your daughter. But here's my husband,
And so much duty as my mother showed
To you, preferring you before her father,
So much I challenge that I may profess   *190*
Due to the Moor my lord.

BRABANTIO.   God be with you! I have done.
Please it Your Grace, on to the state affairs.
I had rather to adopt a child than get it.   *194*
Come hither, Moor.

       (*He joins the hands of Othello and Desdemona.*)

I here do give thee that with all my heart   *196*
Which, but thou hast already, with all my heart   *197*
I would keep from thee.—For your sake, jewel,   *198*
I am glad at soul I have no other child,
For thy escape would teach me tyranny,   *200*
To hang clogs on them.—I have done, my lord.   *201*

DUKE.   Let me speak like yourself, and lay a sentence   *202*
Which, as a grece or step, may help these lovers   *203*
Into your favor.
When remedies are past, the griefs are ended   *205*
By seeing the worst, which late on hopes depended.   *206*

---

184 education upbringing   **185 learn** teach   **186 of duty** to whom duty is due   **190 challenge**
claim   **194 get** beget   **196 with all my heart** wherein my whole affection has been engaged
197 with all my heart willingly, gladly   **198 For your sake** Because of you   **200 escape** elopement
201 clogs (Literally, blocks of wood fastened to the legs of criminals or animals to inhibit escape.)
202 like yourself i.e., as you would, in your proper temper.   **lay a sentence** apply a maxim
203 grece step   **205–6 When . . . depended** When all hope of remedy is past, our sorrows are ended
by realizing that the worst has already happened which lately we hoped would not happen.

To mourn a mischief that is past and gone   207
Is the next way to draw new mischief on.   208
What cannot be preserved when fortune takes,   209
Patience her injury a mock'ry makes.   210
The robbed that smiles steals something from the thief;
He robs himself that spends a bootless grief.   212

BRABANTIO. So let the Turk of Cyprus us beguile,
  We lose it not, so long as we can smile.
  He bears the sentence well that nothing bears   215
  But the free comfort which from thence he hears,   216
  But he bears both the sentence and the sorrow   217
  That, to pay grief, must of poor patience borrow.   218
  These sentences, to sugar or to gall,   219
  Being strong on both sides, are equivocal.   220
  But words are words. I never yet did hear
  That the bruised heart was piercèd through the ear.   222
  I humbly beseech you, proceed to th'affairs of state.

DUKE. The Turk with a most mighty preparation makes
  for Cyprus. Othello, the fortitude of the place is best   225
  known to you; and though we have there a substitute   226
  of most allowed sufficiency, yet opinion, a sovereign   227
  mistress of effects, throws a more safer voice on you.   228
  You must therefore be content to slubber the gloss of   229
  your new fortunes with this more stubborn and   230
  boisterous expedition.   231

OTHELLO. The tyrant custom, most grave senators,
  Hath made the flinty and steel couch of war
  My thrice-driven bed of down. I do agnize   234
  A natural and prompt alacrity

---

207 **mischief** misfortune, injury   208 **next** nearest   209–10 **What . . . makes** When fortune takes away what cannot be saved, patience makes a mockery of fortune's wrongdoing.   212 **spends a bootless grief** indulges in unavailing grief.   215–18 **He bears . . . borrow** A person can easily be comforted by your maxim that enjoys its platitudinous comfort without having to experience the misfortune that occasions sorrow, but anyone whose grief bankrupts his poor patience is left with your saying and his sorrow, too. (*Bears the sentence* also plays on the meaning, "receives judicial sentence.")   219–20 **These . . . equivocal** These fine maxims are equivocal, being equally appropriate to happiness or bitterness.   222 **piercèd . . . ear** relieved by mere words reaching it through the ear.   225 **fortitude** strength   226 **substitute** deputy   227 **allowed** acknowledged 227–8 **opinion . . . on you** general opinion, an important determiner of affairs, chooses you as the best man.   229 **slubber** soil, sully   230–1 **stubborn . . . expedition** rough and violent expedition, for which haste is needed.   234 **thrice-driven** thrice sifted, winnowed.   **agnize** know in myself, acknowledge

I find in hardness, and do undertake   *236*
These present wars against the Ottomites.
Most humbly therefore bending to your state,   *238*
I crave fit disposition for my wife,
Due reference of place and exhibition,   *240*
With such accommodation and besort   *241*
As levels with her breeding.   *242*
DUKE. Why, at her father's.
BRABANTIO.   I will not have it so.
OTHELLO. Nor I.
DESDEMONA. Nor I. I would not there reside,
To put my father in impatient thoughts
By being in his eye. Most gracious Duke,
To my unfolding lend your prosperous ear,   *247*
And let me find a charter in your voice,   *248*
T'assist my simpleness.
DUKE. What would you, Desdemona?
DESDEMONA. That I did love the Moor to live with him,
My downright violence and storm of fortunes   *252*
May trumpet to the world. My heart's subdued
Even to the very quality of my lord.   *254*
I saw Othello's visage in his mind,
And to his honors and his valiant parts   *256*
Did I my soul and fortunes consecrate.
So that, dear lords, if I be left behind
A moth of peace, and he go to the war,   *259*
The rites for why I love him are bereft me,   *260*
And I a heavy interim shall support   *261*
By his dear absence. Let me go with him.   *262*
OTHELLO. Let her have your voice.   *263*
Vouch with me, heaven, I therefor beg it not
To please the palate of my appetite,
Nor to comply with heat—the young affects   *266*

---

236 hardness hardship **238 bending . . . state** bowing or kneeling to your authority **240–2 Due . . .**
breeding proper respect for her place (as my wife) and maintenance, with such suitable provision and
attendance as befits her upbringing. **247 my unfolding** what I shall unfold or say. **prosperous**
favorable **248 charter** privilege, authorization **252 My . . . fortunes** my plain and total breach of
social custom **254 quality** moral and spiritual identity **256 parts** qualities **259 moth** i.e., one
who consumes merely **260 rites** rites of love. (With a suggestion, too, of "rights," sharing.)
261 heavy burdensome **262 dear** grievous **263 voice** consent. **266 heat** sexual passion. **young**
affects passions of youth, adolescent desires

In me defunct—and proper satisfaction, 267
But to be free and bounteous to her mind. 268
And heaven defend your good souls that you think 269
I will your serious and great business scant
When she is with me. No, when light-winged toys
Of feathered Cupid seel with wanton dullness 272
My speculative and officed instruments, 273
That my disports corrupt and taint my business, 274
Let huswives make a skillet of my helm,
And all indign and base adversities 276
Make head against my estimation! 277
DUKE. Be it as you shall privately determine,
Either for her stay or going. Th'affair cries haste,
And speed must answer it.
A SENATOR.   You must away tonight.
DESDEMONA. Tonight, my lord?
DUKE.   This night.
OTHELLO.   With all my heart.
DUKE. At nine i'th' morning here we'll meet again.
Othello, leave some officer behind,
And he shall our commission bring to you,
With such things else of quality and respect 285
As doth import you.
OTHELLO.   So please Your Grace, my ancient; 286
A man he is of honesty and trust.
To his conveyance I assign my wife,
With what else needful Your Good Grace shall think
To be sent after me.
DUKE.   Let it be so.
Good night to everyone. (*To Brabantio*) And, noble signor,
If virtue no delighted beauty lack, 292
Your son-in-law is far more fair than black.
FIRST SENATOR. Adieu, brave Moor. Use Desdemona well.
BRABANTIO. Look to her, Moor, if thou hast eyes to see.
She has deceived her father, and may thee.

---

267 **defunct** done with, at an end. **proper** personal   268 **free** generous   269 **defend** forbid. **think** should think   272 **seel** i.e., make blind (as in falconry, by sewing up the eyes of the hawk during training)   273 **My . . . instruments** my eyes, whose function is to see   274 **That . . . business** in such a way that my sexual pastimes interfere with my official duties   276 **indign** unworthy, shameful   277 **Make head** raise an army.   **estimation** reputation.   285 **of quality and respect** of importance and relevance   286 **import** concern   292 **delighted** capable of delighting

(*Exeunt [Duke, Brabantio, Cassio, Senators, and officers].*)

OTHELLO. My life upon her faith!—Honest Iago,
My Desdemona must I leave to thee.
I prithee, let thy wife attend on her,
And bring them after in the best advantage.   *300*
Come, Desdemona. I have but an hour
Of love, of worldly matters and direction,   *302*
To spend with thee. We must obey the time.   *303*

(*Exit [with Desdemona].*)

RODERIGO. Iago—
IAGO. What say'st thou, noble heart?
RODERIGO. What will I do, think'st thou?
IAGO. Why, go to bed and sleep.
RODERIGO. I will incontinently drown myself.   *308*
IAGO. If thou dost, I shall never love thee after. Why, thou
silly gentleman?
RODERIGO. It is silliness to live when to live is torment;
and then have we a prescription to die when death is   *312*
our physician.
IAGO. Oh, villainous! I have looked upon the world for   *314*
four times seven years, and, since I could distinguish
betwixt a benefit and an injury, I never found man
that knew how to love himself. Ere I would say I
would drown myself for the love of a guinea hen, I   *318*
would change my humanity with a baboon.   *319*
RODERIGO. What should I do? I confess it is my shame
to be so fond, but it is not in my virtue to amend it.   *321*
IAGO. Virtue? A fig! 'Tis in ourselves that we are thus or   *322*
thus. Our bodies are our gardens, to the which our
wills are gardeners; so that if we will plant nettles or
sow lettuce, set hyssop and weed up thyme, supply it   *325*
with one gender of herbs or distract it with many,   *326*
either to have it sterile with idleness or manured with   *327*

---

300 in . . . advantage at the most favorable opportunity. **302 direction** instructions **303 the time**
the urgency of the present crisis. **308 incontinently** immediately, without self-restraint **312 prescription** (1) right based on long-established custom (2) doctor's prescription **314 villainous** i.e.,
what perfect nonsense. **318 guinea hen** (A slang term for a prostitute.) **319 change** exchange
321 fond infatuated. **virtue** strength, nature **322 fig** (To give a fig is to thrust the thumb between
the first and second fingers in a vulgar and insulting gesture.) **325 hyssop** a herb of the mint family
326 gender kind. **distract it with** divide it among **327 idleness** want of cultivation

industry—why, the power and corrigible authority of 328
this lies in our wills. If the beam of our lives had not 329
one scale of reason to poise another of sensuality, the 330
blood and baseness of our natures would conduct us 331
to most preposterous conclusions. But we have reason
to cool our raging motions, our carnal stings, our 333
unbitted lusts, whereof I take this that you call love to 334
be a sect or scion. 335

RODERIGO. It cannot be.

IAGO. It is merely a lust of the blood and a permission
of the will. Come, be a man. Drown thyself? Drown
cats and blind puppies. I have professed me thy friend, 339
and I confess me knit to thy deserving with cables of
perdurable toughness. I could never better stead thee 341
than now. Put money in thy purse. Follow thou the
wars; defeat thy favor with an usurped beard. I say, 343
put money in thy purse. It cannot be long that Desdemona should continue her love to the Moor—put
money in thy purse—nor he his to her. It was a violent commencement in her, and thou shalt see an an- 347
swerable sequestration—put but money in thy purse. 348
These Moors are changeable in their wills—fill thy 349
purse with money. The food that to him now is as
luscious as locusts shall be to him shortly as bitter as 351
coloquintida. She must change for youth; when she is 352
sated with his body, she will find the error of her
choice. She must have change, she must. Therefore
put money in thy purse. If thou wilt needs damn thyself, do it a more delicate way than drowning. Make 356
all the money thou canst. If sanctimony and a frail vow 357
betwixt an erring barbarian and a supersubtle Vene- 358
tian be not too hard for my wits and all the tribe of

---

328 corrigible authority power to correct   **329 beam** balance   **330 poise** counterbalance   **331 blood** natural passions   **333 motions** appetites   **334 unbitted** unbridled, uncontrolled   **335 sect or scion** cutting or offshoot.   **339 blind** i.e., newborn and helpless   **341 perdurable** very durable. **stead** assist   **343 defeat thy favor** disguise your face.   **usurped** (The suggestion is that Roderigo is not man enough to have a beard of his own.)   **347–8 an answerable sequestration** a corresponding cutting off or estrangement   **349 wills** carnal appetites   **351 locusts** fruit of the carob tree (see Matthew 3:4), or perhaps honeysuckle   **352 coloquintida** colocynth or bitter apple, a purgative.   **356 Make** Raise, collect   **357 sanctimony** (1) an aura of goodness (2) love-worship   **358 erring** wandering, vagabond, unsteady

hell, thou shalt enjoy her. Therefore make money. A
pox of drowning thyself! It is clean out of the way.   *361*
Seek thou rather to be hanged in compassing thy joy   *362*
than to be drowned and go without her.

RODERIGO. Wilt thou be fast to my hopes if I depend on   *364*
the issue?   *365*

IAGO. Thou art sure of me. Go, make money. I have
told thee often, and I retell thee again and again, I hate
the Moor. My cause is hearted; thine hath no less rea-   *368*
son. Let us be conjunctive in our revenge against him.   *369*
If thou canst cuckold him, thou dost thyself a pleasure,
me a sport. There are many events in the womb of
time which will be delivered. Traverse, go, provide thy   *372*
money. We will have more of this tomorrow. Adieu.

RODERIGO. Where shall we meet i'th' morning?

IAGO. At my lodging.

RODERIGO. I'll be with thee betimes. (*He starts to leave.*)   *376*

IAGO. Go to, farewell.—Do you hear, Roderigo?   *377*

RODERIGO. What say you?

IAGO. No more of drowning, do you hear?

RODERIGO. I am changed.

IAGO. Go to, farewell. Put money enough in your purse.

RODERIGO. I'll sell all my land.   (*Exit.*)

IAGO. Thus do I ever make my fool my purse;
For I mine own gained knowledge should profane
If I would time expend with such a snipe   *386*
But for my sport and profit. I hate the Moor;
And it is thought abroad that twixt my sheets   *388*
He's done my office. I know not if't be true;   *389*
But I, for mere suspicion in that kind,
Will do as if for surety. He holds me well;   *391*
The better shall my purpose work on him.
Cassio's a proper man. Let me see now: *393*
To get his place and to plume up my will   *394*

---

361 **clean . . . way** entirely unsuitable as a course of action.   362 **compassing** encompassing,
embracing   364 **fast** true   365 **issue** (successful) outcome.   368 **hearted** fixed in the heart, heart-
felt   369 **conjunctive** united   372 **Traverse** (A military marching term.)   376 **betimes** early.
377 **Go to** (An expression of impatience or jollying along others.)   386 **snipe** woodcock, i.e., fool
388 **it is thought abroad** it is rumored   389 **my office** i.e., my sexual function as husband.   391 **do
. . . surety** act as if on certain knowledge.   **holds me well** regards me favorably   393 **proper** handsome   394 **plume up** put a feather in the cap of, i.e., glorify, gratify

In double knavery—How, how?—Let's see:
After some time, to abuse Othello's ear   396
That he is too familiar with his wife.   397
He hath a person and a smooth dispose   398
To be suspected, framed to make women false.   399
The Moor is of a free and open nature,   400
That thinks men honest that but seem to be so,
And will as tenderly be led by the nose   402
As asses are.
I have't. It is engendered. Hell and night
Must bring this monstrous birth to the world's light.

                                                    (*Exit.*)

2.1

Enter Montano and two Gentlemen.

MONTANO. What from the cape can you discern at sea?
FIRST GENTLEMAN. Nothing at all. It is a high-wrought flood.   2
   I cannot, twixt the heaven and the main,   3
   Descry a sail.
MONTANO. Methinks the wind hath spoke aloud at land;
   A fuller blast ne'er shook our battlements.
   If it hath ruffianed so upon the sea,   7
   What ribs of oak, when mountains melt on them,   8
   Can hold the mortise? What shall we hear of this?   9
SECOND GENTLEMAN. A segregation of the Turkish fleet.   10
   For do but stand upon the foaming shore,
   The chidden billow seems to pelt the clouds;   12
   The wind-shaked surge, with high and monstrous mane,   13
   Seems to cast water on the burning Bear   14
   And quench the guards of th'ever-fixèd pole.

---

396 abuse deceive   **397 he** Cassio.   **his** Othello's   **398 dispose** disposition   **399 framed** formed, made   **400 free and open** frank and unsuspecting   **402 tenderly** readily
2.1. Location: A seaport in Cyprus. An open place near the quay.
2 high-wrought flood very agitated sea.   **3 main** ocean. (Also at line 41.)   **7 ruffianed** raged   **8 mountains** i.e., of water   **9 hold the mortise** hold their joints together. (A *mortise* is the socket hollowed out in fitting timbers.)   **10 segregation** dispersal   **12 chidden** i.e., rebuked, repelled (by the shore), and thus shot into the air   **13 monstrous mane** (The surf is like the mane of a wild beast.)   **14 the burning Bear** i.e., the constellation Ursa Minor or the Little Bear, which includes the polestar (and hence regarded as the *guards of th'ever-fixèd pole* in the next line; sometimes the term *guards* is applied to the two "pointers" of the Big Bear or Dipper, which may be intended here.)

I never did like molestation view   *16*
On the enchafèd flood.   *17*
MONTANO. If that the Turkish fleet   *18*
 Be not ensheltered and embayed, they are drowned; *19*
 It is impossible to bear it out.   *20*

(*Enter a [Third] Gentleman.*)

THIRD GENTLEMAN. News, lads! Our wars are done.
 The desperate tempest hath so banged the Turks
 That their designment halts. A noble ship of Venice *23*
 Hath seen a grievous wreck and sufferance *24*
 On most part of their fleet.
MONTANO. How? Is this true?
THIRD GENTLEMAN. The ship is here put in,
 A Veronesa; Michael Cassio,   *28*
 Lieutenant to the warlike Moor Othello,
 Is come on shore; the Moor himself at sea,
 And is in full commission here for Cyprus.
MONTANO. I am glad on't. 'Tis a worthy governor.
THIRD GENTLEMAN. But this same Cassio, though he
  speak of comfort
 Touching the Turkish loss, yet he looks sadly *34*
 And prays the Moor be safe, for they were parted
 With foul and violent tempest.
MONTANO.   Pray heaven he be,
 For I have served him, and the man commands
 Like a full soldier. Let's to the seaside, ho! *38*
 As well to see the vessel that's come in
 As to throw out our eyes for brave Othello,
 Even till we make the main and th'aerial blue *41*
 An indistinct regard.
THIRD GENTLEMAN. Come, let's do so,   *42*
 For every minute is expectancy   *43*
 Of more arrivance.   *44*

---

16 like molestation comparable disturbance **17 enchafèd** angry **18 If that** If **19 embayed** sheltered by a bay **20 bear it out** survive, weather the storm. **23 designment halts** enterprise is crippled. (Literally, "is lame.") **24 wreck** shipwreck. **sufferance** damage, disaster **28 Veronesa** from Verona (and perhaps in service with Venice) **34 sadly** gravely **38 full** perfect **41 the main . . . blue** the sea and the sky **42 An indistinct regard** indistinguishable in our view. **43 is expectancy** gives expectation **44 arrivance** arrival.

(*Enter Cassio.*)

CASSIO. Thanks, you the valiant of this warlike isle,
    That so approve the Moor! Oh, let the heavens   *46*
    Give him defense against the elements,
    For I have lost him on a dangerous sea.
MONTANO. Is he well shipped?
CASSIO. His bark is stoutly timbered, and his pilot
    Of very expert and approved allowance;   *51*
    Therefore my hopes, not surfeited to death,   *52*
    Stand in bold cure.
                ([*A cry*] *within:*) "A sail, a sail, a sail!"   *53*
CASSIO. What noise?
A GENTLEMAN. The town is empty. On the brow o'th' sea   *55*
    Stand ranks of people, and they cry "A sail!"
CASSIO. My hopes do shape him for the governor.   *57*

(*A shot within.*)

SECOND GENTLEMAN. They do discharge their shot of
        courtesy;   *58*
    Our friends at least.
CASSIO.   I pray you, sir, go forth,
    And give us truth who 'tis that is arrived.
SECOND GENTLEMAN. I shall.   (*Exit.*)
MONTANO. But, good Lieutenant, is your general wived?
CASSIO. Most fortunately. He hath achieved a maid
    That paragons description and wild fame,   *64*
    One that excels the quirks of blazoning pens,   *65*
    And in th'essential vesture of creation   *66*
    Does tire the engineer.

(*Enter* [*Second*] *Gentleman.*)

                How now? Who has put in?   *67*
SECOND GENTLEMAN. 'Tis one Iago, ancient to the General.
CASSIO. He's had most favorable and happy speed.

---

46 approve admire, honor   **51 approved allowance** tested reputation   **52–3 not ... cure** not worn
thin through repeated application or delayed fulfillment, strongly persist.   **55 brow o'th' sea** cliff-
edge   **57 My ... governor** I hope and imagine this ship to be Othello's.   **58 discharge ... courtesy**
fire a salute in token of respect and courtesy   **64 paragons** surpasses.   **wild fame** extravagant
report   **65 quirks** witty conceits.   **blazoning** setting forth as though in heraldic language
66–7 And in ... engineer and in her real, God-given, beauty, (she) defeats any attempt to praise her.
(An *engineer* is one who devises, here a poet.)   **67 put in** i.e., to harbor.

Tempests themselves, high seas, and howling winds,
The guttered rocks and congregated sands—   *71*
Traitors ensteeped to clog the guiltless keel—   *72*
As having sense of beauty, do omit   *73*
Their mortal natures, letting go safely by   *74*
The divine Desdemona.
MONTANO.   What is she?
CASSIO. She that I spake of, our great captain's captain,
Left in the conduct of the bold Iago,
Whose footing here anticipates our thoughts   *78*
A sennight's speed. Great Jove, Othello guard,   *79*
And swell his sail with thine own powerful breath,
That he may bless this bay with his tall ship,   *81*
Make love's quick pants in Desdemona's arms,
Give renewed fire to our extincted spirits,
And bring all Cyprus comfort!

(*Enter Desdemona, Iago, Roderigo, and Emilia.*)

                        Oh, behold,
The riches of the ship is come on shore!
You men of Cyprus, let her have your knees.

(*The gentlemen make curtsy to Desdemona.*)

Hail to thee, lady! And the grace of heaven
Before, behind thee, and on every hand
Enwheel thee round!
DESDEMONA.   I thank you, valiant Cassio.
What tidings can you tell me of my lord?
CASSIO. He is not yet arrived, nor know I aught
But that he's well and will be shortly here.
DESDEMONA. Oh, but I fear—How lost you company?
CASSIO. The great contention of the sea and skies
Parted our fellowship.
                        (*Within*) "A sail, a sail!" (*A shot.*)
                        But hark. A sail!
SECOND GENTLEMAN. They give their greeting to the citadel.
This likewise is a friend.

---

71 **guttered** jagged, trenched   72 **ensteeped** lying under water   73 **As** as if.   **omit** forbear to exercise   74 **mortal** deadly   78–9 **Whose ... speed** whose arrival here has happened a week sooner than we expected.   81 **tall** tall-masted

CASSIO.   See for the news.

      (*Exit Second Gentleman.*)

Good Ancient, you are welcome. (*Kissing Emilia.*)
  Welcome, mistress.
Let it not gall your patience, good Iago,
That I extend my manners; 'tis my breeding   *100*
That gives me this bold show of courtesy.
IAGO. Sir, would she give you so much of her lips
  As of her tongue she oft bestows on me,
  You would have enough.
DESDEMONA. Alas, she has no speech!   *105*
IAGO. In faith, too much.
  I find it still, when I have list to sleep.   *107*
  Marry, before Your Ladyship, I grant,
  She puts her tongue a little in her heart
  And chides with thinking.
EMILIA.   You have little cause to say so.   *110*
IAGO. Come on, come on. You are pictures out of doors,   *111*
  Bells in your parlors, wildcats in your kitchens,   *112*
  Saints in your injuries, devils being offended,   *113*
  Players in your huswifery, and huswives in your beds.   *114*
DESDEMONA. Oh, fie upon thee, slanderer!
IAGO. Nay, it is true, or else I am a Turk.   *116*
  You rise to play, and go to bed to work.
EMILIA. You shall not write my praise.
IAGO.   No, let me not.
DESDEMONA. What wouldst write of me, if thou shouldst
   praise me?
IAGO. Oh, gentle lady, do not put me to't,
  For I am nothing if not critical.   *121*
DESDEMONA. Come on, essay.—There's one gone to the
   harbor?   *122*
IAGO. Ay, madam.

---

100 **extend** give scope to.   **breeding** training in the niceties of etiquette   105 **she has no speech** i.e., she's not a chatterbox, as you allege.   107 **still** always.   **list** desire   110 **with thinking** i.e., in her thoughts only.   111 **pictures out of doors** i.e., as pretty as pictures, and silently well-behaved in public   112 **Bells** i.e., jangling, noisy, and brazen.   **in your kitchens** i.e., in domestic affairs. (Ladies would not do the cooking.)   113 **Saints ... injuries** i.e., putting on airs of sanctity and innocence when wronged by others   114 **Players ... beds** play-actors at domesticity and truly energetic only as lovers in bed.   116 **a Turk** an infidel, not to be believed.   121 **critical** censorious.   122 **essay** try.

DESDEMONA. I am not merry, but I do beguile
   The thing I am by seeming otherwise.   *125*
   Come, how wouldst thou praise me?
IAGO. I am about it, but indeed my invention
   Comes from my pate as birdlime does from frieze—   *128*
   It plucks out brains and all. But my Muse labors,   *129*
   And thus she is delivered:
   If she be fair and wise, fairness and wit,
   The one's for use, the other useth it.   *132*
DESDEMONA. Well praised! How if she be black and witty?   *133*
IAGO. If she be black, and thereto have a wit,
   She'll find a white that shall her blackness fit.   *135*
DESDEMONA. Worse and worse.
EMILIA.   How if fair and foolish?
IAGO. She never yet was foolish that was fair,
   For even her folly helped her to an heir.   *138*
DESDEMONA. These are old fond paradoxes to make fools   *139*
   laugh i'th'alehouse. What miserable praise hast thou
   for her that's foul and foolish?   *141*
IAGO. There's none so foul and foolish thereunto,   *142*
   But does foul pranks which fair and wise ones do.   *143*
DESDEMONA. Oh, heavy ignorance! Thou praisest the worst
   best. But what praise couldst thou bestow on a deserv-
   ing woman indeed, one that, in the authority of her mer-
   it, did justly put on the vouch of very malice itself?   *147*
IAGO. She that was ever fair, and never proud,
   Had tongue at will, and yet was never loud,   *149*
   Never lacked gold and yet went never gay,   *150*
   Fled from her wish, and yet said, "Now I may,"   *151*
   She that being angered, her revenge being nigh,
   Bade her wrong stay and her displeasure fly,   *153*

---

125 The thing I am i.e., my anxious self   **128 birdlime** sticky substance used to catch small birds. **frieze** coarse woolen cloth   **129 labors** (1) exerts herself (2) prepares to deliver a child. (With a following pun on *delivered* in line 130.)   **132 The one's . . . it** i.e., her cleverness will make use of her beauty.   **133 black** dark-complexioned, brunette   **135 She'll . . . fit** she will find a fair-complexioned mate suited to her dark complexion. (Punning on *wight*, person, and contrasting *white* and *black*, with suggestion of sexual coupling.)   **138 folly** (With added meaning of "lechery, wantonness.")   **to an heir** i.e., to bear a child.   **139 fond** foolish   **141 foul** ugly   **142 thereunto** in addition   **143 foul** sluttish   **147 put . . . vouch** compel the approval   **149 Had . . . will** was never at a loss for words   **150 gay** extravagantly clothed   **151 Fled . . . may** avoided temptation where the choice was hers   **153 Bade . . . stay** i.e., resolved to put up with her injury and bade her anger to cease

She that in wisdom never was so frail
To change the cod's head for the salmon's tail, 155
She that could think and ne'er disclose her mind,
See suitors following and not look behind,
She was a wight, if ever such wight were—
DESDEMONA. To do what?
IAGO. To suckle fools and chronicle small beer. 160
DESDEMONA. Oh, most lame and impotent conclusion! Do
not learn of him, Emilia, though he be thy husband.
How say you, Cassio? Is he not a most profane and 163
liberal counselor? 164
CASSIO. He speaks home, madam. You may relish him 165
more in the soldier than in the scholar. 166

(*Cassio and Desdemona stand together, conversing intimately.*)

IAGO (*aside*). He takes her by the palm. Ay, well said, 167
whisper. With as little a web as this will I ensnare as
great a fly as Cassio. Ay, smile upon her, do; I will
gyve thee in thine own courtship. You say true; 'tis so, 170
indeed. If such tricks as these strip you out of your
lieutenantry, it had been better you had not kissed
your three fingers so oft, which now again you are
most apt to play the sir in. Very good; well kissed! An 174
excellent courtesy! 'Tis so, indeed. Yet again your fingers to your lips? Would they were clyster pipes for 176
your sake! (*Trumpet within.*) The Moor! I know his
trumpet.
CASSIO. 'Tis truly so.
DESDEMONA. Let's meet him and receive him.
CASSIO. Lo, where he comes!

(*Enter Othello and attendants.*)

OTHELLO. Oh, my fair warrior!

---

155 **To . . . tail** i.e., to be selfishly demanding and ambitious. (The fish's lower body, below the rib cage, has fewest bones and is generally the succulent portion. With sexual implication as well: *cod's head* can be slang for "penis," and *tail* for "pudendum.") 160 **To . . . beer** i.e., To breastfeed babies and keep petty household accounts. 163–4 **profane and liberal** irreverent and licentious 165 **home** right to the target. (A term from fencing.) **relish** appreciate 166 **in** in the character of 167 **well said** well done 170 **gyve** fetter, shackle. **courtship** courtesy, show of courtly manners. **You say true** i.e., That's right, go ahead 174 **the sir** i.e., the fine gentleman 176 **clyster pipes** tubes used for enemas and douches

DESDEMONA.   My dear Othello!
OTHELLO. It gives me wonder great as my content
    To see you here before me. O my soul's joy,
    If after every tempest come such calms,
    May the winds blow till they have wakened death,
    And let the laboring bark climb hills of seas
    Olympus-high, and duck again as low
    As hell's from heaven! If it were now to die,
    'Twere now to be most happy, for I fear
    My soul hath her content so absolute
    That not another comfort like to this
    Succeeds in unknown fate.
DESDEMONA.   The heavens forbid   192
    But that our loves and comforts should increase
    Even as our days do grow!
OTHELLO. Amen to that, sweet powers!
    I cannot speak enough of this content.
    It stops me here; it is too much of joy.
    And this, and this, the greatest discords be   198

(*They kiss.*)

    That e'er our hearts shall make!
IAGO (*aside*). Oh, you are well tuned now!
    But I'll set down the pegs that make this music,   201
    As honest as I am.   202
OTHELLO. Come, let us to the castle.
    News, friends! Our wars are done, the Turks are drowned.
    How does my old acquaintance of this isle?—
    Honey, you shall be well desired in Cyprus;   206
    I have found great love amongst them. Oh, my sweet,
    I prattle out of fashion, and I dote   208
    In mine own comforts.—I prithee, good Iago,
    Go to the bay and disembark my coffers.   210
    Bring thou the master to the citadel;   211
    He is a good one, and his worthiness
    Does challenge much respect.—Come, Desdemona.—   213
    Once more, well met at Cyprus!

---

192 Succeeds ... fate i.e., can follow in the unknown future.   **198.1 *They kiss*** (The direction is from the Quarto.)   **201 set down** loosen (and hence untune the instrument)   **202 As ... I am** for all my supposed honesty.   **206 desired** sought after   **208 out of fashion** indecorously, incoherently   **210 coffers** chests, baggage.   **211 master** ship's captain   **213 challenge** lay claim to, deserve

(Exeunt Othello and Desdemona [and all but Iago and Roderigo].)

IAGO *(to a departing attendant)*. Do thou meet me
    presently at the harbor. *(To Roderigo)* Come hither. If
    thou be'st valiant—as, they say, base men being in love   *217*
    have then a nobility in their natures more than is
    native to them—list me. The Lieutenant tonight   *219*
    watches on the court of guard. First, I must tell thee   *220*
    this: Desdemona is directly in love with him.
RODERIGO. With him? Why, 'tis not possible.
IAGO. Lay thy finger thus, and let thy soul be instructed.   *223*
    Mark me with what violence she first loved the Moor,
    but for bragging and telling her fantastical lies. To love *225*
    him still for prating? Let not thy discreet heart think it.
    Her eye must be fed; and what delight shall she have
    to look on the devil? When the blood is made dull with
    the act of sport, there should be, again to inflame it   *229*
    and to give satiety a fresh appetite, loveliness in favor, *230*
    sympathy in years, manners, and beauties—all which   *231*
    the Moor is defective in. Now, for want of these
    required conveniences, her delicate tenderness will   *233*
    find itself abused, begin to heave the gorge, disrelish   *234*
    and abhor the Moor. Very nature will instruct her in it   *235*
    and compel her to some second choice. Now, sir, this
    granted—as it is a most pregnant and unforced   *237*
    position—who stands so eminent in the degree of this   *238*
    fortune as Cassio does? A knave very voluble, no   *239*
    further conscionable than in putting on the mere form   *240*
    of civil and humane seeming for the better compass-   *241*
    ing of his salt and most hidden loose affection. Why,   *242*
    none, why, none. A slipper and subtle knave, a finder   *243*
    out of occasions, that has an eye can stamp and   *244*
    counterfeit advantages, though true advantage never   *245*

---

217 base men even ignoble men   **219 list** listen to   **220 court of guard** guardhouse. (Cassio is in charge of the watch.)   **223 thus** i.e., on your lips   **225 but** only   **229 the act of sport** sex   **230 favor** appearance   **231 sympathy** correspondence, similarity   **233 required conveniences** things conducive to sexual compatibility   **234 abused** cheated, revolted.   **heave the gorge** experience nausea   **235 Very nature** Her very instincts   **237 pregnant** evident, cogent   **238 in . . . of** as next in line for   **239 voluble** facile, glib   **240 conscionable** conscientious, conscience-bound   **241 humane** polite, courteous   **242 salt** licentious.   **affection** passion.   **243 slipper** slippery   **244 an eye can stamp** an eye that can coin, create   **245 advantages** favorable opportunities

present itself; a devilish knave. Besides, the knave is
handsome, young, and hath all those requisites in him
that folly and green minds look after. A pestilent   *248*
complete knave, and the woman hath found him   *249*
already.

RODERIGO. I cannot believe that in her. She's full of
most blessed condition.   *252*

IAGO. Blessed fig's end! The wine she drinks is made of   *253*
grapes. If she had been blessed, she would never have
loved the Moor. Blessed pudding! Didst thou not see   *255*
her paddle with the palm of his hand? Didst not mark
that?

RODERIGO. Yes, that I did; but that was but courtesy.

IAGO. Lechery, by this hand. An index and obscure pro-   *259*
logue to the history of lust and foul thoughts. They
met so near with their lips that their breaths embraced
together. Villainous thoughts, Roderigo! When these
mutualities so marshal the way, hard at hand comes   *263*
the master and main exercise, th'incorporate conclu-   *264*
sion. Pish! But, sir, be you ruled by me. I have brought
you from Venice. Watch you tonight; for the com-   *266*
mand, I'll lay't upon you. Cassio knows you not. I'll   *267*
not be far from you. Do you find some occasion to
anger Cassio, either by speaking too loud, or tainting   *269*
his discipline, or from what other course you please,
which the time shall more favorably minister.   *271*

RODERIGO. Well.

IAGO. Sir, he's rash and very sudden in choler, and haply   *273*
may strike at you. Provoke him that he may, for
even out of that will I cause these of Cyprus to mutiny,   *275*
whose qualification shall come into no true taste again   *276*
but by the displanting of Cassio. So shall you have a
shorter journey to your desires by the means I shall
then have to prefer them, and the impediment most   *279*

---

248 **folly** wantonness. **green** immature   249 **found him** sized him up, perceived his intent
252 **condition** disposition.   253 **fig's end** (See 1.3.322 for the vulgar gesture of the fig.)   255 **pud-**
ding sausage.   259 **index** table of contents. **obscure** veiled, hidden   263 **mutualities** exchanges,
intimacies. **hard at hand** closely following   264 **th'incorporate** the carnal   266 **Watch you** Stand
watch   266-7 **for . . . you** I'll arrange for you to be appointed, given orders; or, I'll put you in charge.
269 **tainting** disparaging   271 **minister** provide.   273 **choler** wrath. **haply** perhaps   275 **mutiny**
riot   276 **qualification** pacification. **true taste** i.e., acceptable state   279 **prefer** advance

profitably removed, without the which there were no
expectation of our prosperity.

RODERIGO. I will do this, if you can bring it to any
opportunity.

IAGO. I warrant thee. Meet me by and by at the citadel.   284
I must fetch his necessaries ashore. Farewell.

RODERIGO. Adieu.   (*Exit.*)

IAGO. That Cassio loves her, I do well believe't;
That she loves him, 'tis apt and of great credit.   288
The Moor, howbeit that I endure him not,
Is of a constant, loving, noble nature,
And I dare think he'll prove to Desdemona
A most dear husband. Now, I do love her too,
Not out of absolute lust—though peradventure
I stand accountant for as great a sin—   294
But partly led to diet my revenge   295
For that I do suspect the lusty Moor
Hath leaped into my seat, the thought whereof
Doth, like a poisonous mineral, gnaw my innards;
And nothing can or shall content my soul
Till I am evened with him, wife for wife,
Or failing so, yet that I put the Moor
At least into a jealousy so strong
That judgment cannot cure. Which thing to do,
If this poor trash of Venice, whom I trace   304
For his quick hunting, stand the putting on,   305
I'll have our Michael Cassio on the hip,   306
Abuse him to the Moor in the rank garb—   307
For I fear Cassio with my nightcap too—   308
Make the Moor thank me, love me, and reward me
For making him egregiously an ass
And practicing upon his peace and quiet   311
Even to madness. 'Tis here, but yet confused.
Knavery's plain face is never seen till used.   (*Exit.*)

---

284 warrant assure. **by and by** immediately   **288 apt** probable.   **credit** credibility.
294 accountant accountable   **295 diet** feed   **304 trace** i.e., pursue, dog; or, keep hungry (?) or
perhaps *trash,* a hunting term, meaning to put weights on a hunting dog in order to slow him down
305 For to make more eager for.   **stand ... on** responds properly when I incite him to quarrel
306 on the hip at my mercy, where I can throw him. (A wrestling term.)   **307 Abuse** slander.
rank garb coarse manner, gross fashion   **308 with my nightcap** i.e., as a rival in my bed, as one
who gives me cuckold's horns   **311 practicing upon** plotting against

2.2

Enter Othello's Herald with a proclamation.

HERALD. It is Othello's pleasure, our noble and valiant
general, that, upon certain tidings now arrived, im-
porting the mere perdition of the Turkish fleet, every   *3*
man put himself into triumph: some to dance, some to   *4*
make bonfires, each man to what sport and revels his
addiction leads him. For, besides these beneficial   *6*
news, it is the celebration of his nuptial. So much was
his pleasure should be proclaimed. All offices are open,   *8*
and there is full liberty of feasting from this present
hour of five till the bell have told eleven. Heaven bless
the isle of Cyprus and our noble general Othello!

(Exit.)

2.3

Enter Othello, Desdemona, Cassio, and attendants.

OTHELLO. Good Michael, look you to the guard tonight.
 Let's teach ourselves that honorable stop   *2*
 Not to outsport discretion.   *3*
CASSIO. Iago hath direction what to do,
 But notwithstanding, with my personal eye
 Will I look to't.
OTHELLO.   Iago is most honest.
 Michael, good night. Tomorrow with your earliest   *7*
 Let me have speech with you. (*To Desdemona*) Come,
  my dear love,
 The purchase made, the fruits are to ensue;   *9*
 That profit's yet to come 'tween me and you.—   *10*
 Good night.

2.2. Location: Cyprus.
3 **mere perdition** complete destruction 4 **triumph** public celebration 6 **addiction** inclination
8 **offices** rooms where food and drink are kept
2.3. Location: Cyprus. The citadel.
2 **stop** restraint 3 **outsport** celebrate beyond the bounds of 7 **with your earliest** at your earliest
convenience 9–10 **The purchase ... you** i.e., though married, we haven't yet consummated our
love. (Possibly, too, Othello is referring to pregnancy. At all events, his desire for sexual union is
manifest.)

(*Exit [Othello, with Desdemona and attendants].*)

(*Enter Iago.*)

CASSIO. Welcome, Iago. We must to the watch.

IAGO. Not this hour, Lieutenant; 'tis not yet ten o'th'   *13*
    clock. Our general cast us thus early for the love of his   *14*
    Desdemona; who let us not therefore blame. He hath   *15*
    not yet made wanton the night with her, and she is
    sport for Jove.

CASSIO. She's a most exquisite lady.

IAGO. And, I'll warrant her, full of game.

CASSIO. Indeed, she's a most fresh and delicate creature.

IAGO. What an eye she has! Methinks it sounds a parley   *21*
    to provocation.

CASSIO. An inviting eye, and yet methinks right modest.

IAGO. And when she speaks, is it not an alarum to love?   *24*

CASSIO. She is indeed perfection.

IAGO. Well, happiness to their sheets! Come, Lieutenant,
    I have a stoup of wine, and here without are a brace of   *27*
    Cyprus gallants that would fain have a measure to the   *28*
    health of black Othello.

CASSIO. Not tonight, good Iago. I have very poor and
    unhappy brains for drinking. I could well wish cour-
    tesy would invent some other custom of entertain-
    ment.

IAGO. Oh, they are our friends. But one cup! I'll drink for   *34*
    you.   *35*

CASSIO. I have drunk but one cup tonight, and that was
    craftily qualified too, and behold what innovation it   *37*
    makes here. I am unfortunate in the infirmity and   *38*
    dare not task my weakness with any more.

IAGO. What, man? 'Tis a night of revels. The gallants
    desire it.

CASSIO. Where are they?

IAGO. Here at the door. I pray you, call them in.

---

13 Not this hour Not for an hour yet   **14 cast** dismissed   **15 who** i.e., Othello   **21 sounds a parley**
calls for a conference, issues an invitation   **24 alarum** signal calling men to arms. (Continuing the
military metaphor of *parley*, line 21.)   **27 stoup** measure of liquor, two quarts.   **without** outside.
brace pair   **28 fain have a measure** gladly drink a toast   **34–5 for you** in your place. (Iago will do
the steady drinking to keep the gallants company while Cassio has only one cup.)   **37 qualified**
diluted.   **innovation** disturbance, insurrection   **38 here** i.e., in my head.

CASSIO. I'll do't, but it dislikes me.   (*Exit.*)   44
IAGO. If I can fasten but one cup upon him,
    With that which he hath drunk tonight already,
    He'll be as full of quarrel and offense   47
    As my young mistress' dog. Now, my sick fool
        Roderigo,
    Whom love hath turned almost the wrong side out,
    To Desdemona hath tonight caroused   50
    Potations pottle-deep; and he's to watch.   51
    Three lads of Cyprus—noble swelling spirits,   52
    That hold their honors in a wary distance,   53
    The very elements of this warlike isle—   54
    Have I tonight flustered with flowing cups,
    And they watch too. Now, 'mongst this flock of
        drunkards   56
    Am I to put our Cassio in some action
    That may offend the isle.—But here they come.

(*Enter Cassio, Montano, and gentlemen; [servants following
with wine].*)

    If consequence do but approve my dream,   59
    My boat sails freely both with wind and stream.   60
CASSIO. 'Fore God, they have given me a rouse already.   61
MONTANO. Good faith, a little one; not past a pint, as I
    am a soldier.
IAGO. Some wine, ho!
    (*He sings.*). "And let me the cannikin clink, clink,   65
        And let me the cannikin clink.
          A soldier's a man,
          Oh, man's life's but a span;   68
        Why, then, let a soldier drink."
    Some wine, boys!
CASSIO. 'Fore God, an excellent song.
IAGO. I learned it in England, where indeed they are
    most potent in potting. Your Dane, your German, and   73

---

44 it dislikes me i.e., I'm reluctant. **47 offense** readiness to give or take offense **50 caroused**
drunk off **51 pottle-deep** to the bottom of the tankard. **watch** stand watch. **52 swelling** proud
53 hold ... distance i.e., are extremely sensitive of their honor **54 elements** lifeblood **56 watch**
are members of the guard **59 If ... dream** If subsequent events will only confirm my dreams and
hopes **60 stream** current. **61 rouse** full draft of liquor **65 cannikin** small drinking vessel
68 span brief span of time. (Compare Psalm 39:5 as rendered in the Book of Common Prayer:
"Thou hast made my days as it were a span long.") **73 potting** drinking.

your swag-bellied Hollander—drink, ho!—are nothing to your English.

CASSIO. Is your Englishman so exquisite in his drinking?

IAGO. Why, he drinks you, with facility, your Dane   77
dead drunk; he sweats not to overthrow your Almain;   78
he gives your Hollander a vomit ere the next pottle can
be filled.

CASSIO. To the health of our general!

MONTANO. I am for it, Lieutenant, and I'll do you justice.   82

IAGO. O sweet England! (*He sings.*)

"King Stephen was and-a worthy peer,
    His breeches cost him but a crown;
He held them sixpence all too dear,
    With that he called the tailor lown.   87

He was a wight of high renown,
    And thou art but of low degree.
'Tis pride that pulls the country down;   90
    Then take thy auld cloak about thee."   91

Some wine, ho!

CASSIO. 'Fore God, this is a more exquisite song than
the other.

IAGO. Will you hear't again?

CASSIO. No, for I hold him to be unworthy of his place
that does those things. Well, God's above all; and
there be souls must be saved, and there be souls must
not be saved.

IAGO. It's true, good Lieutenant.

CASSIO. For mine own part—no offense to the General,
nor any man of quality—I hope to be saved.   102

IAGO. And so do I too, Lieutenant.

CASSIO. Ay, but, by your leave, not before me; the lieutenant is to be saved before the ancient. Let's have no
more of this; let's to our affairs.—God forgive us our
sins!—Gentlemen, let's look to our business. Do not
think, gentlemen, I am drunk. This is my ancient; this

---

77 drinks you drinks.   **your Dane** your typical Dane   **78 sweats not** i.e., need not exert himself.
Almain German   **82 I'll . . . justice** i.e., I'll drink as much as you.   **87 lown** lout, rascal.   **90 pride**
i.e., extravagance in dress   **91 auld** old   **102 quality** rank

is my right hand, and this is my left. I am not drunk
now. I can stand well enough, and speak well enough.

GENTLEMEN. Excellent well.

CASSIO. Why, very well then; you must not think then
that I am drunk. (*Exit.*)

MONTANO. To th' platform, masters. Come, let's set the
watch. 114

(*Exeunt Gentlemen.*)

IAGO. You see this fellow that is gone before.
He's a soldier fit to stand by Caesar
And give direction; and do but see his vice.
'Tis to his virtue a just equinox, 118
The one as long as th'other. 'Tis pity of him.
I fear the trust Othello puts him in,
On some odd time of his infirmity,
Will shake this island.

MONTANO. But is he often thus?

IAGO. 'Tis evermore the prologue to his sleep.
He'll watch the horologe a double set, 124
If drink rock not his cradle.

MONTANO. It were well
The General were put in mind of it.
Perhaps he sees it not, or his good nature
Prizes the virtue that appears in Cassio
And looks not on his evils. Is not this true?

(*Enter Roderigo.*)

IAGO (*aside to him*). How now, Roderigo?
I pray you, after the Lieutenant; go. (*Exit Roderigo.*)

MONTANO. And 'tis great pity that the noble Moor
Should hazard such a place as his own second 133
With one of an engraffed infirmity. 134
It were an honest action to say so
To the Moor.

IAGO. Not I, for this fair island.

---

114 **set the watch** mount the guard.   118 **just equinox** exact counterpart. (*Equinox* is an equal
length of days and nights.)   124 **watch ... set** stay awake twice around the clock or *horologe*
133–4 **hazard ... With** risk giving such an important position as his second in command to
134 **engraffed** engrafted, inveterate

I do love Cassio well and would do much
To cure him of this evil.   (*Cry within:* "Help! Help!")
                    But, hark! What noise?   138

(*Enter Cassio, pursuing Roderigo.*)

CASSIO. Zounds, you rogue! You rascal!
MONTANO. What's the matter, Lieutenant?
CASSIO. A knave teach me my duty? I'll beat the knave
   into a twiggen bottle.   142
RODERIGO. Beat me?
CASSIO. Dost thou prate, rogue? (*He strikes Roderigo.*)
MONTANO. Nay, good Lieutenant. (*Restraining him.*) I
   pray you, sir, hold your hand.
CASSIO. Let me go, sir, or I'll knock you o'er the mazard.   148
MONTANO. Come, come, you're drunk.
CASSIO. Drunk?   (*They fight.*)
IAGO (*aside to Roderigo*).
   Away, I say. Go out and cry a mutiny.   151

                    (*Exit Roderigo.*)

Nay, good Lieutenant—God's will, gentlemen—
Help, ho!—Lieutenant—sir—Montano—sir—
Help, masters!—Here's a goodly watch indeed!   154

(*A bell rings.*)

Who's that which rings the bell?—Diablo, ho!   155
The town will rise. God's will, Lieutenant, hold!   156
You'll be ashamed forever.

(*Enter Othello and attendants [with weapons].*)

OTHELLO. What is the matter here?
MONTANO.   Zounds, I bleed still.
   I am hurt to th' death. He dies! (*He thrusts at Cassio.*)
OTHELLO.   Hold, for your lives!

138.1 *pursuing* (The Quarto text reads, "*driuing in*.") **142 twiggen** wicker-covered. (Cassio vows to assail Roderigo until his skin resembles wickerwork or until he has driven Roderigo through the holes in a wickerwork.) **148 mazard** i.e., head. (Literally, a drinking vessel.) **151 mutiny** riot. **154 masters** sirs. **154.1 *A bell rings*** (This direction is from the Quarto, as are *Exit Roderigo* at line 131, *They fight* at line 150, and *with weapons* at line 157.1.) **155 Diablo** The devil **156 rise** grow riotous.

495

IAGO. Hold, ho! Lieutenant—sir—Montano—gentlemen—
    Have you forgot all sense of place and duty?
    Hold! The General speaks to you. Hold, for shame!
OTHELLO. Why, how now, ho! From whence ariseth this?
    Are we turned Turks, and to ourselves do that   *164*
    Which heaven hath forbid the Ottomites?   *165*
    For Christian shame, put by this barbarous brawl!
    He that stirs next to carve for his own rage   *167*
    Holds his soul light; he dies upon his motion.   *168*
    Silence that dreadful bell. It frights the isle
    From her propriety. What is the matter, masters?   *170*
    Honest Iago, that looks dead with grieving,
    Speak. Who began this? On thy love, I charge thee.
IAGO. I do not know. Friends all but now, even now,
    In quarter and in terms like bride and groom   *174*
    Devesting them for bed; and then, but now—   *175*
    As if some planet had unwitted men—
    Swords out, and tilting one at others' breasts
    In opposition bloody. I cannot speak   *178*
    Any beginning to this peevish odds;   *179*
    And would in action glorious I had lost
    Those legs that brought me to a part of it!
OTHELLO. How comes it, Michael, you are thus forgot?   *182*
CASSIO. I pray you, pardon me. I cannot speak.
OTHELLO. Worthy Montano, you were wont be civil;   *184*
    The gravity and stillness of your youth   *185*
    The world hath noted, and your name is great
    In mouths of wisest censure. What's the matter   *187*
    That you unlace your reputation thus   *188*
    And spend your rich opinion for the name   *189*
    Of a night-brawler? Give me answer to it.
MONTANO. Worthy Othello, I am hurt to danger.
    Your officer, Iago, can inform you—

164–5 to ourselves . . . Ottomites inflict on ourselves the harm that heaven has prevented the Turks
from doing (by destroying their fleet).   **167 carve for** i.e., indulge, satisfy with his sword
168 Holds . . . light i.e., places little value on his life.   **upon his motion** if he moves.   **170 propriety**
proper state or condition.   **174 In quarter . . . terms** in conduct and speech   **175 Devesting them**
undressing themselves   **178 speak** explain   **179 peevish odds** childish quarrel   **182 are thus forgot**
have forgotten yourself thus.   **184 wont be** accustomed to be   **185 stillness** sobriety   **187 censure**
judgment.   **188 unlace** undo, lay open (as one might loose the strings of a purse containing reputation)   **189 opinion** reputation

While I spare speech, which something now offends
    me—   *193*
Of all that I do know; nor know I aught
By me that's said or done amiss this night,
Unless self-charity be sometimes a vice,
And to defend ourselves it be a sin
When violence assails us.

OTHELLO.   Now, by heaven,
My blood begins my safer guides to rule, *199*
And passion, having my best judgment collied, *200*
Essays to lead the way. Zounds, if I stir, *201*
Or do but lift this arm, the best of you
Shall sink in my rebuke. Give me to know
How this foul rout began, who set it on; *204*
And he that is approved in this offense, *205*
Though he had twinned with me, both at a birth,
Shall lose me. What? In a town of war *207*
Yet wild, the people's hearts brim full of fear,
To manage private and domestic quarrel? *209*
In night, and on the court and guard of safety? *210*
'Tis monstrous. Iago, who began't?

MONTANO (*to Iago*). If partially affined, or leagued in office, *212*
Thou dost deliver more or less than truth,
Thou art no soldier.

IAGO.   Touch me not so near.
I had rather have this tongue cut from my mouth
Than it should do offense to Michael Cassio;
Yet, I persuade myself, to speak the truth
Shall nothing wrong him. Thus it is, General:
Montano and myself being in speech,
There comes a fellow crying out for help,
And Cassio following him with determined sword
To execute upon him. Sir, this gentleman *222*

(*indicating Montano*)

---

193 something somewhat. **offends** pains **199 blood** passion (of anger). **guides** i.e., reason
200 collied darkened **201 Essays** undertakes **204 rout** riot **205 approved in** found guilty of
207 town of town garrisoned for **209 manage** undertake **210 on . . . safety** at the main guardhouse
or headquarters and on watch. **212 If . . . office** If made partial by personal relationship or by your
being fellow officers **222 execute upon him** (1) proceed violently against him (2) execute him.

Steps in to Cassio and entreats his pause. 223
Myself the crying fellow did pursue,
Lest by his clamor—as it so fell out—
The town might fall in fright. He, swift of foot,
Outran my purpose, and I returned, the rather 227
For that I heard the clink and fall of swords
And Cassio high in oath, which till tonight
I ne'er might say before. When I came back—
For this was brief—I found them close together
At blow and thrust, even as again they were
When you yourself did part them.
More of this matter cannot I report.
But men are men; the best sometimes forget. 235
Though Cassio did some little wrong to him,
As men in rage strike those that wish them best, 237
Yet surely Cassio, I believe, received
From him that fled some strange indignity,
Which patience could not pass.
OTHELLO.   I know, Iago, 240
Thy honesty and love doth mince this matter,
Making it light to Cassio. Cassio, I love thee,
But nevermore be officer of mine.

(*Enter Desdemona, attended.*)

Look if my gentle love be not raised up.
I'll make thee an example.
DESDEMONA. What is the matter, dear?
OTHELLO.   All's well now, sweeting;
Come away to bed. (*To Montano*) Sir, for your hurts,
Myself will be your surgeon.—Lead him off. 248

(*Montano is led off.*)

Iago, look with care about the town
And silence those whom this vile brawl distracted.
Come, Desdemona. 'Tis the soldiers' life
To have their balmy slumbers waked with strife.

(*Exit [with all but Iago and Cassio].*)

---

223 his pause him to stop.   **227 rather** sooner   **235 forget** forget themselves.   **237 those . . . best** i.e., even those who are well disposed toward them   **240 pass** pass over, overlook.   **248 be your surgeon** i.e., make sure you receive medical attention.

IAGO. What, are you hurt, Lieutenant?

CASSIO. Ay, past all surgery.

IAGO. Marry, God forbid!

CASSIO. Reputation, reputation, reputation! Oh, I have lost my reputation! I have lost the immortal part of myself, and what remains is bestial. My reputation, Iago, my reputation!

IAGO. As I am an honest man, I thought you had received some bodily wound; there is more sense in that than in reputation. Reputation is an idle and most false imposition, oft got without merit and lost without deserving. You have lost no reputation at all, unless you repute yourself such a loser. What, man, there are more ways to recover the General again. You are but now cast in his mood—a punishment more in policy than in malice, even so as one would beat his offenseless dog to affright an imperious lion. Sue to him again and he's yours. 263 266 267 268 269

CASSIO. I will rather sue to be despised than to deceive so good a commander with so slight, so drunken, and so indiscreet an officer. Drunk? And speak parrot? And squabble? Swagger? Swear? And discourse fustian with one's own shadow? O thou invisible spirit of wine, if thou hast no name to be known by, let us call thee devil! 272 273

IAGO. What was he that you followed with your sword? What had he done to you?

CASSIO. I know not.

IAGO. Is't possible?

CASSIO. I remember a mass of things, but nothing distinctly; a quarrel, but nothing wherefore. Oh, God, that men should put an enemy in their mouths to steal away their brains! That we should, with joy, pleasance, revel, and applause transform ourselves into beasts! 283 286

---

263 false imposition thing artificially imposed and of no real value **266 recover** regain favor with **267 cast in his mood** dismissed in a moment of anger **267–8 in policy** done for expediency's sake and as a public gesture **268–9 would . . . lion** i.e., would make an example of a minor offender in order to deter more important and dangerous offenders. **269 Sue** Petition **272 slight** worthless **273 speak parrot** talk nonsense, rant. (*Discourse fustian*, lines 274–5, has much the same meaning.) **283 wherefore** why. **286 applause** desire for applause

IAGO. Why, but you are now well enough. How came you thus recovered?

CASSIO. It hath pleased the devil drunkenness to give place to the devil wrath. One unperfectness shows me another, to make me frankly despise myself.

IAGO. Come, you are too severe a moraler. As the time, the place, and the condition of this country stands, I could heartily wish this had not befallen; but since it is as it is, mend it for your own good. 293

CASSIO. I will ask him for my place again; he shall tell me I am a drunkard. Had I as many mouths as Hydra, such an answer would stop them all. To be now a sensible man, by and by a fool, and presently a beast! Oh, strange! Every inordinate cup is unblessed, and the ingredient is a devil. 298 301

IAGO. Come, come, good wine is a good familiar creature, if it be well used. Exclaim no more against it. And, good Lieutenant, I think you think I love you.

CASSIO. I have well approved it, sir. I drunk! 306

IAGO. You or any man living may be drunk at a time, man. I'll tell you what you shall do. Our general's wife is now the general—I may say so in this respect, for that he hath devoted and given up himself to the contemplation, mark, and denotement of her parts and graces. Confess yourself freely to her; importune her help to put you in your place again. She is of so free, so kind, so apt, so blessed a disposition, she holds it a vice in her goodness not to do more than she is requested. This broken joint between you and her husband entreat her to splinter; and, my fortunes against any lay worth naming, this crack of your love shall grow stronger than it was before. 307 309 310 311 314 317 318

CASSIO. You advise me well.

IAGO. I protest, in the sincerity of love and honest kindness. 321

---

293 moraler moralizer.   **298 Hydra** the Lernaean Hydra, a monster with many heads and the ability to grow two heads when one was cut off, slain by Hercules as the second of his twelve labors **301 inordinate** immoderate   **306 approved** proved by experience   **307 at a time** at one time or another   **309–10 for that** that   **311 mark, and denotement** (Both words mean "observation.") **parts** qualities   **314 free** generous   **317 splinter** bind with splints   **318 lay** stake, wager **321 protest** insist, declare

CASSIO. I think it freely; and betimes in the morning I 323
  will beseech the virtuous Desdemona to undertake for
  me. I am desperate of my fortunes if they check me 325
  here.
IAGO. You are in the right. Good night, Lieutenant. I
  must to the watch.
CASSIO. Good night, honest Iago.   (*Exit Cassio.*)
IAGO. And what's he then that says I play the villain,
  When this advice is free I give, and honest, 331
  Probal to thinking, and indeed the course 332
  To win the Moor again? For 'tis most easy
  Th'inclining Desdemona to subdue 334
  In any honest suit; she's framed as fruitful 335
  As the free elements. And then for her 336
  To win the Moor—were't to renounce his baptism,
  All seals and symbols of redeemèd sin— 338
  His soul is so enfettered to her love
  That she may make, unmake, do what she list,
  Even as her appetite shall play the god 341
  With his weak function. How am I then a villain, 342
  To counsel Cassio to this parallel course 343
  Directly to his good? Divinity of hell! 344
  When devils will the blackest sins put on, 345
  They do suggest at first with heavenly shows, 346
  As I do now. For whiles this honest fool
  Plies Desdemona to repair his fortune,
  And she for him pleads strongly to the Moor,
  I'll pour this pestilence into his ear,
  That she repeals him for her body's lust; 351
  And by how much she strives to do him good,
  She shall undo her credit with the Moor.
  So will I turn her virtue into pitch, 354

---

323 **freely** unreservedly   325 **check** repulse   331 **free** (1) free from guile (2) freely given
332 **Probal** probable, reasonable   334 **Th'inclining** the favorably disposed.   **subdue** persuade
335 **framed as fruitful** created as generous   336 **free elements** i.e., earth, air, fire, and water, unrestrained and spontaneous.   338 **seals** tokens   341 **her appetite** her desire, or, perhaps, his desire for
her   342 **function** exercise of faculties (weakened by his fondness for her).   343 **parallel** i.e., seemingly in his best interests but at the same time threatening   344 **Divinity of hell!** Inverted theology
of hell (which seduces the soul to its damnation)!   345 **put on** further, instigate   346 **suggest** tempt
351 **repeals him** attempts to get him restored   354 **pitch** i.e., (1) foul blackness (2) a snaring
substance

And out of her own goodness make the net
That shall enmesh them all.

(*Enter Roderigo.*)

How now, Roderigo?

RODERIGO. I do follow here in the chase, not like a
hound that hunts, but one that fills up the cry. My   *358*
money is almost spent; I have been tonight exceedingly well cudgeled; and I think the issue will be I shall   *360*
have so much experience for my pains, and so,   *361*
with no money at all and a little more wit, return again
to Venice.

IAGO. How poor are they that have not patience!
What wound did ever heal but by degrees?
Thou know'st we work by wit, and not by witchcraft,
And wit depends on dilatory time.
Does't not go well? Cassio hath beaten thee,
And thou, by that small hurt, hast cashiered Cassio.   *369*
Though other things grow fair against the sun,   *370*
Yet fruits that blossom first will first be ripe.   *371*
Content thyself awhile. By the Mass, 'tis morning!
Pleasure and action make the hours seem short.
Retire thee; go where thou art billeted.
Away, I say! Thou shalt know more hereafter.
Nay, get thee gone.   (*Exit Roderigo.*)
Two things are to be done.
My wife must move for Cassio to her mistress;   *377*
I'll set her on;
Myself the while to draw the Moor apart
And bring him jump when he may Cassio find   *380*
Soliciting his wife. Ay, that's the way.
Dull not device by coldness and delay.   (*Exit.*)   *382*

3.1

Enter Cassio [and] Musicians.

---

358 fills up the cry merely takes part as one of the pack. **360 issue** outcome **361 so much** just so much and no more **369 cashiered** dismissed from service **370–1 Though . . . ripe** i.e., Plans that are well prepared and set expeditiously in motion will soonest ripen into success. **377 move** plead **380 jump** precisely **382 device** plot. **coldness** lack of zeal
3.1. Location: Before the chamber of Othello and Desdemona.

CASSIO. Masters, play here—I will content your pains— 1
    Something that's brief, and bid "Good morrow,
      General." (*They play.*)

([*Enter*] *Clown.*)

CLOWN. Why, masters, have your instruments been in
    Naples, that they speak i'th' nose thus? 4
A MUSICIAN. How, sir, how?
CLOWN. Are these, I pray you, wind instruments?
A MUSICIAN. Ay, marry, are they, sir.
CLOWN. Oh, thereby hangs a tail.
A MUSICIAN. Whereby hangs a tale, sir?
CLOWN. Marry, sir, by many a wind instrument that I 10
    know. But, masters, here's money for you. (*He gives*
    money.) And the General so likes your music that he
    desires you, for love's sake, to make no more noise
    with it.
A MUSICIAN. Well, sir, we will not.
CLOWN. If you have any music that may not be heard, 16
    to't again; but, as they say, to hear music the General
    does not greatly care.
A MUSICIAN. We have none such, sir.
CLOWN. Then put up your pipes in your bag, for I'll
    away. Go, vanish into air, away! (*Exeunt Musicians.*)
CASSIO. Dost thou hear, mine honest friend?
CLOWN. No, I hear not your honest friend; I hear you.
CASSIO. Prithee, keep up thy quillets. There's a poor 24
    piece of gold for thee. (*He gives money.*) If the gentle-
    woman that attends the General's wife be stirring, tell
    her there's one Cassio entreats her a little favor of 27
    speech. Wilt thou do this? 28
CLOWN. She is stirring, sir. If she will stir hither, I shall 29
    seem to notify unto her. 30
CASSIO. Do, good my friend. (*Exit Clown.*)

---

1 Masters Good sirs. **content your pains** reward your efforts   **4 speak i'th' nose** (1) sound nasal
(2) sound like one whose nose has been attacked by syphilis. (Naples was popularly supposed to
have a high incidence of venereal disease.)   **10 wind instrument** (With a joke on flatulence. The
tail, line 8, that hangs nearby the *wind instrument* suggests the penis.)   **16 may not** cannot
24 keep . . . quillets refrain from quibbling.   **27–8 a little . . . speech** the favor of a brief talk.
29 stir bestir herself. (With a play on *stirring*, "rousing herself from rest.")   **30 seem** deem it good,
think fit

(*Enter Iago.*)

                               In happy time, Iago.   *31*

IAGO. You have not been abed, then?

CASSIO. Why, no. The day had broke
    Before we parted. I have made bold, Iago,
    To send in to your wife. My suit to her
    Is that she will to virtuous Desdemona
    Procure me some access.

IAGO. I'll send her to you presently;
    And I'll devise a mean to draw the Moor
    Out of the way, that your converse and business
    May be more free.

CASSIO. I humbly thank you for't.   (*Exit [Iago].*)
                            I never knew
    A Florentine more kind and honest.   *43*

(*Enter Emilia.*)

EMILIA. Good morrow, good Lieutenant. I am sorry
    For your displeasure; but all will sure be well.   *45*
    The General and his wife are talking of it,
    And she speaks for you stoutly. The Moor replies   *47*
    That he you hurt is of great fame in Cyprus   *48*
    And great affinity, and that in wholesome wisdom   *49*
    He might not but refuse you; but he protests he loves you   *50*
    And needs no other suitor but his likings
    To take the safest occasion by the front   *52*
    To bring you in again.

CASSIO.   Yet I beseech you,
    If you think fit, or that it may be done,
    Give me advantage of some brief discourse
    With Desdemon alone.

EMILIA.   Pray you, come in.
    I will bestow you where you shall have time
    To speak your bosom freely.   *58*

CASSIO. I am much bound to you.   (*Exeunt.*)

---

31 **In happy time** i.e., Well met   43 **Florentine** i.e., even a fellow Florentine. (Iago is a Venetian;
Cassio is a Florentine.)   45 **displeasure** fall from favor   47 **stoutly** spiritedly.   48 **fame** reputation,
importance   49 **affinity** kindred, family connection   50 **protests** insists   52 **occasion . . . front**
opportunity by the forelock   58 **bosom** inmost thoughts

3.2

Enter Othello, Iago, and Gentlemen.

OTHELLO (*giving letters*). These letters give, Iago, to the pilot,
    And by him do my duties to the Senate.   *2*
    That done, I will be walking on the works;   *3*
    Repair there to me.
IAGO.   Well, my good lord, I'll do't.   *4*
OTHELLO. This fortification, gentlemen, shall we see't?
GENTLEMEN. We'll wait upon Your Lordship.   (*Exeunt.*)   *6*

3.3

Enter Desdemona, Cassio, and Emilia.

DESDEMONA. Be thou assured, good Cassio, I will do
    All my abilities in thy behalf.
EMILIA. Good madam, do. I warrant it grieves my husband
    As if the cause were his.
DESDEMONA. Oh, that's an honest fellow. Do not doubt,
       Cassio,
    But I will have my lord and you again
    As friendly as you were.
CASSIO.   Bounteous madam,
    Whatever shall become of Michael Cassio,
    He's never anything but your true servant.
DESDEMONA. I know't. I thank you. You do love my lord;
    You have known him long, and be you well assured
    He shall in strangeness stand no farther off   *12*
    Than in a politic distance.
CASSIO.   Ay, but, lady,   *13*
    That policy may either last so long,
    Or feed upon such nice and waterish diet,   *15*
    Or breed itself so out of circumstance,   *16*

3.2. Location: The citadel.
2 do my duties convey my respects   **3 works** breastworks, fortifications   **4 Repair** return, come
6 wait upon attend
3.3. Location: The garden of the citadel.
12 strangeness aloofness   **13 politic** required by wise policy   **15 Or ... diet** or sustain itself at
length upon such trivial and meager technicalities   **16 breed ... circumstance** continually renew
itself so out of chance events, or yield so few chances for my being pardoned

That, I being absent and my place supplied,　　　　　*17*
My general will forget my love and service.
DESDEMONA. Do not doubt that. Before Emilia here　*19*
　I give thee warrant of thy place. Assure thee,　　*20*
　If I do vow a friendship I'll perform it
　To the last article. My lord shall never rest.
　I'll watch him tame and talk him out of patience;　*23*
　His bed shall seem a school, his board a shrift;　*24*
　I'll intermingle everything he does
　With Cassio's suit. Therefore be merry, Cassio,
　For thy solicitor shall rather die　　　　　　　　*27*
　Than give thy cause away.　　　　　　　　　　　*28*

(*Enter Othello and Iago [at a distance].*)

EMILIA. Madam, here comes my lord.
CASSIO. Madam, I'll take my leave.
DESDEMONA. Why, stay, and hear me speak.
CASSIO. Madam, not now. I am very ill at ease,
　Unfit for mine own purposes.
DESDEMONA. Well, do your discretion.　　(*Exit Cassio.*)　*34*
IAGO. Ha? I like not that.
OTHELLO. What dost thou say?
IAGO. Nothing, my lord; or if—I know not what.
OTHELLO. Was not that Cassio parted from my wife?
IAGO. Cassio, my lord? No, sure, I cannot think it,
　That he would steal away so guiltylike,
　Seeing you coming.
OTHELLO. I do believe 'twas he.
DESDEMONA (*joining them*). How now, my lord?
　I have been talking with a suitor here,
　A man that languishes in your displeasure.
OTHELLO. Who is't you mean?
DESDEMONA. Why, your lieutenant, Cassio. Good my lord,
　If I have any grace or power to move you,
　His present reconciliation take;　　　　　　　　*49*
　For if he be not one that truly loves you,

---

17 supplied filled by another person　**19 doubt** fear　**20 warrant** guarantee　**23 watch him tame**
tame him by keeping him from sleeping. (A term from falconry.)　**out of patience** past his
endurance　**24 board** dining table.　**shrift** confessional　**27 solicitor** advocate　**28 away** up.
34 do your discretion do as you think fit.　**49 His . . . take** let him be reconciled to you right away

That errs in ignorance and not in cunning,   *51*

I have no judgment in an honest face.

I prithee, call him back.

OTHELLO. Went he hence now?

DESDEMONA. Yes, faith, so humbled

That he hath left part of his grief with me

To suffer with him. Good love, call him back.

OTHELLO. Not now, sweet Desdemon. Some other time.

DESDEMONA. But shall't be shortly?

OTHELLO. The sooner, sweet, for you.

DESDEMONA. Shall't be tonight at supper?

OTHELLO. No, not tonight.

DESDEMONA. Tomorrow dinner, then?   *63*

OTHELLO. I shall not dine at home.

I meet the captains at the citadel.

DESDEMONA. Why, then, tomorrow night, or Tuesday morn,

On Tuesday noon, or night, on Wednesday morn.

I prithee, name the time, but let it not

Exceed three days. In faith, he's penitent;

And yet his trespass, in our common reason—   *70*

Save that, they say, the wars must make example   *71*

Out of her best—is not almost a fault   *72*

T'incur a private check. When shall he come?   *73*

Tell me, Othello. I wonder in my soul

What you would ask me that I should deny,

Or stand so mamm'ring on. What? Michael Cassio,   *76*

That came a-wooing with you, and so many a time,

When I have spoke of you dispraisingly,

Hath ta'en your part—to have so much to do

To bring him in! By'r Lady, I could do much—   *80*

OTHELLO. Prithee, no more. Let him come when he will;

I will deny thee nothing.

DESDEMONA. Why, this is not a boon.

'Tis as I should entreat you wear your gloves,

Or feed on nourishing dishes, or keep you warm,

Or sue to you to do a peculiar profit   *86*

---

51 in cunning wittingly   **63 dinner** (The noontime meal.)   **70 common reason** everyday judgments   **71–2 Save . . . best** were it not that, as the saying goes, military discipline requires making an example of the very best men. (*Her* refers to wars as a singular concept.)   **72 not almost** scarcely **73 a private check** even a private reprimand.   **76 mamm'ring on** wavering or muttering about. **80 bring him in** restore him to favor.   **86 peculiar** particular, personal

To your own person. Nay, when I have a suit
Wherein I mean to touch your love indeed,   88
It shall be full of poise and difficult weight,   89
And fearful to be granted.
OTHELLO. I will deny thee nothing.
Whereon, I do beseech thee, grant me this,   92
To leave me but a little to myself.
DESDEMONA. Shall I deny you? No. Farewell, my lord.
OTHELLO. Farewell, my Desdemona. I'll come to thee straight.   95
DESDEMONA. Emilia, come.—Be as your fancies teach you;   96
Whate'er you be, I am obedient. (*Exit [with Emilia].*)
OTHELLO. Excellent wretch! Perdition catch my soul   98
But I do love thee! And when I love thee not,   99
Chaos is come again.   100
IAGO. My noble lord—
OTHELLO. What dost thou say, Iago?
IAGO. Did Michael Cassio, when you wooed my lady,
Know of your love?
OTHELLO. He did, from first to last. Why dost thou ask?
IAGO. But for a satisfaction of my thought;
No further harm.
OTHELLO.   Why of thy thought, Iago?
IAGO. I did not think he had been acquainted with her.
OTHELLO. Oh, yes, and went between us very oft.
IAGO. Indeed?
OTHELLO. Indeed? Ay, indeed. Discern'st thou aught in that?
Is he not honest?
IAGO. Honest, my lord?
OTHELLO. Honest. Ay, honest.
IAGO. My lord, for aught I know.
OTHELLO. What dost thou think?
IAGO. Think, my lord?
OTHELLO. "Think, my lord?" By heaven, thou echo'st me,
As if there were some monster in thy thought

---

88 **touch** test   89 **poise . . . weight** delicacy and weightiness   92 **Whereon** In return for which
95 **straight** straightway.   96 **fancies** inclinations   98 **wretch** (A term of affectionate endearment.)
99–100 **And . . . again** i.e., My love for you will last forever, until the end of time when chaos will
return. (But with an unconscious, ironic suggestion that, if anything should induce Othello to cease
loving Desdemona, the result would be chaos.)

Too hideous to be shown. Thou dost mean something.
I heard thee say even now, thou lik'st not that,
When Cassio left my wife. What didst not like?
And when I told thee he was of my counsel   *123*
In my whole course of wooing, thou criedst "Indeed?"
And didst contract and purse thy brow together   *125*
As if thou then hadst shut up in thy brain
Some horrible conceit. If thou dost love me,   *127*
Show me thy thought.

IAGO. My lord, you know I love you.

OTHELLO. I think thou dost;
And, for I know thou'rt full of love and honesty,   *131*
And weigh'st thy words before thou giv'st them breath,
Therefore these stops of thine fright me the more;   *133*
For such things in a false disloyal knave
Are tricks of custom, but in a man that's just   *135*
They're close dilations, working from the heart   *136*
That passion cannot rule.

IAGO.   For Michael Cassio,   *137*
I dare be sworn I think that he is honest.

OTHELLO. I think so too.

IAGO.   Men should be what they seem;
Or those that be not, would they might seem none!   *140*

OTHELLO. Certain, men should be what they seem.

IAGO. Why, then, I think Cassio's an honest man.

OTHELLO. Nay, yet there's more in this.
I prithee, speak to me as to thy thinkings,
As thou dost ruminate, and give thy worst of thoughts
The worst of words.

IAGO.   Good my lord, pardon me.
Though I am bound to every act of duty,
I am not bound to that all slaves are free to.   *148*
Utter my thoughts? Why, say they are vile and false,
As where's that palace whereinto foul things
Sometimes intrude not? Who has that breast so pure
But some uncleanly apprehensions

---

123 **of my counsel** in my confidence   125 **purse** knit   127 **conceit** fancy.   131 **for** because   133 **stops** pauses   135 **of custom** customary   136–7 **They're . . . rule** they are secret or involuntary expressions of feeling that are too strong to be kept back.   137 **For** As for   140 **seem none** not seem at all, not seem to be honest.   148 **that** that which.   **free to** free with respect to.

Keep leets and law days, and in sessions sit   *153*
With meditations lawful?   *154*

OTHELLO. Thou dost conspire against thy friend, Iago,   *155*
    If thou but think'st him wronged and mak'st his ear
    A stranger to thy thoughts.

IAGO.   I do beseech you,
    Though I perchance am vicious in my guess—   *158*
    As I confess it is my nature's plague
    To spy into abuses, and oft my jealousy   *160*
    Shapes faults that are not—that your wisdom then,
    From one that so imperfectly conceits,   *162*
    Would take no notice, nor build yourself a trouble
    Out of his scattering and unsure observance.   *164*
    It were not for your quiet nor your good,
    Nor for my manhood, honesty, and wisdom,
    To let you know my thoughts.

OTHELLO.   What dost thou mean?

IAGO. Good name in man and woman, dear my lord,
    Is the immediate jewel of their souls.   *169*
    Who steals my purse steals trash; 'tis something, nothing;
    'Twas mine, 'tis his, and has been slave to thousands;
    But he that filches from me my good name
    Robs me of that which not enriches him
    And makes me poor indeed.

OTHELLO. By heaven, I'll know thy thoughts.

IAGO. You cannot, if my heart were in your hand,   *176*
    Nor shall not, whilst 'tis in my custody.

OTHELLO. Ha?

IAGO. Oh, beware, my lord, of jealousy.
    It is the green-eyed monster, which doth mock   *179*
    The meat it feeds on. That cuckold lives in bliss   *180*
    Who, certain of his fate, loves not his wronger;   *181*

---

153 Keep leets and law days i.e., hold court, set up their authority in one's heart. (*Leets* are a kind of manor court; *law days* are the days courts sit in session, or those sessions.) **153–4 and . . . lawful** i.e., and coexist in a kind of spiritual conflict with virtuous thoughts. **155 thy friend** i.e., Othello **158 vicious** wrong **160 jealousy** suspicious nature **162 one** i.e., myself, Iago. **conceits** judges, conjectures **164 scattering** random **169 immediate** essential, most precious **176 if** even if **179–80 which . . . feeds on** (Jealousy mocks both itself and the sufferer of jealousy; it is self-devouring and is its own punishment.) **180–1 That . . . wronger** A cuckolded husband who knows his wife to be unfaithful can at least take comfort in knowing the truth, so that he will not continue to love her or to befriend her lover. (Othello echoes this sentiment in lines 204–6, when he vows that he would end uncertainty and cease to love an unfaithful wife.)

But oh, what damnèd minutes tells he o'er 182
Who dotes, yet doubts, suspects, yet fondly loves!
OTHELLO. Oh, misery!
IAGO. Poor and content is rich, and rich enough, 185
But riches fineless is as poor as winter 186
To him that ever fears he shall be poor.
Good God, the souls of all my tribe defend
From jealousy!
OTHELLO. Why, why is this?
Think'st thou I'd make a life of jealousy,
To follow still the changes of the moon 192
With fresh suspicions? No! To be once in doubt 193
Is once to be resolved. Exchange me for a goat 194
When I shall turn the business of my soul
To such exsufflicate and blown surmises 196
Matching thy inference. 'Tis not to make me jealous 197
To say my wife is fair, feeds well, loves company,
Is free of speech, sings, plays, and dances well;
Where virtue is, these are more virtuous.
Nor from mine own weak merits will I draw
The smallest fear or doubt of her revolt, 202
For she had eyes, and chose me. No, Iago,
I'll see before I doubt; when I doubt, prove;
And on the proof, there is no more but this—
Away at once with love or jealousy.
IAGO. I am glad of this, for now I shall have reason
To show the love and duty that I bear you
With franker spirit. Therefore, as I am bound,
Receive it from me. I speak not yet of proof.
Look to your wife; observe her well with Cassio.
Wear your eyes thus, not jealous nor secure. 212
I would not have your free and noble nature,
Out of self-bounty, be abused. Look to't. 214
I know our country disposition well;

---

182 tells counts **185 Poor . . . enough** To be content with what little one has is the greatest wealth of all. (Proverbial.) **186 fineless** boundless **192–3 To follow . . . suspicions?** to be constantly imagining new causes for suspicion, changing incessantly like the moon? **194 once** once and for all. **resolved** free of doubt, having settled the matter. **196 exsufflicate and blown** inflated and blown up or flyblown, hence, loathsome, disgusting **197 inference** description or allegation. **202 doubt . . . revolt** fear of her unfaithfulness **212 not** neither. **secure** free from uncertainty. **214 self-bounty** inherent or natural goodness and generosity. **abused** deceived.

In Venice they do let God see the pranks
They dare not show their husbands; their best
　　　conscience
Is not to leave't undone, but keep't unknown.
OTHELLO. Dost thou say so?
IAGO. She did deceive her father, marrying you;
　　　And when she seemed to shake and fear your looks,
　　　She loved them most.
OTHELLO.　　　　　　　　And so she did.
IAGO.　　　　　　　　　　　　Why, go to, then!　　　222
　　　She that, so young, could give out such a seeming,　　　223
　　　To seel her father's eyes up close as oak,　　　224
　　　He thought 'twas witchcraft! But I am much to blame.
　　　I humbly do beseech you of your pardon
　　　For too much loving you.
OTHELLO. I am bound to thee forever.　　　228
IAGO. I see this hath a little dashed your spirits.
OTHELLO. Not a jot, not a jot.
IAGO.　　　　　　　　　　I'faith, I fear it has.
　　　I hope you will consider what is spoke
　　　Comes from my love. But I do see you're moved.
　　　I am to pray you not to strain my speech
　　　To grosser issues nor to larger reach　　　234
　　　Than to suspicion.
OTHELLO. I will not.
IAGO. Should you do so, my lord,
　　　My speech should fall into such vile success　　　238
　　　Which my thoughts aimed not. Cassio's my worthy friend.
　　　My lord, I see you're moved.
OTHELLO.　　　　　　　No, not much moved.
　　　I do not think but Desdemona's honest.　　　241
IAGO. Long live she so! And long live you to think so!
OTHELLO. And yet, how nature erring from itself—
IAGO. Ay, there's the point! As—to be bold with you—
　　　Not to affect many proposèd matches　　　245
　　　Of her own clime, complexion, and degree,　　　246

---

222 **go to** (An expression of impatience.) 223 **seeming** false appearance 224 **seel** blind. (A term from falconry.) **oak** (A close-grained wood.) 228 **bound** indebted. (But perhaps with ironic sense of "tied.") 234 **issues** significances. **reach** meaning, scope 238 **success** effect, result 241 **honest** chaste. 245 **affect** prefer, desire 246 **clime ... degree** country, temperament or skin color, and social position

Whereto we see in all things nature tends—
Foh! One may smell in such a will most rank,   *248*
Foul disproportion, thoughts unnatural.   *249*
But pardon me. I do not in position   *250*
Distinctly speak of her, though I may fear
Her will, recoiling to her better judgment,   *252*
May fall to match you with her country forms   *253*
And happily repent.
OTHELLO.   Farewell, farewell!   *254*
   If more thou dost perceive, let me know more.
   Set on thy wife to observe. Leave me, Iago.
IAGO (*going*). My lord, I take my leave.
OTHELLO. Why did I marry? This honest creature doubtless
   Sees and knows more, much more, than he unfolds.
IAGO (*returning*). My lord, I would I might entreat Your Honor
   To scan this thing no farther. Leave it to time.   *261*
   Although 'tis fit that Cassio have his place—
   For, sure, he fills it up with great ability—
   Yet, if you please to hold him off awhile,
   You shall by that perceive him and his means.   *265*
   Note if your lady strain his entertainment   *266*
   With any strong or vehement importunity;
   Much will be seen in that. In the meantime,
   Let me be thought too busy in my fears—   *269*
   As worthy cause I have to fear I am—
   And hold her free, I do beseech Your Honor.   *271*
OTHELLO. Fear not my government.   *272*
IAGO. I once more take my leave.   (*Exit.*)
OTHELLO. This fellow's of exceeding honesty,
   And knows all qualities, with a learnèd spirit,   *275*
   Of human dealings. If I do prove her haggard,   *276*
   Though that her jesses were my dear heartstrings,   *277*

---

248 will sensuality, appetite   **249 disproportion** abnormality   **250 in position** in making this argument or proposition   **252 recoiling** reverting.   **better** i.e., more natural and reconsidered **253 fall . . . forms** undertake to compare you with Venetian norms of handsomeness   **254 happily repent** haply repent her marriage.   **261 scan** scrutinize   **265 his means** the method he uses (to regain his post).   **266 strain his entertainment** urge his reinstatement   **269 busy** officious **271 hold her free** regard her as innocent   **272 government** self-control, conduct.   **275 qualities** natures, types   **276 haggard** wild (like a wild female hawk)   **277 jesses** straps fastened around the legs of a trained hawk

I'd whistle her off and let her down the wind   *278*
To prey at fortune. Haply, for I am black   *279*
And have not those soft parts of conversation   *280*
That chamberers have, or for I am declined   *281*
Into the vale of years—yet that's not much—
She's gone. I am abused, and my relief   *283*
Must be to loathe her. Oh, curse of marriage,
That we can call these delicate creatures ours
And not their appetites! I had rather be a toad
And live upon the vapor of a dungeon
Than keep a corner in the thing I love
For others' uses. Yet, 'tis the plague of great ones;
Prerogatived are they less than the base.   *290*
'Tis destiny unshunnable, like death.
Even then this forkèd plague is fated to us   *292*
When we do quicken. Look where she comes.   *293*

(*Enter Desdemona and Emilia.*)

If she be false, oh, then heaven mocks itself!
I'll not believe't.
DESDEMONA.   How now, my dear Othello?
Your dinner, and the generous islanders   *296*
By you invited do attend your presence.   *297*
OTHELLO. I am to blame.
DESDEMONA.   Why do you speak so faintly?
Are you not well?
OTHELLO. I have a pain upon my forehead here.
DESDEMONA. Faith, that's with watching. 'Twill away again.   *301*

(*She offers her handkerchief.*)

Let me but bind it hard, within this hour
It will be well.

---

278 **I'd ... wind** i.e., I'd let her go forever. (To release a hawk downwind was to turn it loose.)
279 **prey at fortune** fend for herself in the wild. **Haply, for** Perhaps because 280 **soft ... conversa-**
tion pleasing social graces 281 **chamberers** drawing-room gallants 283 **abused** deceived
290 **Prerogatived** privileged (to have honest wives). **the base** ordinary citizens. (Socially prominent
men are especially prone to the common destiny of being cuckolded and to the public shame that goes
with it.) 292 **forkèd** (An allusion to the horns of the cuckold.) 293 **quicken** receive life. (*Quicken*
may also mean to swarm with maggots as the body festers, as in 4.2.69, in which case lines 292–3 suggest
that *even then*, in death, we are cuckolded by *forkèd* worms.) 296 **generous** noble 297 **attend** await
301 **watching** too little sleep.

OTHELLO.   Your napkin is too little.   *303*
    Let it alone. Come, I'll go in with you.   *304*

(*He puts the handkerchief from him, and it drops.*)

DESDEMONA. I am very sorry that you are not well.

                                (*Exit [with Othello].*)

EMILIA (*picking up the handkerchief*).
    I am glad I have found this napkin.
    This was her first remembrance from the Moor.
    My wayward husband hath a hundred times   *308*
    Wooed me to steal it, but she so loves the token—
    For he conjured her she should ever keep it—
    That she reserves it evermore about her
    To kiss and talk to. I'll have the work ta'en out,   *312*
    And give't Iago. What he will do with it
    Heaven knows, not I;
    I nothing but to please his fantasy.   *315*

(*Enter Iago.*)

IAGO. How now? What do you here alone?
EMILIA. Do not you chide. I have a thing for you.
IAGO. You have a thing for me? It is a common thing—   *318*
EMILIA. Ha?
IAGO. To have a foolish wife.
EMILIA. Oh, is that all? What will you give me now
    For that same handkerchief?
IAGO. What handkerchief?
EMILIA. What handkerchief?
    Why, that the Moor first gave to Desdemona;
    That which so often you did bid me steal.
IAGO. Hast stolen it from her?
EMILIA. No, faith. She let it drop by negligence,
    And to th'advantage I, being here, took't up.   *329*
    Look, here 'tis.
IAGO.   A good wench! Give it me.

---

303 napkin handkerchief   **304 Let it alone** i.e., Never mind.   **308 wayward** capricious   **312 work ta'en out** design of the embroidery copied   **315 fantasy** whim.   **318 common thing** (With bawdy suggestion; *common* suggests coarseness and availability to all comers, and *thing* is a slang term for the pudendum.)   **329 to th'advantage** taking the opportunity

EMILIA. What will you do with't, that you have been so earnest
    To have me filch it?
IAGO (*snatching it*).   Why, what is that to you?
EMILIA. If it be not for some purpose of import,
    Give't me again. Poor lady, she'll run mad
    When she shall lack it.
IAGO.   Be not acknown on't.   *335*
    I have use for it. Go, leave me.   (*Exit Emilia.*)
    I will in Cassio's lodging lose this napkin   *337*
    And let him find it. Trifles light as air
    Are to the jealous confirmations strong
    As proofs of Holy Writ. This may do something.
    The Moor already changes with my poison.
    Dangerous conceits are in their natures poisons,   *342*
    Which at the first are scarce found to distaste,   *343*
    But with a little act upon the blood   *344*
    Burn like the mines of sulfur.

(*Enter Othello.*)

                  I did say so.
    Look where he comes! Not poppy nor mandragora   *346*
    Nor all the drowsy syrups of the world
    Shall ever medicine thee to that sweet sleep
    Which thou owed'st yesterday.
OTHELLO.   Ha, ha, false to me?   *349*
IAGO. Why, how now, General? No more of that.
OTHELLO. Avaunt! Begone! Thou hast set me on the rack.
    I swear 'tis better to be much abused
    Than but to know't a little.
IAGO.   How now, my lord?
OTHELLO. What sense had I of her stolen hours of lust?
    I saw't not, thought it not, it harmed not me.
    I slept the next night well, fed well, was free and merry;   *356*
    I found not Cassio's kisses on her lips.
    He that is robbed, not wanting what is stolen,   *358*
    Let him not know't and he's not robbed at all.

---

335 **lack** miss. **Be . . . on't** Do not confess knowledge of it; keep out of this.   337 **lose** (The Folio spelling, "loose," is a normal spelling for "lose," but it may also contain the idea of "let go," "release.") 342 **conceits** fancies, ideas   343 **distaste** be distasteful   344 **act** action, working   346 **mandragora** an opiate made of the mandrake root   349 **thou owed'st** you did own   356 **free** carefree 358 **wanting** missing

IAGO. I am sorry to hear this.

OTHELLO. I had been happy if the general camp,
    Pioneers and all, had tasted her sweet body,   *362*
    So I had nothing known. Oh, now, forever   *363*
    Farewell the tranquil mind! Farewell content!
    Farewell the plumèd troops and the big wars   *365*
    That makes ambition virtue! Oh, farewell!
    Farewell the neighing steed and the shrill trump,
    The spirit-stirring drum, th'ear-piercing fife,
    The royal banner, and all quality,   *369*
    Pride, pomp, and circumstance of glorious war!   *370*
    And O you mortal engines, whose rude throats   *371*
    Th'immortal Jove's dread clamors counterfeit,   *372*
    Farewell! Othello's occupation's gone.

IAGO. Is't possible, my lord?

OTHELLO. Villain, be sure thou prove my love a whore!
    Be sure of it. Give me the ocular proof,
    Or, by the worth of mine eternal soul,
    Thou hadst been better have been born a dog
    Than answer my waked wrath!

IAGO.   Is't come to this?

OTHELLO. Make me to see't, or at the least so prove it
    That the probation bear no hinge nor loop   *381*
    To hang a doubt on, or woe upon thy life!

IAGO. My noble lord—

OTHELLO. If thou dost slander her and torture me,
    Never pray more; abandon all remorse;   *385*
    On horror's head horrors accumulate;   *386*
    Do deeds to make heaven weep, all earth amazed;   *387*
    For nothing canst thou to damnation add
    Greater than that.

IAGO.   O grace! O heaven forgive me!
    Are you a man? Have you a soul or sense?
    God b'wi'you; take mine office. O wretched fool,   *391*
    That lov'st to make thine honesty a vice!   *392*

---

362 Pioneers diggers of mines, the lowest grade of soldiers   **363 So** provided   **365 big** mighty
369 quality character, essential nature   **370 Pride** rich display. **circumstance** pageantry
371 mortal engines i.e., cannon. (*Mortal* means "deadly.")   **372 Jove's dread clamors** i.e., thunder
381 probation proof   **385 remorse** pity, penitent hope for salvation   **386 horrors accumulate** add
still more horrors   **387 amazed** confounded with horror   **391 O wretched fool** (Iago addresses
himself as a fool for having carried honesty too far.)   **392 vice** failing, something overdone.

O monstrous world! Take note, take note, O world,
To be direct and honest is not safe.
I thank you for this profit, and from hence   395
I'll love no friend, sith love breeds such offense.   396

OTHELLO. Nay, stay. Thou shouldst be honest.   397

IAGO. I should be wise, for honesty's a fool
And loses that it works for.

OTHELLO.   By the world,   399
I think my wife be honest and think she is not;
I think that thou art just and think thou art not.
I'll have some proof. My name, that was as fresh
As Dian's visage, is now begrimed and black   403
As mine own face. If there be cords, or knives,
Poison, or fire, or suffocating streams,
I'll not endure it. Would I were satisfied!

IAGO. I see, sir, you are eaten up with passion.
I do repent me that I put it to you.
You would be satisfied?

OTHELLO.   Would? Nay, and I will.

IAGO. And may; but how? How satisfied, my lord?
Would you, the supervisor, grossly gape on?   411
Behold her topped?

OTHELLO.   Death and damnation! Oh!

IAGO. It were a tedious difficulty, I think,
To bring them to that prospect. Damn them then,   414
If ever mortal eyes do see them bolster   415
More than their own. What then? How then?   416
What shall I say? Where's satisfaction?
It is impossible you should see this,
Were they as prime as goats, as hot as monkeys,   419
As salt as wolves in pride, and fools as gross   420
As ignorance made drunk. But yet I say,
If imputation and strong circumstances   422
Which lead directly to the door of truth

---

395 profit profitable instruction. **hence** henceforth   **396 sith** since.   **offense** i.e., harm to the one who offers help and friendship.   **397 Thou shouldst be** It appears that you are. (But Iago replies in the sense of "ought to be.")   **399 that** what   **403 Dian** Diana, goddess of the moon and of chastity **411 supervisor** onlooker   **414 Damn them then** i.e., They would have to be really incorrigible **415 bolster** go to bed together, share a bolster   **416 More** other.   **own** own eyes.   **419 prime** lustful   **420 salt** wanton, sensual.   **pride** heat   **422 imputation . . . circumstances** strong circumstantial evidence

Will give you satisfaction, you might have't.
OTHELLO. Give me a living reason she's disloyal.
IAGO. I do not like the office.
> But sith I am entered in this cause so far, 427
> Pricked to't by foolish honesty and love, 428
> I will go on. I lay with Cassio lately,
> And being troubled with a raging tooth
> I could not sleep. There are a kind of men
> So loose of soul that in their sleeps will mutter
> Their affairs. One of this kind is Cassio.
> In sleep I heard him say, "Sweet Desdemona,
> Let us be wary, let us hide our loves!"
> And then, sir, would he grip and wring my hand,
> Cry "O sweet creature!", then kiss me hard,
> As if he plucked up kisses by the roots
> That grew upon my lips; then laid his leg
> Over my thigh, and sighed, and kissed, and then
> Cried, "Cursèd fate that gave thee to the Moor!"
OTHELLO. Oh, monstrous! Monstrous!
IAGO.   Nay, this was but his dream.
OTHELLO. But this denoted a foregone conclusion. 443
> 'Tis a shrewd doubt, though it be but a dream. 444
IAGO. And this may help to thicken other proofs
> That do demonstrate thinly.
OTHELLO.   I'll tear her all to pieces.
IAGO. Nay, but be wise. Yet we see nothing done;
> She may be honest yet. Tell me but this:
> Have you not sometimes seen a handkerchief
> Spotted with strawberries in your wife's hand? 450
OTHELLO. I gave her such a one. 'Twas my first gift.
IAGO. I know not that; but such a handkerchief—
> I am sure it was your wife's—did I today
> See Cassio wipe his beard with.
OTHELLO.   If it be that—
IAGO. If it be that, or any that was hers,
> It speaks against her with the other proofs.
OTHELLO. Oh, that the slave had forty thousand lives! 457

---

427 sith since   **428 Pricked** spurred   **443 foregone conclusion** previous experience or action.
444 shrewd doubt suspicious circumstance   **450 Spotted with strawberries** embroidered with a
strawberry pattern   **457 the slave** i.e., Cassio

One is too poor, too weak for my revenge.
Now do I see 'tis true. Look here, Iago,
All my fond love thus do I blow to heaven.   *460*
'Tis gone.
Arise, black vengeance, from the hollow hell!
Yield up, O love, thy crown and hearted throne   *463*
To tyrannous hate! Swell, bosom, with thy freight,   *464*
For 'tis of aspics' tongues!   *465*

IAGO. Yet be content.   *466*

OTHELLO. Oh, blood, blood, blood!

IAGO. Patience, I say. Your mind perhaps may change.

OTHELLO. Never, Iago. Like to the Pontic Sea,   *469*
Whose icy current and compulsive course
Ne'er feels retiring ebb, but keeps due on
To the Propontic and the Hellespont,   *472*
Even so my bloody thoughts with violent pace
Shall ne'er look back, ne'er ebb to humble love,
Till that a capable and wide revenge   *475*
Swallow them up. Now, by yond marble heaven,   *476*
(*Kneeling*) In the due reverence of a sacred vow
I here engage my words.

IAGO.   Do not rise yet.
(*He kneels.*) Witness, you ever-burning lights above,   *479*
You elements that clip us round about,   *480*
Witness that here Iago doth give up
The execution of his wit, hands, heart,   *482*
To wronged Othello's service. Let him command,
And to obey shall be in me remorse,   *484*
What bloody business ever.   (*They rise.*)

OTHELLO.   I greet thy love,   *485*
Not with vain thanks, but with acceptance bounteous,
And will upon the instant put thee to't.   *487*
Within these three days let me hear thee say

---

460 fond foolish. (But also suggesting "affectionate.")   **463 hearted** fixed in the heart   **464 freight** burden   **465 aspics'** venomous serpents'   **466 content** calm.   **469 Pontic Sea** Black Sea **472 Propontic** Sea of Marmora, between the Black Sea and the Aegean.   **Hellespont** Dardanelles, straits where the Sea of Marmora joins with the Aegean   **475 capable** ample, comprehensive **476 marble** i.e., gleaming, polished, and indifferent to human suffering   **479 s.d. *He kneels*** (In the Quarto text, Iago kneels here after Othello has knelt at line 477.)   **480 clip** encompass   **482 execution** exercise, action.   **wit** mind   **484 remorse** pity (for Othello's wrongs)   **485 ever** soever. **487 to't** to the proof.

That Cassio's not alive.

IAGO.   My friend is dead;
'Tis done at your request. But let her live.

OTHELLO. Damn her, lewd minx! Oh, damn her, damn her!   491
Come, go with me apart. I will withdraw
To furnish me with some swift means of death
For the fair devil. Now art thou my lieutenant.

IAGO. I am your own forever.   (*Exeunt.*)

3.4

Enter Desdemona, Emilia, and Clown.

DESDEMONA. Do you know, sirrah, where Lieutenant   1
Cassio lies?   2

CLOWN. I dare not say he lies anywhere.

DESDEMONA. Why, man?

CLOWN. He's a soldier, and for me to say a soldier lies,
'tis stabbing.

DESDEMONA. Go to. Where lodges he?

CLOWN. To tell you where he lodges is to tell you where
I lie.

DESDEMONA. Can anything be made of this?

CLOWN. I know not where he lodges, and for me to devise a lodging and say he lies here, or he lies there,
were to lie in mine own throat.   13

DESDEMONA. Can you inquire him out, and be edified
by report?

CLOWN. I will catechize the world for him; that is, make
questions, and by them answer.

DESDEMONA. Seek him, bid him come hither. Tell him I
have moved my lord on his behalf and hope all will be   19
well.

CLOWN. To do this is within the compass of man's wit,
and therefore I will attempt the doing it. (*Exit Clown.*)

DESDEMONA. Where should I lose that handkerchief, Emilia?

EMILIA. I know not, madam.

DESDEMONA. Believe me, I had rather have lost my purse

---

491 minx wanton.
3.4. Location: Before the citadel.
1 sirrah (A form of address to an inferior.)   **2 lies** lodges. (But the Clown makes the obvious pun.)
13 lie . . . throat lie egregiously and deliberately.   **19 moved my lord** petitioned Othello

Full of crusadoes; and but my noble Moor   26
    Is true of mind and made of no such baseness
    As jealous creatures are, it were enough
    To put him to ill thinking.
EMILIA.   Is he not jealous?
DESDEMONA. Who, he? I think the sun where he was born
    Drew all such humors from him.
EMILIA.   Look where he comes.   *31*

(*Enter Othello.*)

DESDEMONA. I will not leave him now till Cassio
    Be called to him.—How is't with you, my lord?
OTHELLO. Well, my good lady. (*Aside*) Oh, hardness to
        dissemble!—
    How do you, Desdemona?
DESDEMONA.   Well, my good lord.
OTHELLO. Give me your hand. (*She gives her hand.*) This
        hand is moist, my lady.
DESDEMONA. It yet hath felt no age nor known no sorrow.
OTHELLO. This argues fruitfulness and liberal heart.   38
      Hot, hot, and moist. This hand of yours requires
      A sequester from liberty, fasting and prayer,   40
      Much castigation, exercise devout;   41
      For here's a young and sweating devil here
      That commonly rebels. 'Tis a good hand,
      A frank one.
DESDEMONA.   You may indeed say so,   44
    For 'twas that hand that gave away my heart.
OTHELLO. A liberal hand. The hearts of old gave hands,   46
    But our new heraldry is hands, not hearts.   47
DESDEMONA. I cannot speak of this. Come now, your promise.
OTHELLO. What promise, chuck?   49

---

26 **crusadoes** Portuguese gold coins   31 **humors** (Refers to the four bodily fluids thought to determine temperament.)   38 **argues** gives evidence of. **fruitfulness** generosity, amorousness, and fecundity. **liberal** generous and sexually free 40 **sequester** sequestration 41 **castigation** corrective discipline. **exercise devout** i.e., prayer, religious meditation, etc. 44 **frank** generous, open. (With sexual suggestion.) 46–7 **The hearts . . . hands** i.e., In former times, people would give their hearts when they gave their hands to something, but in our dedacent present age the joining of hands no longer has that spiritual sense. 49 **chuck** (A term of endearment.)

DESDEMONA. I have sent to bid Cassio come speak with
    you.
OTHELLO. I have a salt and sorry rheum offends me;   *51*
    Lend me thy handkerchief.
DESDEMONA. Here, my lord.   (*She offers a handkerchief.*)
OTHELLO. That which I gave you.
DESDEMONA.   I have it not about me.
OTHELLO. Not?
DESDEMONA. No, faith, my lord.
OTHELLO. That's a fault. That handkerchief
    Did an Egyptian to my mother give.
    She was a charmer, and could almost read   *59*
    The thoughts of people. She told her, while she kept it
    'Twould make her amiable and subdue my father   *61*
    Entirely to her love, but if she lost it
    Or made a gift of it, my father's eye
    Should hold her loathèd and his spirits should hunt
    After new fancies. She, dying, gave it me,   *65*
    And bid me, when my fate would have me wived,
    To give it her. I did so; and take heed on't;   *67*
    Make it a darling like your precious eye.
    To lose't or give't away were such perdition   *69*
    As nothing else could match.
DESDEMONA.   Is't possible?
OTHELLO. 'Tis true. There's magic in the web of it.   *71*
    A sibyl, that had numbered in the world
    The sun to course two hundred compasses,   *73*
    In her prophetic fury sewed the work;   *74*
    The worms were hallowed that did breed the silk,
    And it was dyed in mummy which the skillful   *76*
    Conserved of maidens' hearts.
DESDEMONA.   I'faith! Is't true?   *77*
OTHELLO. Most veritable. Therefore look to't well.
DESDEMONA. Then would to God that I had never seen't!
OTHELLO. Ha? Wherefore?

---

51 **salt ... rheum** distressful head cold or watering of the eyes   59 **charmer** sorceress   61 **amiable** desirable   65 **fancies** loves.   67 **her** i.e., to my wife.   69 **perdition** loss   71 **web** fabric, weaving   73 **compasses** annual circlings. (The *sibyl*, or prophetess, was two hundred years old.)   74 **prophetic fury** frenzy of prophetic inspiration.   **work** embroidered pattern   76 **mummy** medicinal or magical preparation drained from mummified bodies   77 **Conserved of** prepared or preserved out of

DESDEMONA. Why do you speak so startingly and rash?   *81*
OTHELLO. Is't lost? Is't gone? Speak, is't out o'th' way?   *82*
DESDEMONA. Heaven bless us!
OTHELLO. Say you?
DESDEMONA. It is not lost; but what an if it were?   *85*
OTHELLO. How?
DESDEMONA. I say it is not lost.
OTHELLO.   Fetch't, let me see't.
DESDEMONA. Why, so I can, sir, but I will not now.
    This is a trick to put me from my suit.
    Pray you, let Cassio be received again.
OTHELLO. Fetch me the handkerchief! My mind misgives.
DESDEMONA. Come, come,
    You'll never meet a more sufficient man.   *93*
OTHELLO. The handkerchief!
DESDEMONA.   I pray, talk me of Cassio.   *94*
OTHELLO. The handkerchief!
DESDEMONA.   A man that all his time   *95*
    Hath founded his good fortunes on your love,   *96*
    Shared dangers with you—
OTHELLO. The handkerchief!
DESDEMONA. I'faith, you are to blame.
OTHELLO. Zounds!   (*Exit Othello.*)
EMILIA. Is not this man jealous?
DESDEMONA. I ne'er saw this before.
    Sure, there's some wonder in this handkerchief.
    I am most unhappy in the loss of it.   *104*
EMILIA. 'Tis not a year or two shows us a man.   *105*
    They are all but stomachs, and we all but food;   *106*
    They eat us hungerly, and when they are full   *107*
    They belch us.

(*Enter Iago and Cassio.*)

        Look you, Cassio and my husband.
IAGO (*to Cassio*). There is no other way; 'tis she must do't.
    And, lo, the happiness! Go and importune her.   *110*

---

81 startingly and rash disjointedly and impetuously, excitedly.   **82 out o'th' way** lost, misplaced.
85 an if if   **93 sufficient** able, complete   **94 talk** talk to   **95–6 A man . . . love** A man who throughout his career has relied on your favor for his advancement   **104 unhappy** (1) unfortunate (2) sad
105 'Tis . . . man A year or two is not enough time for us women to know what men really are.
106 but nothing but   **107 hungerly** hungrily   **110 the happiness** in happy time, fortunately met.

DESDEMONA. How now, good Cassio? What's the news
    with you?
CASSIO. Madam, my former suit. I do beseech you
    That by your virtuous means I may again   *113*
    Exist and be a member of his love
    Whom I, with all the office of my heart,   *115*
    Entirely honor. I would not be delayed.
    If my offense be of such mortal kind   *117*
    That nor my service past, nor present sorrows,   *118*
    Nor purposed merit in futurity
    Can ransom me into his love again,
    But to know so must be my benefit;   *121*
    So shall I clothe me in a forced content,
    And shut myself up in some other course,   *123*
    To fortune's alms.
DESDEMONA.   Alas, thrice-gentle Cassio,   *124*
    My advocation is not now in tune.   *125*
    My lord is not my lord; nor should I know him,
    Were he in favor as in humor altered.   *127*
    So help me every spirit sanctified   *128*
    As I have spoken for you all my best
    And stood within the blank of his displeasure   *130*
    For my free speech! You must awhile be patient.   *131*
    What I can do I will, and more I will
    Than for myself I dare. Let that suffice you.
IAGO. Is my lord angry?
EMILIA.   He went hence but now,
    And certainly in strange unquietness.
IAGO. Can he be angry? I have seen the cannon
    When it hath blown his ranks into the air,
    And like the devil from his very arm
    Puffed his own brother—and is he angry?
    Something of moment then. I will go meet him.   *140*
    There's matter in't indeed, if he be angry.

---

113 virtuous (1) efficacious (2) morally good   **115 office** loyal service   **117 mortal** fatal
118 nor . . . nor neither . . . nor   **121 But . . . benefit** merely to know that my case is hopeless will
have to content me (and will be better than uncertainty)   **123 And shut . . . in** commit myself to
124 To fortune's alms throwing myself on the mercy of fortune.   **125 advocation** advocacy
127 favor appearance.   **humor** mood   **128 So . . . sanctified** So help me all the heavenly host
130 within the blank within point-blank range. (The *blank* is the center of the target.)   **131 free**
frank   **140 of moment** of immediate importance, momentous

DESDEMONA. I prithee, do so.   (*Exit [Iago].*)
                              Something, sure, of state,   142
Either from Venice, or some unhatched practice   143
Made demonstrable here in Cyprus to him,
Hath puddled his clear spirit; and in such cases   145
Men's natures wrangle with inferior things,
Though great ones are their object. 'Tis even so;
For let our finger ache, and it indues   148
Our other, healthful members even to a sense
Of pain. Nay, we must think men are not gods,
Nor of them look for such observancy   151
As fits the bridal. Beshrew me much, Emilia,   152
I was, unhandsome warrior as I am,   153
Arraigning his unkindness with my soul;   154
But now I find I had suborned the witness,   155
And he's indicted falsely.
EMILIA.   Pray heaven it be
State matters, as you think, and no conception
Nor no jealous toy concerning you.   158
DESDEMONA. Alas the day! I never gave him cause.
EMILIA. But jealous souls will not be answered so;
They are not ever jealous for the cause,
But jealous for they're jealous. It is a monster   162
Begot upon itself, born on itself.   163
DESDEMONA. Heaven keep that monster from Othello's mind!
EMILIA. Lady, amen.
DESDEMONA. I will go seek him. Cassio, walk hereabout.
If I do find him fit, I'll move your suit
And seek to effect it to my uttermost.
CASSIO. I humbly thank Your Ladyship.

(*Exit [Desdemona with Emilia].*)

(*Enter Bianca.*)

BIANCA. Save you, friend Cassio!

---

142 **of state** concerning state affairs   143 **unhatched practice** as yet unexecuted or undiscovered plot   145 **puddled** muddied   148 **indues** endows, brings to the same condition   151 **observancy** attentiveness   152 **bridal** wedding (when a bridegroom is newly attentive to his bride).   **Beshrew me** (A mild oath.)   153 **unhandsome** insufficient, unskillful   154 **with** before the bar of   155 **suborned the witness** induced the witness to give false testimony   158 **toy** fancy   162 **for** because   163 **Begot upon itself** generated solely from itself

CASSIO.   What make you from home?   *170*
   How is't with you, my most fair Bianca?
   I' faith, sweet love, I was coming to your house.
BIANCA. And I was going to your lodging, Cassio.
   What, keep a week away? Seven days and nights?
   Eightscore-eight hours? And lovers' absent hours   *175*
   More tedious than the dial eightscore times?   *176*
   Oh, weary reck'ning!
CASSIO.   Pardon me, Bianca.
   I have this while with leaden thoughts been pressed;
   But I shall, in a more continuate time,
   Strike off this score of absence. Sweet Bianca,

(*giving her Desdemona's handkerchief*)

   Take me this work out.
BIANCA.   Oh, Cassio, whence came this?   *181*
   This is some token from a newer friend.   *182*
   To the felt absence now I feel a cause.
   Is't come to this? Well, well.
CASSIO.   Go to, woman!
   Throw your vile guesses in the devil's teeth,
   From whence you have them. You are jealous now
   That this is from some mistress, some remembrance.
   No, by my faith, Bianca.
BIANCA.   Why, whose is it?
CASSIO. I know not, neither. I found it in my chamber.
   I like the work well. Ere it be demanded—   *190*
   As like enough it will—I would have it copied   *191*
   Take it and do't, and leave me for this time.
BIANCA. Leave you? Wherefore?
CASSIO. I do attend here on the General,
   And think it no addition, nor my wish,   *195*
   To have him see me womaned.
BIANCA. Why, I pray you?
CASSIO. Not that I love you not.

---

170 **Save** God save. **make** do 175 **Eightscore-eight** one hundred sixty-eight, the number of hours
in a week 176 **the dial** a complete revolution of the clock 179 **continuate** uninterrupted
180 **Strike . . . score** settle this account 181 **Take . . . out** copy this embroidery for me. 182 **friend**
mistress. 190 **demanded** inquired for 191 **like** likely 195 **addition** i.e., addition to my
reputation

BIANCA. But that you do not love me.
    I pray you, bring me on the way a little,   *200*
    And say if I shall see you soon at night.
CASSIO. 'Tis but a little way that I can bring you,
    For I attend here; but I'll see you soon.
BIANCA. 'Tis very good. I must be circumstanced.   *204*

(*Exeunt omnes.*)

4.1

Enter Othello and Iago.

IAGO. Will you think so?
OTHELLO.   Think so, Iago?
IAGO.   What,
    To kiss in private?
OTHELLO.   An unauthorized kiss!
IAGO. Or to be naked with her friend in bed
    An hour or more, not meaning any harm?
OTHELLO. Naked in bed, Iago, and not mean harm?
    It is hypocrisy against the devil.
    They that mean virtuously and yet do so,
    The devil their virtue tempts, and they tempt heaven.
IAGO. If they do nothing, 'tis a venial slip.   *9*
    But if I give my wife a handkerchief—
OTHELLO. What then?
IAGO. Why then, 'tis hers, my lord, and being hers,
    She may, I think, bestow't on any man.
OTHELLO. She is protectress of her honor too.
    May she give that?
IAGO. Her honor is an essence that's not seen;
    They have it very oft that have it not.   *17*
    But, for the handkerchief—
OTHELLO. By heaven, I would most gladly have forgot it.
    Thou said'st—Oh, it comes o'er my memory
    As doth the raven o'er the infectious house,   *21*
    Boding to all—he had my handkerchief.

---

200 bring accompany   **204 be circumstanced** be governed by circumstance, yield to your conditions.
4.1. Location: Before the citadel.
9 venial pardonable   **17 They have it** i.e., They enjoy a reputation for it   **21 raven ... house**
(Allusion to the belief that the raven hovered over a house of sickness or infection, such as one visited by the plague.)

IAGO. Ay, what of that?

OTHELLO.   That's not so good now.

IAGO.   What
    If I had said I had seen him do you wrong?
    Or heard him say—as knaves be such abroad,   *25*
    Who having, by their own importunate suit,   *26*
    Or voluntary dotage of some mistress,   *27*
    Convincèd or supplied them, cannot choose   *28*
    But they must blab—

OTHELLO.   Hath he said anything?   *29*

IAGO. He hath, my lord; but, be you well assured,
    No more than he'll unswear.

OTHELLO.   What hath he said?

IAGO. Faith, that he did—I know not what he did.

OTHELLO. What? What?

IAGO. Lie—

OTHELLO. With her?

IAGO.   With her, on her; what you will.

OTHELLO. Lie with her? Lie on her? We say "lie on her"
    when they belie her. Lie with her? Zounds, that's ful-   *36*
    some.—Handkerchief—confessions—handkerchief!   *37*
    —To confess and be hanged for his labor—first to be   *38*
    hanged and then to confess.—I tremble at it. Nature   *39*
    would not invest herself in such shadowing passion   *40*
    without some instruction. It is not words that shakes   *41*
    me thus. Pish! Noses, ears, and lips.—Is't possible?
    —Confess—handkerchief!—O devil!

(*Falls in a trance.*)

IAGO. Work on,
    My medicine, work! Thus credulous fools are caught,
    And many worthy and chaste dames even thus,
    All guiltless, meet reproach.—What, ho! My lord!
    My lord, I say! Othello!

25–9 as . . . blab— since there are rascals enough who, having seduced a woman either through their own importunity or through the woman's willing infatuation, cannot keep quiet about it— **36 belie** slander   **36–7 fulsome** foul.   **38–9 first . . . to confess** (Othello reverses the proverbial *confess and be hanged*; Cassio is to be given no time to confess before he dies.)   **39–41 Nature . . . instruction** i.e., Without some foundation in fact, nature would not have dressed herself in such an overwhelming passion that comes over me now and fills my mind with images, or in such a lifelike fantasy as Cassio had in his dream of lying with Desdemona.   **41 words** mere words

(*Enter Cassio.*)

How now, Cassio?

CASSIO. What's the matter?

IAGO. My lord is fall'n into an epilepsy.
This is his second fit. He had one yesterday.

CASSIO. Rub him about the temples.

IAGO.   No, forbear.   *53*
The lethargy must have his quiet course.
If not, he foams at mouth, and by and by
Breaks out to savage madness. Look, he stirs.
Do you withdraw yourself a little while.
He will recover straight. When he is gone,
I would on great occasion speak with you.   *58*

(*Exit Cassio.*)

How is it, General? Have you not hurt your head?

OTHELLO. Dost thou mock me?

IAGO.   I mock you not, by heaven.   *60*
Would you would bear your fortune like a man!

OTHELLO. A hornèd man's a monster and a beast.

IAGO. There's many a beast then in a populous city,
And many a civil monster.   *64*

OTHELLO. Did he confess it?

IAGO. Good sir, be a man.
Think every bearded fellow that's but yoked   *67*
May draw with you. There's millions now alive   *68*
That nightly lie in those unproper beds   *69*
Which they dare swear peculiar. Your case is better.   *70*
Oh, 'tis the spite of hell, the fiend's arch-mock,
To lip a wanton in a secure couch   *72*
And to suppose her chaste! No, let me know,
And knowing what I am, I know what she shall be.   *74*

OTHELLO. Oh, thou art wise. 'Tis certain.

---

53 lethargy coma. **his** its   **58 on great occasion** on a matter of great importance   **60 mock me** (Othello takes Iago's question about hurting his head to be a mocking reference to the cuckold's horns.)   **64 civil** i.e., dwelling in a city   **67 yoked** (1) married (2) put into the yoke of infamy and cuckoldry   **68 draw with you** pull as you do, like oxen who are yoked, i.e., share your fate as cuckold. **69 unproper** not exclusively their own   **70 peculiar** private, their own.   **better** i.e., because you know the truth.   **72 lip** kiss.   **secure** free from suspicion   **74 And . . . shall be** and, knowing myself to be a cuckold, I'll know for certain that she's a whore.

IAGO. Stand you awhile apart;
    Confine yourself but in a patient list.   *77*
    Whilst you were here o'erwhelmèd with your grief—
    A passion most unsuiting such a man—
    Cassio came hither. I shifted him away,   *80*
    And laid good 'scuse upon your ecstasy,   *81*
    Bade him anon return and here speak with me,
    The which he promised. Do but encave yourself   *83*
    And mark the fleers, the gibes, and notable scorns   *84*
    That dwell in every region of his face;
    For I will make him tell the tale anew,
    Where, how, how oft, how long ago, and when
    He hath and is again to cope your wife.   *88*
    I say, but mark his gesture. Marry, patience!
    Or I shall say you're all-in-all in spleen,   *90*
    And nothing of a man.
OTHELLO.   Dost thou hear, Iago?
    I will be found most cunning in my patience;
    But—dost thou hear?—most bloody.
IAGO.   That's not amiss;
    But yet keep time in all. Will you withdraw?   *94*

(*Othello stands apart.*)

    Now will I question Cassio of Bianca,
    A huswife that by selling her desires   *96*
    Buys herself bread and clothes. It is a creature
    That dotes on Cassio—as 'tis the strumpet's plague
    To beguile many and be beguiled by one.
    He, when he hears of her, cannot restrain   *100*
    From the excess of laughter. Here he comes.

(*Enter Cassio.*)

    As he shall smile, Othello shall go mad;
    And his unbookish jealousy must conster   *103*
    Poor Cassio's smiles, gestures, and light behaviors
    Quite in the wrong.—How do you now, Lieutenant?

---

77 in . . . list within the bounds of patience.   **80–1 I shifted . . . ecstasy** I got him out of the way, using your fit as my excuse for doing so   **83 encave** conceal   **84 fleers** sneers   **88 cope** encounter with, have sex with   **90 all-in-all in spleen** utterly governed by passionate impulses   **94 keep time** keep yourself steady (as in music)   **96 huswife** hussy   **100 restrain** refrain   **103 his unbookish** Othello's uninstructed.   **conster** construe

CASSIO. The worser that you give me the addition   *106*
    Whose want even kills me.   *107*

IAGO. Ply Desdemona well and you are sure on't.
    (*Speaking lower*) Now, if this suit lay in Bianca's power,
    How quickly should you speed!

CASSIO (*laughing*). Alas, poor caitiff!   *111*

OTHELLO (*aside*). Look how he laughs already!

IAGO. I never knew a woman love man so.

CASSIO. Alas, poor rogue! I think, i'faith, she loves me.

OTHELLO (*aside*). Now he denies it faintly, and laughs it out.

IAGO. Do you hear, Cassio?

OTHELLO (*aside*).   Now he importunes him
    To tell it o'er. Go to! Well said, well said.   *117*

IAGO. She gives it out that you shall marry her.
    Do you intend it?

CASSIO. Ha, ha, ha!

OTHELLO (*aside*). Do you triumph, Roman? Do you triumph?   *121*

CASSIO. I marry her? What? A customer? Prithee, bear   *122*
    some charity to my wit; do not think it so unwhole-   *123*
    some. Ha, ha, ha!

OTHELLO (*aside*). So, so, so, so! They laugh that win.   *125*

IAGO. Faith, the cry goes that you shall marry her.   *126*

CASSIO. Prithee, say true.

IAGO. I am a very villain else.   *128*

OTHELLO (*aside*). Have you scored me? Well.   *129*

CASSIO. This is the monkey's own giving out. She is
    persuaded I will marry her out of her own love and
    flattery, not out of my promise.   *132*

OTHELLO (*aside*). Iago beckons me. Now he begins the story.   *133*

CASSIO. She was here even now; she haunts me in every
    place. I was the other day talking on the seabank with   *136*
    certain Venetians, and thither comes the bauble, and,   *137*
    by this hand, she falls me thus about my neck—   *138*

---

106 **addition** title   107 **Whose want** the lack of which   111 **caitiff** wretch.   117 **Go to** (An expression of remonstrance.)   **Well said** Well done. (Sarcastic.)   121 **Roman** (The Romans were noted for their *triumphs* or triumphal processions.)   122 **A customer?** Who, I, the whore's customer? (Or, *customer* could mean "prostitute.")   122–3 **bear . . . wit** be more charitable to my judgment   125 **They . . . win** i.e., They that laugh last laugh best.   126 **cry** rumor   128 **I . . . else** Call me a complete rogue if I'm not telling the truth.   129 **scored me** scored off me, beaten me, made up my reckoning, branded me.   132 **flattery** self-flattery, self-deception   133 **beckons** signals to   136 **seabank** seashore   137 **bauble** plaything   138 **by this hand** I make my vow

(*He embraces Iago.*)

OTHELLO (*aside*). Crying, "Oh, dear Cassio!" as it were; his
  gesture imports it.
CASSIO. So hangs and lolls and weeps upon me, so
  shakes and pulls me. Ha, ha, ha!
OTHELLO (*aside*). Now he tells how she plucked him to my
  chamber. Oh, I see that nose of yours, but not that dog   144
  I shall throw it to.   145
CASSIO. Well, I must leave her company.
IAGO. Before me, look where she comes.   147

(*Enter Bianca [with Othello's handkerchief].*)

CASSIO. 'Tis such another fitchew! Marry, a perfumed   148
  one.—What do you mean by this haunting of me?
BIANCA. Let the devil and his dam haunt you! What did   150
  you mean by that same handkerchief you gave me
  even now? I was a fine fool to take it. I must take out
  the work? A likely piece of work, that you should find   153
  it in your chamber and know not who left it there!
  This is some minx's token, and I must take out the   156
  work? There; give it your hobbyhorse. (*She gives him
  the handkerchief.*) Wheresoever you had it, I'll take out
  no work on't.
CASSIO. How now, my sweet Bianca? How now? How
  now?
OTHELLO (*aside*). By heaven, that should be my hand-   160
  kerchief!
BIANCA. If you'll come to supper tonight, you may; if
  you will not, come when you are next prepared for.   163

(*Exit.*)

IAGO. After her, after her.
CASSIO. Faith, I must. She'll rail in the streets else.
IAGO. Will you sup there?
CASSIO. Faith, I intend so.

144–5 **not . . . to** (Othello imagines himself cutting off Cassio's nose and throwing it to a dog.)
147 **Before me** i e., On my soul   148 **'Tis . . . fitchew!** What a whore she is! Just like all the others.
(*Fitchew* or "polecat" was a common term of contempt for a courtesan or prostitute.)   150 **dam**
mother   153 **A likely . . . work** A fine story   156 **hobbyhorse** harlot.   160 **should be** must be
163 **when . . . for** when I'm ready for you (i.e., never).

IAGO. Well, I may chance to see you, for I would very
fain speak with you.

CASSIO. Prithee, come. Will you?

IAGO. Go to. Say no more.   (*Exit Cassio.*)   171

OTHELLO (*advancing*). How shall I murder him, Iago?

IAGO. Did you perceive how he laughed at his vice?

OTHELLO. Oh, Iago!

IAGO. And did you see the handkerchief?

OTHELLO. Was that mine?

IAGO. Yours, by this hand. And to see how he prizes
the foolish woman your wife! She gave it him, and he
hath given it his whore.

OTHELLO. I would have him nine years a-killing. A fine
woman! A fair woman! A sweet woman!

IAGO. Nay, you must forget that.

OTHELLO. Ay, let her rot and perish, and be damned
tonight, for she shall not live. No, my heart is turned
to stone; I strike it, and it hurts my hand. Oh, the world
hath not a sweeter creature! She might lie by an emperor's side and command him tasks.

IAGO. Nay, that's not your way.   188

OTHELLO. Hang her! I do but say what she is. So delicate
with her needle! An admirable musician! Oh, she will
sing the savageness out of a bear. Of so high and plen-
teous wit and invention!   192

IAGO. She's the worse for all this.

OTHELLO. Oh, a thousand, a thousand times! And then,
of so gentle a condition!   195

IAGO. Ay, too gentle.   196

OTHELLO. Nay, that's certain. But yet the pity of it, Iago!
Oh, Iago, the pity of it, Iago!

IAGO. If you are so fond over her iniquity, give her patent 199
to offend, for if it touch not you it comes near nobody.

OTHELLO. I will chop her into messes. Cuckold me?   201

IAGO. Oh, 'tis foul in her.

OTHELLO. With mine officer?

IAGO. That's fouler.

---

171 **Go to** (An expression of remonstrance.)   188 **your way** i.e., the way you should think of her.
192 **invention** imagination.   195 **gentle a condition** wellborn and well-bred.   196 **gentle** generous,
yielding (to other men).   199 **fond** foolish.   **patent** license   201 **messes** portions of meat, i.e., bits.

OTHELLO. Get me some poison, Iago, this night. I'll not
  expostulate with her, lest her body and beauty unpro-   *206*
  vide my mind again. This night, Iago.   *207*
IAGO. Do it not with poison. Strangle her in her bed,
  even the bed she hath contaminated.
OTHELLO. Good, good! The justice of it pleases. Very good.
IAGO. And for Cassio, let me be his undertaker. You   *211*
  shall hear more by midnight.
OTHELLO. Excellent good. (*A trumpet within.*) What
  trumpet is that same?
IAGO. I warrant, something from Venice.

(*Enter Lodovico, Desdemona, and attendants.*)

  'Tis Lodovico. This comes from the Duke.
  See, your wife's with him.
LODOVICO. God save you, worthy General!
OTHELLO.   With all my heart, sir.   *217*
LODOVICO (*giving him a letter*). The Duke and the senators
  of Venice greet you.
OTHELLO. I kiss the instrument of their pleasures.

(*He opens the letter, and reads.*)

DESDEMONA. And what's the news, good cousin Lodovico?
IAGO. I am very glad to see you, signor.
  Welcome to Cyprus.
LODOVICO. I thank you. How does Lieutenant Cassio?
IAGO. Lives, sir.
DESDEMONA. Cousin, there's fall'n between him and my
    lord
  An unkind breach; but you shall make all well.   *226*
OTHELLO. Are you sure of that?
DESDEMONA. My lord?
OTHELLO (*reads*). "This fail you not to do, as you will—"
LODOVICO. He did not call; he's busy in the paper.
  Is there division twixt my lord and Cassio?
DESDEMONA. A most unhappy one. I would do much
  T'atone them, for the love I bear to Cassio.   *233*

206–7 **unprovide** weaken, disarm   211 **be his undertaker** undertake to dispatch him.   217 **With all
my heart** i.e., I thank you most heartily   226 **unkind** unnatural, contrary to their natures; hurtful
233 **T'atone** to reconcile

OTHELLO. Fire and brimstone!

DESDEMONA. My lord?

OTHELLO. Are you wise?

DESDEMONA. What, is he angry?

LODOVICO.   Maybe the letter moved him;
    For, as I think, they do command him home,
    Deputing Cassio in his government.   239

DESDEMONA. By my troth, I am glad on't.   240

OTHELLO. Indeed?

DESDEMONA. My lord?

OTHELLO. I am glad to see you mad.   243

DESDEMONA. Why, sweet Othello—

OTHELLO (*striking her*). Devil!

DESDEMONA. I have not deserved this.

LODOVICO. My lord, this would not be believed in Venice,
    Though I should swear I saw't. 'Tis very much.   248
    Make her amends; she weeps.

OTHELLO.   Oh, devil, devil!
    If that the earth could teem with woman's tears,   250
    Each drop she falls would prove a crocodile.   251
    Out of my sight!

DESDEMONA.   I will not stay to offend you. (*Going.*)

LODOVICO. Truly, an obedient lady.
    I do beseech Your Lordship, call her back.

OTHELLO (*calling*). Mistress!

DESDEMONA (*returning*). My lord?

OTHELLO. What would you with her, sir?   257

LODOVICO. Who, I, my lord?

OTHELLO. Ay, you did wish that I would make her turn.
    Sir, she can turn, and turn, and yet go on
    And turn again; and she can weep, sir, weep;
    And she's obedient, as you say, obedient,   262
    Very obedient.—Proceed you in your tears.—
    Concerning this, sir—Oh, well-painted passion!—   264
    I am commanded home.—Get you away;

---

239 government office.   **240 on't** of it.   **243 I am ... mad** i.e., I am glad to see that you are insane enough to rejoice in Cassio's promotion. (? Othello bitterly plays on Desdemona's *I am glad.*) **248 very much** too much, outrageous.   **250 teem** breed, be impregnated   **251 falls** lets fall. **crocodile** (Crocodiles were supposed to weep hypocritical tears for their victims.)   **257 What ... sir?** (Othello implies that Desdemona is pliant and will do a *turn*, lines 257–9, for any man.)   **262 obedient** (With much the same sexual connotation as *turn* in lines 257–9.)   **264 passion** i.e., grief.

I'll send for you anon.—Sir, I obey the mandate
And will return to Venice.—Hence, avaunt!

(*Exit Desdemona.*)

Cassio shall have my place. And, sir, tonight
I do entreat that we may sup together.
You are welcome, sir, to Cyprus.—Goats and
    monkeys! (*Exit.*)   *270*
LODOVICO. Is this the noble Moor whom our full Senate
  Call all in all sufficient? Is this the nature
  Whom passion could not shake? Whose solid virtue
  The shot of accident nor dart of chance
  Could neither graze nor pierce?
IAGO.   He is much changed.
LODOVICO. Are his wits safe? Is he not light of brain?
IAGO. He's that he is. I may not breathe my censure   *277*
  What he might be. If what he might he is not,   *278*
  I would to heaven he were!
LODOVICO.   What, strike his wife?   *279*
IAGO. Faith, that was not so well; yet would I knew
  That stroke would prove the worst!
LODOVICO.   Is it his use?   *281*
  Or did the letters work upon his blood   *282*
  And new-create his fault?
IAGO.   Alas, alas!
  It is not honesty in me to speak
  What I have seen and known. You shall observe him,
  And his own courses will denote him so   *286*
  That I may save my speech. Do but go after,
  And mark how he continues.
LODOVICO. I am sorry that I am deceived in him. (*Exeunt.*)

4.2

Enter Othello and Emilia.

OTHELLO. You have seen nothing, then?

---

270 Goats and monkeys (See 3.3.419.)   **277–9 I may . . . were!** I dare not venture an opinion as to whether he's of unsound mind, as you suggest, but, if he isn't, then it might be better to wish he were in fact insane, since only that could excuse his wild behavior!   **281 use** custom.   **282 blood** passions   **286 courses will denote** actions will reveal
4.2. Location: The citadel.

EMILIA. Nor ever heard, nor ever did suspect.

OTHELLO. Yes, you have seen Cassio and she together.

EMILIA. But then I saw no harm, and then I heard
    Each syllable that breath made up between them.

OTHELLO. What, did they never whisper?

EMILIA. Never, my lord.

OTHELLO. Nor send you out o'th' way?

EMILIA. Never.

OTHELLO. To fetch her fan, her gloves, her mask, nor nothing?

EMILIA. Never, my lord.

OTHELLO. That's strange.

EMILIA. I durst, my lord, to wager she is honest,
    Lay down my soul at stake. If you think other,   *14*
    Remove your thought; it doth abuse your bosom.   *15*
    If any wretch have put this in your head,
    Let heaven requite it with the serpent's curse!   *17*
    For if she be not honest, chaste, and true,
    There's no man happy; the purest of their wives
    Is foul as slander.

OTHELLO.   Bid her come hither. Go.

                        (*Exit Emilia.*)

    She says enough; yet she's a simple bawd   *21*
    That cannot say as much. This is a subtle whore,   *22*
    A closet lock and key of villainous secrets.   *23*
    And yet she'll kneel and pray; I have seen her do't.

(*Enter Desdemona and Emilia.*)

DESDEMONA. My lord, what is your will?

OTHELLO. Pray you, chuck, come hither.

DESDEMONA. What is your pleasure?

OTHELLO.   Let me see your eyes.
    Look in my face.

DESDEMONA.   What horrible fancy's this?

OTHELLO (*to Emilia*). Some of your function, mistress.   *29*

---

14 at stake as the wager.   **15 abuse your bosom** deceive your breast, your heart.   **17 the serpent's curse** the curse pronounced by God on the serpent for deceiving Eve, just as some man has done to Othello and Desdemona. (See Genesis 3:14.)   **21–2 she's . . . much** i.e., any procuress or go-between who couldn't make up as plausible a story as Emilia's would have to be pretty stupid.   **22 This** i.e., Desdemona   **23 closet lock and key** i.e., concealer   **29 Some . . . function** i.e., Practice your chosen profession, that of bawd (by guarding the door)

Leave procreants alone and shut the door; 30
Cough or cry "hem" if anybody come.
Your mystery, your mystery! Nay, dispatch. 32

(*Exit Emilia.*)

DESDEMONA (*kneeling*). Upon my knees, what doth your
    speech import?
I understand a fury in your words,
But not the words.
OTHELLO. Why, what art thou?
DESDEMONA.   Your wife, my lord, your true
And loyal wife.
OTHELLO.   Come, swear it, damn thyself,
Lest, being like one of heaven, the devils themselves 38
Should fear to seize thee. Therefore be double damned:
Swear thou art honest.
DESDEMONA.   Heaven doth truly know it.
OTHELLO. Heaven truly knows that thou art false as hell.
DESDEMONA. To whom, my lord? With whom? How am I
    false?
OTHELLO (*weeping*). Ah, Desdemon! Away, away, away!
DESDEMONA. Alas the heavy day! Why do you weep?
Am I the motive of these tears, my lord? 45
If haply you my father do suspect
An instrument of this your calling back,
Lay not your blame on me. If you have lost him,
I have lost him too.
OTHELLO.   Had it pleased heaven
To try me with affliction, had they rained 50
All kinds of sores and shames on my bare head,
Steeped me in poverty to the very lips,
Given to captivity me and my utmost hopes,
I should have found in some place of my soul
A drop of patience. But, alas, to make me
A fixèd figure for the time of scorn 56
To point his slow and moving finger at! 57
Yet could I bear that too, well, very well.

---

30 procreants mating couples   **32 mystery** trade, occupation   **38 being ... heaven** looking like an
angel   **45 motive** cause   **50 they** the heavenly powers   **56–7 A fixèd ... finger at** a figure of
ridicule to be pointed at scornfully for all of eternity by the slowly moving finger of Time.

But there where I have garnered up my heart,   *59*
Where either I must live or bear no life,
The fountain from the which my current runs   *61*
Or else dries up—to be discarded thence!
Or keep it as a cistern for foul toads   *63*
To knot and gender in! Turn thy complexion there,   *64*
Patience, thou young and rose-lipped cherubin—   *65*
Ay, there look grim as hell!   *66*

DESDEMONA. I hope my noble lord esteems me honest.   *67*

OTHELLO. Oh, ay, as summer flies are in the shambles,   *68*
That quicken even with blowing. O thou weed,   *69*
Who art so lovely fair and smell'st so sweet
That the sense aches at thee, would thou hadst ne'er
    been born!

DESDEMONA. Alas, what ignorant sin have I committed?   *72*

OTHELLO. Was this fair paper, this most goodly book,
Made to write "whore" upon? What committed?
Committed? Oh, thou public commoner!   *75*
I should make very forges of my cheeks,
That would to cinders burn up modesty,
Did I but speak thy deeds. What committed?
Heaven stops the nose at it and the moon winks;   *79*
The bawdy wind, that kisses all it meets,   *80*
Is hushed within the hollow mine of earth   *81*
And will not hear't. What committed?
Impudent strumpet!

DESDEMONA.   By heaven, you do me wrong.

OTHELLO. Are not you a strumpet?

DESDEMONA. No, as I am a Christian.
If to preserve this vessel for my lord   *86*
From any other foul unlawful touch
Be not to be a strumpet, I am none.

OTHELLO. What, not a whore?

DESDEMONA. No, as I shall be saved.

---

59 garnered stored   **61 fountain** spring   **63 cistern** cesspool   **64 To ... gender in** to couple sexually and conceive in.   **64–6 Turn ... hell!** Direct your gaze there, Patience, and your youthful and rosy cherubic countenance will turn grim and pale at this hellish spectacle!   **67 honest** chaste.
68 shambles slaughterhouse   **69 That ... blowing** that come to life with the puffing up of the rotten meat on which the flies and their maggots are breeding.   **72 ignorant sin** sin in ignorance
75 commoner prostitute.   **79 winks** closes her eyes. (The moon symbolizes chastity.)   **80 bawdy** kissing one and all   **81 mine** cave (where the winds were thought to dwell)   **86 vessel** body

OTHELLO. Is't possible?

DESDEMONA. Oh, heaven forgive us!

OTHELLO.   I cry you mercy, then.   92
    I took you for that cunning whore of Venice
    That married with Othello. (*Calling out*) You, mistress,
    That have the office opposite to Saint Peter
    And keep the gate of hell!

(*Enter Emilia.*)

                         You, you, ay, you!
    We have done our course. There's money for your   97
        pains. (*He gives money.*)
    I pray you, turn the key and keep our counsel. (*Exit.*)

EMILIA. Alas, what does this gentleman conceive?   99
    How do you, madam? How do you, my good lady?

DESDEMONA. Faith, half asleep.   101

EMILIA. Good madam, what's the matter with my lord?

DESDEMONA. With who?

EMILIA. Why, with my lord, madam.

DESDEMONA. Who is thy lord?

EMILIA.   He that is yours, sweet lady.

DESDEMONA. I have none. Do not talk to me, Emilia.
    I cannot weep, nor answers have I none
    But what should go by water. Prithee, tonight   108
    Lay on my bed my wedding sheets, remember;
    And call thy husband hither.

EMILIA. Here's a change indeed!   (*Exit.*)

DESDEMONA. 'Tis meet I should be used so, very meet.   112
    How have I been behaved, that he might stick   113
    The small'st opinion on my least misuse?   114

(*Enter Iago and Emilia.*)

IAGO. What is your pleasure, madam? How is't with you?

DESDEMONA. I cannot tell. Those that do teach young babes
    Do it with gentle means and easy tasks.

---

92 cry you mercy beg your pardon. (Sarcastic.) **97 course** business. (With an indecent suggestion of "trick," turn at sex.) **99 conceive** suppose, think. **101 half asleep** i.e., dazed. **108 go by water** be conveyed by tears. **112 'Tis ... very meet** i.e., It must be I somehow have deserved this.
113–14 How ... misuse? What have I done that prompts Othello to attach even the slightest censure to whatever little fault I may have committed?

He might have chid me so, for, in good faith,
I am a child to chiding.

IAGO. What is the matter, lady?

EMILIA. Alas, Iago, my lord hath so bewhored her,
Thrown such despite and heavy terms upon her,
That true hearts cannot bear it.

DESDEMONA. Am I that name, Iago?

IAGO. What name, fair lady?

DESDEMONA. Such as she said my lord did say I was.

EMILIA. He called her whore. A beggar in his drink
Could not have laid such terms upon his callet.   128

IAGO. Why did he so?

DESDEMONA (*weeping*). I do not know. I am sure I am
none such.

IAGO. Do not weep, do not weep. Alas the day!

EMILIA. Hath she forsook so many noble matches,
Her father and her country and her friends,
To be called whore? Would it not make one weep?

DESDEMONA. It is my wretched fortune.

IAGO.   Beshrew him for't!   135
How comes this trick upon him?   136

DESDEMONA.   Nay, heaven doth know.

EMILIA. I will be hanged if some eternal villain,   137
Some busy and insinuating rogue,   138
Some cogging, cozening slave, to get some office,   139
Have not devised this slander. I will be hanged else.

IAGO. Fie, there is no such man. It is impossible.

DESDEMONA. If any such there be, heaven pardon him!

EMILIA. A halter pardon him! And hell gnaw his bones!
Why should he call her whore? Who keeps her company?
What place? What time? What form? What likelihood?   145
The Moor's abused by some most villainous knave,
Some base notorious knave, some scurvy fellow.
Oh, heavens, that such companions thou'dst unfold,   148
And put in every honest hand a whip
To lash the rascals naked through the world

---

128 **callet** whore.   135 **Beshrew** May evil befall. (An oath.)   136 **trick** strange behavior, delusion
137 **eternal** inveterate   138 **insinuating** ingratiating, fawning, wheedling   139 **cogging, cozening**
cheating, defrauding   143 **halter** hangman's noose   145 **form** manner, circumstance.   148 **that . . .**
unfold would that you would expose such fellows

Even from the east to th' west!

IAGO.   Speak within door.   *151*

EMILIA. Oh, fie upon them! Some such squire he was   *152*
　　　That turned your wit the seamy side without   *153*
　　　And made you to suspect me with the Moor.

IAGO. You are a fool. Go to.   *155*

DESDEMONA.   O God, Iago,
　　　What shall I do to win my lord again?
　　　Good friend, go to him; for, by this light of heaven,
　　　I know not how I lost him. Here I kneel. (*She kneels.*)
　　　If e'er my will did trespass 'gainst his love,
　　　Either in discourse of thought or actual deed,   *160*
　　　Or that mine eyes, mine ears, or any sense   *161*
　　　Delighted them in any other form;   *162*
　　　Or that I do not yet, and ever did,   *163*
　　　And ever will—though he do shake me off
　　　To beggarly divorcement—love him dearly,
　　　Comfort forswear me! Unkindness may do much,   *166*
　　　And his unkindness may defeat my life,   *167*
　　　But never taint my love. I cannot say "whore."
　　　It does abhor me now I speak the word;   *169*
　　　To do the act that might the addition earn   *170*
　　　Not the world's mass of vanity could make me.   *171*

(*She rises.*)

IAGO. I pray you, be content. 'Tis but his humor.   *172*
　　　The business of the state does him offense,
　　　And he does chide with you.

DESDEMONA. If 'twere no other—

IAGO. It is but so, I warrant. (*Trumpets within.*)
　　　Hark, how these instruments summon you to supper!
　　　The messengers of Venice stays the meat.   *178*
　　　Go in, and weep not. All things shall be well.

---

151 **within door** i.e., not so loud.　152 **squire** fellow　153 **seamy side without** wrong side out
155 **Go to** i.e., That's enough.　160 **discourse of thought** process of thinking　161 **that** if. (Also in
line 163.)　162 **Delighted them** took delight　163 **yet** still　166 **Comfort forswear** may heavenly
comfort forsake　167 **defeat** destroy　169 **abhor** (1) fill me with abhorrence (2) make me whorelike
170 **addition** title　171 **vanity** showy splendor　172 **humor** mood.　178 **stays the meat** are waiting
to dine.

(Exeunt Desdemona and Emilia.)

(Enter Roderigo.)

How now, Roderigo?

RODERIGO. I do not find that thou deal'st justly with me.

IAGO. What in the contrary?

RODERIGO. Every day thou daff'st me with some device,   *183*
Iago, and rather, as it seems to me now, keep'st
from me all conveniency than suppliest me with the   *185*
least advantage of hope. I will indeed no longer   *186*
endure it, nor am I yet persuaded to put up in peace   *187*
what already I have foolishly suffered.

IAGO. Will you hear me, Roderigo?

RODERIGO. Faith, I have heard too much, for your words
and performances are no kin together.

IAGO. You charge me most unjustly.

RODERIGO. With naught but truth. I have wasted myself
out of my means. The jewels you have had from me to
deliver Desdemona would half have corrupted a vo-   *195*
tarist. You have told me she hath received them and   *196*
returned me expectations and comforts of sudden re-   *197*
spect and acquaintance, but I find none.   *198*

IAGO. Well, go to, very well.

RODERIGO. "Very well"! "Go to"! I cannot go to, man,   *200*
nor 'tis not very well. By this hand, I think it is scurvy,
and begin to find myself fopped in it.   *202*

IAGO. Very well.

RODERIGO. I tell you 'tis not very well. I will make myself   *204*
known to Desdemona. If she will return me my jewels,
I will give over my suit and repent my unlawful solicitation; if not, assure yourself I will seek satisfaction   *207*
of you.

IAGO. You have said now?   *209*

---

183 **thou daff'st me** you put me off.   183–4 **device** excuse, trick   185 **conveniency** advantage, opportunity   186 **advantage** increase   187 **put up** submit to, tolerate   195 **deliver** deliver to   195–6 **votarist** nun   197–8 **sudden respect** immediate consideration   200 **I cannot go to** (Roderigo changes Iago's *go to*, an expression urging patience, to *I cannot go to*, "I have no opportunity for success in wooing.")   202 **fopped** fooled, duped   204 **not very well** (Roderigo changes Iago's *very well*, "all right, then," to *not very well*, "not at all good.")   207 **satisfaction** repayment. (The term normally means settling of accounts in a duel.)   209 **You . . . now?** Have you finished?

RODERIGO. Ay, and said nothing but what I protest 210
intendment of doing. 211

IAGO. Why, now I see there's mettle in thee, and even
from this instant do build on thee a better opinion
than ever before. Give me thy hand, Roderigo. Thou
hast taken against me a most just exception; but yet I
protest I have dealt most directly in thy affair.

RODERIGO. It hath not appeared.

IAGO. I grant indeed it hath not appeared, and your
suspicion is not without wit and judgment. But,
Roderigo, if thou hast that in thee indeed which I have
greater reason to believe now than ever—I mean
purpose, courage, and valor—this night show it. If
thou the next night following enjoy not Desdemona,
take me from this world with treachery and devise
engines for my life. 225

RODERIGO. Well, what is it? Is it within reason and
compass?

IAGO. Sir, there is especial commission come from
Venice to depute Cassio in Othello's place.

RODERIGO. Is that true? Why, then Othello and Desdemona return again to Venice.

IAGO. Oh, no; he goes into Mauritania and takes away
with him the fair Desdemona, unless his abode be
lingered here by some accident; wherein none can be
so determinate as the removing of Cassio. 235

RODERIGO. How do you mean, removing of him?

IAGO. Why, by making him uncapable of Othello's
place—knocking out his brains.

RODERIGO. And that you would have me to do?

IAGO. Ay, if you dare do yourself a profit and a right.
He sups tonight with a harlotry, and thither will I go to 241
him. He knows not yet of his honorable fortune. If
you will watch his going thence, which I will fashion
to fall out between twelve and one, you may take him 244
at your pleasure. I will be near to second your attempt,
and he shall fall between us. Come, stand not amazed
at it, but go along with me. I will show you such a

210–11 **protest intendment** avow my intention   225 **engines** plots, snares   235 **determinate** conclusive, instrumental   241 **harlotry** slut   244 **fall out** occur

necessity in his death that you shall think yourself
bound to put it on him. It is now high suppertime,   *249*
and the night grows to waste. About it.   *250*
RODERIGO. I will hear further reason for this.
IAGO. And you shall be satisfied.   (*Exeunt.*)

4.3

Enter Othello, Lodovico, Desdemona, Emilia, and attendants.

LODOVICO. I do beseech you, sir, trouble yourself no further.
OTHELLO. Oh, pardon me; 'twill do me good to walk.
LODOVICO. Madam, good night. I humbly thank Your Ladyship.
DESDEMONA. Your Honor is most welcome.
OTHELLO.   Will you walk, sir?
    Oh, Desdemona!
DESDEMONA. My lord?
OTHELLO. Get you to bed on th'instant. I will be re-
    turned forthwith. Dismiss your attendant there. Look't
    be done.
DESDEMONA. I will, my lord.

    (*Exit [Othello, with Lodovico and attendants].*)

EMILIA. How goes it now? He looks gentler than he did.
DESDEMONA. He says he will return incontinent,   *12*
    And hath commanded me to go to bed,
    And bid me to dismiss you.
EMILIA. Dismiss me?
DESDEMONA. It was his bidding. Therefore, good Emilia,
    Give me my nightly wearing, and adieu.
    We must not now displease him.
EMILIA. I would you had never seen him!
DESDEMONA. So would not I. My love doth so approve him
    That even his stubbornness, his checks, his frowns—   *21*
    Prithee, unpin me—have grace and favor in them.

(*Emilia prepares Desdemona for bed.*)

EMILIA. I have laid those sheets you bade me on the bed.

---

249 **high** fully   250 **grows to waste** wastes away.
4.3 Location: The citadel.
12 **incontinent** immediately   21 **stubbornness** roughness.   **checks** rebukes

DESDEMONA. All's one. Good faith, how foolish are our minds! 25
    If I do die before thee, prithee shroud me
    In one of these same sheets.
EMILIA.   Come, come, you talk. 27
DESDEMONA. My mother had a maid called Barbary.
    She was in love, and he she loved proved mad 29
    And did forsake her. She had a song of "Willow."
    An old thing 'twas, but it expressed her fortune,
    And she died singing it. That song tonight
    Will not go from my mind; I have much to do 33
    But to go hang my head all at one side 34
    And sing it like poor Barbary. Prithee, dispatch.
EMILIA. Shall I go fetch your nightgown? 36
DESDEMONA. No, unpin me here.
    This Lodovico is a proper man. 38
EMILIA. A very handsome man.
DESDEMONA. He speaks well.
EMILIA. I know a lady in Venice would have walked barefoot
    to Palestine for a touch of his nether lip.
DESDEMONA (*singing*).
        "The poor soul sat sighing by a sycamore tree,
           Sing all a green willow; 44
        Her hand on her bosom, her head on her knee,
           Sing willow, willow, willow.
        The fresh streams ran by her and murmured her
             moans;
           Sing willow, willow, willow;
        Her salt tears fell from her, and softened the
             stones—"
    Lay by these.
    (*Singing*) "Sing willow, willow, willow—"
    Prithee, hie thee. He'll come anon. 52
    (*Singing*) "Sing all a green willow must be my garland.
        Let nobody blame him; his scorn I approve—"
    Nay, that's not next.—Hark! Who is't that knocks?
EMILIA. It's the wind.

---

25 All's one All right. It doesn't really matter.   **27 talk** i.e., prattle.   **29 mad** wild, lunatic
33-4 I . . . hang I can scarcely keep myself from hanging   **36 nightgown** dressing gown.
38 proper handsome   **44 willow** (A conventional emblem of disappointed love.)   **52 hie thee**
hurry. **anon** right away.

DESDEMONA (*singing*).
  "I called my love false love; but what said he then?
    Sing willow, willow, willow;
  If I court more women, you'll couch with more men."
So, get thee gone. Good night. Mine eyes do itch;
Doth that bode weeping?
EMILIA.   'Tis neither here nor there.
DESDEMONA. I have heard it said so. Oh, these men, these men!
  Dost thou in conscience think—tell me, Emilia—
  That there be women do abuse their husbands   64
  In such gross kind?
EMILIA.   There be some such, no question.
DESDEMONA. Wouldst thou do such a deed for all the world?
EMILIA. Why, would not you?
DESDEMONA.   No, by this heavenly light!
EMILIA. Nor I neither by this heavenly light;
  I might do't as well i'th' dark.
DESDEMONA. Wouldst thou do such a deed for all the world?
EMILIA. The world's a huge thing. It is a great price
  For a small vice.
DESDEMONA. Good troth, I think thou wouldst not.
EMILIA. By my troth, I think I should, and undo't when
  I had done. Marry, I would not do such a thing for a
  joint ring, nor for measures of lawn, nor for gowns,   76
  petticoats, nor caps, nor any petty exhibition. But for   77
  all the whole world! Uds pity, who would not make   78
  her husband a cuckold to make him a monarch? I
  should venture purgatory for't.
DESDEMONA. Beshrew me if I would do such a wrong
  For the whole world.
EMILIA. Why, the wrong is but a wrong i'th' world, and
  having the world for your labor, 'tis a wrong in your
  own world, and you might quickly make it right.
DESDEMONA. I do not think there is any such woman.
EMILIA. Yes, a dozen, and as many   87
  To th' vantage as would store the world they played for.   88
  But I do think it is their husbands' faults

---

64 abuse deceive **76 joint ring** a ring made in separate halves. **lawn** fine linen **77 exhibition**
gift. **78 Uds** God's **87–8 and . . . played for** and enough additionally to stock the world men have
gambled and sported sexually for.

If wives do fall. Say that they slack their duties   90
And pour our treasures into foreign laps,   91
Or else break out in peevish jealousies,
Throwing restraint upon us? Or say they strike us,   93
Or scant our former having in despite?   94
Why, we have galls, and though we have some grace,   95
Yet have we some revenge. Let husbands know
Their wives have sense like them. They see, and smell,   97
And have their palates both for sweet and sour,
As husbands have. What is it that they do   99
When they change us for others? Is it sport?   100
I think it is. And doth affection breed it?   101
I think it doth. Is't frailty that thus errs?
It is so, too. And have not we affections,
Desires for sport, and frailty, as men have?
Then let them use us well; else let them know,
The ills we do, their ills instruct us so.
DESDEMONA. Good night, good night. God me such uses
    send   107
Not to pick bad from bad, but by bad mend!

(Exeunt.)

5.1

Enter Iago and Roderigo.

IAGO. Here stand behind this bulk. Straight will he come.   1
    Wear thy good rapier bare, and put it home.   2
    Quick, quick! Fear nothing. I'll be at thy elbow.
    It makes us or it mars us. Think on that,
    And fix most firm thy resolution.
RODERIGO. Be near at hand. I may miscarry in't.

---

90 they our husbands.   **duties** marital duties   **91 pour ... laps** i.e., are unfaithful, give what is
rightfully ours (semen) to other women   **93 Throwing ... us** jealously restricting our freedom.
94 Or ... despite or spitefully take away from us whatever we enjoyed before.   **95 have galls** i.e., are
capable of resenting injury and insult.   **grace** inclination to be merciful   **97 sense** sensory perception and appetite   **99 they** husbands   **100 change** exchange.   **sport** sexual pastime.   **101 affection**
passion   **107 uses** habit, practice   **108 Not ... mend** i.e., not to learn bad conduct from others'
badness (as Emilia has suggested women learn from men), but to mend my ways by perceiving what
badness is, making spiritual benefit out of evil and adversity.
5.1 Location: A street in Cyprus.
1 bulk framework projecting from the front of a shop.   **2 bare** unsheathed.   **home** all the way into
the target.

IAGO. Here, at thy hand. Be bold, and take thy stand.

(*Iago stands aside, Roderigo conceals himself.*)

RODERIGO. I have no great devotion to the deed;
　　　And yet he hath given me satisfying reasons.
　　　'Tis but a man gone. Forth, my sword! He dies.

(*He draws.*)

IAGO. I have rubbed this young quat almost to the sense,　　　*11*
　　　And he grows angry. Now, whether he kill Cassio
　　　Or Cassio him, or each do kill the other,
　　　Every way makes my gain. Live Roderigo,　　　*14*
　　　He calls me to a restitution large
　　　Of gold and jewels that I bobbed from him　　　*16*
　　　As gifts to Desdemona.
　　　It must not be. If Cassio do remain,
　　　He hath a daily beauty in his life
　　　That makes me ugly; and besides, the Moor
　　　May unfold me to him; there stand I in much peril.　　　*21*
　　　No, he must die. Be't so. I hear him coming.

(*Enter Cassio.*)

RODERIGO (*coming forth*). I know his gait, 'tis he.—
　　　Villain, thou diest!

(*He attacks Cassio.*)

CASSIO. That thrust had been mine enemy indeed,
　　　But that my coat is better than thou know'st.　　　*25*
　　　I will make proof of thine.

(*He draws, and wounds Roderigo.*)

RODERIGO.　　　　　　Oh, I am slain!　　(*He falls.*　　　*26*
　　　　　(*Iago, from behind, wounds Cassio
　　　　　　　in the leg, and exit.*)

CASSIO. I am maimed forever. Help, ho! Murder! Murder!

(*Enter Othello.*)

---

11 quat pimple, pustule.　**to the sense** to the quick　**14 Live Roderigo** If Roderigo lives　**16 bobbed** swindled　**21 unfold** expose　**25 coat** (Possibly a garment of mail under the outer clothing, or simply a tougher coat than Roderigo expected.)　**26 proof** a test

OTHELLO. The voice of Cassio! Iago keeps his word.

RODERIGO. Oh, villain that I am!

OTHELLO. It is even so.

CASSIO. Oh, help, ho! Light! A surgeon!

OTHELLO. 'Tis he. O brave Iago, honest and just,
  That hast such noble sense of thy friend's wrong!
  Thou teachest me.—Minion, your dear lies dead,   34
  And your unblest fate hies. Strumpet, I come.   35
  Forth of my heart those charms, thine eyes, are blotted;   36
  Thy bed, lust-stained, shall with lust's blood be
      spotted.   (*Exit Othello.*)

(*Enter Lodovico and Gratiano.*)

CASSIO. What ho! No watch? No passage? Murder! Murder!   38

GRATIANO. 'Tis some mischance. The voice is very direful.

CASSIO. Oh, help!

LODOVICO. Hark!

RODERIGO. Oh, wretched villain!

LODOVICO. Two or three groan. 'Tis heavy night;   43
  These may be counterfeits. Let's think't unsafe
  To come in to the cry without more help.   45

(*They remain near the entrance.*)

RODERIGO. Nobody come? Then shall I bleed to death.

(*Enter Iago [in his shirtsleeves, with a light].*)

LODOVICO. Hark!

GRATIANO. Here's one comes in his shirt, with light and
      weapons.

IAGO. Who's there? Whose noise is this that cries on murder?   49

LODOVICO. We do not know.

IAGO.   Did not you hear a cry?

CASSIO. Here, here! For heaven's sake, help me!

IAGO.   What's the matter?

(*He moves toward Cassio.*)

GRATIANO (*to Lodovico*). This is Othello's ancient, as I take it.

---

34 **Minion** Hussy (i.e., Desdemona)   35 **hies** hastens on.   36 **Forth of** From out   38 **passage** people passing by.   43 **heavy** thick, dark   45 **come in to** approach   49 **cries** cries out

LODOVICO (*to Gratiano*). The same indeed, a very valiant
  fellow.

IAGO (*to Cassio*). What are you here that cry so grievously? *54*

CASSIO. Iago? Oh, I am spoiled, undone by villains! *55*
  Give me some help.

IAGO. Oh, me, Lieutenant! What villains have done this?

CASSIO. I think that one of them is hereabout,
  And cannot make away.

IAGO.   Oh, treacherous villains! *59*
  (*To Lodovico and Gratiano*) What are you there? Come in,
      and give some help.   (*They advance.*)

RODERIGO. Oh, help me there!

CASSIO. That's one of them.

IAGO.   Oh, murderous slave! Oh, villain!

(*He stabs Roderigo.*)

RODERIGO. Oh, damned Iago! Oh, inhuman dog!

IAGO. Kill men i'th' dark?—Where be these bloody thieves?—
  How silent is this town!—Ho! Murder, murder!—
  (*To Lodovico and Gratiano*) What may you be? Are you
      of good or evil?

LODOVICO. As you shall prove us, praise us. *67*

IAGO. Signor Lodovico?

LODOVICO. He, sir.

IAGO. I cry you mercy. Here's Cassio hurt by villains. *70*

GRATIANO. Cassio?

IAGO. How is't, brother?

CASSIO. My leg is cut in two.

IAGO. Marry, heaven forbid!
  Light, gentlemen! I'll bind it with my shirt.

(*He hands them the light, and tends to Cassio's wound.*)

(*Enter Bianca.*)

BIANCA. What is the matter, ho? Who is't that cried?

IAGO. Who is't that cried?

BIANCA   Oh, my dear Cassio!
  My sweet Cassio! Oh, Cassio, Cassio, Cassio!

IAGO. Oh, notable strumpet! Cassio, may you suspect

---

54 What Who. (Also at lines 60 and 66.) **55 spoiled** ruined, done for **59 make** get **67 prove us**
prove us to be. **praise** appraise **70 I cry you mercy** I beg your pardon.

552

Who they should be that have thus mangled you?

CASSIO. No.

GRATIANO. I am sorry to find you thus. I have been to seek you.

IAGO. Lend me a garter. (*He applies a tourniquet.*) So.—
  Oh, for a chair,   *83*
  To bear him easily hence!

BIANCA. Alas, he faints! Oh, Cassio, Cassio, Cassio!

IAGO. Gentlemen all, I do suspect this trash
  To be a party in this injury.—
  Patience awhile, good Cassio.—Come, come;
  Lend me a light. (*He shines the light on Roderigo.*) Know
    we this face or no?
  Alas, my friend and my dear countryman
  Roderigo! No.—Yes, sure.—Oh, heaven! Roderigo!

GRATIANO. What, of Venice?

IAGO. Even he, sir. Did you know him?

GRATIANO. Know him? Ay.

IAGO. Signor Gratiano? I cry your gentle pardon.   *95*
  These bloody accidents must excuse my manners *96*
  That so neglected you.

GRATIANO.   I am glad to see you.

IAGO. How do you, Cassio?—Oh, a chair, a chair!

GRATIANO. Roderigo!

IAGO. He, he, 'tis he. (*A litter is brought in.*) Oh, that's well
    said; the chair.   *100*
  Some good man bear him carefully from hence;
  I'll fetch the General's surgeon. (*To Bianca*) For you,
    mistress,   *102*
  Save you your labor.—He that lies slain here, Cassio, *103*
  Was my dear friend. What malice was between you? *104*

CASSIO. None in the world, nor do I know the man.

IAGO (*to Bianca*)
  What, look you pale?—Oh, bear him out o'th'air. *106*

(*Cassio and Roderigo are borne off.*)

  Stay you, good gentlemen.—Look you pale, mistress?— *107*
  Do you perceive the gastness of her eye?—   *108*

---

83 chair litter **95 gentle** noble **96 accidents** sudden events **100 well said** well done **102 For** As for **103 Save ... labor** i.e., never you mind tending Cassio. **104 malice** enmity **106 bear ... air** (Fresh air was thought to be dangerous for a wound.) **107 Stay you** (Lodovico and Gratiano are evidently about to leave.) **108 gastness** terror

Nay, if you stare, we shall hear more anon.— 109
Behold her well; I pray you, look upon her.
Do you see, gentlemen? Nay, guiltiness
Will speak, though tongues were out of use.

(*Enter Emilia.*)

EMILIA. 'Las, what's the matter? What's the matter, husand?
IAGO. Cassio hath here been set on in the dark
By Roderigo and fellows that are scaped.
He's almost slain, and Roderigo dead.
EMILIA. Alas, good gentleman! Alas, good Cassio!
IAGO. This is the fruits of whoring. Prithee, Emilia,
Go know of Cassio where he supped tonight. 119
(*To Bianca*) What, do you shake at that?
BIANCA. He supped at my house, but I therefore shake not.
IAGO. Oh, did he so? I charge you go with me.
EMILIA. Oh, fie upon thee, strumpet!
BIANCA. I am no strumpet, but of life as honest 124
As you that thus abuse me.
EMILIA. As I? Faugh! Fie upon thee!
IAGO. Kind gentlemen, let's go see poor Cassio dressed.— 127
Come, mistress, you must tell 's another tale.—
Emilia, run you to the citadel
And tell my lord and lady what hath happed.—
Will you go on afore? (*Aside*) This is the night
That either makes me or fordoes me quite. (*Exeunt.*) 132

5.2

Enter Othello (with a light), and Desdemona in her bed.

OTHELLO. It is the cause, it is the cause, my soul. 1
Let me not name it to you, you chaste stars!
It is the cause. Yet I'll not shed her blood,
Nor scar that whiter skin of hers than snow,

---

109 stare (Iago pretends to interpret Bianca's wild looks as an involuntary confession of guilt.)
119 know learn 124 honest chaste 127 Cassio dressed Cassio's wounds dressed. 132 fordoes
undoes, ruins
5.2. Location: A bedchamber in the citadel.
0.1–2 in her bed (Either the curtains are drawn back to reveal the bed in a recessed area backstage,
or the bed is "thrust out" onstage as the scene begins.) 1 cause i.e., cause of justice, the offense
itself, which must be corrected in the name of justice

And smooth as monumental alabaster.   5
Yet she must die, else she'll betray more men.
Put out the light, and then put out the light.   7
If I quench thee, thou flaming minister,   8
I can again thy former light restore,
Should I repent me; but once put out thy light,   10
Thou cunning'st pattern of excelling nature,   11
I know not where is that Promethean heat   12
That can thy light relume. When I have plucked thy rose,   13
I cannot give it vital growth again;
It needs must wither. I'll smell thee on the tree.

(*He kisses her.*)

Oh, balmy breath, that dost almost persuade
Justice to break her sword! One more, one more.
Be thus when thou art dead, and I will kill thee,
And love thee after. One more, and that's the last.

(*He kisses her.*)

So sweet was ne'er so fatal. I must weep,
But they are cruel tears. This sorrow's heavenly;   21
It strikes where it doth love. She wakes.   22
DESDEMONA. Who's there? Othello?
OTHELLO. Ay, Desdemona.
DESDEMONA. Will you come to bed, my lord?
OTHELLO. Have you prayed tonight, Desdemon?
DESDEMONA. Ay, my lord.
OTHELLO. If you bethink yourself of any crime   28
    Unreconciled as yet to heaven and grace,
    Solicit for it straight.   30
DESDEMONA. Alack, my lord, what may you mean by that?
OTHELLO. Well, do it, and be brief. I will walk by.
    I would not kill thy unprepar`ed` spirit.
    No, heaven forfend! I would not kill thy soul.   34

---

5 monumental i.e., used in making tombs and funeral monuments   **7 the light . . . light** the torch
or lamp . . . Desdemona's life.   **8 minister** servant   **10 repent me** change my mind   **11 Thou . . .
pattern** you skillfully wrought perfect example   **12 Promethean heat** (Alludes to two myths: that of
Prometheus stealing fire from heaven for humanity, and that of his creating humankind.)
13 relume rekindle.   **21 they are cruel tears** these tears betoken a sorrowful cruelty, regrettable but
just.   **22 It . . . love** (Compare Hebrews 12:6: "For whom the Lord loveth he chasteneth.")   **28 crime**
sin   **30 Solicit** petition, pray.   **straight** immediately.   **34 forfend** forbid.

DESDEMONA. Talk you of killing?

OTHELLO.   Ay, I do.

DESDEMONA.   Then heaven
 Have mercy on me!

OTHELLO.   Amen, with all my heart!

DESDEMONA. If you say so, I hope you will not kill me.

OTHELLO. Humh!

DESDEMONA. And yet I fear you; for you're fatal then
 When your eyes roll so. Why I should fear I know not,
 Since guiltiness I know not; but yet I feel I fear.

OTHELLO. Think on thy sins.

DESDEMONA.   They are loves I bear to you.   *42*

OTHELLO. Ay, and for that thou diest.

DESDEMONA. That death's unnatural that kills for loving.
 Alas, why gnaw you so your nether lip?
 Some bloody passion shakes your very frame.
 These are portents; but yet I hope, I hope,
 They do not point on me.

OTHELLO. Peace, and be still!

DESDEMONA. I will so. What's the matter?

OTHELLO. That handkerchief which I so loved and gave thee
 Thou gav'st to Cassio.

DESDEMONA.   No, by my life and soul!
 Send for the man and ask him.

OTHELLO. Sweet soul, take heed, take heed of perjury.
 Thou art on thy deathbed.

DESDEMONA. Ay, but not yet to die.

OTHELLO.   Yes, presently.   *56*
 Therefore confess thee freely of thy sin;
 For to deny each article with oath
 Cannot remove nor choke the strong conception   *59*
 That I do groan withal. Thou art to die.   *60*

DESDEMONA. Then Lord have mercy on me!

OTHELLO.   I say, amen.

DESDEMONA. And have you mercy too! I never did
 Offend you in my life; never loved Cassio

---

42 They . . . you i.e., My only sins are my idolatry of loving you too much. **56 presently** immediately. **59 conception** (1) belief in your guilt (2) plan in my mind **60 groan withal** (1) groan at in sorrow (2) as in giving birth.

But with such general warranty of heaven   64
    As I might love. I never gave him token.
OTHELLO. By heaven, I saw my handkerchief in 's hand.
    Oh, perjured woman! Thou dost stone my heart,   67
    And makes me call what I intend to do
    A murder, which I thought a sacrifice.
    I saw the handkerchief.
DESDEMONA.   He found it, then.
    I never gave it him. Send for him hither;
    Let him confess a truth.
OTHELLO.   He hath confessed.
DESDEMONA. What, my lord?
OTHELLO. That he hath used thee.
DESDEMONA.   How? Unlawfully?
OTHELLO.   Ay.
DESDEMONA. He will not say so.
OTHELLO.   No, his mouth is stopped;
    Honest Iago hath ta'en order for't.   76
DESDEMONA. Oh, my fear interprets. What, is he dead?
OTHELLO. Had all his hairs been lives, my great revenge
    Had stomach for them all.
DESDEMONA. Alas, he is betrayed and I undone! (*She weeps.*)
OTHELLO. Out, strumpet! Weep'st thou for him to my face?
DESDEMONA. Oh, banish me, my lord, but kill me not!
OTHELLO. Down, strumpet!
DESDEMONA. Kill me tomorrow; let me live tonight!
OTHELLO. Nay, if you strive—
DESDEMONA. But half an hour!
OTHELLO.   Being done, there is no pause.   86
DESDEMONA. But while I say one prayer!
OTHELLO.   It is too late.

(*Smothers her.*)

EMILIA (*at the door*). My lord, my lord! What, ho! My lord,
    my lord!
OTHELLO. What noise is this? Not dead? Not yet quite dead?
    I that am cruel am yet merciful;
    I would not have thee linger in thy pain.

---

64 warranty sanction   **67 stone** turn to stone, harden   **76 ta'en order** taken measures   **86 Being done** i.e., Since justice has begun its relentless course

(*He dispatches her.*)

So, so.

EMILIA (*within*). What, ho! My lord, my lord!

OTHELLO.   Who's there?

EMILIA (*within*). Oh, good my lord, I would speak a word
    with you!

OTHELLO. Yes, 'tis Emilia.—By and by.—She's dead.
    'Tis like she comes to speak of Cassio's death.—   95
    The noise was here. Ha! No more moving?   96
    Still as the grave. Shall she come in? Were't good?—
    I think she stirs again. No. What's best to do?
    If she come in, she'll sure speak to my wife.
    My wife! My wife! What wife? I have no wife.
    Oh, insupportable! Oh, heavy hour!
    Methinks it should be now a huge eclipse
    Of sun and moon, and that th'affrighted globe
    Should yawn at alteration.

EMILIA (*within*).   I do beseech you   104
    That I may speak with you, oh, good my lord!

OTHELLO. I had forgot thee. Oh, come in, Emilia.—
    Soft, by and by. Let me the curtains draw.—   107

(*He closes the bedcurtains and opens the door.*)

    Where art thou?

(*Enter Emilia.*)

                What's the matter with thee now?

EMILIA. Oh, my good lord, yonder's foul murders done!

OTHELLO. What, now?

EMILIA. But now, my lord.

OTHELLO. It is the very error of the moon;   112
    She comes more nearer earth than she was wont,   113
    And makes men mad.   114

---

95 like likely that   **96 here** (The Folio's "high" is possible, suggesting that the commotion of the attack on Cassio was loud.)   **104 Should ... alteration** should gape wide in an earthquake, as if expressing amazement at an eclipse. (According to Pliny, earthquakes often happen during eclipses. The cataclismic event here is especially terrifying in that it imagines the impossible concurrence of a solar and lunar eclipse—an apocalyptic scenario befitting the horror of Desdemona's death.)
107 Soft Wait a minute   **112 error** aberration, irregularity   **113 She** Luna, the moon goddess
114 mad i.e., "lunatic."

EMILIA. Cassio, my lord, hath killed a young Venetian
    Called Roderigo.
OTHELLO.   Roderigo killed?
    And Cassio killed?
EMILIA.   No, Cassio is not killed.
OTHELLO. Not Cassio killed? Then murder's out of tune,
    And sweet revenge grows harsh.
DESDEMONA. Oh, falsely, falsely murdered!
EMILIA. Oh, Lord, what cry is that?
OTHELLO. That? What?
EMILIA. Out and alas, that was my lady's voice.   *123*

(*She opens the bedcurtains.*)

    Help, help, ho, help! O lady, speak again!
    Sweet Desdemona! O sweet mistress, speak!
DESDEMONA. A guiltless death I die.
EMILIA. Oh, who hath done this deed?
DESDEMONA. Nobody; I myself. Farewell.
    Commend me to my kind lord. Oh, farewell! (*She dies.*)
OTHELLO. Why, how should she be murdered?
EMILIA.   Alas, who knows?
OTHELLO. You heard her say herself it was not I.
EMILIA. She said so. I must needs report the truth.
OTHELLO. She's like a liar gone to burning hell!
    'Twas I that killed her.
EMILIA.   Oh, the more angel she,
    And you the blacker devil!
OTHELLO. She turned to folly, and she was a whore.   *136*
EMILIA. Thou dost belie her, and thou art a devil.   *137*
OTHELLO. She was false as water.
EMILIA. Thou art rash as fire to say
    That she was false. Oh, she was heavenly true!
OTHELLO. Cassio did top her. Ask thy husband else.   *141*
    Oh, I were damned beneath all depth in hell
    But that I did proceed upon just grounds
    To this extremity. Thy husband knew it all.
EMILIA. My husband?

---

123 **Out** (A cry of dismay, intensifying *alas.*)   **136 folly** i.e., wantonness, fleshly sin   **137 belie** slander   **141 else** i.e., if you don't believe me.

OTHELLO. Thy husband.

EMILIA. That she was false to wedlock?

OTHELLO. Ay, with Cassio. Nay, had she been true,
    If heaven would make me such another world
    Of one entire and perfect chrysolite,   *150*
    I'd not have sold her for it.

EMILIA. My husband?

OTHELLO. Ay, 'twas he that told me on her first.
    An honest man he is, and hates the slime
    That sticks on filthy deeds.

EMILIA. My husband?

OTHELLO. What needs this iterance, woman? I say thy husband.   *157*

EMILIA. Oh, mistress, villainy hath made mocks with love!   *158*
    My husband say she was false?

OTHELLO.   He, woman;
    I say thy husband. Dost understand the word?
    My friend, thy husband, honest, honest Iago.

EMILIA. If he say so, may his pernicious soul
    Rot half a grain a day! He lies to th' heart.
    She was too fond of her most filthy bargain.

OTHELLO. Ha? (*He draws.*)

EMILIA. Do thy worst!
    This deed of thine is no more worthy heaven
    Than thou wast worthy her.

OTHELLO.   Peace, you were best.   *168*

EMILIA. Thou hast not half that power to do me harm
    As I have to be hurt. O gull! O dolt!   *170*
    As ignorant as dirt! Thou hast done a deed—
    I care not for thy sword; I'll make thee known,
    Though I lost twenty lives.—Help! Help, ho, help!
    The Moor hath killed my mistress! Murder, murder!

(*Enter Montano, Gratiano, and Iago.*)

MONTANO. What is the matter? How now, General?

EMILIA. Oh, are you come, Iago? You have done well,
    That men must lay their murders on your neck.   *177*

GRATIANO. What is the matter?

---

150 **chrysolite** precious topaz   157 **iterance** iteration, repetition   158 **made mocks with** made a mockery of   168 **Peace . . . best** You'd better be quiet.   170 **to be hurt** i.e., to endure hurt. **gull** dupe.   177 **on your neck** to your charge.

EMILIA (*to Iago*). Disprove this villain, if thou be'st a man.
    He says thou told'st him that his wife was false.
    I know thou didst not; thou'rt not such a villain.   *181*
    Speak, for my heart is full.
IAGO. I told him what I thought, and told no more
    Than what he found himself was apt and true.   *184*
EMILIA. But did you ever tell him she was false?
IAGO. I did.
EMILIA. You told a lie, an odious, damnèd lie!
    Upon my soul, a lie, a wicked lie.
    She false with Cassio? Did you say with Cassio?
IAGO. With Cassio, mistress. Go to, charm your tongue.   *190*
EMILIA. I will not charm my tongue; I am bound to speak.
    My mistress here lies murdered in her bed—
ALL. Oh, heavens forfend!
EMILIA. And your reports have set the murder on.
OTHELLO. Nay, stare not, masters. It is true indeed.
GRATIANO. 'Tis a strange truth.
MONTANO. Oh, monstrous act!
EMILIA.   Villainy, villainy, villainy!
    I think upon't—I think I smell't! O villainy!
    I thought so then—I'll kill myself for grief—   *199*
    Oh, villainy, villainy!
IAGO. What, are you mad? I charge you, get you home.
EMILIA. Good gentlemen, let me have leave to speak.
    'Tis proper I obey him, but not now.
    Perchance, Iago, I will ne'er go home.
OTHELLO. Oh! Oh! Oh! (*Othello falls on the bed.*)
EMILIA.   Nay, lay thee down and roar,   *205*
    For thou hast killed the sweetest innocent
    That e'er did lift up eye.
OTHELLO (*rising*).   Oh, she was foul!   *207*
    I scarce did know you, uncle. There lies your niece,
    Whose breath indeed these hands have newly stopped.
    I know this act shows horrible and grim.   *210*

---

181 such a villain such a villain as all that.   **184 apt** plausible   **190 charm** control   **199 then** (Perhaps at 3.3.331–2 and 4.2.137–54.)   **205 s.d. Othello . . . bed** (This direction is from the Quarto, as also *He kisses her* at line 19 and *She dies* at line 129.)   **207 lift up eye** i.e., lift her eyes to heaven. **210 shows** looks

GRATIANO. Poor Desdemon! I am glad thy father's dead.
    Thy match was mortal to him, and pure grief
    Shore his old thread in twain. Did he live now,   *213*
    This sight would make him do a desperate turn,   *214*
    Yea, curse his better angel from his side,
    And fall to reprobance.   *216*
OTHELLO. 'Tis pitiful. But yet Iago knows
    That she with Cassio hath the act of shame
    A thousand times committed. Cassio confessed it;
    And she did gratify his amorous works   *220*
    With that recognizance and pledge of love   *221*
    Which I first gave her. I saw it in his hand;
    It was a handkerchief, an antique token
    My father gave my mother.
EMILIA. Oh, God! Oh, heavenly God!
IAGO. Zounds, hold your peace.
EMILIA.   'Twill out, 'twill out! I peace?
    No, I will speak as liberal as the north.   *227*
    Let heaven and men and devils, let them all,
    All, all, cry shame against me, yet I'll speak.
IAGO. Be wise, and get you home.
EMILIA.   I will not.

(*Iago threatens Emilia.*)

GRATIANO.   Fie,
    Your sword upon a woman?
EMILIA. Oh, thou dull Moor! That handkerchief thou
        speak'st of
    I found by fortune and did give my husband;
    For often, with a solemn earnestness,
    More than indeed belonged to such a trifle,   *235*
    He begged of me to steal't.
IAGO.   Villainous whore!
EMILIA. She give it Cassio? No, alas! I found it,
    And I did give't my husband.
IAGO.   Filth, thou liest!
EMILIA. By heaven, I do not, I do not, gentlemen.

---

213 Shore...thread sheared the thread of his old age (as Atropos, one of the three Fates, was thought to do). **214 turn** deed   **216 reprobance** damnation, i.e., suicide.   **220 gratify** reward   **221 recognizance** token   **227 liberal as the north** freely as the north wind (blows).   **235 belonged** was appropriate

Oh, murderous coxcomb! What should such a fool   240
Do with so good a wife?
OTHELLO. Are there no stones in heaven   242
But what serves for the thunder?—Precious villain!   243

(*He runs at Iago; Montano disarms Othello. Iago, from
behind, stabs Emilia.*)

GRATIANO. The woman falls! Sure he hath killed his wife.
EMILIA. Ay, ay. Oh, lay me by my mistress' side.

(*Exit Iago.*)

GRATIANO. He's gone, but his wife's killed.
MONTANO. 'Tis a notorious villain. Take you this weapon,
Which I have here recovered from the Moor.
Come, guard the door without. Let him not pass,
But kill him rather. I'll after that same villain,
For 'tis a damnèd slave.

(*Exit [with all but Othello and Emilia,
who has been laid by Desdemona's side].*)

OTHELLO. I am not valiant neither,
But every puny whipster gets my sword.   253
But why should honor outlive honesty?   254
Let it go all.
EMILIA.   What did thy song bode, lady?
Hark, canst thou hear me? I will play the swan,
And die in music. (*She sings*) "Willow, willow, willow."
Moor, she was chaste. She loved thee, cruel Moor.
So come my soul to bliss as I speak true.
So speaking as I think, alas, I die. (*She dies.*)
OTHELLO. I have another weapon in this chamber;
It was a sword of Spain, the ice-brook's temper—   262
Oh, here it is. (*He finds a sword.*) Uncle, I must come forth.
GRATIANO (*within*). If thou attempt it, it will cost thee dear.
Thou hast no weapon, and perforce must suffer.

---

240 **coxcomb** fool. (Addressed to Othello.)   242 **stones** bolts, such as those used for thunderbolts
243 **Precious** i.e., Arrant, utter.   243.1–2 **He . . . Emilia** (The Quarto text reads, "*The Moore runnes
at Iago. Iago kils his wife.*" The Quarto also specifies the exit of Iago at line 245 and the death of
Emilia at line 260.)   253 **every . . . sword** every whipper-snapper can get the better of me and my
sword.   254 **why . . . honesty?** why should a soldier's reputation for bravery outlive true integrity?
262 **the icebrook's temper** tempered in ice-cold water

OTHELLO. Look in upon me then and speak with me,
    Or, naked as I am, I will assault thee.   *267*

(*Enter Gratiano.*)

GRATIANO. What is the matter?
OTHELLO.   Behold, I have a weapon;
    A better never did itself sustain
    Upon a soldier's thigh. I have seen the day
    That, with this little arm and this good sword,
    I have made my way through more impediments
    Than twenty times your stop. But oh, vain boast!   *273*
    Who can control his fate? 'Tis not so now.
    Be not afraid, though you do see me weaponed;
    Here is my journey's end, here is my butt   *276*
    And very seamark of my utmost sail.   *277*

(*Gratiano steps back.*)

    Do you go back dismayed? 'Tis a lost fear;   *278*
    Man but a rush against Othello's breast   *279*
    And he retires. Where should Othello go?

(*He turns to Desdemona.*)

    Now, how dost thou look now? Oh, ill-starred wench!
    Pale as thy smock! When we shall meet at compt,   *282*
    This look of thine will hurl my soul from heaven,
    And fiends will snatch at it. Cold, cold, my girl?
    Even like thy chastity. Oh, cursèd, cursèd slave!   *285*
    Whip me, ye devils,
    From the possession of this heavenly sight!
    Blow me about in winds! Roast me in sulfur!
    Wash me in steep-down gulfs of liquid fire!
    Oh, Desdemon! Dead, Desdemon! Dead! Oh! Oh!   *290*

(*Enter Lodovico, Cassio* [*carried in a litter*],
Montano, and Iago [*prisoner*], *with officers.*)

---

267 naked unarmed   **273 your stop** the obstruction you present.   **276 butt** goal, limit. (An archery term.)   **277 seamark** beacon (marking his destination or limit)   **278 lost** groundless   **279 Man . . . rush** wield no more than a reed   **282 compt** account, judgment day   **285 slave** i.e., Othello himself. **290.1 in a litter** (The Quarto specifies that Cassio is "*in a Chaire*.")

LODOVICO. Where is this rash and most unfortunate man?
OTHELLO. That's he that was Othello. Here I am.
LODOVICO. Where is that viper? Bring the villain forth.

(*Iago is led forward.*)

OTHELLO. I look down towards his feet; but that's a fable.   294
    If that thou be'st a devil, I cannot kill thee.

(*He wounds Iago.*)

LODOVICO. Wrench his sword from him.

                  (*Othello is disarmed.*)

IAGO.   I bleed, sir, but not killed.
OTHELLO. I am not sorry neither. I'd have thee live,
    For in my sense 'tis happiness to die.   298
LODOVICO. O thou Othello, that was once so good,
    Fall'n in the practice of a cursèd slave,   300
    What shall be said to thee?
OTHELLO.   Why, anything.
    An honorable murderer, if you will,
    For naught I did in hate, but all in honor.
LODOVICO. This wretch hath part confessed his villainy.
    Did you and he consent in Cassio's death?   305
OTHELLO. Ay.
CASSIO. Dear General, I never gave you cause.
OTHELLO. I do believe it, and I ask your pardon.
    Will you, I pray, demand that demi-devil
    Why he hath thus ensnared my soul and body?
IAGO. Demand me nothing. What you know, you know.
    From this time forth I never will speak word.
LODOVICO. What, not to pray?
GRATIANO. Torments will ope your lips.   314
OTHELLO. Well, thou dost best.   315
LODOVICO. Sir, you shall understand what hath befall'n,
    Which, as I think, you know not. Here is a letter
    Found in the pocket of the slain Roderigo;
    And here another. (*He produces letters.*) The one of
        them imports

---

294 towards his feet i.e., to see if they are cloven, as the devil's are fabled to be   **298 in my sense** to one who feels as I do   **300 in the practice** through the plotting, into the snare.   **slave** villain   **305 consent** agree   **314 Torments** Torture   **315 thou dost best** you (Iago) do best not to talk.

The death of Cassio, to be undertook
By Roderigo.

OTHELLO. Oh, villain!

CASSIO.　　　　　　　Most heathenish and most gross!　　　322

LODOVICO (*showing another paper*).
Now here's another discontented paper　　　323
Found in his pocket too. And this, it seems,
Roderigo meant t'have sent this damnèd villain;
But that belike Iago in the interim　　　326
Came in and satisfied him.　　　327

OTHELLO (*to Iago*). Oh, thou pernicious caitiff!—
How came you, Cassio, by that handkerchief
That was my wife's?

CASSIO.　　　　　　　I found it in my chamber;
And he himself confessed but even now
That there he dropped it for a special purpose
Which wrought to his desire.

OTHELLO.　　　　　　　Oh, fool, fool, fool!　　　333

CASSIO. There is besides in Roderigo's letter
How he upbraids Iago, that he made him
Brave me upon the watch, whereon it came　　　336
That I was cast; and even but now he spake,　　　337
After long seeming dead, Iago hurt him,
Iago set him on.

LODOVICO (*to Othello*). You must forsake this room and
　　　go with us.
Your power and your command is taken off,　　　341
And Cassio rules in Cyprus. For this slave,
If there be any cunning cruelty
That can torment him much and hold him long,　　　344
It shall be his. You shall close prisoner rest　　　345
Till that the nature of your fault be known
To the Venetian state.—Come, bring away.

OTHELLO. Soft you; a word or two before you go.　　　348
I have done the state some service, and they know't.
No more of that. I pray you, in your letters,

---

322 **gross** monstrous.　323 **discontented** full of discontent　326 **belike** most likely　327 **Came . . . him** interposed and gave him satisfactory explanation.　333 **wrought . . . desire** worked out as he wished, fitted in with his plan.　336 **Brave** defy.　**whereon it came** whereof it came about　337 **cast** dismissed　341 **taken off** taken away　344 **hold him long** keep him alive a long time (during his torture)　345 **rest** remain　348 **Soft you** One moment

When you shall these unlucky deeds relate,   *351*
Speak of me as I am; nothing extenuate,
Nor set down aught in malice. Then must you speak
Of one that loved not wisely but too well;
Of one not easily jealous but, being wrought,   *355*
Perplexed in the extreme; of one whose hand,   *356*
Like the base Indian, threw a pearl away   *357*
Richer than all his tribe; of one whose subdued eyes,   *358*
Albeit unusèd to the melting mood,
Drops tears as fast as the Arabian trees
Their medicinable gum. Set you down this;   *361*
And say besides that in Aleppo once,
Where a malignant and a turbaned Turk
Beat a Venetian and traduced the state,
I took by th' throat the circumcisèd dog
And smote him, thus. (*He stabs himself.*)   *366*
LODOVICO. Oh, bloody period!
GRATIANO. All that is spoke is marred.
OTHELLO. I kissed thee ere I killed thee. No way but this,
    Killing myself, to die upon a kiss.

([*He kisses Desdemona and*] *dies.*)

CASSIO. This did I fear, but thought he had no weapon;
    For he was great of heart.
LODOVICO (*to Iago*).   O Spartan dog,   *372*
    More fell than anguish, hunger, or the sea!   *373*
    Look on the tragic loading of this bed.
    This is thy work. The object poisons sight;
    Let it be hid. Gratiano, keep the house,   *376*

(*The bedcurtains are drawn.*)

---

351 **unlucky** unfortunate   355 **wrought** worked upon, worked into a frenzy   356 **Perplexed** distraught   357 **Indian** (This reading from the Quarto pictures an ignorant savage who cannot recognize the value of a precious jewel. The Folio reading, "Iudean," i.e., infidel or disbeliever, may refer to Herod, who slew Miriamne in a fit of jealousy, or to Judas Iscariot, the betrayer of Christ.)   358 **subdued** i.e., overcome by grief   361 **gum** i.e., myrrh.   366 **s.d.** *He stabs himself* (This direction is in the Quarto text.)   367 **period** termination, conclusion.   372 **Spartan dog** (Spartan dogs were noted for their savagery and silence.)   373 **fell** cruel   376 **Let it be hid** i.e., draw the bedcurtains. (No stage direction specifies that the dead are to be carried offstage at the end of the play.)   **keep** guard

And seize upon the fortunes of the Moor,   *377*
For they succeed on you. (*To Cassio*) To you, Lord
    Governor,   *378*
Remains the censure of this hellish villain,   *379*
The time, the place, the torture. Oh, enforce it!
Myself will straight aboard, and to the state
This heavy act with heavy heart relate.   (*Exeunt.*)

[1603–1604]

---

377 seize upon take legal possession of **378 succeed on** pass as though by inheritance to
379 censure sentencing

Shall I Compare Thee to a Summer's Day?

WILLIAM SHAKESPEARE

Shall I compare thee to a summer's day?
Thou art more lovely and more temperate.
Rough winds do shake the darling buds of May,
And summer's lease hath all too short a date.
Sometime too hot the eye of heaven shines,   5
And often is his gold complexion dimmed;
And every fair from fair sometimes declines,
By chance, or nature's changing course, untrimmed.
But thy eternal summer shall not fade,
Nor lose possession of that fair thou ow'st;   10
Nor shall death brag thou wand'rest in his shade,
When in eternal lines to time thou grow'st.
   So long as men can breathe or eyes can see,
   So long lives this, and this gives life to thee.

[1609]

First published in the 1609 *Shake-speares sonnets*.

Sophocles
[C. 496–406 B.C.E.]

In ancient Greece, plays were performed annually at a religious festival for Dionysus, the god of wine. These performances were competitive, and the Athenian playwright SOPHOCLES *remarkably earned approximately twenty first prizes in these drama contests. During his long lifetime, this master trage-dian wrote an estimated one hundred plays, yet only seven remain:* Oedipus the King, Electra, Antigone, Trachinian Women, Ajax, Philoctetes, *and* Oedipus at Colonus.

*Ironically, the influential tragedy for which Sophocles is perhaps most famous—*Oedipus Rex *(*Oedipus the King*)—won only second prize. The three "Theban Plays"—*Oedipus Rex, Oedipus at Colonus, *and* Antigone*—depict the fate of Oedipus, king of Thebes, and his children. Sophocles drew Oedipus, a man who unwittingly killed his father and married his mother, from familiar Greek myth. Through his dramatic depictions of Oedipus's life, Sophocles addressed the question of destiny and fate. These tragedies ask if man is master of his own fate, or if he is merely a puppet directed by the will of higher power. During the twentieth century, the Oedipus myth was famously invoked by the psychologist Sigmund Freud in his theory of the Oedipus Complex. Here, Freud hypothesized that a crucial stage in childhood development was characterized by the male child's desire for sexual involvement with the mother and the attendant rivalry with the father.*

Sophocles is credited with a number of important theatrical innovations. He introduced props and scenic backdrops, which established for the audience the location of the the story. He reduced the size of the chorus and instituted the prac-tice of providing a third actor on the stage. Traditionally, two actors performed all of the roles in classical drama; with the addition of this third actor, plots became more complex. Sophocles also began to present the whole of dramatic action in one play, rather than offering it in a trilogy, as his predecessor and teacher Aeschylus had done. This new plot structure, which often centered on inevitabil-ity and doubt, increased psychological depth for dramatic characters. Sophocles also provided readers and audiences with rich and complex characterizations of tragic women, such as Electra and Antigone.

Throughout his life, Sophocles was involved in public issues as a statesman, general, and priest. He lived through the height of Athenian power during the fifth century B.C.E. *and actively contributed to the rise of Athens following the Persian Wars. He died at age ninety, having witnessed the decline of Athens dur-ing the thirty-year Peloponnesian War waged among the Greek states.*

CHARACTERS

Chorus
Antigone
Nurse
Ismene
Haemon
Creon
First Guard (*Jonas*)
Second Guard (*a Corporal*)
Third Guard
Messenger
Page
Eurydice

Reprinted from *Five Plays* Vol. 1 (1969), Farrar, Straus & Giroux.

571

ANTIGONE

ANTIGONE, *her hands clasped round her knees, sits on the top step. The* THREE GUARDS *sit on the steps, in a small group, playing cards. The* CHORUS *stands on the top step.* EURYDICE *sits on the top step, just left of center, knitting. The* NURSE *sits on the second step, left of* EURYDICE. ISMENE *stands in front of arch, left, facing* HAEMON, *who stands left of her.* CREON *sits in the chair at right end of the table, his arm over the shoulder of his* PAGE, *who sits on the stool beside his chair. The* MESSENGER *is leaning against the downstage portal of the right arch.*

The curtain rises slowly; then the CHORUS *turns and moves downstage.*

CHORUS. Well, here we are.

These people are about to act out for you the story of Antigone.

That thin little creature sitting by herself, staring straight ahead, seeing nothing, is Antigone. She is thinking. She is thinking that the instant I finish telling you who's who and what's what in this play, she will burst forth as the tense, sallow, willful girl whose family would never take her seriously and who is about to rise up alone against Creon, her uncle, the King.

Another thing that she is thinking is this: she is going to die. Antigone is young. She would much rather live than die. But there is no help for it. When your name is Antigone, there is only one part you can play; and she will have to play hers through to the end.

From the moment the curtain went up, she began to feel that inhuman forces were whirling her out of this world, snatching her away from her sister Ismene, whom you see smiling and chatting with that young man; from all of us who sit or stand here, looking at her, not in the least upset ourselves—for we are not doomed to die tonight.

CHORUS *turns and indicates* HAEMON.

The young man talking to Ismene—to the gay and beautiful Ismene—is Haemon. He is the King's son,

3

Creon's son. Antigone and he are engaged to be married. You wouldn't have thought she was his type. He likes dancing, sports, competition; he likes women, too. Now look at Ismene again. She is certainly more beautiful than Antigone. She is the girl you'd think he'd go for. Well . . . There was a ball one night. Ismene wore a new evening frock. She was radiant. Haemon danced every dance with her. And yet, that same night, before the dance was over, suddenly he went in search of Antigone, found her sitting alone—like that, with her arms clasped round her knees—and asked her to marry him. We still don't know how it happened. It didn't seem to surprise Antigone in the least. She looked up at him out of those solemn eyes of hers, smiled sort of sadly and said "yes." That was all. The band struck up another dance. Ismene, surrounded by a group of young men, laughed out loud. And . . . well, here is Haemon expecting to marry Antigone. He won't, of course. He didn't know, when he asked her, that the earth wasn't meant to hold a husband of Antigone, and that this princely distinction was to earn him no more than the right to die sooner than he might otherwise have done.

CHORUS *turns toward* CREON.

That gray-haired, powerfully built man sitting lost in thought, with his little page at his side, is Creon, the King. His face is lined. He is tired. He practices the difficult art of a leader of men. When he was younger, when Oedipus was King and Creon was no more than the King's brother-in-law, he was different. He loved music, bought rare manuscripts, was a kind of art patron. He would while away whole afternoons in the antique shops of this city of Thebes. But Oedipus died. Oedipus' sons died. Creon had to roll up his sleeves and take over the kingdom. Now and then, when he goes to bed weary with the day's work, he wonders whether this business of being a leader of men is worth the trouble. But when he wakes up, the problems are there to be solved; and like a conscientious workman, he does his job.

Creon has a wife, a Queen. Her name is Eurydice. There she sits, the old lady with the knitting, next to the

Nurse who brought up the two girls. She will go on knitting all through the play, till the times comes for her to go to her room and die. She is a good woman, a worthy, loving soul. But she is no help to her husband. Creon has to face the music alone. Alone with his Page, who is too young to be of any help.

The others? Well, let's see.

He points toward the Messenger.

That pale young man leaning against the wall is the Messenger. Later on he will come running in to announce that Haemon is dead. He has a premonition of catastrophe. That's what he is brooding over. That's why he won't mingle with the others.

As for those three red-faced card players—they are the guards. One smells of garlic, another of beer; but they're not a bad lot. They have wives they are afraid of, kids who are afraid of them; they're bothered by the little day-to-day worries that beset us all. At the same time—they are policemen: eternally innocent, no matter what crimes are committed; eternally indifferent, for nothing that happens can matter to them. They are quite prepared to arrest anybody at all, including Creon himself, should the order be given by a new leader.

That's the lot. Now for the play.

Oedipus, who was the father of the two girls, Antigone and Ismene, had also two sons, Eteocles and Polynices. After Oedipus died, it was agreed that the two sons should share his throne, each to reign over Thebes in alternate years.

Gradually, the lights on the stage have been dimmed.

But when Eteocles, the elder son, had reigned a full year, and time had come for him to step down, he refused to yield up the throne to his younger brother. There was civil war. Polynices brought up allies—six foreign princes; and in the course of the war he and his foreigners were defeated, each in front of one of the seven gates of the city. The two brothers fought, and they killed one another in single combat just outside the city walls. Now Creon is King.

CHORUS *is leaning, at this point, against the left proscenium arch. By now the stage is dark, with only the cyclorama bathed in dark blue. A single spot lights up the face of* CHORUS.

Creon has issued a solemn edict that Eteocles, with whom he had sided, is to be buried with pomp and honours, and that Polynices is to be left to rot. The vultures and the dogs are to bloat themselves on his carcass. Nobody is to go into mourning for him. No gravestone is to be set up in his memory. And above all, any person who attempts to give him religious burial will himself be put to death.

While CHORUS *has been speaking the characters have gone out one by one.* CHORUS *disappears through the left arch.*

It is dawn, gray and ashen, in a house asleep. ANTIGONE *steals in from out-of-doors, through the arch, right. She is carrying her sandals in her hand. She pauses, looking off through the arch, taut, listening, then turns and moves across downstage. As she reaches the table, she sees the* NURSE *approaching through the arch, left. She runs quickly toward the exit. As she reaches the steps, the* NURSE *enters through arch and stands still when she sees* ANTIGONE.

Nurse. Where have you been?
Antigone. Nowhere. It was beautiful. The whole world was gray when I went out. And now—you wouldn't recognize it. It's like a post card: all pink, and green, and yellow. You'll have to get up earlier, Nurse, if you want to see a world without color.
Nurse. It was still pitch black when I got up. I went to your room, for I thought you might have flung off your blanket in the night. You weren't there.
Antigone [*comes down the steps*]. The garden was lovely. It was still asleep. Have you ever thought how lovely a garden is when it is not yet thinking of men?

Nurse. You hadn't slept in your bed. I couldn't find you. I went to the back door. You'd left it open.

Antigone. The fields were wet. They were waiting for something to happen. The whole world was breathless, waiting. I can't tell you what a roaring noise I seemed to make alone on the road. It bothered me that whatever was waiting wasn't waiting for me. I took off my sandals and slipped into a field. [*She moves down to the stool and sits.*]

Nurse [kneels at ANTIGONE'S *feet to chafe them and put on the sandals*]. You'll do well to wash your feet before you go back to bed, Miss.

Antigone. I'm not going back to bed.

Nurse. Don't be a fool! You get some sleep! And me, getting up to see if she hasn't flung off her blanket; and I find her bed cold and nobody in it!

Antigone. Do you think that if a person got up every morning like this, it would be just as thrilling every morning to be the first girl out-of-doors?

NURSE *puts* ANTIGONE'S *left foot down, lifts her other foot and chafes it.*

Nurse. Morning my grandmother! It was night. It still is. And now, my girl, you'll stop trying to squirm out of this and tell me what you were up to. Where've you been?

Antigone. That's true. It was still night. There wasn't a soul out of doors but me, who thought that it was morning. Don't you think it's marvelous—to be the first person who is aware that it is morning?

Nurse. Oh, my little flibbertigibbet! Just can't imagine what I'm talking about, can she? Go on with you! I know that game. Where have you been, wicked girl?

Antigone [soberly]. No. Not wicked.

Nurse. You went out to meet someone, didn't you? Deny it if you can.

Antigone. Yes. I went out to meet someone.

Nurse. A lover?

Antigone. Yes, Nurse. Yes, the poor dear. I have a lover.

Nurse [stands up; bursting out]. Ah, that's very nice now, isn't it? Such goings-on! You, the daughter of a king, running out to meet lovers. And we work our fingers to the bone for you, we slave to bring you up like young ladies!

[*She sits on chair, right of table.*] You're all alike, all of you. Even you—who never used to stop to primp in front of a looking glass, or smear your mouth with rouge, or dindle and dandle to make the boys ogle you, and you ogle back. How many times I'd say to myself, "Now that one, now: I wish she was a little more of a coquette— always wearing the same dress, her hair tumbling round her face. One thing's sure," I'd say to myself, "none of the boys will look at her while Ismene's about, all curled and cute and tidy and trim. I'll have this one on my hands for the rest of my life." And now, you see? Just like your sister, after all. Only worse: a hypocrite. Who is the lad? Some little scamp, eh? Somebody you can't bring home and show to your family, and say, "Well, this is him, and I mean to marry him and no other." That's how it is, is it? Answer me!

Antigone [*smiling faintly*]. That's how it is. Yes, Nurse.

Nurse. Yes, says she! God save us! I took her when she wasn't that high. I promised her poor mother I'd make a lady of her. And look at her! But don't you go thinking this is the end of this, my young 'un. I'm only your nurse and you can play deaf and dumb with me; I don't count. But your Uncle Creon will hear of this! That, I promise you.

Antigone [*a little weary*]. Yes. Creon will hear of this.

Nurse. And we'll hear what he has to say when he finds out that you go wandering alone o' nights. Not to mention Haemon. For the girl's engaged! Going to be married! Going to be married, and she hops out of bed at four in the morning to meet somebody else in a field. Do you know what I ought to do to you? Take you over my knee the way I used to do when you were little.

Antigone. Please, Nurse, I want to be alone.

Nurse. And if you so much as speak of it, she says she wants to be alone!

Antigone. Nanny, you shouldn't scold, dear. This isn't a day when you should be losing your temper.

Nurse. Not scold, indeed! Along with the rest of it, I'm to like it. Didn't I promise your mother? What would she say if she was here? "Old Stupid!" That's what she'd call me. "Old Stupid. Not to know how to keep my little girl pure! Spend your life making them behave, watching over them like a mother hen, running after them with mufflers and sweaters to keep them warm, and eggnogs to make them strong; and then at four o'clock in the morning, you who always complained you never could sleep a wink, snoring in your bed and letting them slip out into the bushes." That's what she'd say, your mother. And I'd stand there, dying of shame if I wasn't dead already. And all I could do would be not to dare look her in the face; and "That's true," I'd say. "That's all true what you say, Your Majesty."

Antigone. Nanny, dear. Dear Nanny. Don't cry. You'll be able to look Mamma in the face when it's your time to see her. And she'll say, "Good morning, Nanny. Thank you for my little Antigone. You did look after her so well." She knows why I went out this morning.

Nurse. Not to meet a lover?

Antigone. No. Not to meet a lover.

Nurse. Well, you've a queer way of teasing me, I must say! Not to know when she's teasing me! [*Rises to stand behind* ANTIGONE.] I must be getting awfully old, that's what it is. But if you loved me, you'd tell me the truth. You'd tell me why your bed was empty when I went along to tuck you in. Wouldn't you?

Antigone. Please, Nanny, don't cry any more. [ANTIGONE *turns partly toward* NURSE, *puts an arm up to* NURSE's *shoulder. With her other hand,* ANTIGONE *caresses* NURSE's *face.*] There now, my sweet red apple. Do you remember how I used to rub your cheeks to make them shine? My dear, wrinkled red apple! I didn't do anything tonight that was worth sending tears down the little gullies of your dear face. I am pure, and I swear that I have no other lover that Haemon. If you like, I'll swear that I shall never have any other lover than Haemon. Save your tears, Nanny, save them, Nanny dear; you may still need them. When you cry like that, I become a little girl again; and I mustn't be a little girl today. [ANTIGONE *rises and moves upstage.*]

ISMENE *enters through arch, left. She pauses in front of arch.*

Ismene. Antigone! What are you doing up at this hour? I've just been to your room.

Nurse. The two of you, now! You're both going mad, to

be up before the kitchen fire has been started. Do you
like running about without a mouthful of breakfast? Do
you think it's decent for the daughters of a king? [*She
turns to* ISMENE.] And look at you, with nothing on, and
the sun not up! I'll have you both on my hands with colds
before I know it.

Antigone. Nanny dear, go away now. It's not chilly,
really. Summer's here. Go and make us some coffee.
Please, Nanny, I'd love some coffee. It would do me so
much good.

Nurse. My poor baby! Her head's swimming, what with
nothing on her stomach, and me standing here like an idiot
when I could be getting her something hot to drink. [*Exit
NURSE.*]

A pause.

Ismene. Aren't you well?

Antigone. Of course I am. Just a little tired. I got up
too early. [ANTIGONE *sits on a chair, suddenly tired.*]

Ismene. I couldn't sleep, either.

Antigone. Ismene, you ought not to go without your
beauty sleep.

Ismene. Don't make fun of me.

Antigone. I'm not, Ismene, truly. This particular morning, seeing how beautiful you are makes everything easier
for me. Wasn't I a miserable little beast when we were
small? I used to fling mud at you, and put worms down
your neck. I remember tying you to a tree and cutting off
your hair. Your beautiful hair! How easy it must be never
to be unreasonable with all that smooth silken hair so
beautifully set round your head.

Ismene [*abruptly*]. Why do you insist upon talking
about other things?

Antigone [*gently*]. I am not talking about other things.

Ismene. Antigone, I've thought about it a lot.

Antigone. Have you?

Ismene. I thought about it all night long. Antigone,
you're mad.

Antigone. Am I?

Ismene. We cannot do it.

Antigone. Why not?

Ismene. Creon will have us put to death.

Antigone. Of course he will. That's what he's here for.

He will do what he has to do, and we will do what we have to do. He is bound to put us to death. We are bound to go out and bury our brother. That's the way it is. What do you think we can do to change it?

Ismene [*releases* ANTIGONE's *hand; draws back a step*]. I don't want to die.

Antigone. I'd prefer not to die, myself.

Ismene. Listen to me, Antigone. I thought about it all night. I'm older than you are. I always think things over, and you don't. You are impulsive. You get a notion in your head and you jump up and do the thing straight off. And if it's silly, well, so much the worse for you. Whereas, I think things out.

Antigone. Sometimes it is better not to think too much.

Ismene. I don't agree with you! [ANTIGONE *looks at* ISMENE, *then turns and moves to chair behind table.* ISMENE *leans on end of table top, toward* ANTIGONE.] Oh, I know it's horrible. And I pity Polynices just as much as you do. But all the same, I sort of see what Uncle Creon means.

Antigone. I don't want to "sort of see" anything.

Ismene. Uncle Creon is the king. He has to set an example!

Antigone. But I am not the king; and I don't have to set people examples. Little Antigone gets a notion in her head—the nasty brat, the willful, wicked girl; and they put her in a corner all day, or they lock her up in the cellar. And she deserves it. She shouldn't have disobeyed!

Ismene. There you go, frowning, glowering, wanting your own stubborn way in everything. Listen to me. I'm right oftener than you are.

Antigone. I don't want to be right!

Ismene. At least you can try to understand.

Antigone. Understand! The first word I ever heard out of any of you was that word "understand." Why didn't I "understand" that I must not play with water—cold, black, beautiful flowing water—because I'd spill it on the palace tiles. Or with earth, because earth dirties a little girl's frock. Why didn't I "understand" that nice children don't eat out of every dish at once; or give everything in their pockets to beggars; or run in the wind so fast that they fall down; or ask for a drink when they're perspiring; or want to go swimming when it's either too early or too late, merely because they happen to feel like swimming. Understand! I don't want to understand. There'll be time enough to understand when I'm old. . . . If I ever *am* old. But not now.

Ismene. He is stronger than we are, Antigone. He is the king. And the whole city is with him. Thousands and thousands of them, swarming through all the streets of Thebes.

Antigone. I am not listening to you.

Ismene. His mob will come running, howling as it runs. A thousand arms will seize our arms. A thousand breaths will breathe into our faces. Like one single pair of eyes, a thousand eyes will stare at us. We'll be driven in a tumbrel through their hatred, through the smell of them and their cruel, roaring laughter. We'll be dragged to the scaffold for torture, surrounded by guards with their idiot faces all bloated, their animal hands clean-washed for the sacrifice, their beefy eyes squinting as they stare at us. And we'll know that no shrieking and no begging will make them understand that we want to live, for they are like slaves who do exactly as they've been told, without caring about right or wrong. And we shall suffer, we shall feel pain rising in us until it becomes so unbearable that we *know* it must stop. But it won't stop; it will go on rising and rising, like a screaming voice. Oh, I can't, I can't, Antigone!

A *pause.*

Antigone. How well have you thought it all out.

Ismene. I thought of it all night long. Didn't you?

Antigone. Oh, yes.

Ismene. I'm an awful coward, Antigone.

Antigone. So am I. But what has that to do with it?

Ismene. But, Antigone! Don't you want to go on living?

Antigone. Go on living! Who was it that was always the first out of bed because she loved the touch of the cold morning air on her bare skin? Who was always the last to bed because nothing less than infinite weariness could wean her from the lingering night? Who wept when she was little because there were too many grasses in the meadow, too many creatures in the field, for her to know and touch them all?

Ismene [*clasps* ANTIGONE'S *hands, in a sudden rush of tenderness*]. Darling little sister!

Antigone [*repulsing her*]. No! For heaven's sake! Don't paw me! And don't let us start sniveling! You say you've thought it all out. The howling mob—the torture—the fear of death. . . . They've made up your mind for you. Is that it?

Ismene. Yes.

Antigone. All right. They're as good excuses as any.

Ismene. Antigone, be sensible. It's all very well for men to believe in ideas and die for them. But you are a girl!

Antigone. Don't I know I'm a girl? Haven't I spent my life cursing the fact that I was a girl?

Ismene [*with spirit*]. Antigone! You have everything in the world to make you happy. All you have to do is reach out for it. You are going to be married; you are young; you are beautiful——

Antigone. I am not beautiful.

Ismene. Yes, you are! Not the way other girls are. But it's always you that the little boys turn to look back at when they pass us in the street. And when you go by, the little girls stop talking. They stare and stare at you, until we've turned a corner.

Antigone [*a faint smile*]. "Little boys—little girls."

Ismene [*challengingly*]. And what about Haemon?

A pause.

Antigone. I shall see Haemon this morning. I'll take care of Haemon. You always said I was mad; and it didn't matter how little I was or what I wanted to do. Go back to bed now, Ismene. The sun is coming up, and, as you see, there is nothing I can do today. Our brother Polynices is as well guarded as if he had won the war and were sitting on his throne. Go along. You are pale with weariness.

Ismene. What are you going to do?

Nurse [*calls from off-stage*]. Come along, my dove. Come to breakfast.

Antigone. I don't feel like going to bed. However, if you like, I'll promise not to leave the house till you wake up. Nurse is getting me breakfast. Go and get some sleep.

The sun is just up. Look at you: you can't keep your eyes open. Go.

Ismene. And you will listen to reason, won't you? You'll let me talk to you about this again? Promise?

Antigone. I promise. I'll let you talk. I'll let all of you talk. Go to bed, now. [ISMENE *goes to arch; exit.*] Poor Ismene!

Nurse [*enters through arch, speaking as she enters*]. Come along, my dove. I've made you some coffee and toast and jam. [*She turns towards arch as if to go out.*]

Antigone. I'm not really hungry, Nurse.

NURSE *stops, looks at* ANTIGONE, *then moves behind her.*

Nurse [*very tenderly*]. Where is your pain?

Antigone. Nowhere, Nanny dear. But you must keep me warm and safe, the way you used to do when I was little. Nanny! Stronger than all fever, stronger than any nightmare, stronger than the shadow of the cupboard that used to snarl at me and turn into a dragon on the bedroom wall. Stronger than the thousand insects gnawing and nibbling in the silence of the night. Stronger than the night itself, with the weird hooting of the night birds that frightened me even when I couldn't hear them. Nanny, stronger than death. Give me your hand, Nanny, as if I were ill in bed, and you sitting beside me.

Nurse. My sparrow, my lamb! What is it that's eating your heart out?

Antigone. Oh, it's just that I'm a little young still for what I have to go through. But nobody but you must know that.

Nurse [*places her other arm around* ANTIGONE's *shoulder*]. A little young for what, my kitten?

Antigone. Nothing in particular, Nanny. Just—all this. Oh, it's so good that you are here. I can hold your callused hand, your hand that is so prompt to ward off evil. You are very powerful, Nanny.

Nurse. What is it you want me to do for you, my baby?

Antigone. There isn't anything to do, except put your hand like this against my cheek [*She places the* NURSE's *hand against her cheek. A pause, then, as* ANTIGONE *leans back, her eyes shut.*] There! I'm not afraid any more. Not afraid of the wicked ogre, nor of the sandman, nor of the dwarf who steals little children. [A *pause*. ANTIGONE *resumes on another note.*] Nanny . . .

Nurse. Yes?

Antigone. My dog, Puff . . .

Nurse [*straightens up, draws her hand away*]. Well?

Antigone. Promise me that you will never scold her again.

Nurse. Dogs that dirty up a house with their filthy paws deserve to be scolded.

Antigone. I know. Just the same, promise me.

Nurse. You mean you want me to let her make a mess all over the place and not say a thing?

Antigone. Yes, Nanny.

Nurse. You're asking a lot. The next time she wets my living-room carpet, I'll——

Antigone. Please, Nanny, I beg of you!

Nurse. It isn't fair to take me on my weak side, just because you look a little peaked today. . . . Well, have it your own way. We'll mop up and keep our mouth shut. You're making a fool of me, though.

Antigone. And promise me that you will talk to her. That you will talk to her often.

Nurse [*turns and looks at* ANTIGONE]. Me, talk to a dog!

Antigone. Yes. But mind you: you are not to talk to her the way people usually talk to dogs. You're to talk to her the way I talk to her.

Nurse. I don't see why both of us have to make fools of ourselves. So long as you're here, one ought to be enough.

Antigone. But if there was a reason why I couldn't go on talking to her——

Nurse [*interrupting*]. Couldn't go on talking to her! And why couldn't you go on talking to her? What kind of poppycock——?

Antigone. And if she got too unhappy, if she moaned and moaned, waiting for me with her nose under the door as she does when I'm out all day, then the best thing, Nanny, might be to have her mercifully put to sleep.

Nurse. Now what *has* got into you this morning? [HAEMON *enters through arch*]. Running around in the darkness, won't sleep, won't eat—[ANTIGONE *sees* HAEMON.]—and now it's her dog she wants killed. I never.

Antigone [*interrupting*]. Nanny! Haemon is here. Go inside, please. And don't forget that you've promised me.

[Nurse *goes to arch; exit.* Antigone *rises.*] Haemon, Haemon! Forgive me for quarreling with you last night. [*She crosses quickly to* Haemon *and they embrace.*] Forgive me for everything. It was all my fault. I beg you to forgive me.

Haemon. You know that I've forgiven you. You had hardly slammed the door, your perfume still hung in the room, when I had already forgiven you. [*He holds her in his arms and smiles at her. Then draws slightly back.*] You stole that perfume. From whom?

Antigone. Ismene.

Haemon. And the rouge? and the face powder? and the frock? Whom did you steal them from?

Antigone. Ismene.

Haemon. And in whose honor did you get yourself up so elegantly?

Antigone. I'll tell you everything. [*She draws him closer.*] Oh, darling, what a fool I was! To waste a whole evening! A whole, beautiful evening!

Haemon. We'll have other evenings, my sweet.

Antigone. Perhaps we won't.

Haemon. And other quarrels, too. A happy love is full of quarrels, you know.

Antigone. A happy love, yes. Haemon, listen to me.

Haemon. Yes?

Antigone. Don't laugh at me this morning. Be serious.

Haemon. I am serious.

Antigone. And hold me tight. Tighter than you have ever held me. I want all your strength to flow into me.

Haemon. There! With all my strength.

A pause.

Antigone [*breathless*]. That's good. [*They stand for a moment, silent and motionless.*] Haemon! I wanted to tell you. You know—the little boy we were going to have when we were married?

Haemon. Yes?

Antigone. I'd have protected him against everything in the world.

Haemon. Yes, dearest.

Antigone. Oh, you don't know how I should have held him in my arms and given him my strength. He wouldn't have been afraid of anything, I swear he wouldn't. Not of the falling night, nor of the terrible noonday sun, nor of all the shadows, or all the walls in the world. Our little boy, Haemon! His mother wouldn't have been very imposing: her hair wouldn't always have been brushed; but she would have been strong where he was concerned, so much stronger than all those real mothers with their real bosoms and their aprons around their middle. You believe that, don't you, Haemon?

Haemon [*soothingly*]. Yes, yes, my darling.

Antigone. And you believe me when I say that you would have had a real wife?

Haemon. Darling, you are my real wife.

Antigone [*pressing against him and crying out*]. Haemon, you loved me! You did love me that night, didn't you? You're sure of it!

Haemon [*rocking her gently*]. What night, my sweet?

Antigone. And you are very sure, aren't you, that that night, at the dance, when you came to the corner where I was sitting, there was no mistake? It was me you were looking for? It wasn't another girl? And you're sure that never, not in your most secret heart of hearts, have you said to yourself that it was Ismene you ought to have asked to marry you?

Haemon [*reproachfully*]. Antigone, you are idiotic. You might give me credit for knowing my own mind. It's you I love, and no one else.

Antigone. But you love me as a woman—as a woman wants to be loved, don't you? Your arms around me aren't lying, are they? Your hands, so warm against my back— they're not lying? This warmth that's in me; this confidence, this sense that I am safe, secure, that flows through me as I stand here with my cheek in the hollow of your shoulder: they are not lies, are they?

Haemon. Antigone, darling, I love you exactly as you love me. With all of myself.

They kiss.

Antigone. I'm sallow, and I'm scrawny. Ismene is pink and golden. She's like a fruit.

Haemon. Look here, Antigone——

Antigone. Ah, dearest, I am ashamed of myself. But this

morning, this special morning, I must know. Tell me the
truth! I beg you to tell me the truth! When you think
about me, when it strikes you suddenly that I am going to
belong to you—do you have the feeling that—that a great
empty space is being hollowed out inside you, that there is
something inside you that is just—dying?

Haemon. Yes, I do, I do.

A pause.

Antigone. That's the way I feel. And another thing. I
wanted you to know that I should have been very proud
to be your wife—the woman whose shoulder you would
put your hand on as you sat down to table, absent-
mindedly, as upon a thing that belonged to you. [*After a
moment, draws away from him. Her tone changes.*] There!
Now I have two things more to tell you. And when I have
told them to you, you must go away instantly, without
asking any questions. However strange they may seem to
you. However much they may hurt you. Swear that you
will!

Haemon [*beginning to be troubled*]. What are these
things that you are going to tell me?

Antigone. Swear, first, that you will go away without
one word. Without so much as looking at me. [*She looks
at him, wretchedness in her face.*] You hear me, Haemon.
Swear it, please. This is the last mad wish that you will
ever have to grant me.

A pause.

Haemon. I swear it, since you insist. But I must tell you
that I don't like this at all.

Antigone. Please, Haemon. It's very serious. You must
listen to me and do as I ask. First, about last night, when
I came to your house. You asked me a moment ago why
I wore Ismene's dress and rouge. It was because I was
stupid. I wasn't very sure that you loved me as a woman;
and I did it—because I wanted you to want me. I was trying to be more like other girls.

Haemon. Was *that* the reason? My poor— -

Antigone. Yes. And you laughed at me. And we

quarreled; and my awful temper got the better of me and I flung out of the house. . . . The real reason was that I wanted you to take me; I wanted to be your wife before——

Haemon. Oh, my darling——

Antigone [*shuts him off*]. You swore you wouldn't ask any questions. You swore, Haemon. [*Turns her face away and goes on in a hard voice.*] As a matter of fact, I'll tell you why. I wanted to be your wife last night because I love you that way very—very strongly. And also because—— Oh, my darling, my darling, forgive me; I'm going to cause you quite a lot of pain. [*She draws away from him.*] I wanted it also because I shall never, never be able to marry you, never! [HAEMON *is stupefied and mute; then he moves a step towards her.*] Haemon! You took a solemn oath! You swore! Leave me quickly! Tomorrow the whole thing will be clear to you. Even before tomorrow: this afternoon. If you please, Haemon, go now. It is the only thing left that you can do for me if you still love me. [*A pause as* HAEMON *stares at her. Then he turns and goes out through the arch.* ANTIGONE *stands motionless, then moves to a chair at end of table and lets herself gently down on it. In a mild voice, as of calm after storm.*] Well, it's over for Haemon, Antigone.

ISMENE *enters through arch, pauses for a moment in front of it when she sees* ANTIGONE, *then crosses behind table.*

Ismene. I can't sleep. I'm terrified. I'm so afraid that, even though it is daylight, you'll still try to bury Polynices. Antigone, little sister, we all want to make you happy— Haemon, and Nurse, and I, and Puff whom you love. We love you, we are alive, we need you. And you remember what Polynices was like. He was our brother, of course. But he's dead; and he never loved you. He was a bad brother. He was like an enemy in the house. He never thought of you. Why should you think of him? What if his soul does have to wander through endless time without rest or peace? Don't try something that is beyond your strength. You are always defying the world, but you're only a girl, after all. Stay at home tonight. Don't try to do it, I beg you. It's Creon's doing, not ours.

Antigone. You are too late, Ismene. When you first saw me this morning, I had just come in from burying him. [*Exit* ANTIGONE *through arch.*]

The lighting, which by this time has reached a point of early morning sun, is quickly dimmed out, leaving the stage bathed in a light blue color. ISMENE *runs out after* ANTIGONE. *On* ISMENE'S *exit the lights are brought up suddenly to suggest a later period of the day.* CREON *and* PAGE *enter through curtain upstage.* CREON *stands on the top step; his* PAGE *stands at his right side.*

Creon. A private of the guards, you say? One of those standing watch over the body? Show him in.

The PAGE *crosses to arch; exit.* CREON *moves down to end of table.* PAGE *re-enters, preceded by the* FIRST GUARD, *livid with fear.* PAGE *remains on upstage side of arch.* GUARD *salutes.*

Guard. Private Jonas, Second Battalion.
Creon. What are you doing here?
Guard. It's like this, sir. Soon as it happened, we said: "Got to tell the chief about this before anybody else spills it. He'll want to know right away." So we tossed a coin to see which one would come up and tell you about it. You see, sir, we thought only one man had better come, because, after all, you don't want to leave the body without a guard. Right? I mean, there's three of us on duty, guarding the body.
Creon. What's wrong about the body?
Guard. Sir, I've been seventeen years in the service. Volunteer. Wounded three times. Two mentions. My record's clean. I know my business and I know my place. I carry out orders. Sir, ask any officer in the battalion; they'll tell you. "Leave it to Jonas. Give him an order: he'll carry it out." That's what they'll tell you, sir. Jonas, that's me—that's my name.
Creon. What's the matter with you, man? What are you shaking for?
Guard. By rights it's the corporal's job, sir. I've been recommended for a corporal, but they haven't put it through yet. June, it was supposed to go through.

Creon [*interrupts*]. Stop chattering and tell me why you are here. If anything has gone wrong, I'll break all three of you.

Guard. Nobody can say we didn't keep our eye on that body. We had the two-o'clock watch—the tough one. You know how it is, sir. It's nearly the end of the night. Your eyes are like lead. You've got a crick in the back of your neck. There's shadows, and the fog is beginning to roll in. A fine watch they give us! And me, seventeen years in the service. But we was doing our duty all right. On our feet, all of us. Anybody says we were sleeping is a liar. First place, it was too cold. Second place—— [CREON *makes a gesture of impatience.*] Yes, sir. Well, I turned around and looked at the body. We wasn't only ten feet away from it, but that's how I am. I was keeping my eye on it. [*Shouts.*] Listen, sir, I was the first man to see it! Me! They'll tell you. I was the one let out that yell!

Creon. What for? What was the matter?

Guard. Sir, the body! Somebody had been there and buried it. [CREON *comes down a step on the stair. The* GUARD *becomes more frightened.*] It wasn't much, you understand. With us three there, it couldn't have been. Just covered over with a little dirt, that's all. But enough to hide it from the buzzards.

Creon. By God, I'll——| [*He looks intently at the* GUARD.] You are sure that it couldn't have been a dog, scratching up the earth?

Guard. Not a chance, sir. That's kind of what we hoped it was. But the earth was scattered over the body just like the priests tell you you should do it. Whoever did that job knew what he was doing, all right.

Creon. Who could have dared? [*He turns and looks at the* GUARD.] Was there anything to indicate who might have done it?

Guard. Not a thing, sir. Maybe we heard a footstep— I can't swear to it. Of course we started right in to search, and the corporal found a shovel, a kid's shovel no bigger than that, all rusty and everything. Corporal's got the shovel for you. We thought maybe a kid did it.

Creon [*to himself*]. A kid! [*He looks away from the* GUARD.] I broke the back of the rebellion; but like a snake, it is coming together again. Polynices' friends, with their gold, blocked by my orders in the banks of Thebes.

The leaders of the mob, stinking of garlic and allied to envious princes. And the temple priests, always ready foɪ a bit of fishing in troubled waters. A kid! I can imagine what he is like, their kid: a baby-faced killer, creeping in the night with a toy shovel under his jacket. [*He looks at his* PAGE.] Though why shouldn't they have corrupted a real child? Very touching! Very useful to the party, an innocent child. A martyr. A real white-faced baby of fourteen who will spit with contempt at the guards who kill him. A free gift to their cause: the precious, innocent blood of a child on my hands. [*He turns to the* GUARD.] They must have accomplices in the Guard itself. Look here, you. Who knows about this?

Guard. Only us three, sir. We flipped a coin, and I came right over.

Creon. Right. Listen, now. You will continue on duty. When the relief squad comes up, you will tell them to return to barracks. You will uncover the body. If another attempt is made to bury it, I shall expect you to make an arrest and bring the person straight to me. And you will keep your mouths shut. Not one word of this to a human soul. You are all guilty of neglect of duty, and you will be punished; but if the rumor spreads through Thebes that the body received burial, you will be shot—all three of you.

Guard [*excitedly*]. Sir, we never told nobody, I swear we didn't! Anyhow, I've been up here. Suppose my pals spilled it to the relief; I couldn't have been with them and here too. That wouldn't be my fault if they talked. Sir, I've got two kids. You're my witness, sir, it couldn't have been me. I was here with you. I've got a witness! If anybody talked, it couldn't have been me! I was——

Creon [*interrupting*]. Clear out! If the story doesn't get around, you won't be shot. [*The* GUARD *salutes, turns, and exits at the double.* CREON *turns and paces upstage, then comes down to end of the table.*] A child! [*He looks at* PAGE.] Come along, my lad. Since we can't hope to keep this to ourselves, we shall have to be the first to give out the news. And after that, we shall have to clean up the mess. [PAGE *crosses to side of* CREON. CREON *puts his hand on* PAGE's *shoulder.*] Would you be willing to die for me? Would you defy the Guard with your little shovel? [PAGE *looks up at* CREON.] Of course you would. You would do it, too. [*A pause.* CREON *looks away from* PAGE *and murmurs*] A child! [CREON *and* PAGE *go slowly upstage center to top step.* PAGE *draws aside the curtain, through which exit* CREON *with* PAGE *behind him.*]

As soon as CREON *and* PAGE *have disappeared,* CHORUS *enters and leans against the upstage portal or arch, left. The lighting is brought up to its brightest point to suggest mid-afternoon.* CHORUS *allows a a pause to indicate that a crucial moment has been reached in the play, then moves slowly downstage, center. He stands for a moment silent, reflecting, and then smiles faintly.*

Chorus. The spring is wound up tight. It will uncoil of itself. That is what is so convenient in tragedy. The least little turn of the wrist will do the job. Anything will set it going: a glance at a girl who happens to be lifting her arms to her hair as you go by; a feeling when you wake up on a fine morning that you'd like a little respect paid to you today, as if it were as easy to order as a second cup of coffee; one question too many, idly thrown out over a friendly drink—and the tragedy is on.

The rest is automatic. You don't need to lift a finger. The machine is in perfect order; it has been oiled ever since time began, and it runs without friction. Death, treason, and sorrow are on the march; and they move in the wake of storm, of tears, of stillness. Every kind of stillness. The hush when the executioner's ax goes up at the end of the last act. The unbreathable silence when, at the beginning of the play, the two lovers, their hearts bared, their bodies naked, stand for the first time face to face in the darkened room, afraid to stir. The silence inside you when the roaring crowd acclaims the winner—so that you think of a film without a sound track, mouths agape and no sound coming out of them, a clamor that is no more than a picture; and you, the victor, already vanquished, alone in the desert of your silence. That is tragedy.

Tragedy is clean, it is restful, it is flawless. It has nothing to do with melodrama—with wicked villains, persecuted maidens, avengers, sudden revelations, and eleventh-hour repentances. Death, in a melodrama, is really horrible because it is never inevitable. The dear old father might so easily have been saved; the honest young man might so easily have brought in the police five minutes earlier.

In a tragedy, nothing is in doubt and everyone's destiny is known. That makes for tranquillity. There is a sort of fellow-feeling among characters in a tragedy: he who kills is as innocent as he who gets killed: it's all a matter of what part you are playing. Tragedy is restful; and the reason is that hope, that foul, deceitful thing, has no part in it. There isn't any hope. You're trapped. The whole sky has fallen on you, and all you can do about it is to shout.

Don't mistake me: I said "shout": I did not say groan, whimper, complain. That, you cannot do. But you can shout aloud; you can get all those things said that you never thought you'd be able to say—or never even knew you had it in you to say. And you don't say these things because it will do any good to say them: you know better than that. You say them for their own sake; you say them because you learn a lot from them.

In melodrama you argue and struggle in the hope of escape. That is vulgar; it's practical. But in tragedy, where there is no temptation to try to escape, argument is gratuitous: it's kingly.

Voices of the GUARDS *and scuffling sound heard through the archway.* CHORUS *looks in that direction; then, in a changed tone:*

The play is on. Antigone has been caught. For the first time in her life, little Antigone is going to be able to be herself.

Exit CHORUS *through arch. A pause, while the offstage voices rise in volume, then the* FIRST GUARD *enters, followed by* SECOND *and* THIRD GUARDS, *holding the arms of* ANTIGONE *and dragging her along. The* FIRST GUARD, *speaking as he enters, crosses swiftly to end of the table. The* TWO GUARDS *and* ANTIGONE *stop downstage.*

First Guard [*recovered from his fright*]. Come on, now, Miss, give it a rest. The chief will be here in a minute and you can tell him about it. All I know is my orders. I don't want to know what you were doing there. People always have excuses; but I can't afford to listen to them, see. Why, if we had to listen to all the people who want to tell us what's the matter with this country, we'd never get our work done. [*To the* GUARDS.] You keep hold of her and I'll see that she keeps her face shut.

Antigone. They are hurting me. Tell them to take their dirty hands off me.

First Guard. Dirty hands, eh? The least you can do is try to be polite, Miss. Look at me: I'm polite.

Antigone. Tell them to let me go. I shan't run away. My father was King Oedipus. I am Antigone.

First Guard. King Oedipus' little girl! Well, well, well! Listen, Miss, the night watch never picks up a lady but they say, you better be careful: I'm sleeping with the police commissioner.

The GUARDS *laugh.*

Antigone. I don't mind being killed, but I don't want them to touch me.

First Guard. And what about stiffs, and dirt, and such like? You wasn't afraid to touch them, was you? "Their dirty hands!" Take a look at your own hands. [ANTIGONE, *handcuffed, smiles despite herself as she looks down at her hands. They are grubby.*] You must have lost your shovel, didn't you? Had to go at it with your fingernails the second time, I'll bet. By God, I never saw such nerve! I turn my back for about five seconds; I ask a pal for a chew; I say "thanks"; I get the tobacco stowed away in my cheek—the whole thing don't take ten seconds; and there she is, clawing away like a hyena. Right out in broad daylight! And did she scratch and kick when I grabbed her! Straight for my eyes with them nails she went. And yelling something fierce about, "I haven't finished yet; let me finish!" She ain't got all her marbles!

Second Guard. I pinched a nut like that the other day. Right on the main square she was, hoisting up her skirts and showing her behind to anybody that wanted to take a look.

First Guard. Listen, we're going to get a bonus out of this. What do you say we throw a party, the three of us?

Second Guard. At the old woman's? Behind Market Street?

Third Guard. Suits me. Sunday would be a good day. We're off duty Sunday. What do you say we bring our wives?

First Guard. No. Let's have some fun this time. Bring your wife, there's always something goes wrong. First place, what do you do with the kids? Bring them, they always want to go to the can just when you're right in the middle of a game of cards or something. Listen, who would have thought an hour ago that us three would be talking about throwing a party now? The way I felt when the old man was interrogating me, we'd be lucky if we got off with being docked a month's pay. I want to tell you, I was scared.

Second Guard. You sure we're going to get a bonus?

First Guard. Yes. Something tells me this is big stuff.

Third Guard [to SECOND GUARD]. What's-his-name, you know—in the Third Battalion? He got an extra month's pay for catching a firebug.

Second Guard. If we get an extra month's pay, I vote we throw the party at the Arabian's.

First Guard. You're crazy! He charges twice as much for liquor as anybody else in town. Unless you want to go upstairs, of course. Can't do that at the old woman's.

Third Guard. Well, we can't keep this from our wives, no matter how you work it out. You get an extra month's pay, and what happens? Everybody in the battalion knows it, and your wife knows it too. They might even line up the battalion and give it to you in front of everybody, so how could you keep your wife from finding out?

First Guard. Well, we'll see about that. If they do the job out in the barrack yard—of course that means women, kids, everything.

Antigone. I should like to sit down, if you please.

A pause, as the FIRST GUARD *thinks it over.*

First Guard. Let her sit down. But keep hold of her. [*The two* GUARDS *start to lead her toward the chair at end of table. The curtain upstage opens, and* CREON *enters, followed by his* PAGE. FIRST GUARD *turns and moves upstage a few steps, sees* CREON.] 'Tenshun! [*The three* GUARDS *salute.* CREON, *seeing* ANTIGONE *handcuffed to* THIRD GUARD, *stops on the top step, astonished.*]

Creon. Antigone! [*To the* First Guard.] Take off those handcuffs! [First Guard *crosses above table to left of* Antigone.] What is this? [Creon *and his* Page *come down off the steps.*]

First Guard *takes key from his pocket and unlocks the cuff on* Antigone's *hand.* Antigone *rubs her wrist as she crosses below table toward chair at end of table.* Second *and* Third Guards *step back to front of arch.* First Guard *turns upstage toward* Creon.

First Guard. The watch, sir. We all came this time.
Creon. Who is guarding the body?
First Guard. We sent for the relief.

Creon *comes down.*

Creon. But I gave orders that the relief was to go back to barracks and stay there! [Antigone *sits on chair at left of table.*] I told you not to open your mouth about this!
First Guard. Nobody's said anything, sir. We made this arrest, and brought the party in, the way you said we should.
Creon [*to* Antigone]. Where did these men find you?
First Guard. Right by the body.
Creon. What were you doing near your brother's body? You knew what my orders were.
First Guard. What was she doing? Sir, that's why we brought her in. She was digging up the dirt with her nails. She was trying to cover up the body all over again.
Creon. Do you realize what you are saying?
First Guard. Sir, ask these men here. After I reported to you, I went back, and first thing we did, we uncovered the body. The sun was coming up and it was beginning to smell, so we moved it up on a little rise to get him in the wind. Of course, you wouldn't expect any trouble in broad daylight. But just the same, we decided one of us had better keep his eye peeled all the time. About noon, what with the sun and the smell, and as the wind dropped and I wasn't feeling none too good, I went over to my pal to get a chew. I just had time to say "thanks" and stick it in my mouth, when I turned round and there she was, clawing away at the dirt with both hands. Right out in

broad daylight! Wouldn't you think when she saw me come running she'd stop and leg it out of there? Not her! She went right on digging as fast as she could, as if I wasn't there at all. And when I grabbed her, she scratched and bit and yelled to leave her alone, she hadn't finished yet, the body wasn't all covered yet, and the like of that.

Creon [*to* ANTIGONE]. Is this true?

Antigone. Yes, it is true.

First Guard. We scraped the dirt off as fast as we could, then we sent for the relief and we posted them. But we didn't tell them a thing, sir. And we brought in the party so's you could see her. And that's the truth, so help me God.

Creon [*to* ANTIGONE.] And was it you who covered the body the first time? In the night?

Antigone. Yes, it was. With a toy shovel we used to take to the seashore when we were children. It was Poly-nices' own shovel; he had cut his name in the handle. That was why I left it with him. But these men took it away; so the next time, I had to do it with my hands.

First Guard. Sir, she was clawing away like a wild animal. Matter of fact, first minute we saw her, what with the heat haze and everything, my pal says, "That must be a dog," he says. "Dog!" I says, "that's a girl, that is!" And it was.

Creon. Very well. [*Turns to the* PAGE.] Show these men to the anteroom. [*The* PAGE *crosses to the arch, stands there, waiting.* CREON *moves behind the table. To the* FIRST GUARD.] You three men will wait outside. I may want a report from you later.

First Guard. Do I put the cuffs back on her, sir?

Creon. No. [*The three* GUARDS *salute, do an about-turn, and exeunt through arch, right.* PAGE *follows them out. A pause.*] Had you told anybody what you meant to do?

Antigone. No.

Creon. Did you meet anyone on your way—coming or going?

Antigone. No, nobody.

Creon. Sure of that, are you?

Antigone. Perfectly sure.

Creon. Very well. Now listen to me. You will go straight to your room. When you get there, you will go

to bed. You will say that your are not well and that you
have not been out since yesterday. Your nurse will tell
the same story. [*He looks toward arch, through which
the* GUARDS *have gone out.*] And I'll get rid of those three
men.

Antigone. Uncle Creon, you are going to a lot of
trouble for no good reason. You must know that I'll do
it all over again tonight.

A pause. They look one another in the eye.

Creon. Why did you try to bury your brother?
Antigone. I owed it to him.
Creon. I had forbidden it.
Antigone. I owed it to him. Those who are not buried
wander eternally and find no rest. If my brother were
alive, and he came home weary after a long day's hunting,
I should kneel down and unlace his boots, I should fetch
him food and drink, I should see that his bed was ready
for him. Polynices is home from the hunt. I owe it to him
to unlock the house of the dead in which my father and
my mother are waiting to welcome him. Polynices has
earned his rest.

Creon. Polynices was a rebel and a traitor, and you
know it.

Antigone. He was my brother.

Creon. You heard my edict. It was proclaimed throughout Thebes. You read my edict. It was posted up on the
city walls.

Antigone. Of course I did.

Creon. You knew the punishment I decreed for any
person who attempted to give him burial.

Antigone. Yes, I knew the punishment.

Creon. Did you by any chance act on the assumption
that a daughter of Oedipus, a daughter of Oedipus' stubborn pride, was above the law?

Antigone. No, I did not act on that assumption.

Creon. Because if you had acted on that assumption,
Antigone, you would have been deeply wrong. Nobody
has a more sacred obligation to obey the law than those
who make the law. You are a daughter of lawmakers, a
daughter of kings, Antigone. You must observe the law.

Antigone. Had I been a scullery maid washing my

dishes when that law was read aloud to me, I should have scrubbed the greasy water from my arms and gone out in my apron to bury my brother.

Creon. What nonsense! If you had been a scullery maid, there would have been no doubt in your mind about the seriousness of that edict. You would have known that it meant death; and you would have been satisfied to weep for your brother in your kitchen. But you! You thought that because you come of the royal line, because you were my niece and were going to marry my son, I shouldn't dare have you killed.

Antigone. You are mistaken. Quite the contrary. I never doubted for an instant that you would have me put to death.

> *A pause, as* CREON *stares fixedly at her.*

Creon. The pride of Oedipus! Oedipus and his headstrong pride all over again. I can see your father in you— and I believe you. Of course you thought that I should have you killed! Proud as you are, it seemed to you a natural climax in your existence. Your father was like that. For him as for you human happiness was meaningless; and mere human misery was not enough to satisfy his passion for torment. [*He sits on stool behind the table.*] You come of people for whom the human vestment is a kind of straitjacket: it cracks at the seams. You spend your lives wriggling to get out of it. Nothing less than a cosy tea party with death and destiny will quench your thirst. The happiest hour of your father's life came when he listened greedily to the story of how, unknown to himself, he had killed his own father and dishonored the bed of his own mother. Drop by drop, word by word, he drank in the dark story that the gods had destined him first to live and then to hear. How avidly men and women drink the brew of such a tale when their names are Oedipus— and Antigone! And it is so simple, afterwards, to do what your father did, to put out one's eyes and take one's daughter begging on the highways.

Let me tell you, Antigone: those days are over for Thebes. Thebes has a right to a king without a past. My name, thank God, is only Creon. I stand here with both feet firm on the ground; with both hands in my pockets; and I have decided that so long as I am king—being less

599

ambitious than your father was—I shall merely devote myself to introducing a little order into this absurd kingdom; if that is possible.

Don't think that being a king seems to me romantic. It is my trade; a trade a man has to work at every day; and like every other trade, it isn't all beer and skittles. But since it is my trade, I take it seriously. And if, tomorrow, some wild and bearded messenger walks in from some wild and distant valley—which is what happened to your dad—and tells me that he's not quite sure who my parents were, but thinks that my wife Eurydice is actually my mother, I shall ask him to do me the kindness to go back where he came from; and I shan't let a little matter like that persuade me to order my wife to take a blood test and the police to let me know whether or not my birth certificate was forged. Kings, my girl, have other things to do than to surrender themselves to their private feelings. [*He looks at her and, smiles.*] Hand *you* over to be killed! [*He rises, moves to end of table and sits on the top of table.*] I have other plans for you. You're going to marry Haemon; and I want you to fatten up a bit so that you can give him a sturdy boy. Let me assure you that Thebes needs that boy a good deal more than it needs your death. You will go to your room, now, and do as you have been told; and you won't say a word about this to anybody. Don't fret about the guards: I'll see that their mouths are shut. And don't annihilate me with those eyes. I know that you think I am a brute, and I'm sure you must consider me very prosaic. But the fact is, I have always been fond of you, stubborn though you always were. Don't forget that the first doll you ever had came from me. [*A pause.* ANTIGONE *says nothing, rises, and crosses slowly below the table toward the arch.* CREON *turns and watches her; then*] Where are you going?

Antigone [*stops downstage. Without any show of rebellion*]. You know very well where I am going.

Creon [*after a pause*]. What sort of game are you playing?

Antigone. I am not playing games.

Creon. Antigone, do you realize that if, apart from those three guards, a single soul finds out what you have tried to do, it will be impossible for me to avoid putting you to death? There is still a chance that I can save you;

but only if you keep this to yourself and give up your crazy purpose. Five minutes more, and it will be too late. You understand that?

Antigone. I must go and bury my brother. Those men uncovered him.

Creon. What good will it do? You know that there are other men standing guard over Polynices. And even if you did cover him over with earth again, the earth would again be removed.

Antigone. I know all that. I know it. But that much, at least, I can do. And what a person can do, a person ought to do.

Pause.

Creon. Tell me, Antigone, do you believe all that flummery about religious burial? Do you really believe that a so-called shade of your brother is condemned to wander for ever homeless if a little earth is not flung on his corpse to the accompaniment of some priestly abracadabra? Have you ever listened to the priests of Thebes when they were mumbling their formula? Have you ever watched those dreary bureaucrats while they were preparing the dead for burial—skipping half the gestures required by the ritual, swallowing half their words, hustling the dead into their graves out of fear that they might be late for lunch?

Antigone. Yes, I have seen all that.

Creon. And did you never say to yourself as you watched them, that if someone you really loved lay dead under the shuffling, mumbling ministrations of the priests, you would scream aloud and beg the priests to leave the dead in peace?

Antigone. Yes, I've thought all that.

Creon. And you still insist upon being put to death—merely because I refuse to let your brother go out with that grotesque passport; because I refuse his body the wretched consolation of that mass-production jibber-jabber, which you would have been the first to be embarrassed by if I had allowed it. The whole thing is absurd!

Antigone. Yes, it's absurd.

Creon. Then why, Antigone, why? For whose sake? For the sake of them that believe in it? To raise them against me?

Antigone. No.

Creon. For whom then if not for them and not for Polynices either?

Antigone. For nobody. For myself.

A pause as they stand looking at one another.

Creon. You must want very much to die. You look like a trapped animal.

Antigone. Stop feeling sorry for me. Do as I do. Do your job. But if you are a human being, do it quickly. That is all I ask of you. I'm not going to be able to hold out for ever.

Creon [*takes a step toward her*]. I want to save you, Antigone.

Antigone. You are the king, and you are all-powerful. But that you cannot do.

Creon. You think not?

Antigone. Neither save me nor stop me.

Creon. Prideful Antigone! Little Oedipus!

Antigone. Only this can you do: have me put to death.

Creon. Have you tortured, perhaps?

Antigone. Why would you do that? To see me cry? To hear me beg for mercy? Or swear whatever you wish, and then begin over again?

A pause.

Creon. You listen to me. You have cast me for the villain in this little play of yours, and yourself for the heroine. And you know it, you damned little mischief-maker! But don't you drive me too far! If I were one of your preposterous little tyrants that Greece is full of, you would be lying in a ditch this minute with your tongue pulled out and your body drawn and quartered. But you can see something in my face that makes me hesitate to send for the guards and turn you over to them. Instead, I let you go on arguing; and you taunt me, you take the offensive. [*He grasps her left wrist.*] What are you driving at, you she devil?

Antigone. Let me go. You are hurting my arm.

Creon [*gripping her tighter*]. I will not let you go.

Antigone [*moans*]. Oh!

Creon. I was a fool to waste words. I should have done this from the beginning. [*He looks at her.*] I may be your uncle—but we are not a particularly affectionate family. Are we, eh? [*Through his teeth, as he twists.*] Are we? [CREON *propels* ANTIGONE *round below him to his side.*] What fun for you, eh? To be able to spit in the face of a king who has all the power in the world; a man who has done his own killing in his day; who has killed people just as pitiable as you are—and who is still soft enough to go to all this trouble in order to keep you from being killed.

A pause.

Antigone. Now you are squeezing my arm too tightly. It doesn't hurt any more.

CREON *stares at her, then drops her arm.*

Creon. I shall save you yet. [*He goes below the table to the chair at end of table, takes off his coat, and places it on the chair.*] God knows, I have things enough to do today without wasting my time on an insect like you. There's plenty to do, I assure you, when you've just put down a revolution. But urgent things can wait. I am not going to let politics be the cause of your death. For it is a fact that this whole business is nothing but politics: the mournful shade of Polynices, the decomposing corpse, the sentimental weeping, and the hysteria that you mistake for heroism—nothing but politics.

Look here. I may not be soft, but I'm fastidious. I like things clean, shipshape, well scrubbed. Don't think that I am not just as offended as you are by the thought of that meat rotting in the sun. In the evening, when the breeze comes in off the sea, you can smell it in the palace, and it nauseates me. But I refuse even to shut my window. It's vile; and I can tell you what I wouldn't tell anybody else: it's stupid, monstrously stupid. But the people of Thebes have got to have their noses rubbed into it a little longer. My God! If it was up to me, I should have had them bury your brother long ago as a mere matter of public hygiene. I admit that what I am doing is childish. But if the featherheaded rabble I govern are to under-

stand what's what, that stench has got to fill the town
for a month!

Antigone [*turns to him*]. You are a loathsome man!

Creon. I agree. My trade forces me to be. We could
argue whether I ought or ought not to follow my trade;
but once I take on the job, I must do it properly.

Antigone. Why do you do it at all?

Creon. My dear, I woke up one morning and found
myself King of Thebes. God knows, there were other
things I loved in life more than power.

Antigone. Then you should have said no.

Creon. Yes, I could have done that. Only, I felt that it
would have been cowardly. I should have been like a
workman who turns down a job that has to be done. So
I said yes.

Antigone. So much the worse for you, then. I didn't
say yes. I can say no to anything I think vile, and I don't
have to count the cost. But because you said yes, all that
you can do, for all your crown and your trappings, and
your guards—all that you can do is to have me killed.

Creon. Listen to me.

Antigone. If I want to. I don't have to listen to you if
I don't want to. You've said your *yes*. There is nothing
more you can tell me that I don't know. You stand there,
drinking in my words. [*She moves behind chair.*] Why is
it that you don't call your guards? I'll tell you why? You
want to hear me out to the end; that's why.

Creon. You amuse me.

Antigone. Oh, no, I don't. I frighten you. That is why
you talk about saving me. Everything would be so much
easier if you had a docile, tongue-tied little Antigone living
in the palace. I'll tell you something, Uncle Creon: I'll
give you back one of your own words. You are too fastidious to make a good tyrant. But you are going to have to
put me to death today, and you know it. And that's what
frightens you. God! Is there anything uglier than a frightened man!

Creon. Very well. I am afraid, then. Does that satisfy
you? I am afraid that if you insist upon it, I shall have to
have you killed. And I don't want to.

Antigone. I don't have to do things that I think are
wrong. If it comes to that, you didn't really want to leave

my brother's body unburied, did you? Say it! Admit that you didn't.

Creon. I have said it already.

Antigone. But you did it just the same. And now, though you don't want to do it, you are going to have me killed. And you call that being a king!

Creon. Yes, I call that being a king.

Antigone. Poor Creon! My nails are broken, my fingers are bleeding, my arms are covered with the welts left by the paws of your guards—but I am a queen!

Creon. Then why not have pity on me, and live? Isn't your brother's corpse, rotting there under my windows, payment enough for peace and order in Thebes? My son loves you. Don't make me add your life to the payment. I've paid enough.

Antigone. No, Creon! You said yes, and made yourself king. Now you will never stop paying.

Creon. But God in heaven! Won't you try to understand me! I'm trying hard enough to understand you! There had to be one man who said yes. Somebody had to agree to captain the ship. She had sprung a hundred leaks; she was loaded to the water line with crime, ignorance, poverty. The wheel was swinging with the wind. The crew refused to work and were looting the cargo. The officers were building a raft, ready to slip overboard and desert the ship. The mast was splitting, the wind was howling, the sails were beginning to rip. Every man jack on board was about to drown—and only because the only thing they thought of was their own skins and their cheap little day-to-day traffic. Was that a time, do you think, for playing with words like yes and no? Was that a time for a man to be weighing the pros and cons, wondering if he wasn't going to pay too dearly later on; if he wasn't going to lose his life, or his family, or his touch with other men? You grab the wheel, you right the ship in the face of a mountain of water. You shout an order, and if one man refuses to obey, you shoot straight into the mob. Into the mob, I say! The beast as nameless as the wave that crashes down upon your deck; as nameless as the whipping wind. The thing that drops when you shoot may be someone who poured you a drink the night before; but it has no name. And you, braced at the wheel, you have no name, either. Nothing has a name—

except the ship, and the storm. [A *pause as he looks at her.*] Now do you understand?

Antigone. I am not here to understand. That's all very well for you. I am here to say no to you, and die.

Creon. It is easy to say no.

Antigone. Not always.

Creon. It is easy to say no. To say yes, you have to sweat and roll up your sleeves and plunge both hands into life up to the elbows. It is easy to say no, even if saving no means death. All you have to do is to sit still and wait. Wait to go on living; wait to be killed. That is the coward's part. No is one of your man-made words. Can you imagine a world in which trees say *no* to the sap? In which beasts say *no* to hunger or to propagation? Animals are good, simple, tough. They move in droves, nudging one another onwards, all traveling the same road. Some of them keel over, but the rest go on; and no matter how many may fall by the wayside, there are always those few left that go on bringing their young into the world, traveling the same road with the same obstinate will, unchanged from those who went before.

Antigone. Animals, eh, Creon! What a king you could be if only men were animals!

A *pause.* CREON *turns and looks at her.*

Creon. You despise me, don't you? [ANTIGONE *is silent.* CREON *goes on, as if to himself.*] Strange. Again and again, I have imagined myself holding this conversation with a pale young man I have never seen in the flesh. He would have come to assassinate me, and would have failed. I would be trying to find out from him why he wanted to kill me. But with all my logic and all my powers of debate, the only thing I could get out of him would be that he despised me. Who would have thought that the white-faced boy would turn out to be you? And that the debate would arise out of something so meaningless as the burial of your brother?

Antigone [*repeats contemptuously.*] Meaningless!

Creon [*earnestly, almost desperately*]. And yet, you must hear me out. My part is not an heroic one, but I shall play my part. I shall have you put to death. Only, before I do, I want to make one last appeal. I want to be

sure that you know what you are doing as well as I know
what I am doing. Antigone, do you know what you are
dying for? Do you know the sordid story to which you
are going to sign your name in blood, for all time to
come?

Antigone. What story?

Creon. The story of Éteocles and Polynices, the story of
your brothers. You think you know it, but you don't.
Nobody in Thebes knows that story but me. And it
seems to me, this afternoon, that you have a right to
know it too. [*A pause as* ANTIGONE *moves to chair and
sits.*] It's not a pretty story. [*He turns, gets stool from
behind the table and places it between the table and the
chair.*] You'll see. [*He looks at her for a moment.*] Tell
me, first. What do you remember about your brothers?
They were older than you, so they must have looked
down on you. And I imagine that they tormented you—
pulled your pigtails, broke your dolls, whispered secrets
to each other to put you in a rage.

Antigone. They were big and I was little.

Creon. And later on, when they came home wearing
evening clothes, smoking cigarettes, they would have
nothing to do with you; and you thought they were
wonderful.

Antigone. They were boys and I was a girl.

Creon. You didn't know why, exactly, but you knew
that they were making your mother unhappy. You saw
her in tears over them; and your father would fly into a
rage because of them. You heard them come in, slamming
doors, laughing noisily in the corridors—insolent, spineless, unruly, smelling of drink.

Antigone [*staring outward*]. Once, it was very early and
we had just got up. I saw them coming home, and hid
behind a door. Polynices was very pale and his eyes were
shining. He was so handsome in his evening clothes. He
saw me, and said: "Here, this is for you"; and he gave
me a big paper flower that he had brought home from
his night out.

Creon. And of course you still have that flower. Last
night, before you crept out, you opened a drawer and
looked at it for a time, to give yourself courage.

Antigone. Who told you so?

Creon. Poor Antigone! With her night club flower. Do you know what your brother was?

Antigone. Whatever he was, I know that you will say vile things about him.

Creon. A cheap, idiotic bounder, that is what he was. A cruel, vicious little voluptuary. A little beast with just wit enough to drive a car faster and throw more money away than any of his pals. I was with your father one day when Polynices, having lost a lot of money gambling, asked him to settle the debt; and when your father refused, the boy raised his hand against him and called him a vile name.

Antigone. That's a lie!

Creon. He struck your father in the face with his fist. It was pitiful. Your father sat at his desk with his head in his hands. His nose was bleeding. He was weeping with anguish. And in a corner of your father's study, Polynices stood sneering and lighting a cigarette.

Antigone. That's a lie.

A pause.

Creon. When did you last see Polynices alive? When you were twelve years old. *That's* true, isn't it?

Antigone. Yes, that's true.

Creon. Now you know why. Oedipus was too chicken-hearted to have the boy locked up. Polynices was allowed to go off and join the Argive army. And as soon as he reached Argos, the attempts upon your father's life began —upon the life of an old man who couldn't make up his mind to die, couldn't bear to be parted from his kingship. One after another, men slipped into Thebes from Argos for the purpose of assassinating him, and every killer we caught always ended by confessing who had put him up to it, who had paid him to try it. And it wasn't only Polynices. That is really what I am trying to tell you. I want you to know what went on in the back room, in the kitchen of politics; I want you to know what took place in the wings of this drama in which you are burning to play a part.

Yesterday, I gave Eteocles a State funeral, with pomp and honors. Today, Eteocles is a saint and a hero in the eyes of all Thebes. The whole city turned out to bury him. The schoolchildren emptied their saving boxes to buy wreaths for him. Old men, orating in quavering, hypocritical voices, glorified the virtues of the great-hearted brother, the devoted son, the loyal prince. I made a speech myself; and every temple priest was present with an appropriate show of sorrow and solemnity in his stupid face. And military honors were accorded the dead hero.

Well, what else could I have done? People had taken sides in the civil war. Both sides couldn't be wrong; that would be too much. I couldn't have made them swallow the truth. Two gangsters was more of a luxury than I could afford. [*He pauses for a moment.*] And this is the whole point of my story. Eteocles, that virtuous brother, was just as rotten as Polynices. That great-hearted son had done his best, too, to procure the assassination of his father. That loyal prince had also offered to sell out Thebes to the highest bidder.

Funny, isn't it? Polynices lies rotting in the sun while Eteocles is given a hero's funeral and will be housed in a marble vault. Yet I have absolute proof that everything that Polynices did, Eteocles had plotted to do. They were a pair of blackguards—both engaged in selling out Thebes, and both engaged in selling out each other; and they died like the cheap gangsters they were, over a division of the spoils.

But, as I told you a moment ago, I had to make a martyr of one of them. I sent out to the holocaust for their bodies; they were found clasped in one another's arms—for the first time in their lives, I imagine. Each had been spitted on the other's sword, and the Argive cavalry had trampled them down. They were mashed to a pulp, Antigone. I had the prettier of the two carcasses brought in and gave it a State funeral; and I left the other to rot. I don't know which was which. And I assure you, I don't care.

Long silence, neither looking at the other.

Antigone [*in a mild voice*]. Why do you tell me all this?

Creon. Would it have been better to let you die a victim to that obscene story?

Antigone. It might have been. I had my faith.

Creon. What are you going to do now?

Antigone [*rises to her feet in a daze*]. I shall go up to my room.

Creon. Don't stay alone. Go and find Haemon. And get married quickly.

Antigone [*in a whisper*]. Yes.

Creon. All this is really beside the point. You have your whole life ahead of you—and life is a treasure.

Antigone. Yes.

Creon. And you were about to throw it away. Don't think me fatuous if I say that I understand you; and that at your age I should have done the same thing. A moment ago, when we were quarreling, you said I was drinking in your words. I was. But it wasn't you I was listening to; it was a lad named Creon who lived here in Thebes many years ago. He was thin and pale, as you are. His mind, too, was filled with thoughts of self-sacrifice. Go and find Haemon. And get married quickly, Antigone. Be happy. Life flows like water, and you young people let it run away through your fingers. Shut your hands; hold on to it, Antigone. Life is not what you think it is. Life is a child playing around your feet, a tool you hold firmly in your grip, a bench you sit down upon in the evening, in your garden. People will tell you that that's not life, that life is something else. They will tell you that because they need your strength and your fire, and they will want to make use of you. Don't listen to them. Believe me, the only poor consolation that we have in our old age is to discover that what I have just said to you is true. Life is nothing more than the happiness that you get out of it.

Antigone [*murmurs, lost in thought*]. Happiness . . .

Creon [*suddenly a little self-conscious*]. Not much of a word, is it?

Antigone [*quietly*]. What kind of happiness do you foresee for me? Paint me the picture of your happy Antigone. What are the unimportant little sins that I shall have to commit before I am allowed to sink my teeth into life and tear happiness from it? Tell me: to whom shall I have to lie? Upon whom shall I have to fawn? To whom must I sell myself? Whom do you want me to leave dying, while I turn away my eyes?

Creon. Antigone, be quiet.

Antigone. Why do you tell me to be quiet when all I

want to know is what I have to do to be happy? This
minute; since it is this very minute that I must make my
choice. You tell me that life is so wonderful. I want to
know what I have to do in order to be able to say that
myself.

Creon. Do you love Haemon?

Antigone. Yes, I love Haemon. The Haemon I love is
hard and young, faithful and difficult to satisfy, just as
I am. But if what I love in Haemon is to be worn away
like a stone step by the tread of the thing you call life, the
thing you call happiness, if Haemon reaches the point
where he stops growing pale with fear when I grow pale,
stops thinking that I must have been killed in an accident
when I am five minutes late, stops feeling that he is alone on
earth when I laugh and he doesn't know why—if he too
has to learn to say yes to everything—why, no, then, no!
I do not love Haemon!

Creon. You don't know what you are talking about!

Antigone. I do know what I am talking about! Now
it is you who have stopped understanding. I am too far
away from you now, talking to you from a kingdom you
can't get into, with your quick tongue and your hollow
heart. [Laughs.] I laugh, Creon, because I see you suddenly as you must have been at fifteen: the same look
of impotence in your face and the same inner conviction
that there was nothing you couldn't do. What has life
added to you, except those lines in your face, and that
fat on your stomach?

Creon. Be quiet, I tell you!

Antigone. Why do you want me to be quiet? Because
you know that I am right? Do you think I can't see in
your face that what I am saying is true? You can't admit
it, of course; you have to go on growling and defending
the bone you call happiness.

Creon. It is your happiness, too, you little fool!

Antigone. I spit on your happiness! I spit on your idea
of life—that life that must go on, come what may. You
are all like dogs that lick everything they smell. You with
your promise of a humdrum happiness—provided a person doesn't ask too much of life. I want everything of
life, I do; and I want it now! I want it total, complete:
otherwise I reject it! I will not be moderate. I will not be
satisfied with the bit of cake you offer me if I promise to
be a good little girl. I want to be sure of everything this

very day; sure that everything will be as beautiful as when I was a little girl. If not, I want to die!

Creon. Scream on, daughter of Oedipus! Scream on, in your father's own voice!

Antigone. In my father's own voice, yes! We are of the tribe that asks questions, and we ask them to the bitter end. Until no tiniest chance of hope remains to be strangled by our hands. We are of the tribe that hates your filthy hope, your docile, female hope; hope, your whore——

Creon [grasps her by her arms]. Shut up! If you could see how ugly you are, shrieking those words!

Antigone. Yes, I am ugly! Father was ugly, too. [CREON *releases her arms, turns and moves away. Stands with his back to* ANTIGONE.] But Father became beautiful. And do you know when? [*She follows him to behind the table.*] At the very end. When all his questions had been answered. When he could no longer doubt that he *had* killed his own father; that he *had* gone to bed with his own mother. When all hope was gone, stamped out like a beetle. When it was absolutely certain that nothing, nothing could save him. Then he was at peace; then he could smile, almost; then he became beautiful. . . . Whereas you! Ah, those faces of yours, you candidates for election to happiness! It's you who are the ugly ones, even the handsomest of you—with that ugly glint in the corner of your eyes, that ugly crease at the corner of your mouths. Creon, you spoke the word a moment ago: the kitchen of politics. You look it and you smell of it.

Creon [struggles to put his hand over her mouth]. I order you to shut up! Do you hear me?

Antigone. You order me? Cook! Do you really believe that you can give me orders?

Creon. Antigone! The anteroom is full of people! Do you want them to hear you?

Antigone. Open the doors! Let us make sure that they can hear me!

Creon. By God! You shut up, I tell you!

ISMENE *enters through arch.*

Ismene [distraught]. Antigone!

Antigone [turns to ISMENE]. You, too? What do you want?

Ismene. Oh, forgive me, Antigone. I've come back. I'll be brave. I'll go with you now.

Antigone. Where will you go with me?

Ismene [*to* CREON]. Creon! If you kill her, you'll have to kill me too.

Antigone. Oh, no, Ismene. Not a bit of it. I die alone. You don't think I'm going to let you die with me after what I've been through? You don't deserve it.

Ismene. If you die, I don't want to live. I don't want to be left behind, alone.

Antigone. You chose life and I chose death. Now stop blubbering. You had your chance to come with me in the black night, creeping on your hands and knees. You had your chance to claw up the earth with your nails, as I did; to get yourself caught like a thief, as I did. And you refused it.

Ismene. Not any more. I'll do it alone tonight.

Antigone [*turns round toward* CREON]. You hear that, Creon? The thing is catching! Who knows but that lots of people will catch the disease from me! What are you waiting for? Call in your guards! Come on, Creon! Show a little courage! It only hurts for a minute! Come on, cook!

Creon [*turns toward arch and calls*]. Guard!

GUARDS *enter through arch.*

Antigone [*in a great cry of relief*]. At last, Creon!

CHORUS *enters through left arch.*

Creon [*to the* GUARDS]. Take her away! [CREON *goes up on top step.*]

GUARDS *grasp* ANTIGONE *by her arms, turn and hustle her toward the arch, right, and exeunt.* ISMENE *mimes horror, backs away toward the arch, left, then turns and runs out through the arch. A long pause, as* CREON *moves slowly downstage.*

Chorus [*behind* CREON. *Speaks in a deliberate voice*]. You are out of your mind, Creon. What have you done?

Creon [*his back to* CHORUS]. She had to die.

Chorus. You must not let Antigone die. We shall carry the scar of her death for centuries.

Creon. She insisted. No man on earth was strong enough to dissuade her. Death was her purpose, whether she knew it or not. Polynices was a mere pretext. When she had to give up that pretext, she found another one—that life and happiness were tawdry things and not worth possessing. She was bent upon only one thing: to reject life and to die.

Chorus. She is a mere child, Creon.

Creon. What do you want me to do for her? Condemn her to live?

Haemon [*calls from offstage*]. Father! [HAEMON *enters through arch, right.* CREON *turns toward him.*]

Creon. Haemon, forget Antigone. Forget her, my dearest boy.

Haemon. How can you talk like that?

Creon [*grasps* HAEMON *by the hands*]. I did everything I could to save her, Haemon. I used every argument. I swear I did. The girl doesn't love you. She could have gone on living for you; but she refused. She wanted it this way; she wanted to die.

Haemon. Father! The guards are dragging Antigone away! You've got to stop them! [*He breaks away from* CREON.]

Creon [*looks away from* HAEMON]. I can't stop them. It's too late. Antigone has spoken. The story is all over Thebes. I cannot save her now.

Chorus. Creon, you must find a way. Lock her up. Say that she has gone out of her mind.

Creon. Everybody will know it isn't so. The nation will say that I am making an exception of her because my son loves her. I cannot.

Chorus. You can still gain time, and get her out of Thebes.

Creon. The mob already knows the truth. It is howling for her blood. I can do nothing.

Haemon. But, Father, you are master in Thebes!

Creon. I am master under the law. Not above the law.

Haemon. You cannot let Antigone be taken from me. I am your son!

Creon. I cannot do anything else, my poor boy. She must die and you must live.

Haemon. Live, you say! Live a life without Antigone? A life in which I am to go on admiring you as you busy yourself about your kingdom, make your persuasive speeches, strike your attitudes? Not without Antigone. I love Antigone. I will not live without Antigone!

Creon. Haemon—you will have to resign yourself to life without Antigone. [*He moves to left of* HAEMON.] Sooner or later there comes a day of sorrow in each man's life when he must cease to be a child and take up the burden of manhood. That day has come for you.

Haemon [*backs away a step*]. That giant strength, that courage. That massive god who used to pick me up in his arms and shelter me from shadows and monsters—was that you, Father? Was it of you I stood in awe? Was that man you?

Creon. For God's sake, Haemon, do not judge me! Not you, too!

Haemon [*pleading now*]. This is all a bad dream, Father. You are not yourself. It isn't true that we have been backed up against a wall, forced to surrender. We don't have to say *yes* to this terrible thing. You are still king. You are still the father I revered. You have no right to desert me, to shrink into nothingness. The world will be too bare, I shall be too alone in the world, if you force me to disown you.

Creon. The world *is* bare, Haemon, and you *are* alone. You must cease to think your father all-powerful. Look straight at me. See your father as he is. That is what it means to grow up and be a man.

Haemon [*stares at* CREON *for a moment*]. I tell you that I will not live without Antigone. [*Turns and goes quickly out through arch.*]

Chorus. Creon, the boy will go mad.

Creon. Poor boy! He loves her.

Chorus. Creon, the boy is wounded to death.

Creon. We are all wounded to death.

FIRST GUARD *enters through arch, right, followed by* SECOND *and* THIRD GUARDS *pulling* ANTIGONE *along with them.*

First Guard. Sir, the people are crowding into the palace!

Antigone. Creon, I don't want to see their faces. I don't want to hear them howl. You are going to kill me; let that be enough. I want to be alone until it is over.

Creon. Empty the palace! Guards at the gates!

CREON *quickly crosses toward the arch; exit. Two* GUARDS *release* ANTIGONE; *exeunt behind* CREON. CHORUS *goes out through arch, left. The lighting dims so that only the area about the table is lighted. The cyclorama is covered with a dark blue color. The scene is intended to suggest a prison cell, filled with shadows and dimly lit.* ANTIGONE *moves to stool and sits. The* FIRST GUARD *stands upstage. He watches* ANTIGONE, *and as she sits, he begins pacing slowly downstage, then upstage. A pause.*

Antigone [*turns and looks at the* GUARD]. It's you, is it?

Guard. What do you mean, me?

Antigone. The last human face that I shall see. [*A pause as they look at each other, then* GUARD *paces upstage, turns, and crosses behind table.*] Was it you that arrested me this morning?

Guard. Yes, that was me.

Antigone. You hurt me. There was no need for you to hurt me. Did I act as if I was trying to escape?

Guard. Come on now, Miss. It was my business to bring you in. I did it. [*A pause. He paces to and fro upstage. Only the sound of his boots is heard.*]

Antigone. How old are you?

Guard. Thirty-nine.

Antigone. Have you any children?

Guard. Yes. Two.

Antigone. Do you love your children?

Guard. What's that got to with you? [*A pause. He paces upstage and downstage.*]

Antigone. How long have you been in the Guard?

Guard. Since the war. I was in the army. Sergeant. Then I joined the Guard.

Antigone. Does one have to have been an army sergeant to get into the Guard?

Guard. Supposed to be. Either that or on special detail. But when they make you a guard, you lose your stripes.

Antigone [*murmurs*]. I see.

Guard. Yes. Of course, if you're a guard, everybody knows you're something special; they know you're an old N.C.O. Take pay, for instance. When you're a guard you get your pay, and on top of that you get six months' extra pay, to make sure you don't lose anything by not being a sergeant any more. And of course you do better than that. You get a house, coal, rations, extras for the wife and kids. If you've got two kids, like me, you draw better than a sergeant.

Antigone [barely audible]. I see.

Guard. That's why sergeants, now, they don't like guards. Maybe you noticed they try to make out they're better than us? Promotion, that's what it is. In the army, anybody can get promoted. All you need is good conduct. Now in the Guard, it's slow, and you have to know your business—like how to make out a report and the like of that. But when you're an N.C.O. in the Guard, you've got something that even a sergeant-major ain't got. For instance——

Antigone [breaking him off]. Listen.

Guard. Yes, Miss.

Antigone. I'm going to die soon.

The GUARD *looks at her for a moment, then turns and moves away.*

Guard. For instance, people have a lot of respect for guards, they have. A guard may be a soldier, but he's kind of in the civil service, too.

Antigone. Do you think it hurts to die?

Guard. How would I know? Of course, if somebody sticks a saber in your guts and turns it round, it hurts.

Antigone. How are they going to put me to death?

Guard. Well, I'll tell you. I heard the proclamation all right. Wait a minute. How did it go now? [*He stares into space and recites from memory.*] "In order that our fair city shall not be pol-luted with her sinful blood, she shall be im-mured—immured." That means, they shove you in a cave and wall up the cave.

Antigone. Alive?

Guard. Yes. . . . [*He moves away a few steps.*]

Antigone [murmurs]. O tomb! O bridal bed! Alone! [ANTIGONE *sits there, a tiny figure in the middle of the stage. You would say she felt a little chilly. She wraps her arms round herself.*]

Guard. Yes! Outside the southeast gate of the town. In the Cave of Hades. In broad daylight. Some detail, eh, for them that's on the job! First they thought maybe it was a job for the army. Now it looks like it's going to be the Guard. There's an outfit for you! Nothing the Guard can't do. No wonder the army's jealous.

Antigone. A pair of animals.

Guard. What do you mean, a pair of animals?

Antigone. When the winds blow cold, all they need do is to press close against one another. I am all alone.

Guard. Is there anything you want? I can send out for it, you know.

Antigone. You are very kind. [*A pause.* ANTIGONE *looks up at the* GUARD.] Yes, there is something I want. I want you to give someone a letter from me, when I am dead.

Guard. How's that again? A letter?

Antigone. Yes, I want to write a letter; and I want you to give it to someone for me.

Guard [*straightens up*]. Now, wait a minute. Take it easy. It's as much as my job is worth to go handing out letters from prisoners.

Antigone [*removes a ring from her finger and holds it out toward him*]. I'll give you this ring if you will do it.

Guard. Is it gold? [*He takes the ring from her.*]

Antigone. Yes, it is gold.

Guard [*shakes his head*]. Uh-uh. No can do. Suppose they go through my pockets. I might get six months for a thing like that. [*He stares at the ring, then glances off right to make sure that he is not being watched.*] Listen, tell you what I'll do. You tell me what you want to say, and I'll write it down in my book. Then, afterwards, I'll tear out the pages and give them to the party, see? If it's in my handwriting, it's all right.

Antigone [*winces*]. In your handwriting? [*She shudders slightly.*] No. That would be awful. The poor darling! In your handwriting.

Guard [*offers back the ring*]. O.K. It's no skin off my nose.

Antigone [*quickly*]. Of course, of course. No, keep the ring. But hurry. Time is getting short. Where is your notebook? [*The* GUARD *pockets the ring, takes his notebook and pencil from his pocket, puts his foot up on chair, and rests the notebook on his knee, licks his pencil.*] Ready? [*He nods.*] Write, now. "My darling . . ."

Guard [*writes as he mutters*]. The boy friend, eh?

Antigone. "My darling. I wanted to die, and perhaps you will not love me any more . . ."

Guard [*mutters as he writes*] ". . . will not love me any more."

Antigone. "Creon was right. It is terrible to die."

Guard [*repeats as he writes*] ". . . terrible to die."

Antigone. "And I don't even know what I am dying for. I am afraid . . ."

Guard [*looks at her*]. Wait a minute! How fast do you think I can write?

Antigone [*takes hold of herself*]. Where are you?

Guard [*reads from his notebook*]. "And I don't even know what I am dying for."

Antigone. No. Scratch that out. Nobody must know that. They have no right to know. It's as if they saw me naked and touched me, after I was dead. Scratch it all out. Just write: "Forgive me."

Guard [*looks at* ANTIGONE]. I cut out everything you said there at the end, and I put down, "Forgive me"?

Antigone. Yes. "Forgive me, my darling. You would all have been so happy except for Antigone. I love you."

Guard [*finishes the letter*] ". . . I love you." [*He looks at her.*] Is that all?

Antigone. That's all.

Guard [*straightens up, looks at notebook*]. Damn funny letter.

Antigone. I know.

Guard [*looks at her*]. Who is it to? [*A sudden roll of drums begins and continues until after* ANTIGONE'S *exit. The* FIRST GUARD *pockets the notebook and shouts at* ANTIGONE.] O.K. That's enough out of you! Come on!

At the sound of the drum roll, SECOND *and* THIRD GUARDS *enter through the arch.* ANTIGONE *rises.* GUARDS *seize her and exeunt with her. The lighting moves up to suggest late afternoon.* CHORUS *enters.*

Chorus. And now it is Creon's turn.

MESSENGER *runs through the arch, right.*

Messenger. The Queen . . . the Queen! Where is the Queen?

Chorus. What do you want with the Queen? What have you to tell the Queen?

Messenger. News to break her heart. Antigone had just been thrust into the cave. They hadn't finished heaving the last block of stone into place when Creon and the rest heard a sudden moaning from the tomb. A hush fell over us all, for it was not the voice of Antigone. It was Haemon's voice that came forth from the tomb. Everybody looked at Creon; and he howled like a man demented: "Take away the stones! Take away the stones!" The slaves leaped at the wall of stones, and Creon worked with them, sweating and tearing at the blocks with his bleeding hands. Finally a narrow opening was forced, and into it slipped the smallest guard.

Antigone had hanged herself by the cord of her robe, by the red and golden twisted cord of her robe. The cord was round her neck like a child's collar. Haemon was on his knees, holding her in his arms and moaning, his face buried in her robe. More stones were removed, and Creon went into the tomb. He tried to raise Haemon to his feet. I could hear him begging Haemon to rise to his feet. Haemon was deaf to his father's voice, till suddenly he stood up of his own accord, his eyes dark and burning. Anguish was in his face, but it was the face of a little boy. He stared at his father. Then suddenly he struck him —hard; and he drew his sword. Creon leaped out of range. Haemon went on staring at him, his eyes full of contempt —a glance that was like a knife, and that Creon couldn't escape. The King stood trembling in the far corner of the tomb, and Haemon went on staring. Then, without a word, he stabbed himself and lay down beside Antigone, embracing her in a great pool of blood.

A pause as CREON *and* PAGE *enter through arch on the* MESSENGER'S *last words.* CHORUS *and the* MESSENGER *both turn to look at* CREON; *then exit the* MESSENGER *through curtain.*

Creon. I have had them laid out side by side. They are together at last, and at peace. Two lovers on the morrow of their bridal. Their work is done.

Chorus. But not yours, Creon. You have still one thing to learn. Eurydice, the Queen, your wife——

Creon. A good woman. Always busy with her garden, her preserves, her sweaters—those sweaters she never stopped knitting for the poor. Strange, how the poor never stop needing sweaters. One would almost think that was all they needed.

Chorus. The poor in Thebes are going to be cold this winter, Creon. When the Queen was told of her son's death, she waited carefully until she had finished her row, then put down her knitting calmly—as she did everything. She went up to her room, her lavender-scented room, with its embroidered doilies and its pictures framed in plush; and there, Creon, she cut her throat. She is laid out now in one of those two old-fashioned twin beds, exactly where you went to her one night when she was still a maiden. Her smile is still the same, scarcely a shade more melancholy. And if it were not for that great red blot on the bed linen by her neck, one might think she was asleep.

Creon [*in a dull voice*]. She, too. They are all asleep. [*Pause.*] It must be good to sleep.

Chorus. And now you are alone, Creon.

Creon. Yes, all alone. [*To* Page.] My lad.

Page. Sir?

Creon. Listen to me. They don't know it, but the truth is the work is there to be done, and a man can't fold his arms and refuse to do it. They say it's dirty work. But if we didn't do it, who would?

Page. I don't know, sir.

Creon. Of course you don't. You'll be lucky if you never find out. In a hurry to grow up, aren't you?

Page. Oh, yes, sir.

Creon. I shouldn't be if I were you. Never grow up if you can help it. [*He is lost in thought as the hour chimes.*] What time is it?

Page. Five o'clock, sir.

Creon. What have we on at five o'clock?

Page. Cabinet meeting, sir.

Creon. Cabinet meeting. Then we had better go along to it.

Exeunt CREON *and* PAGE *slowly through arch, left, and* CHORUS *moves downstage.*

Chorus. And there we are. It is quite true that if it had not been for Antigone they would all have been at peace. But that is over now. And they are all at peace. All those who were meant to die have died: those who believed one thing, those who believed the contrary thing, and even those who believed nothing at all, yet were caught up in the web without knowing why. All dead: stiff, useless, rotting. And those who have survived will now begin quietly to forget the dead: they won't remember who was who or which was which. It is all over. Antigone is calm tonight, and we shall never know the name of the fever that consumed her. She has played her part.

Three GUARDS *enter, resume their places on steps as at the rise of the curtain, and begin to play cards.*

A great melancholy wave of peace now settles down upon Thebes, upon the empty palace, upon Creon, who can now begin to wait for his own death.

Only the guards are left, and none of this matters to them. It's no skin off. their noses. They go on playing cards.

CHORUS *walks toward the arch, left, as the curtain falls.*

Oedipus Rex

SOPHOCLES
TRANSLATED BY DUDLEY FITTS AND ROBERT FITZGERALD

CHARACTERS

OEDIPUS,	King of Thebes, supposed son of Polybos and Merope, King and Queen of Corinth
IOKASTE[1],	wife of Oedipus and widow of the late King Laios
KREON,	brother of Iokaste, a prince of Thebes
TEIRESIAS,	a blind seer who serves Apollo
PRIEST MESSENGER,	from Corinth
SHEPHERD,	former servant of Laios
SECOND MESSENGER,	from the palace
CHORUS OF THEBAN ELDERS CHORAGOS,	leader of the Chorus
ANTIGONE and ISMENE,	young daughters of Oedipus and Iokaste. They appear in the Exodos but do not speak.
SUPPLIANTS, GUARDS, SERVANTS	

THE SCENE

Before the palace of Oedipus, King of Thebes. A central door and two lateral doors open onto a platform which runs the length of the facade. On the platform, right and left, are altars; and three steps lead down into the orchestra, or chorus-ground. At the beginning of the action these steps are crowded by suppliants who have brought branches and chaplets of olive leaves and who sit in various attitudes of despair. Oedipus enters.

---

[1]Iokaste has been translated as Jocasta in other versions of the play.

Translated by Dudley Fitts and Robert Fitzgerald. Copyright © 1949 by Harcourt, Inc. and renewed 1977 by Cornelia Fitts and Robert Fitzgerald. Reprinted by permission of Harcourt, Inc.

623

PROLOGUE[2]

OEDIPUS. My children, generations of the living
　　In the line of Kadmos,[3] nursed at his ancient hearth:
　　Why have you strewn yourselves before these altars
　　In supplication, with your boughs and garlands?
　　The breath of incense rises from the city 　　　　　　　5
　　With a sound of prayer and lamentation.

　　　　　　　　　　　　　　　　　　Children,

　　I would not have you speak through messengers,
　　And therefore I have come myself to hear you—
　　I, Oedipus, who bear the famous name.
　　(*To a Priest.*) You, there, since you are eldest in the company, 　10
　　Speak for them all, tell me what preys upon you,
　　Whether you come in dread, or crave some blessing:
　　Tell me, and never doubt that I will help you
　　In every way I can; I should be heartless
　　Were I not moved to find you suppliant here. 　　　　　15
PRIEST. Great Oedipus, O powerful king of Thebes!
　　You see how all the ages of our people
　　Cling to your altar steps: here are boys
　　Who can barely stand alone, and here are priests
　　By weight of age, as I am a priest of God, 　　　　　20
　　And young men chosen from those yet unmarried;
　　As for the others, all that multitude,
　　They wait with olive chaplets in the squares,
　　At the two shrines of Pallas,[4] and where Apollo[5]
　　Speaks in the glowing embers.

　　　　　　　　　　　　　　　　Your own eyes 　25

　　Must tell you: Thebes is tossed on a murdering sea
　　And can not lift her head from the death surge.
　　A rust consumes the buds and fruits of the earth;
　　The herds are sick; children die unborn,
　　And labor is vain. The god of plague and pyre 　　　　30
　　Raids like detestable lightning through the city,

---

[2]Part of play that explains background and current action.

[3]Founder of Thebes.

[4]Pallas Athene, goddess of wisdom

[5]God of the sun.

And all the house of Kadmos is laid waste,
All emptied, and all darkened: Death alone
Battens upon the misery of Thebes.
You are not one of the immortal gods, we know;   *35*
Yet we have come to you to make our prayer
As to the man surest in mortal ways
And wisest in the ways of God. You saved us
From the Sphinx,[6] that flinty singer, and the tribute
We paid to her so long; yet you were never   *40*
Better informed than we, nor could we teach you:
A god's touch, it seems, enabled you to help us.

Therefore, O mighty power, we turn to you:
Find us our safety, find us a remedy,
Whether by counsel of the gods or of men.   *45*
A king of wisdom tested in the past
Can act in a time of troubles, and act well.
Noblest of men, restore
Life to your city! Think how all men call you
Liberator for your boldness long ago;   *50*
Ah, when your years of kingship are remembered,
Let them not say *We rose, but later fell*—
Keep the State from going down in the storm!
Once, years ago, with happy augury,
You brought us fortune; be the same again!   *55*
No man questions your power to rule the land:
But rule over men, not over a dead city!
Ships are only hulls, high walls are nothing,
When no life moves in the empty passageways.
OEDIPUS. Poor children! You may be sure I know   *60*
All that you longed for in your coming here.
I know that you are deathly sick; and yet,
Sick as you are, not one is as sick as I.
Each of you suffers in himself alone
His anguish, not another's; but my spirit   *65*
Groans for the city, for myself, for you.

---

[6]Mythological winged creature with lion's body and human head that tormented Thebes by demanding the answer to this riddle: What has one voice and yet becomes four-footed and two-footed and three-footed? When the riddle was answered incorrectly, she ate the respondent. Oedipus gives the correct answer: A man crawls on all fours in infancy, walks on two feet when grown, and leans on a staff in old age. After Oedipus answers correctly, the Sphinx kills herself.

I was not sleeping, you are not waking me.
No, I have been in tears for a long while
And in my restless thought walked many ways.
In all my search I found one remedy,   *70*
And I have adopted it: I have sent Kreon,
Son of Menoikeus, brother of the queen,
To Delphi,[7] Apollo's place of revelation,
To learn there, if he can,
What act or pledge of mine may save the city.   *75*
I have counted the days, and now, this very day,
I am troubled, for he has overstayed his time.
What is he doing? He has been gone too long.
Yet whenever he comes back, I should do ill
Not to take any action the god orders.   *80*

PRIEST. It is a timely promise. At this instant
    They tell me Kreon is here.

OEDIPUS. O Lord Apollo!
    May his news be fair as his face is radiant!

PRIEST. Good news, I gather! he is crowned with bay,
    The chaplet is thick with berries.

OEDIPUS. We shall soon know;   *85*
    He is near enough to hear us now. (*Enter Kreon.*) O prince:
    Brother: son of Menoikeus:
    What answer do you bring us from the god?

KREON. A strong one. I can tell you, great afflictions
    Will turn out well, if they are taken well.   *90*

OEDIPUS. What was the oracle? These vague words
    Leave me still hanging between hope and fear.

KREON. Is it your pleasure to hear me with all these
    Gathered around us? I am prepared to speak,
    But should we not go in?

OEDIPUS. Speak to them all,   *95*
    It is for them I suffer, more than for myself.

KREON. Then I will tell you what I heard at Delphi.
    In plain words
    The god commands us to expel from the land of Thebes
    An old defilement we are sheltering.   *100*
    It is a deathly thing, beyond cure;
    We must not let it feed upon us longer.

---

[7]Greek temple and oracle of Apollo.

OEDIPUS. What defilement? How shall we rid ourselves of it?

KREON. By exile or death, blood for blood. It was
    Murder that brought the plague-wind on the city. 105

OEDIPUS. Murder of whom? Surely the god has named him?

KREON. My Lord: Laios once ruled this land,
    Before you came to govern us.

OEDIPUS. I know;
    I learned of him from others; I never saw him.

KREON. He was murdered; and Apollo commands us now 110
    To take revenge upon whoever killed him.

OEDIPUS. Upon whom? Where are they? Where shall we find a clue
    To solve that crime, after so many years?

KREON. Here in this land, he said. Search reveals
    Things that escape an inattentive man. 115

OEDIPUS. Tell me: Was Laios murdered in his house,
    Or in the fields, or in some foreign country?

KREON. He said he planned to make a pilgrimage.
    He did not come home again.

OEDIPUS. And was there no one,
    No witness, no companion, to tell what happened? 120

KREON. They were all killed but one, and he got away
    So frightened that he could remember one thing only.

OEDIPUS. What was that one thing? One may be the key
    To everything, if we resolve to use it.

KREON. He said that a band of highwaymen attacked them, 125
    Outnumbered them, and overwhelmed the king.

OEDIPUS. Strange, that a highwayman should be so daring—
    Unless some faction here bribed him to do it.

KREON. We thought of that. But after Laios' death
    New troubles arose and we had no avenger. 130

OEDIPUS. What troubles could prevent your hunting down the killers?

KREON. The riddling Sphinx's song
    Made us deaf to all mysteries but her own.

OEDIPUS. Then once more I must bring what is dark to light.
    It is most fitting that Apollo shows, 135
    As you do, this compunction for the dead.
    You shall see how I stand by you, as I should,
    Avenging this country and the god as well,
    And not as though it were for some distant friend,
    But for my own sake, to be rid of evil. 140
    Whoever killed King Laios might—who knows?—

Lay violent hands even on me—and soon.
I act for the murdered king in my own interest.
Come, then, my children: leave the altar steps,
Lift up your olive boughs!

One of you go 145

And summon the people of Kadmos to gather here.
I will do all that I can; you may tell them that.

(Exit a Page.)

So, with the help of God,
We shall be saved—or else indeed we are lost.
PRIEST. Let us rise, children. It was for this we came,   *150*
And now the king has promised it.
Phoibos[8] has sent us an oracle; may he descend
Himself to save us and drive out the plague.

(Exeunt[9] Oedipus and Kreon into the palace by the central door. The Priest and the Suppliants disperse right and left. After a short pause the Chorus enters the orchestra.)

PARADOS[10]

Strophe[11] 1

CHORUS. What is God singing in his profound
    Delphi of gold and shadow?
    What oracle for Thebes, the Sunwhipped city?
    Fear unjoints me, the roots of my heart tremble.
    Now I remember, O Healer, your power, and wonder: *5*
    Will you send doom like a sudden cloud, or weave it
    Like nightfall of the past?
    Speak to me, tell me, O
    Child of golden Hope, immortal Voice.

---

[8]Apollo

[9]They go out. (Latin)

[10]Song or ode the Chorus chants when they enter the stage.

[11]Song the Chorus sings as they dance from stage right to stage left.

Antistrophe[12] 1

Let me pray to Athene, the immortal daughter of Zeus,   *10*
And to Artemis[13] her sister
Who keeps her famous throne in the market ring,
And to Apollo, archer from distant heaven—
O gods, descend! Like three streams leap against
The fires of our grief, the fires of darkness;   *15*
Be swift to bring us rest!
As in the old time from the brilliant house
Of air you stepped to save us, come again!

Strophe 2

Now our afflictions have no end,
Now all our stricken host lies down   *20*
And no man fights off death with his mind;
The noble plowland bears no grain,
And groaning mothers can not bear—
See, how our lives like birds take wing,
Like sparks that fly when a fire soars,   *25*
To the shore of the god of evening.

Antistrophe 2

The plague burns on, it is pitiless,
Though pallid children laden with death
Lie unwept in the stony ways,
And old gray women by every path   *30*
Flock to the strand about the altars
There to strike their breasts and cry
Worship of Phoibos in wailing prayers:
Be kind, God's golden child!

Strophe 3

There are no swords in this attack by fire,   *35*
No shields, but we are ringed with cries.
Send the besieger plunging from our homes

---

[12]Song the Chorus sings as they dance back from stage left to stage right.

[13]Goddess of wild animals and the hunt.

629

Into the vast sea-room of the Atlantic
Or into the waves that foam eastward of Thrace—
For the day ravages what the night spares—   *40*
Destroy our enemy, lord of the thunder!
Let him be riven by lightning from heaven!

Antistrophe 3

Phoibos Apollo, stretch the sun's bowstring,
That golden cord, until it sing for us,
Flashing arrows in heaven!
Artemis, Huntress,   *45*
Race with flaring lights upon our mountains!
O scarlet god,[14] O golden-banded brow,
O Theban Bacchos in a storm of Maenads,[15]

(*Enter Oedipus, center.*)

Whirl upon Death, that all the Undying hate!
Come with blinding torches, come in joy!   *50*

SCENE 1

OEDIPUS. Is this your prayer? It may be answered. Come,
    Listen to me, act as the crisis demands,
    And you shall have relief from all these evils.

    Until now I was a stranger to this tale,
    As I had been a stranger to the crime.   *5*
    Could I track down the murderer without a clue?
    But now, friends,
    As one who became a citizen after the murder,
    I make this proclamation to all Thebans:
    If any man knows by whose hand Laios, son of Labdakos,   *10*
    Met his death, I direct that man to tell me everything,
    No matter what he fears for having so long withheld it.
    Let it stand as promised that no further trouble
    Will come to him, but he may leave the land in safety.
    Moreover: If anyone knows the murderer to be foreign,   *15*
    Let him not keep silent: he shall have his reward from me.

---

[14]Bacchus, god of wine, creative ecstasy, and dramatic poetry

[15]Women who worship Bacchus.

However, if he does conceal it; if any man
Fearing for his friend or for himself disobeys this edict,
Hear what I propose to do:
I solemnly forbid the people of this country,   *20*
Where power and throne are mine, ever to receive that man
Or speak to him, no matter who he is, or let him
Join in sacrifice, lustration, or in prayer.
I decree that he be driven from every house,
Being, as he is, corruption itself to us: the Delphic   *25*
Voice of Apollo has pronounced this revelation.
Thus I associate myself with the oracle
And take the side of the murdered king.

As for the criminal, I pray to God—
Whether it be a lurking thief, or one of a number—   *30*
I pray that that man's life be consumed in evil and wretchedness.
And as for me, this curse applies no less
If it should turn out that the culprit is my guest here,
Sharing my hearth.

                     You have heard the penalty.
I lay it on you now to attend to this   *35*
For my sake, for Apollo's, for the sick
Sterile city that heaven has abandoned.
Suppose the oracle had given you no command:
Should this defilement go uncleansed for ever?
You should have found the murderer: your king,   *40*
A noble king, had been destroyed!

                          Now I,
Having the power that he held before me,
Having his bed, begetting children there
Upon his wife, as he would have, had he lived—
Their son would have been my children's brother,   *45*
If Laios had had luck in fatherhood!
(And now his bad fortune has struck him down)—
I say I take the son's part, just as though
I were his son, to press the fight for him
And see it won! I'll find the hand that brought   *50*
Death to Labdakos' and Polydoros' child,
Heir of Kadmos' and Agenor's line.[16]

---

[16]Labdakos, Polydoros, Kadmos, Agenor, father, grandfather, great-grandfather, and great-great-
grandfather of Laios.

And as for those who fail me,
May the gods deny them the fruit of the earth,
Fruit of the womb, and may they rot utterly!   55
Let them be wretched as we are wretched, and worse!

For you, for loyal Thebans, and for all
Who find my actions right, I pray the favor
Of justice, and of all the immortal gods.
CHORAGOS. Since I am under oath, my lord, I swear   60
    I did not do the murder, I can not name
    The murderer. Phoibos ordained the search;
    Why did he not say who the culprit was?
OEDIPUS. An honest question. But no man in the world
    Can make the gods do more than the gods will.   65
CHORAGOS. There is an alternative, I think—
OEDIPUS.   Tell me.
    Any or all, you must not fail to tell me.
CHORAGOS. A lord clairvoyant to the lord Apollo,
    As we all know, is the skilled Teiresias.
    One might learn much about this from him, Oedipus.   70
OEDIPUS. I am not wasting time:
    Kreon spoke of this, and I have sent for him—
    Twice, in fact; it is strange that he is not here.
CHORAGOS. The other matter—that old report—seems useless.
OEDIPUS. What was that? I am interested in all reports.   75
CHORAGOS. The king was said to have been killed by highwaymen.
OEDIPUS. I know. But we have no witnesses to that.
CHORAGOS. If the killer can feel a particle of dread,
    Your curse will bring him out of hiding!
OEDIPUS.   No.
    The man who dared that act will fear no curse.   80

(*Enter the blind seer Teiresias, led by a Page.*)

CHORAGOS. But there is one man who may detect the criminal.
    This is Teiresias, this is the holy prophet
    In whom, alone of all men, truth was born.
OEDIPUS. Teiresias: seer: student of mysteries,
    Of all that's taught and all that no man tells,   85
    Secrets of Heaven and secrets of the earth:
    Blind though you are, you know the city lies
    Sick with plague; and from this plague, my lord,
    We find that you alone can guard or save us.

632

Possibly you did not hear the messengers? 90
Apollo, when we sent to him,
Sent us back word that this great pestilence
Would lift, but only if we established clearly
The identity of those who murdered Laios.
They must be killed or exiled.

                                            Can you use 95

Birdflight[17] or any art of divination
To purify yourself, and Thebes, and me
From this contagion? We are in your hands.
There is no fairer duty
Than that of helping others in distress. 100
TEIRESIAS. How dreadful knowledge of the truth can be
    When there's no help in truth! I knew this well,
    But did not act on it; else I should not have come.
OEDIPUS. What is troubling you? Why are your eyes so cold?
TEIRESIAS. Let me go home. Bear your own fate, and I'll 105
    Bear mine. It is better so: trust what I say.
OEDIPUS. What you say is ungracious and unhelpful
    To your native country. Do not refuse to speak.
TEIRESIAS. When it comes to speech, your own is neither temperate
    Nor opportune. I wish to be more prudent. 110
OEDIPUS. In God's name, we all beg you—
TEIRESIAS.   You are all ignorant.
    No; I will never tell you what I know.
    Now it is my misery; then, it would be yours.
OEDIPUS. What! You do know something, and will not tell us?
    You would betray us all and wreck the State? 115
TEIRESIAS. I do not intend to torture myself, or you.
    Why persist in asking? You will not persuade me.
OEDIPUS. What a wicked old man you are! You'd try a stone's
    Patience! Out with it! Have you no feeling at all?
TEIRESIAS. You call me unfeeling. If you could only see 120
    The nature of your own feelings . . .
OEDIPUS.   Why,
    Who would not feel as I do? Who could endure
    Your arrogance toward the city?
TEIRESIAS.   What does it matter?
    Whether I speak or not, it is bound to come.

---

[17]Prophets predicted the future by observing the flight of birds.

OEDIPUS. Then, if "it" is bound to come, you are bound to tell me. *125*
TEIRESIAS. No, I will not go on. Rage as you please.
OEDIPUS. Rage? Why not!
>   And I'll tell you what I think:
> You planned it, you had it done, you all but
> Killed him with your own hands: if you had eyes,
> I'd say the crime was yours, and yours alone. *130*
TEIRESIAS. So? I charge you, then,
> Abide by the proclamation you have made:
> From this day forth
> Never speak again to these men or to me;
> You yourself are the pollution of this country. *135*
OEDIPUS. You dare say that! Can you possibly think you have
> Some way of going free, after such insolence?
TEIRESIAS. I have gone free. It is the truth sustains me.
OEDIPUS. Who taught you shamelessness? It was not your craft.
TEIRESIAS. You did. You made me speak. I did not want to. *140*
OEDIPUS. Speak what? Let me hear it again more clearly.
TEIRESIAS. Was it not clear before? Are you tempting me?
OEDIPUS. I did not understand it. Say it again.
TEIRESIAS. I say that you are the murderer whom you seek.
OEDIPUS. Now twice you have spat out infamy.
> You'll pay for it! *145*
TEIRESIAS. Would you care for more? Do you wish to be really angry?
OEDIPUS. Say what you will. Whatever you say is worthless.
TEIRESIAS. I say you live in hideous shame with those
> Most dear to you. You can not see the evil.
OEDIPUS. Can you go on babbling like this for ever? *150*
TEIRESIAS. I can, if there is power in truth.
OEDIPUS.   There is:
> But not for you, not for you,
> You sightless, witless, senseless, mad old man!
TEIRESIAS. You are the madman. There is no one here
> Who will not curse you soon, as you curse me. *155*
OEDIPUS. You child of total night! I would not touch you;
> Neither would any man who sees the sun.
TEIRESIAS. True: it is not from you my fate will come.
> That lies within Apollo's competence,
> As it is his concern.
OEDIPUS.   Tell me, who made *160*
> These fine discoveries? Kreon? or someone else?

TEIRESIAS. Kreon is no threat. You weave your own doom.
OEDIPUS. Wealth, power, craft of statemanship!
    Kingly position, everywhere admired!
    What savage envy is stored up against these,   *165*
    If Kreon, whom I trusted, Kreon my friend,
    For this great office which the city once
    Put in my hands unsought—if for this power
    Kreon desires in secret to destroy me!

    He has bought this decrepit fortune-teller, this   *170*
    Collector of dirty pennies, this prophet fraud—
    Why, he is no more clairvoyant than I am!
                                                Tell us:
    Has your mystic mummery ever approached the truth?
    When that hellcat the Sphinx was performing here,
    What help were you to these people?   *175*
    Her magic was not for the first man who came along:
    It demanded a real exorcist. Your birds—
    What good were they? or the gods, for the matter of that?
    But I came by,
    Oedipus, the simple man, who knows nothing—   *180*
    I thought it out for myself, no birds helped me!
    And this is the man you think you can destroy,
    That you may be close to Kreon when he's king!
    Well, you and your friend Kreon, it seems to me,
    Will suffer most. If you were not an old man,   *185*
    You would have paid already for your plot.
CHORAGOS. We can not see that his words or yours
    Have been spoken except in anger, Oedipus,
    And of anger we have no need. How to accomplish
    The god's will best: that is what most concerns us.   *190*
TEIRESIAS. You are a king. But where argument's concerned
    I am your man, as much a king as you.
    I am not your servant, but Apollo's.
    I have no need of Kreon or Kreon's name.

    Listen to me. You mock my blindness, do you?   *195*
    But I say that you, with both your eyes, are blind:
    You can not see the wretchedness of your life,
    Nor in whose house you live, no, nor with whom.
    Who are your father and mother? Can you tell me?

You do not even know the blind wrongs   *200*
That you have done them, on earth and in the world below.
But the double lash of your parents' curse will whip you
Out of this land some day, with only night
Upon your precious eyes.
Your cries then—where will they not be heard?   *205*
What fastness of Kithairon[18] will not echo them?
And that bridal-descant of yours—you'll know it then,
The song they sang when you came here to Thebes
And found your misguided berthing.
All this, and more, that you can not guess at now,   *210*
Will bring you to yourself among your children.

Be angry, then. Curse Kreon. Curse my words.
I tell you, no man that walks upon the earth
Shall be rooted out more horribly than you.   *215*
OEDIPUS. Am I to bear this from him?—Damnation
   Take you! Out of this place! Out of my sight!
TEIRESIAS. I would not have come at all if you had not asked me.
OEDIPUS. Could I have told that you'd talk nonsense, that
   You'd come here to make a fool of yourself, and of me?
TEIRESIAS. A fool? Your parents thought me sane enough.   *220*
OEDIPUS. My parents again!—Wait: who were my parents?
TEIRESIAS. This day will give you a father, and break your heart.
OEDIPUS. Your infantile riddles! Your damned abracadabra!
TEIRESIAS. You were a great man once at solving riddles.
OEDIPUS. Mock me with that if you like; you will find it true.   *225*
TEIRESIAS. It was true enough. It brought about your ruin.
OEDIPUS. But if it saved this town?
TEIRESIAS (*to the Page*).   Boy, give me your hand.
OEDIPUS.   Yes, boy; lead him away.
   —While you are here
   We can do nothing. Go; leave us in peace.
TEIRESIAS. I will go when I have said what I have to say.   *230*
   How can you hurt me? And I tell you again:
   The man you have been looking for all this time,
   The damned man, the murderer of Laios,
   That man is in Thebes. To your mind he is foreign-born,   *235*
   But it will soon be shown that he is a Theban,

---

[18]As a baby, Oedipus was abandoned at this mountain.

A revelation that will fail to please.

A blind man,

Who has his eyes now; a penniless man, who is rich now;
And he will go tapping the strange earth with his staff.
To the children with whom he lives now he will be   240
Brother and father—the very same; to her
Who bore him, son and husband—the very same
Who came to his father's bed, wet with his father's blood.
Enough. Go think that over.
If later you find error in what I have said,   245
You may say that I have no skill in prophecy.

(*Exit Teiresias, led by his Page. Oedipus goes into the palace.*)

ODE[19] 1

Strophe 1

CHORUS. The Delphic stone of prophecies
　　Remembers ancient regicide
　　And a still bloody hand.
　　That killer's hour of flight has come.
　　He must be stronger than riderless   5
　　Coursers of untiring wind,
　　For the son of Zeus[20] armed with his father's thunder
　　Leaps in lightning after him;
　　And the Furies[21] hold his track, the sad Furies.

Antistrophe 1

　　Holy Parnassos'[22] peak of snow   10
　　Flashes and blinds that secret man,
　　That all shall hunt him down:
　　Though he may roam the forest shade
　　Like a bull gone wild from pasture
　　To rage through glooms of stone.   15

---

[19]Song sung by Chorus.

[20]Ruler of the Olympian gods.

[21]Goddesses of vengeance.

[22]Mountain sacred to Apollo.

Doom comes down on him; flight will not avail him;
For the world's heart calls him desolate,
And the immortal voices follow, for ever follow.

Strophe 2

But now a wilder thing is heard
From the old man skilled at hearing Fate in the wing-beat
   of a bird.   *20*
Bewildered as a blown bird, my soul hovers and can not find
Foothold in this debate, or any reason or rest of mind.
But no man ever brought—none can bring
Proof of strife between Thebes' royal house,
Labdakos' line, and the son of Polybos;[23]   *25*
And never until now has any man brought word
Of Laios' dark death staining Oedipus the King.

Antistrophe 2

Divine Zeus and Apollo hold
Perfect intelligence alone of all tales ever told;
And well though this diviner works, he works in his own night;   *30*
No man can judge that rough unknown or trust in second sight,
For wisdom changes hands among the wise.
Shall I believe my great lord criminal
At a raging word that a blind old man let fall?
I saw him, when the carrion woman[24] faced him of old,   *35*
Prove his heroic mind. These evil words are lies.

SCENE 2

KREON. Men of Thebes:
    I am told that heavy accusations
    Have been brought against me by King Oedipus.

    I am not the kind of man to bear this tamely.

    If in these present difficulties   5
    He holds me accountable for any harm to him

---

[23]King who adopted Oedipus.

[24]Sphinx

Through anything I have said or done—why, then,
I do not value life in this dishonor.
It is not as though this rumor touched upon
Some private indiscretion. The matter is grave.   *10*
The fact is that I am being called disloyal
To the State, to my fellow citizens, to my friends.
CHORAGOS. He may have spoken in anger, not from his mind.
KREON. But did you not hear him say I was the one
Who seduced the old prophet into lying?   *15*
CHORAGOS. The thing was said; I do not know how seriously.
KREON. But you were watching him! Were his eyes steady?
Did he look like a man in his right mind?
CHORAGOS.   I do not know.
I can not judge the behavior of great men.
But here is the king himself.

(*Enter Oedipus.*)

OEDIPUS.   So you dared come back. *20*
Why? How brazen of you to come to my house,
You murderer!
Do you think I do not know
That you plotted to kill me, plotted to steal my throne?
Tell me, in God's name: am I coward, a fool,
That you should dream you could accomplish this?   *25*
A fool who could not see your slippery game?
A coward, not to fight back when I saw it?
You are the fool, Kreon, are you not? hoping
Without support or friends to get a throne?
Thrones may be won or bought: you could do neither.   *30*
KREON. Now listen to me. You have talked; let me talk, too.
You can not judge unless you know the facts.
OEDIPUS. You speak well: there is one fact; but I find it hard
To learn from the deadliest enemy I have.
KREON. That above all I must dispute with you.   *35*
OEDIPUS. That above all I will not hear you deny.
KREON. If you think there is anything good in being stubborn.
Against all reason, then I say you are wrong.
OEDIPUS. If you think a man can sin against his own kind
And not be punished for it, I say you are mad.   *40*
KREON. I agree. But tell me: what have I done to you?
OEDIPUS. You advised me to send for that wizard, did you not?
KREON. I did. I should do it again.

OEDIPUS.   Very well. Now tell me:
>How long has it been since Laios—

KREON.   What of Laios?

OEDIPUS. Since he vanished in that onset by the road?   45

KREON. It was long ago, a long time.

OEDIPUS.   And this prophet,
>Was he practicing here then?

KREON.   He was; and with honor, as now.

OEDIPUS. Did he speak of me at that time?

KREON.   He never did,
>At least, not when I was present.

OEDIPUS.   But . . . the enquiry?
>I suppose you held one?

KREON.   We did, but we learned nothing.   50

OEDIPUS. Why did the prophet not speak against me then?

KREON. I do not know; and I am the kind of man
>Who holds his tongue when he has no facts to go on.

OEDIPUS. There's one fact that you know, and you could tell it.

KREON. What fact is that? If I know it, you shall have it.   55

OEDIPUS. If he were not involved with you, he could not say
>That it was I who murdered Laios.

KREON. If he says that, you are the one that knows it!—
>But now it is my turn to question you.

OEDIPUS. Put your questions. I am no murderer.   60

KREON. First, then: You married my sister?

OEDIPUS.   I married your sister.

KREON. And you rule the kingdom equally with her?

OEDIPUS. Everything that she wants she has from me.

KREON. And I am the third, equal to both of you?

OEDIPUS. That is why I call you a bad friend.   65

KREON. No. Reason it out, as I have done.
>Think of this first: would any sane man prefer
>Power, with all a king's anxieties,
>To that same power and the grace of sleep?
>Certainly not I.   70
>I have never longed for the king's power—only his rights.
>Would any wise man differ from me in this?
>As matters stand, I have my way in everything
>With your consent, and no responsibilities.
>If I were king, I should be a slave to policy.   75
>How could I desire a scepter more
>Than what is now mine—untroubled influence?

No, I have not gone mad; I need no honors,
Except those with the perquisites I have now.
I am welcome everywhere; every man salutes me,   *80*
And those who want your favor seek my ear,
Since I know how to manage what they ask.
Should I exchange this ease for that anxiety?
Besides, no sober mind is treasonable.
I hate anarchy   *85*
And never would deal with any man who likes it.
Test what I have said. Go to the priestess
At Delphi, ask if I quoted her correctly.
And as for this other thing: if I am found
Guilty of treason with Teiresias,   *90*
Then sentence me to death. You have my word
It is a sentence I should cast my vote for—
But not without evidence!
You do wrong
When you take good men for bad, bad men for good.
A true friend thrown aside—why, life itself   *95*
Is not more precious!
In time you will know this well:
For time, and time alone, will show the just man,
Though scoundrels are discovered in a day.
CHORAGOS. This is well said, and a prudent man would ponder it.
   Judgments too quickly formed are dangerous.   *100*
OEDIPUS. But is he not quick in his duplicity?
   And shall I not be quick to parry him?
   Would you have me stand still, hold my peace, and let
   This man win everything, through my inaction?
KREON. And you want—what is it, then? To banish me?   *105*
OEDIPUS. No, not exile. It is your death I want,
   So that all the world may see what treason means.
KREON. You will persist, then? You will not believe me?
OEDIPUS. How can I believe you?
KREON.   Then you are a fool.
OEDIPUS. To save myself?
KREON.   In justice, think of me. *110*
OEDIPUS. You are evil incarnate.
KREON.   But suppose that you are wrong?
OEDIPUS. Still I must rule.
KREON.   But not if you rule badly.
OEDIPUS. O city, city!

KREON. It is my city, too!

CHORAGOS. Now, my lords, be still. I see the queen,
Iokaste, coming from her palace chambers; 115
And it is time she came, for the sake of you both.
This dreadful quarrel can be resolved through her.

(*Enter Iokaste.*)

IOKASTE. Poor foolish men, what wicked din is this?
With Thebes sick to death, is it not shameful
That you should take some private quarrel up? 120
(*To Oedipus.*) Come into the house.
—And you, Kreon, go now:
Let us have no more of this tumult over nothing.

KREON. Nothing? No, sister: what your husband plans for me
Is one of two great evils: exile or death.

OEDIPUS. He is right.
Why, woman I have caught him squarely 125
Plotting against my life.

KREON. No! Let me die
Accurst if ever I have wished you harm!

IOKASTE. Ah, believe it, Oedipus!
In the name of the gods, respect this oath of his
For my sake, for the sake of these people here! 130

Strophe 1

CHORAGOS. Open your mind to her, my lord. Be ruled by her, I beg you!

OEDIPUS. What would you have me do?

CHORAGOS. Respect Kreon's word. He has never spoken like a fool,
And now he has sworn an oath.

OEDIPUS. You know what you ask?

CHORAGOS. I do.

OEDIPUS. Speak on, then.

CHORAGOS. A friend so sworn should not be baited so, 135
In blind malice, and without final proof.

OEDIPUS. You are aware, I hope, that what you say
Means death for me, or exile at the least.

Strophe 2

CHORAGOS. No, I swear by Helios, first in heaven!
May I die friendless and accurst, 140

The worst of deaths, if ever I meant that!
It is the withering fields
That hurt my sick heart:
Must we bear all these ills,
And now your bad blood as well?   *145*
OEDIPUS. Then let him go. And let me die, if I must,
    Or be driven by him in shame from the land of Thebes.
    It is your unhappiness, and not his talk,
    That touches me.

                                       As for him—
    Wherever he goes, hatred will follow him.   *150*
KREON. Ugly in yielding, as you were ugly in rage!
    Natures like yours chiefly torment themselves.
OEDIPUS. Can you not go? Can you not leave me?
KREON.   I can.
    You do not know me; but the city knows me,
    And in its eyes I am just, if not in yours.   *155*

(*Exit Kreon.*)

Antistrophe 1

CHORAGOS. Lady Iokaste, did you not ask the King to go to his
    chambers?
IOKASTE. First tell me what has happened.
CHORAGOS. There was suspicion without evidence; yet it rankled
    As even false charges will.
IOKASTE. On both sides?
CHORAGOS.   On both.
IOKASTE.   But what was said? *160*
CHORAGOS. Oh let it rest, let it be done with!
    Have we not suffered enough?
OEDIPUS. You see to what your decency has brought you:
    You have made difficulties where my heart saw none.

Antistrophe 2

CHORAGOS. Oedipus, it is not once only I have told you—   *165*
    You must know I should count myself unwise
    To the point of madness, should I now forsake you—
    You, under whose hand,
    In the storm of another time,
    Our dear land sailed out free.   *170*
    But now stand fast at the helm!

IOKASTE. In God's name, Oedipus, inform your wife as well:
Why are you so set in this hard anger?
OEDIPUS. I will tell you, for none of these men deserves
My confidence as you do. It is Kreon's work,   *175*
His treachery, his plotting against me.
IOKASTE. Go on, if you can make this clear to me.
OEDIPUS. He charges me with the murder of Laios.
IOKASTE. Has he some knowledge? Or does he speak from hearsay?
OEDIPUS. He would not commit himself to such a charge,   *180*
But he has brought in that damnable soothsayer
To tell his story.
IOKASTE.   Set your mind at rest.
If it is a question of soothsayers, I tell you
That you will find no man whose craft gives knowledge
Of the unknowable.
                                    Here is my proof: *185*
An oracle was reported to Laios once
(I will not say from Phoibos himself, but from
His appointed ministers, at any rate)
That his doom would be death at the hands of his own son—
His son, born of his flesh and of mine!   *190*

Now, you remember the story: Laios was killed
By marauding strangers where three highways meet;
But his child had not been three days in this world
Before the king had pierced the baby's ankles
And left him to die on a lonely mountainside.   *195*

Thus, Apollo never caused that child
To kill his father, and it was not Laios' fate
To die at the hands of his son, as he had feared.
This is what prophets and prophecies are worth!
Have no dread of them.
                                    It is God himself *200*
Who can show us what he wills, in his own way.
OEDIPUS. How strange a shadowy memory crossed my mind,
Just now while you were speaking; it chilled my heart.
IOKASTE. What do you mean? What memory do you speak of?
OEDIPUS. If I understand you, Laios was killed   *205*
At a place where three roads meet.

IOKASTE. So it was said;
    We have no later story.
OEDIPUS. Where did it happen?
IOKASTE. Phokis, it is called: at a place where the Theban Way
    Divides into the roads toward Delphi and Daulia.
OEDIPUS. When?
IOKASTE. We had the news not long before you came   *210*
    And proved the right to your succession here.
OEDIPUS. Ah, what net has God been weaving for me?
IOKASTE. Oedipus! Why does this trouble you?
OEDIPUS. Do not ask me yet.
    First, tell me how Laios looked, and tell me
    How old he was.
IOKASTE. He was tall, his hair just touched *215*
    With white; his form was not unlike your own.
OEDIPUS. I think that I myself may be accurst
    By my own ignorant edict.
IOKASTE. You speak strangely.
    It makes me tremble to look at you, my king.
OEDIPUS. I am not sure that the blind man can not see.   *220*
    But I should know better if you were to tell me—
IOKASTE. Anything—though I dread to hear you ask it.
OEDIPUS. Was the king lightly escorted, or did he ride
    With a large company, as a ruler should?
IOKASTE. There were five men with him in all: one was a herald; *225*
    And a single chariot, which he was driving.
OEDIPUS. Alas, that makes it plain enough!

                               But who—
    Who told you how it happened?
IOKASTE. A household servant,
    The only one to escape.
OEDIPUS. And is he still
    A servant of ours?
IOKASTE. No; for when he came back at last *230*
    And found you enthroned in the place of the dead king,
    He came to me, touched my hand with his, and begged
    That I would send him away to the frontier district
    Where only the shepherds go—
    As far away from the city as I could send him.   *235*
    I granted his prayer; for although the man was a slave,
    He had earned more than this favor at my hands.

OEDIPUS. Can he be called back quickly?

IOKASTE.   Easily.

    But why?

OEDIPUS. I have taken too much upon myself

    Without enquiry; therefore I wish to consult him.   240

IOKASTE. Then he shall come.

                             But am I not one also

    To whom you might confide these fears of yours?

OEDIPUS. That is your right; it will not be denied you,

    Now least of all; for I have reached a pitch

    Of wild foreboding. Is there anyone   245

    To whom I should sooner speak?

    Polybos of Corinth is my father.

    My mother is a Dorian: Merope.

    I grew up chief among the men of Corinth

    Until a strange thing happened—   250

    Not worth my passion, it may be, but strange.

    At a feast, a drunken man maundering in his cups

    Cries out that I am not my father's son!

    I contained myself that night, though I felt anger

    And a sinking heart. The next day I visited   255

    My father and mother, and questioned them. They stormed,

    Calling it all the slanderous rant of a fool;

    And this relieved me. Yet the suspicion

    Remained always aching in my mind;

    I knew there was talk; I could not rest;   260

    And finally, saying nothing to my parents,

    I went to the shrine at Delphi.

    The god dismissed my question without reply;

    He spoke of other things.

                         Some were clear,

    Full of wretchedness, dreadful, unbearable: 265

    As, that I should lie with my own mother, breed

    Children from whom all men would turn their eyes;

    And that I should be my father's murderer.

    I heard all this, and fled. And from that day

    Corinth to me was only in the stars   270

Descending in that quarter of the sky,
As I wandered farther and farther on my way
To a land where I should never see the evil
Sung by the oracle. And I came to this country
Where, so you say, King Laios was killed.   *275*

I will tell you all that happened there, my lady.
There were three highways
Coming together at a place I passed;
And there a herald came towards me, and a chariot
Drawn by horses, with a man such as you describe   *280*
Seated in it. The groom leading the horses
Forced me off the road at his lord's command;
But as this charioteer lurched over towards me
I struck him in my rage. The old man saw me
And brought his double goad down upon my head   *285*
As I came abreast.

                   He was paid back, and more!
Swinging my club in this right hand I knocked him
Out of his car, and he rolled on the ground.

                           I killed him.

I killed them all.
Now if that stranger and Laios were—kin,   *290*
Where is a man more miserable than I?
More hated by the gods? Citizen and alien alike
Must never shelter me or speak to me—
I must be shunned by all.

                     And I myself
Pronounced this malediction upon myself!   *295*

Think of it: I have touched you with these hands,
These hands that killed your husband. What defilement!

Am I all evil, then? It must be so,
Since I must flee from Thebes, yet never again
See my own countrymen, my own country,   *300*
For fear of joining my mother in marriage
And killing Polybos, my father.

                      Ah,

If I was created so, born to this fate,
Who could deny the savagery of God?

O holy majesty of heavenly powers!   305
May I never see that day! Never!
Rather let me vanish from the race of men
Than know the abomination destined me!
CHORAGOS. We too, my lord, have felt dismay at this.
    But there is hope: you have yet to hear the shepherd.   310
OEDIPUS. Indeed, I fear no other hope is left me.
IOKASTE. What do you hope from him when he comes?
OEDIPUS.   This much:
    If his account of the murder tallies with yours,
    Then I am cleared.
IOKASTE.   What was it that I said
    Of such importance?
OEDIPUS.   Why, "marauders," you said,   315
    Killed the king, according to this man's story.
    If he maintains that still, if there were several,
    Clearly the guilt is not mine: I was alone.
    But if he says one man, singlehanded, did it,
    Then the evidence all points to me.   320
IOKASTE. You may be sure that he said there were several;
    And can he call back that story now? He can not.
    The whole city heard it as plainly as I.
    But suppose he alters some detail of it:
    He can not ever show that Laios' death   325
    Fulfilled the oracle: for Apollo said
    My child was doomed to kill him; and my child—
    Poor baby!—it was my child that died first.

    No. From now on, where oracles are concerned,
    I would not waste a second thought on any.   330
OEDIPUS. You may be right.
                              But come: let someone go
    For the shepherd at once. This matter must be settled.
IOKASTE. I will send for him.
    I would not wish to cross you in anything,
    And surely not in this.—Let us go in.   335

(*Exeunt into the palace.*)

ODE 2

Strophe 1

CHORUS. Let me be reverent in the ways of right,
    Lowly the paths I journey on;
    Let all my words and actions keep
    The laws of the pure universe
    From highest Heaven handed down.   *5*
    For Heaven is their bright nurse,
    Those generations of the realms of light;
    Ah, never of mortal kind were they begot,
    Nor are they slaves of memory, lost in sleep:
    Their Father is greater than Time, and ages not.   *10*

Antistrophe 1

    The tyrant is a child of Pride
    Who drinks from his great sickening cup
    Recklessness and vanity,
    Until from his high crest headlong
    He plummets to the dust of hope.   *15*
    That strong man is not strong.
    But let no fair ambition be denied;
    May God protect the wrestler for the State
    In government, in comely policy,
    Who will fear God, and on his ordinance wait.   *20*

Strophe 2

    Haughtiness and the high hand of disdain
    Tempt and outrage God's holy law;
    And any mortal who dares hold
    No immortal Power in awe
    Will be caught up in a net of pain: *25*
    The price for which his levity is sold.
    Let each man take due earnings, then,
    And keep his hands from holy things,
    And from blasphemy stand apart—
    Else the crackling blast of heaven   *30*
    Blows on his head, and on his desperate heart.
    Though fools will honor impious men,
    In their cities no tragic poet sings.

Antistrophe 2

Shall we lose faith in Delphi's obscurities,
We who have heard the world's core   35
Discredited, and the sacred wood
Of Zeus at Elis praised no more?
The deeds and the strange prophecies
Must make a pattern yet to be understood.
Zeus, if indeed you are lord of all,   40
Throned in light over night and day,
Mirror this in your endless mind:
Our masters call the oracle
Words on the wind, and the Delphic vision blind!
Their hearts no longer know Apollo,   45
And reverence for the gods has died away.

SCENE 3

Enter Iokaste.

IOKASTE. Princes of Thebes, it has occurred to me
   To visit the altars of the gods, bearing
   These branches as a suppliant, and this incense.
   Our king is not himself: his noble soul
   Is overwrought with fantasies of dread,   5
   Else he would consider
   The new prophecies in the light of the old.
   He will listen to any voice that speaks disaster,
   And my advice goes for nothing. (*She approaches the
      altar, right.*)
                                        To you, then, Apollo,
   Lycean lord, since you are nearest, I turn in prayer   10
   Receive these offerings, and grant us deliverance
   From defilement. Our hearts are heavy with fear
   When we see our leader distracted, as helpless sailors
   Are terrified by the confusion of their helmsman.

(*Enter Messenger.*)

MESSENGER. Friends, no doubt you can direct me: 15
   Where shall I find the house of Oedipus,
   Or, better still, where is the king himself?
CHORAGOS. It is this very place, stranger; he is inside.
   This is his wife and mother of his children.

MESSENGER. I wish her happiness in a happy house,   *20*
    Blest in all the fulfillment of her marriage.
IOKASTE. I wish as much for you: your courtesy
    Deserves a like good fortune. But now, tell me:
    Why have you come? What have you to say to us?
MESSENGER. Good news, my lady, for your house and your husband. *25*
IOKASTE. What news? Who sent you here?
MESSENGER.   I am from Corinth.
    The news I bring ought to mean joy for you,
    Though it may be you will find some grief in it.
IOKASTE. What is it? How can it touch us in both ways?
MESSENGER. The word is that the people of the Isthmus   *30*
    Intend to call Oedipus to be their king.
IOKASTE. But old King Polybos—is he not reigning still?
MESSENGER. No. Death holds him in his sepulchre.
IOKASTE. What are you saying? Polybos is dead?
MESSENGER. If I am not telling the truth, may I die myself.   *35*
IOKASTE (*to a Maidservant*). Go in, go quickly; tell this to your master.
    O riddlers of God's will, where are you now!
    This was the man whom Oedipus, long ago,
    Feared so, fled so, in dread of destroying him—
    But it was another fate by which he died.   *40*

(*Enter Oedipus, center.*)

OEDIPUS. Dearest Iokaste, why have you sent for me?
IOKASTE. Listen to what this man says, and then tell me
    What has become of the solemn prophecies.
OEDIPUS. Who is this man? What is his news for me?
IOKASTE. He has come from Corinth to announce your father's
    death!   *45*
OEDIPUS. Is it true, stranger? Tell me in your own words.
MESSENGER. I can not say it more clearly: the king is dead.
OEDIPUS. Was it by treason? Or by an attack of illness?
MESSENGER. A little thing brings old men to their rest.
OEDIPUS. It was sickness, then?
MESSENGER.   Yes, and his many years. *50*
OEDIPUS. Ah!
    Why should a man respect the Pythian hearth,[25] or
    Give heed to the birds that jangle above his head?

---

[25]Delphi

They prophesied that I should kill Polybos,
Kill my own father; but he is dead and buried, 55
And I am here—I never touched him, never,
Unless he died of grief for my departure,
And thus, in a sense, through me. No. Polybos
Has packed the oracles off with him underground.
They are empty words.
IOKASTE. Had I not told you so? 60
OEDIPUS. You had; it was my faint heart that betrayed me.
IOKASTE. From now on never think of those things again.
OEDIPUS. And yet—must I not fear my mother's bed?
IOKASTE. Why should anyone in this world be afraid
Since Fate rules us and nothing can be foreseen? 65
A man should live only for the present day.

Have no more fear of sleeping with your mother:
How many men, in dreams, have lain with their mothers!
No reasonable man is troubled by such things.
OEDIPUS. That is true, only— 70
If only my mother were not still alive!
But she is alive. I can not help my dread.
IOKASTE. Yet this news of your father's death is wonderful.
OEDIPUS. Wonderful. But I fear the living woman.
MESSENGER. Tell me, who is this woman that you fear? 75
OEDIPUS. It is Merope, man; the wife of King Polybos.
MESSENGER. Merope? Why should you be afraid of her?
OEDIPUS. An oracle of the gods, a dreadful saying.
MESSENGER. Can you tell me about it or are you sworn to silence?
OEDIPUS. I can tell you, and I will. 80
Apollo said through his prophet that I was the man
Who should marry his own mother, shed his father's blood
With his own hands. And so, for all these years
I have kept clear of Corinth, and no harm has come—
Though it would have been sweet to see my parents again. 85
MESSENGER. And is this the fear that drove you out of Corinth?
OEDIPUS. Would you have me kill my father?
MESSENGER. As for that
You must be reassured by the news I gave you.
OEDIPUS. If you could reassure me, I would reward you.
MESSENGER. I had that in mind, I will confess: I thought 90
I could count on you when you returned to Corinth.

OEDIPUS. No. I will never go near my parents again.
MESSENGER. Ah, son, you still do not know what you are doing—
OEDIPUS. What do you mean? In the name of God tell me!
MESSENGER. —If these are your reasons for not going home.   95
OEDIPUS. I tell you, I fear the oracle may come true.
MESSENGER. And guilt may come upon you through your parents?
OEDIPUS. That is the dread that is always in my heart.
MESSENGER. Can you not see that all your fears are groundless?
OEDIPUS. Groundless? Am I not my parents' son?   100
MESSENGER. Polybos was not your father.
OEDIPUS.   Not my father?
MESSENGER. No more your father than the man speaking to you.
OEDIPUS. But you are nothing to me!
MESSENGER.   Neither was he.
OEDIPUS. Then why did he call me son?
MESSENGER.   I will tell you:
     Long ago he had you from my hands, as a gift.   105
OEDIPUS. Then how could he love me so, if I was not his?
MESSENGER. He had no children, and his heart turned to you.
OEDIPUS. What of you? Did you buy me? Did you find me by chance?
MESSENGER. I came upon you in the woody vales of Kithairon.
OEDIPUS. And what were you doing there?
MESSENGER.   Tending my flocks. 110
OEDIPUS. A wandering shepherd?
MESSENGER.   But your savior, son, that day.
OEDIPUS. From what did you save me?
MESSENGER.   Your ankles should tell you that.
OEDIPUS. Ah, stranger, why do you speak of that childhood pain?
MESSENGER. I pulled the skewer that pinned your feet together.
OEDIPUS. I have had the mark as long as I can remember.   115
MESSENGER. That was why you were given the name[26] you bear.
OEDIPUS. God! Was it my father or my mother who did it?
     Tell me!
MESSENGER.   I do not know. The man who gave you to me
     Can tell you better than I.
OEDIPUS. It was not you that found me, but another?   120
MESSENGER. It was another shepherd gave you to me.
OEDIPUS. Who was he? Can you tell me who he was?
MESSENGER. I think he was said to be one of Laios' people.

---

[26]Oedipus means "swollen foot."

OEDIPUS. You mean the Laios who was king here years ago?

MESSENGER. Yes; King Laios; and the man was one of his herdsmen. *125*

OEDIPUS. Is he still alive? Can I see him?

MESSENGER. These men here
    Know best about such things.

OEDIPUS. Does anyone here
    Know this shepherd that he is talking about?
    Have you seen him in the fields, or in the town?
    If you have, tell me. It is time things were made plain. *130*

CHORAGOS. I think the man he means is that same shepherd
    You have already asked to see. Iokaste perhaps
    Could tell you something.

OEDIPUS. Do you know anything
    About him, Lady? Is he the man we have summoned?
    Is that the man this shepherd means?

IOKASTE. Why think of him? *135*
    Forget this herdsman. Forget it all.
    This talk is a waste of time.

OEDIPUS. How can you say that,
    When the clues to my true birth are in my hands?

IOKASTE. For God's love, let us have no more questioning!
    Is your life nothing to you? *140*
    My own is pain enough for me to bear.

OEDIPUS. You need not worry. Suppose my mother a slave,
    And born of slaves: no baseness can touch you.

IOKASTE. Listen to me, I beg you: do not do this thing!

OEDIPUS. I will not listen; the truth must be made known. *145*

IOKASTE. Everything that I say is for your own good!

OEDIPUS. My own good
    Snaps my patience, then; I want none of it.

IOKASTE. You are fatally wrong! May you never learn who you are!

OEDIPUS. Go, one of you, and bring the shepherd here.
    Let us leave this woman to brag of her royal name. *150*

IOKASTE. Ah, miserable!
    That is the only word I have for you now.
    That is the only word I can ever have.

(*Exit into the palace.*)

CHORAGOS. Why has she left us, Oedipus? Why has she gone
    In such a passion of sorrow? I fear this silence: *155*
    Something dreadful may come of it.

OEDIPUS.   Let it come!
    However base my birth, I must know about it.
    The Queen, like a woman, is perhaps ashamed
    To think of my low origin. But I
    Am a child of Luck, I can not be dishonored.   *160*
    Luck is my mother; the passing months, my brothers,
    Have seen me rich and poor.
                            If this is so,
    How could I wish that I were someone else?
    How could I not be glad to know my birth?

ODE 3

Strophe

CHORUS. If ever the coming time were known
    To my heart's pondering,
    Kithairon, now by Heaven I see the torches
    At the festival of the next full moon
    And see the dance, and hear the choir sing   *5*
    A grace to your gentle shade:
    Mountain where Oedipus was found,
    O mountain guard of a noble race!
    May the god[27] who heals us lend his aid,
    And let that glory come to pass   *10*
    For our king's cradling-ground.

Antistrophe

    Of the nymphs that flower beyond the years,
    Who bore you, royal child,
    To Pan[28] of the hills or the timberline Apollo,
    Cold in delight where the upland clears,   *15*
    Or Hermes[29] for whom Kyllene's[30] heights are piled?
    Or flushed as evening cloud,

---

[27]Apollo

[28]God of nature, shepherds, and fertility; associated with lechery, and often represented as half-man, half-goat.

[29]Messenger of the gods.

[30]Mountain that was birthplace of Hermes.

Great Dionysos,[31] roamer of mountains,
He—was it he who found you there,
And caught you up in his own proud   *20*
Arms from the sweet god-ravisher
Who laughed by the Muses'[32] fountains?

SCENE 4

OEDIPUS. Sirs: though I do not know the man,
    I think I see him coming, this shepherd we want:
    He is old, like our friend here, and the men
    Bringing him seem to be servants of my house.
    But you can tell, if you have ever seen him.   *5*

(*Enter Shepherd escorted by Servants.*)

CHORAGOS. I know him, he was Laios' man. You can trust him.
OEDIPUS. Tell me first, you from Corinth: is this the shepherd
    We were discussing?
MESSENGER.   This is the very man.
OEDIPUS (*to Shepherd*). Come here. No, look at me.
    You must answer
    Everything I ask.—You belonged to Laios?   *10*
SHEPHERD. Yes: born his slave, brought up in his house.
OEDIPUS. Tell me: what kind of work did you do for him?
SHEPHERD. I was a shepherd of his, most of my life.
OEDIPUS. Where mainly did you go for pasturage?
SHEPHERD. Sometimes Kithairon, sometimes the hills near-by. *15*
OEDIPUS. Do you remember ever seeing this man out there?
SHEPHERD. What would he be doing there? This man?
OEDIPUS. This man standing here. Have you ever seen him before?
SHEPHERD. At least, not to my recollection.
MESSENGER. And that is not strange, my lord. But I'll refresh *20*
    His memory: he must remember when we two
    Spent three whole seasons together, March to September,
    On Kithairon or thereabouts. He had two flocks;
    I had one. Each autumn I'd drive mine home
    And he would go back with his to Laios' sheepfold.—   *25*
    Is this not true, just as I have described it?

---

[31]Another name for Bacchus.

[32]Group of sister goddesses, patrons of poetry, music, art, and sciences.

SHEPHERD. True, yes; but it was all so long ago.
MESSENGER. Well, then: do you remember, back in those days,
    That you gave me a baby boy to bring up as my own?
SHEPHERD. What if I did? What are you trying to say?   *30*
MESSENGER. King Oedipus was once that little child.
SHEPHERD. Damn you, hold your tongue!
OEDIPUS.   No more of that!
    It is your tongue needs watching, not this man's.
SHEPHERD. My king, my master, what is it I have done wrong?
OEDIPUS. You have not answered his question about the boy.   *35*
SHEPHERD. He does not know . . . He is only making trouble . . .
OEDIPUS. Come, speak plainly, or it will go hard with you.
SHEPHERD. In God's name, do not torture an old man!
OEDIPUS. Come here, one of you; bind his arms behind him.
SHEPHERD. Unhappy king! What more do you wish to learn?   *40*
OEDIPUS. Did you give this man the child he speaks of?
SHEPHERD.   I did.
    And I would to God I had died that very day.
OEDIPUS. You will die now unless you speak the truth.
SHEPHERD. Yet if I speak the truth, I am worse than dead.
OEDIPUS (*to Attendant*). He intends to draw it out, apparently—   *45*
SHEPHERD. No! I have told you already that I gave him the boy.
OEDIPUS. Where did you get him? From your house?
    From somewhere else?
SHEPHERD. Not from mine, no. A man gave him to me.
OEDIPUS. Is that man here? Whose house did he belong to?
SHEPHERD. For God's love, my king, do not ask me any more!   *50*
OEDIPUS. You are a dead man if I have to ask you again.
SHEPHERD. Then . . .Then the child was from the palace of Laios.
OEDIPUS. A slave child? or a child of his own line?
SHEPHERD. Ah, I am on the brink of dreadful speech!
OEDIPUS. And I of dreadful hearing. Yet I must hear.   *55*
SHEPHERD. If you must be told, then . . .
                     They said it was Laios' child;
    But it is your wife who can tell you about that.
OEDIPUS. My wife—Did she give it to you?
SHEPHERD.   My lord, she did.
OEDIPUS. Do you know why?
SHEPHERD.   I was told to get rid of it.
OEDIPUS. Oh heartless mother!
SHEPHERD.   But in dread of prophecies . . .   *60*

OEDIPUS. Tell me.

SHEPHERD.   It was said that the boy would kill his own father.

OEDIPUS. Then why did you give him over to this old man?

SHEPHERD. I pitied the baby, my king,
  And I thought that this man would take him far away
  To his own country.

                              He saved him—but for what a fate!   *65*
  For if you are what this man says you are,
  No man living is more wretched than Oedipus.

OEDIPUS. Ah God!
  It was true!

                              All the prophecies!
                                        —Now,

  O Light, may I look on you for the last time!   *70*
  I, Oedipus,
  Oedipus, damned in his birth, in his marriage damned,
  Damned in the blood he shed with his own hand!

(*He rushes into the palace.*)

ODE 4

Strophe 1

CHORUS. Alas for the seed of men.
  What measure shall I give these generations
  That breathe on the void and are void
  And exist and do not exist?
  Who bears more weight of joy   *5*
  Than mass of sunlight shifting in images,
  Or who shall make his thought stay on
  That down time drifts away?
  Your splendor is all fallen.
  O naked brow of wrath and tears,   *10*
  O change of Oedipus!
  I who saw your days call no man blest—
  Your great days like ghosts gone.

Antistrophe 1

  That mind was a strong bow.
  Deep, how deep you drew it then, hard archer,   *15*
  At a dim fearful range,

And brought dear glory down!
You overcame the stranger[33]—
The virgin with her hooking lion claws—
And though death sang, stood like a tower   *20*
To make pale Thebes take heart.
Fortress against our sorrow!
True king, giver of laws,
Majestic Oedipus!
No prince in Thebes had ever such renown,   *25*
No prince won such grace of power.

Strophe 2

And now of all men ever known
Most pitiful is this man's story:
His fortunes are most changed; his state
Fallen to a low slave's   *30*
Ground under bitter fate.
O Oedipus, most royal one!
The great door[34] that expelled you to the light
Gave at night—ah, gave night to your glory:
As to the father, to the fathering son.   *35*
All understood too late.
How could that queen whom Laios won,
The garden that he harrowed at his height,
Be silent when that act was done?

Antistrophe 2

But all eyes fail before time's eye,   *40*
All actions come to justice there.
Though never willed, though far down the deep past,
Your bed, your dread sirings,
Are brought to book at last.
Child by Laios doomed to die,   *45*
Then doomed to lose that fortunate little death,
Would God you never took breath in this air
That with my wailing lips I take to cry:

---

[33]The Sphinx

[34]Iokasate's womb

For I weep the world's outcast.
I was blind, and now I can tell why:
Asleep, for you had given ease of breath
To Thebes, while the false years went by.   *50*

EXODOS[35]

Enter, from the palace, Second Messenger.

SECOND MESSENGER. Elders of Thebes, most honored in this land,
    What horrors are yours to see and hear, what weight
    Of sorrow to be endured, if, true to your birth,
    You venerate the line of Labdakos!
    I think neither Istros nor Phasis, those great rivers,   *5*
    Could purify this place of all the evil
    It shelters now, or soon must bring to light—
    Evil not done unconsciously, but willed.

    The greatest griefs are those we cause ourselves.
CHORAGOS. Surely, friend, we have grief enough already;   *10*
    What new sorrow do you mean?
SECOND MESSENGER.   The queen is dead.
CHORAGOS. O miserable queen! But at whose hand?
SECOND MESSENGER.   Her own.
    The full horror of what happened you can not know,
    For you did not see it; but I, who did, will tell you
    As clearly as I can how she met her death.   *15*

    When she had left us,
    In passionate silence, passing through the court,
    She ran to her apartment in the house,
    Her hair clutched by the fingers of both hands.
    She closed the doors behind her; then, by that bed
    Where long ago the fatal son was conceived—   *20*
    That son who should bring about his father's death—
    We heard her call upon Laios, dead so many years,
    And heard her wail for the double fruit of her marriage,
    A husband by her husband, children by her child.   *25*

---

[35]Final scene

Exactly how she died I do not know:
For Oedipus burst in moaning and would not let us
Keep vigil to the end: it was by him
As he stormed about the room that our eyes were caught.
From one to another of us he went, begging a sword, 30
Hunting the wife who was not his wife, the mother
Whose womb had carried his own children and himself.
I do not know: it was none of us aided him,
But surely one of the gods was in control!
For with a dreadful cry 35
He hurled his weight, as though wrenched out of himself,
At the twin doors: the bolts gave, and he rushed in. ·
And there we saw her hanging, her body swaying
From the cruel cord she had noosed about her neck.
A great sob broke from him, heartbreaking to hear, 40
As he loosed the rope and lowered her to the ground.

I would blot out from my mind what happened next!
For the king ripped from her gown the golden brooches
That were her ornament, and raised them, and plunged them
    down
Straight into his own eyeballs, crying, "No more, 45
No more shall you look on the misery about me,
The horrors of my own doing! Too long you have known
The faces of those whom I should never have seen,
Too long been blind to those for whom I was searching!
From this hour, go in darkness!" And as he spoke, 50
He struck at his eyes—not once, but many times;
And the blood spattered his beard,
Bursting from his ruined sockets like red hail.
So from the unhappiness of two this evil has sprung,
A curse on the man and woman alike. The old 55
Happiness of the house of Labdakos
Was happiness enough: where is it today?
It is all wailing and ruin, disgrace, death—all
The misery of mankind that has a name—
And it is wholly and for ever theirs. 60
CHORAGOS. Is he in agony still? Is there no rest for him?
SECOND MESSENGER. He is calling for someone to open the doors
    wide
    So that all the children of Kadmos may look upon
    His father's murderer, his mother's—no,

I can not say it!

And then he will leave Thebes,   *65*

Self-exiled, in order that the curse
Which he himself pronounced may depart from the house.
He is weak, and there is none to lead him,
So terrible is his suffering.

But you will see:

Look, the doors are opening; in a moment   *70*
You will see a thing that would crush a heart of stone.

(*The central door is opened; Oedipus, blinded, is led in.*)

CHORAGOS. Dreadful indeed for men to see.
      Never have my own eyes
      Looked on a sight so full of fear.

      Oedipus!   *75*
      What madness came upon you, what demon
      Leaped on your life with heavier
      Punishment than a mortal man can bear?
      No: I can not even
      Look at you, poor ruined one.   *80*
      And I would speak, question, ponder,
      If I were able. No.
      You make me shudder.
CHORAGOS. God. God.
      Is there a sorrow greater?   *85*
      Where shall I find harbor in this world?
      My voice is hurled far on a dark wind.
      What has God done to me?
CHORAGOS. Too terrible to think of, or to see.

Strophe 1

OEDIPUS. O cloud of night,   *90*
      Never to be turned away: night coming on,
      I can not tell how: night like a shroud!
      My fair winds brought me here.

O God. Again

      The pain of the spikes where I had sight,
      The flooding pain   *95*
      Of memory, never to be gouged out.

CHORAGOS. This is not strange.
>You suffer it all twice over, remorse in pain,
>Pain in remorse.

Antistrophe 1

OEDIPUS. Ah dear friend   *100*
>Are you faithful even yet, you alone?
>Are you still standing near me, will you stay here,
>Patient, to care for the blind?

>>>>>The blind man!

>Yet even blind I know who it is attends me,
>By the voice's tone—   *105*
>Though my new darkness hide the comforter.
CHORAGOS. Oh fearful act!
>What god was it drove you to rake black
>Night across your eyes?

Strophe 2

OEDIPUS. Apollo. Apollo. Dear   *110*
>Children, the god was Apollo.
>He brought my sick, sick fate upon me.
>But the blinding hand was my own!
>How could I bear to see
>When all my sight was horror everywhere?   *115*
CHORAGOS. Everywhere; that is true.
OEDIPUS. And now what is left?
>Images? Love? A greeting even,
>Sweet to the senses? Is there anything?
>Ah, no, friends: lead me away.   *120*
>Lead me away from Thebes.

>>>>Lead the great wreck

>And hell of Oedipus, whom the gods hate.
CHORAGOS. Your misery, you are not blind to that.
>Would God you had never found it out!

Antistrophe 2

OEDIPUS. Death take the man who unbound   *125*
>My feet on that hillside
>And delivered me from death to life! What life?

663

If only I had died,
This weight of monstrous doom
Could not have dragged me and my darlings down.   130
CHORAGOS. I would have wished the same.
OEDIPUS. Oh never to have come here
With my father's blood upon me! Never
To have been the man they call his mother's husband!
Oh accurst! Oh child of evil,   135
To have entered that wretched bed—the selfsame one!
More primal than sin itself, this fell to me.
CHORAGOS. I do not know what words to offer you.
You were better dead than alive and blind.
OEDIPUS. Do not counsel me any more. This punishment   140
That I have laid upon myself is just.
If I had eyes,
I do not know how I could bear the sight
Of my father, when I came to the house of Death,
Or my mother: for I have sinned against them both   145
So vilely that I could not make my peace
By strangling my own life.

                Or do you think my children,
Born as they were born, would be sweet to my eyes?
Ah never, never! Nor this town with its high walls,
Nor the holy images of the gods.

                          For I, 150

Thrice miserable!—Oedipus, noblest of all the line
Of Kadmos, have condemned myself to enjoy
These things no more, by my own malediction
Expelling that man whom the gods declared
To be a defilement in the house of Laios.   155
After exposing the rankness of my own guilt,
How could I look men frankly in the eyes?
No, I swear it,
If I could have stifled my hearing at its source,
I would have done it and made all this body   160
A tight cell of misery, blank to light and sound:
So I should have been safe in my dark mind
Beyond external evil.

                      Ah Kithairon!
Why did you shelter me? When I was cast upon you,
Why did I not die? Then I should never   165
Have shown the world my execrable birth.

Ah Polybos! Corinth, city that I believed
The ancient seat of my ancestors: how fair
I seemed, your child! And all the while this evil
Was cancerous within me!

                                  For I am sick   *170*
In my own being, sick in my origin.
O three roads, dark ravine, woodland and way
Where three roads met; you, drinking my father's blood,
My own blood, spilled by my own hand: can you remember
The unspeakable things I did there, and the things   *175*
I went on from there to do?

                             O marriage, marriage!
The act that engendered me, and again the act
Performed by the son in the same bed—

                             Ah, the net
Of incest, mingling fathers, brothers, sons,
With brides, wives, mothers: the last evil   *180*
That can be known by men: no tongue can say
How evil!

               No. For the love of God, conceal me
Somewhere far from Thebes; or kill me; or hurl me
Into the sea, away from men's eyes for ever.

Come, lead me. You need nor fear to touch me.   *185*
Of all men, I alone can bear this guilt.

(*Enter Kreon.*)

CHORAGOS. Kreon is here now. As to what you ask,
    He may decide the course to take. He only
    Is left to protect the city in your place.
OEDIPUS. Alas, how can I speak to him? What right have I   *190*
    To beg his courtesy whom I have deeply wronged?
KREON. I have not come to mock you, Oedipus,
    Or to reproach you, either.
    (*To Attendants.*)—   You, standing there:
    If you have lost all respect for man's dignity,
    At least respect the flame of Lord Helios:[36]   *195*
    Do not allow this pollution to show itself
    Openly here, an affront to the earth

---

[36]Helios: sun god.

And Heaven's rain and the light of day. No, take him
Into the house as quickly as you can.
  For it is proper   *200*
That only the close kindred see his grief.
OEDIPUS. I pray you in God's name, since your courtesy
  Ignores my dark expectation, visiting
  With mercy this man of all men most execrable:
  Give me what I ask—for your good, not for mine.   *205*
KREON. And what is it that you turn to me begging for?
OEDIPUS. Drive me out of this country as quickly as may be
  To a place where no human voice can ever greet me.
KREON. I should have done that before now—only,
  God's will had not been wholly revealed to me.   *210*
OEDIPUS. But his command is plain: the parricide
  Must be destroyed. I am that evil man.
KREON. That is the sense of it, yes; but as things are,
  We had best discover clearly what is to be done.
OEDIPUS. You would learn more about a man like me?   *215*
KREON. You are ready now to listen to the god.
OEDIPUS. I will listen. But it is to you
  That I must turn for help. I beg you, hear me.

  The woman is there—
  Give her whatever funeral you think proper: *220*
  She is your sister.
                          —But let me go, Kreon!
  Let me purge my father's Thebes of the pollution
  Of my living here, and go out to the wild hills,
  To Kithairon, that has won such fame with me,
  The tomb my mother and father appointed for me,   *225*
  And let me die there, as they willed I should.
  And yet I know
  Death will not ever come to me through sickness
  Or in any natural way: I have been preserved
  For some unthinkable fate. But let that be.   *230*

  As for my sons, you need not care for them.
  They are men, they will find some way to live.
  But my poor daughters, who have shared my table,
  Who never before have been parted from their father—
  Take care of them, Kreon; do this for me.   *235*

And will you let me touch them with my hands
A last time, and let us weep together?
Be kind, my lord,
Great prince, be kind!

Could I but touch them,

They would be mine again, as when I had my eyes.   *240*

(*Enter Antigone and Ismene, attended.*)

Ah, God!
Is it my dearest children I hear weeping?
Has Kreon pitied me and sent my daughters?
KREON. Yes, Oedipus: I knew that they were dear to you
In the old days, and know you must love them still.   *245*
OEDIPUS. May God bless you for this—and be a friendlier
Guardian to you than he has been to me!

Children, where are you?
Come quickly to my hands: they are your brother's—
Hands that have brought your father's once clear eyes   *250*
To this way of seeing—

Ah dearest ones,

I had neither sight nor knowledge then, your father
By the woman who was the source of his own life!
And I weep for you—having no strength to see you—,
I weep for you when I think of the bitterness   *255*
That men will visit upon you all your lives.
What homes, what festivals can you attend
Without being forced to depart again in tears?
And when you come to marriageable age,
Where is the man, my daughters, who would dare   *260*
Risk the bane that lies on all my children?
Is there any evil wanting? Your father killed
His father; sowed the womb of her who bore him;
Engendered you at the fount of his own existence!
That is what they will say of you.

Then, whom *265*

Can you ever marry? There are no bridegrooms for you,
And your lives must wither away in sterile dreaming.

O Kreon, son of Menoikeus!
You are the only father my daughters have,

Since we, their parents, are both of us gone for ever.   *270*
They are your own blood: you will not let them
Fall into beggary and loneliness;
You will keep them from the miseries that are mine!
Take pity on them; see, they are only children,
Friendless except for you. Promise me this,   *275*
Great prince, and give me your hand in token of it.

(*Kreon clasps his right hand.*)

Children:
I could say much, if you could understand me,
But as it is, I have only this prayer for you:
Live where you can, be as happy as you can—   *280*
Happier, please God, than God has made your father.

KREON. Enough. You have wept enough. Now go within.
OEDIPUS. I must, but it is hard.
KREON.   Time eases all things.
OEDIPUS. You know my mind, then?
KREON.   Say what you desire.
OEDIPUS. Send me from Thebes!
KREON.   God grant that I may! *285*
OEDIPUS. But since God hates me . . .
KREON.   No, he will grant your wish.
OEDIPUS. You promise?
KREON. I can not speak beyond my knowledge.
OEDIPUS. Then lead me in.
KREON. Come now, and leave your children.
OEDIPUS. No! Do not take them from me!
KREON.   Think no longer
That you are in command here, but rather think   *290*
How, when you were, you served your own destruction.

(*Exeunt into the house all but the Chorus; the Choragos chants directly to the audience.*)

CHORAGOS. Men of Thebes: look upon Oedipus.
This is the king who solved the famous riddle
And towered up, most powerful of men.
No mortal eyes but looked on him with envy,   *295*
Yet in the end ruin swept over him.

Let every man in mankind's frailty
Consider his last day; and let none
Presume on his good fortune until he find
Life, at his death, a memory without pain.   *300*

[C. 430 B.C.E.]

Alfred, Lord Tennyson
[1809–1892]

ALFRED TENNYSON'S *life spans most of the years of Queen Victoria's reign. He was born in a Lincolnshire rectory into a talented and literate family, the fourth child and one of eight sons and four daughters. All the children were brought up as intellectuals. Tennyson's publication of poetry included the works of his two brothers, Frederick and Charles* (Poems by Two Brothers, *1827*). *Tennyson looked the part of a poet, tall and slender with an elegant head, and he was quickly adopted by the artistic circle at school. At Trinity College, Cambridge, he became a member of the poets' club, The Apostles, where he met Arthur Henry Hallam, whose early death was to shape both Tennyson's temperament and his poetry. Before that event, however, Tennyson won the Chancellor's prize for a poem titled* Timbuctoo *and saw his first volume of poetry published in 1830,* Poems, Chiefly Lyrical. *His second volume appeared in 1832. In 1833, Hallam, by then engaged to Tennyson's sister, Emily, died in Vienna. Tennyson began his poem on faith and doubt,* In Memoriam, *that was eventually to make him famous. He worked on the poem for seventeen years. At the same time, he worked on* Idylls of the King, *a long work retelling the tales of King Arthur from Malory but molded into the Victorian mindset. In 1842, he published* Poems, *which included* Ulysses *and* Morte D'Arthur. *In 1847, his popular satire on women's place in the world,* Princess, *appeared. These were difficult times for Tennyson, despite the success of the latest poems. Then in 1850 he married Emily Sellwood and finally published* In Memoriam. *That year he was chosen to succeed Wordsworth as Poet Laureate. A long formal poem,* Ode on the Death of the Duke of Wellington *(1852) preceded* Maud *(1855), a romantic tale of love and death, followed by* Enoch Arden *and* Northern Farmer *(1964). He dedicated a new edition of* Idylls *to the memory of Queen Victoria's beloved husband Prince Albert, who had died in 1861, and became a great favorite of the queen. In 1884, he became Lord Tennyson and published* Becket, *a successful drama. In his last years, he wrote apace, publishing* Tiresias and Other Poems *in 1885,* Locksley Hall Sixty Years After *in 1886,* Demeter and Other Poems *in 1889, and* The Death of Oenone *in 1892, published just after his death. Assessments of Tennyson's work was, in turn, criticized and then praised in the past century. During most of the twentieth century, he was thought to be too ornate for most readers, but in time his poetic talent and his ability to bring sound and light to life were honored. Those who love a talented wordsmith and those who love a mythic vision of ancient England love Tennyson.*

The Eagle

ALFRED, LORD TENNYSON

He clasps the crag with crooked hands;
Close to the sun in lonely lands,
Ringed with the azure world, he stands.

The wrinkled sea beneath him crawls;
He watches from his mountain walls,   5
And like a thunderbolt he falls.

[1851]

First published in *Poems of Alfred Tennyson* in 1851.

Dylan Thomas
[1914–1953]

A popular image of the poet is, perhaps, as a hard-drinking, womanizing, rabble-rousing, egotistic, irresponsible, and ultimately tragic figure. No poet more conformed to this image than DYLAN THOMAS. *Born in the town of Swansea, Wales, Thomas attended Swansea Grammar School, dropped out of school at sixteen, and became a reporter for* The South Wales Daily Post. *By the age of twenty, he published his first book of poems, drawing high praise. Between 1936 and 1946 he published several more books of poems and prose, made radio broadcasts for the BBC, and by 1950 embarked on the first of his legendary reading tours of the United States. These readings captivated American audiences who were entranced by the force of Thomas's personality, his theatrical performances, and the emotional, lyrical intensity of his poetry.*

Thomas was, as another poet described him, "the maddest of the word-mad poets." Consistent with the Romantic, self-destructive image he cast, Thomas died at thirty-nine after a heavy bout of drinking at the renowned White Horse Tavern in New York City. Always productive, Thomas published In Country Sleep, And Other Poems *and his* Collected Poems *in 1952. In 1954 he published the memoir of his Welsh childhood,* A Child's Christmas in Wales *and a radio play,* Under Milk Wood, *which also recalls memories of the coastal town where he was raised.*

Do Not Go Gentle into That Good Night

DYLAN THOMAS

Do not go gentle into that good night,
Old age should burn and rave at close of day;
Rage, rage against the dying of the light.

Though wise men at their end know dark is right,
Because their words had forked no lightning they   5
Do not go gentle into that good night.

Good men, the last wave by, crying how bright
Their frail deeds might have danced in a green bay,
Rage, rage against the dying of the light.

Wild men who caught and sang the sun in flight,   10
And learn, too late, they grieved it on its way,
Do not go gentle into that good night.

Grave men, near death, who see with blinding sight
Blind eyes could blaze like meteors and be gay,
Rage, rage against the dying of the light.   15

And you, my father, there on the sad height,
Curse, bless, me now with your fierce tears, I pray.
Do not go gentle into that good night.
Rage, rage against the dying of the light.

[1952]

Reprinted from *The Poems of Dylan Thomas,* by permission of New Directions Publishing
Corp. Copyright © 1952 by Dylan Thomas.

John Updike
[1932–2009]

JOHN UPDIKE *was born and raised in Shillington, Pennsylvania, where his early academic success led to a scholarship to Harvard University. After graduating in 1954, Updike studied at the Ruskin School of Drawing and Fine Arts in Oxford, England, returning to the United States the following year to take a position on the staff of* The New Yorker, *where he worked under James Thurber for two years.*

The New Yorker *was also the venue for Updike's earliest publications, and he continued publishing fiction, poems, and essays in the magazine for decades after he left its staff. Updike is numbered among the most prolific contemporary writers, having published some fifty books. His second novel,* Rabbit, Run *(1960), inspired three sequels,* Rabbit Redux *(1972),* Rabbit is Rich *(1981), and* Rabbit at Rest, *(1990); each of the last two was awarded the Pulitzer Prize for fiction. Updike also received the Rosenthal Award from the National Institute of Arts and Letters (1959); the National Book Award in Fiction (1964); the O. Henry Prize (1967); the American Book Award (1982); the National Book Critics Circle Award for fiction (1982 and 1990); the National Arts Club Medal of Honor (1984); and both the National Medal of the Arts (1989) and the National Medal for the Humanities (2003).*

Among Updike's dozens of other notable publications include Bech: A Book *(1970), which introduced Henry Bech, a moderately successful Jewish-American novelist whom many read as Updike's fictional alter ego, and who returned in* Bech is Back *(1982) and* Bech at Bay *(1998). Updike's novel* The Witches of Eastwick *(1984) was adapted for a major motion picture starring Jack Nicholson. Many of his best short stories, such as "A&P," feature an eye for detail and an interest in sexuality and its repressions. These themes have characterized Updike's work throughout his career.*

For nearly five decades, Updike moved fluidly between multiple genres—novels, short stories, poetry, criticism, and other nonfiction—with equal grace. His realistic style, his masterful exploration of the conventions of prose narrative, and his attention to the nuances of life in postwar suburbia make Updike among the most beloved writers of the twentieth century.

A & P

JOHN UPDIKE

IN WALKS THESE THREE girls in nothing but bathing suits. I'm in the third check-out slot, with my back to the door, so I don't see them until they're over by the bread. The one that caught my eye first was the one in the plaid green two-piece. She was a chunky kid, with a good tan and a sweet broad soft-looking can with those two crescents of white just under it, where the sun never seems to hit, at the top of the backs of her legs. I stood there with my hand on a box of HiHo crackers trying to remember if I rang it up or not. I ring it up again and the customer starts giving me hell. She's one of these cash-register-watchers, a witch about fifty with rouge on her cheekbones and no eyebrows, and I know it made her day to trip me up. She'd been watching cash registers for fifty years and probably never seen a mistake before.

By the time I got her feathers smoothed and her goodies into a bag—she gives me a little snort in passing, if she'd been born at the right time they would have burned her over in Salem—by the time I get her on her way the girls had circled around the bread and were coming back, without a pushcart, back my way along the counters, in the aisle between the checkouts and the Special bins. They didn't even have shoes on. There was this chunky one, with the two-piece—it was bright green and the seams on the bra were still sharp and her belly was still pretty pale so I guessed she just got it (the suit)—there was this one, with one of those chubby berry-faces, the lips all bunched together under her nose, this one, and a tall one, with black hair that hadn't quite frizzed right, and one of these sunburns right across under the eyes, and a chin that was too long—you know, the kind of girl other girls think is very "striking" and "attractive" but never quite makes it, as they very well know, which is why they like her so much—and then the third one, that wasn't quite so tall. She was the queen. She kind of led them, the other two peeking around and making their shoulders round. She didn't look around, not this queen, she just walked straight on slowly, on these long white primadonna legs. She came down a little hard on her heels, as if she didn't walk in bare feet that much, putting down her heels and then letting the weight move along to her toes as if she was testing the floor with every step, putting a little deliberate extra

Reprinted from *Pigeon Feathers and Other Stories,* by permission of Alfred A. Knopf, a division of Random House, Inc. Copyright © 1962 and renewed 1990 by John Updike.

action into it. You never know for sure how girls' minds work (do you really think it's a mind in there or just a little buzz like a bee in a glass jar?) but you got the idea she had talked the other two into coming in here with her, and now she was showing them how to do it, walk slow and hold yourself straight.

She had on a kind of dirty-pink—beige maybe, I don't know—bathing suit with a little nubble all over it and, what got me, the straps were down. They were off her shoulders looped loose around the cool tops of her arms, and I guess as a result the suit had slipped a little on her, so all around the top of the cloth there was this shining rim. If it hadn't been there you wouldn't have known there could have been anything whiter than those shoulders. With the straps pushed off, there was nothing between the top of the suit and the top of her head except just *her* this clean bare plane of the top of her chest down from the shoulder bones like a dented sheet of metal tilted in the light. I mean, it was more than pretty.

She had a sort of oaky hair that sun and salt had bleached, done up in a bun that was unravelling, and a kind of prim face. Walking into the A & P with your straps down, I suppose it's the only kind of face you *can* have. She held her head so high her neck, coming up out of those white shoulders, looked kind of stretched, but I didn't mind. The longer her neck was, the more of her there was.

She must have felt in the corner of her eye me and over my shoulder Stokesie in the second slot watching, but she didn't tip. Not this queen. She kept her eyes moving across the racks, and stopped, and turned so slow it made my stomach rub the inside of my apron, and buzzed to the other two, who kind of huddled against her for relief, and then they all three of them went up the cat-and-dog-food-breakfast-cereal-macaroni-rice-raisins-seasonings-spreads-spaghetti-soft-drinks-crackers-and-cookies aisle. From the third slot I look straight up this aisle to the meat counter, and I watched them all the way. The fat one with the tan sort of fumbled with the cookies, but on second thought she put the package back. The sheep pushing their carts down the aisle—the girls were walking against the usual traffic (not that we have one-way signs or anything)—were pretty hilarious. You could see them, when Queenie's white shoulders dawned on them, kind of jerk, or hop, or hiccup, but their eyes snapped back to their own baskets and on they pushed. I bet you could set off dynamite in an A & P and the people would by and large keep reaching and checking oatmeal off their lists and muttering "Let me see, there was a third thing, began with A, asparagus, no, ah, yes, applesauce!" or whatever it is they do mutter. But there was no doubt, this jiggled them. A few house-slaves in pin curlers even looked around after pushing their carts past to make sure what they had seen was correct.

676

You know, it's one thing to have a girl in a bathing suit down on the beach, where what with the glare nobody can look at each other much anyway, and another thing in the cool of the A & P, under the fluorescent lights, against all those stacked packages, with her feet paddling along naked over our checkerboard green-and-cream rubber-tile floor.

"Oh Daddy," Stokesie said beside me. "I feel so faint."

"Darling," I said. "Hold me tight." Stokesie's married, with two babies chalked up on his fuselage already, but as far as I can tell that's the only difference. He's twenty-two, and I was nineteen this April.

"Is it done?" he asks, the responsible married man finding his voice. I forgot to say he thinks he's going to be manager some sunny day, maybe in 1990 when it's called the Great Alexandrov and Petrooshki Tea Company or something.

What he meant was, our town is five miles from a beach, with a big summer colony out on the Point, but we're right in the middle of town, and the women generally put on a shirt or shorts or something before they get out of the car into the street. And anyway these are usually women with six children and varicose veins mapping their legs and nobody, including them, could care less. As I say, we're right in the middle of town, and if you stand at our front doors you can see two banks and the Congregational church and the newspaper store and three real-estate offices and about twenty-seven old freeloaders tearing up Central Street because the sewer broke again. It's not as if we're on the Cape; we're north of Boston and there's people in this town haven't seen the ocean for twenty years.

The girls had reached the meat counter and were asking McMahon something. He pointed, they pointed, and they shuffled out of sight behind a pyramid of Diet Delight peaches. All that was left for us to see was old McMahon patting his mouth and looking after them sizing up their joints. Poor kids, I began to feel sorry for them, they couldn't help it.

Now here comes the sad part of the story, at least my family says it's sad, but I don't think it's so sad myself. The store's pretty empty, it being Thursday afternoon, so there was nothing much to do except lean on the register and wait for the girls to show up again. The whole store was like a pinball machine and I didn't know which tunnel they'd come out of. After a while they come around out of the far aisle, around the light bulbs, records at discount of the Caribbean Six or Tony Martin Sings or some such gunk you wonder they waste wax on, six-packs of candy bars, and plastic toys done up in cellophane that fall apart when a kid looks at them anyway. Around they come, Queenie still leading the way, and holding a little gray jar in her hand. Slots Three through Seven are unmanned and I could see her wondering between Stokes and me, but Stokesie with his usual luck draws an old party in baggy gray pants who stumbles up with four giant cans of pineapple juice (what do these bums *do* with all that pineapple juice? I've often asked myself) so the girls come to me. Queenie puts down the jar and I take it into my fingers icy cold. Kingfish Fancy Herring Snacks in Pure Sour Cream: 49¢. Now her hands are empty, not a ring or a bracelet, bare as God made them, and I wonder where the money's coming from. Still with that prim look she lifts a folded dollar bill out of the hollow at the center of her nubbled pink top. The jar went heavy in my hand. Really, I thought that was so cute.

Then everybody's luck begins to run out. Lengel comes in from haggling with a truck full of cabbages on the lot and is about to scuttle into the door marked MANAGER behind which he hides all day when the girls touch his eye. Lengel's pretty dreary, teaches Sunday school and the rest, but he doesn't miss that much. He comes over and says, "Girls, this isn't the beach."

Queenie blushes, though maybe it's just a brush of sunburn I was noticing for the first time, now that she was so close. "My mother asked me to pick up a jar of herring snacks." Her voice kind of startled me, the way voices do when you see the people first, coming out so flat and dumb yet kind of tony, too, the way it ticked over "pick up" and "snacks." All of a sudden I slid right down her voice into her living room. Her father and the other men were standing around in ice-cream coats and bow ties and the women were in sandals picking up herring snacks on toothpicks off a big glass plate and they were all holding drinks the color of water with olives and sprigs of mint in them. When my parents have somebody over they get lemonade and if it's a real racy affair Schlitz in tall glasses with "They Do It Every Time" cartoons stencilled on.

"That's all right," Lengel said. "But this isn't the beach." His repeating this struck me as funny, as if it had just occurred to him, and he had been thinking all these years the A & P was a great big dune and he was the head lifeguard. He didn't like my smiling—as I say he doesn't miss much—but he concentrates on giving the girls that sad Sunday-school-superintendent stare.

Queenie's blush is no sunburn now, and the plump one in plaid, that I liked better from the back—a really sweet can—pipes up, "We weren't doing any shopping. We just came in for one thing."

"That makes no difference," Lengel tells her, and I could see from the way his eyes went that he hadn't noticed she was wearing a two-piece before. "We want you decently dressed when you come in here."

"We *are* decent," Queenie says suddenly, her lower lip pushing, getting sore now that she remembers her place, a place from which the crowd that runs the A & P must look pretty crummy. Fancy Herring Snacks flashed in her very blue eyes.

"Girls, I don't want to argue with you. After this come in here with your shoulders covered. It's our policy." He turns back. That's policy for you. Policy is what the kingpins want. What the others want is juvenile delinquency.

All this while, the customers had been showing up with their carts but, you know, sheep, seeing a scene, they had all bunched up on Stokesie, who shook open a paper bag as gently as peeling a peach, not wanting to miss a word. I could feel in the silence everybody getting nervous, most of all Lengel, who asks me, "Sammy, have you rung up their purchase?"

I thought and said "No" but it wasn't about that I was thinking. I go through the punches, 4, 9, GROC, TOT—it's more complicated than you think, and after you do it often enough, it begins to make a little song, that you hear words to, in my case "Hello (*bing*) there, you (*gung*) hap-py peepul (*splat*)"— the *splat* being the drawer flying out. I uncreased the bill, tenderly as you may imagine, it just having come from between the two smoothest scoops of vanilla I had ever known there were, and pass a half and a penny into her narrow pink palm, and nestle the herrings in a bag and twist its neck and hand it over, all the time thinking.

The girls, and who'd blame them, are in a hurry to get out, so I say "I quit" to Lengel quick enough for them to hear, hoping they'll stop and watch me, their unsuspected hero. They keep right on going, into the electric eye; the door flies open and they flicker across the lot to their car, Queenie and Plaid and Big Tall Goony-Goony (not that as raw material she was so bad), leaving me with Lengel and a kink in his eyebrow.

"Did you say something, Sammy?"

"I said I quit."

"I thought you did."

"You didn't have to embarrass them."

"It was they who were embarrassing us."

I started to say something that came out "Fiddle-de-doo." It's a saying of my grandmother's, and I know she would have been pleased.

"I don't think you know what you're saying." Lengel said.

"I know you don't," I said. "But I do." I pull the bow at the back of my apron and start shrugging it off my shoulders. A couple of customers that had been heading for my slot begin to knock against each other, like scared pigs in a chute.

Lengel sighs and begins to look very patient and old and gray. He's been a friend of my parents for years. "Sammy, you don't want to do this to your Mom and Dad," he tells me. It's true, I don't. But it seems to me that once you begin a gesture it's fatal not to go through with it. I fold the apron, "Sammy" stitched in red on the pocket, and put it on the counter, and drop the bow tie on top of it. The bow tie is theirs, if you've ever wondered. "You'll feel this for

679

the rest of your life," Lengel says, and I know that's true, too, but remembering how he made that pretty girl blush makes me so scrunchy inside I punch the No Sale tab and the machine whirs "pee-pul" and the drawer splats out. One advantage to this scene taking place in summer, I can follow this up with a clean exit, there's no fumbling around getting your coat and galoshes, I just saunter into the electric eye in my white shirt that my mother ironed the night before, and the door heaves itself open, and outside the sunshine is skating around on the asphalt.

I look around for my girls, but they're gone, of course. There wasn't anybody but some young married screaming with her children about some candy they didn't get by the door of a powder-blue Falcon station wagon. Looking back in the big windows, over the bags of peat moss and aluminum lawn furniture stacked on the pavement, I could see Lengel in my place in the slot, checking the sheep through. His face was dark gray and his back stiff, as if he's just had an injection of iron, and my stomach kind of fell as I felt how hard the world was going to be to me hereafter.

[1961]

William Carlos Williams
[1883–1963]

WILLIAM CARLOS WILLIAMS *is considered by many to be one of the foremost early twentieth-century experimenters of a poetry that would break from the affectations of the previous era. As a contemporary of poets such as T. S. Eliot and Wallace Stevens, he differed from them in his continual search for a distinctly American idiom in poetry in order to distinguish it from its European influences. He desired to write poetry in a language that reflected "the simple order of natural speech," as his friend the poet Ezra Pound expressed to him in a letter. For Williams, this language captured an identity he thought of as uniquely American, with not only the directness of expression, but a rhythm and energy reflective of the sensibilities of the America and the particulars of the physical world. Williams's beliefs about language and poetry can be summed up in perhaps his most famous phrase: "No ideas but in things."*

Williams was born in Rutherford, New Jersey where he spent most of his life. His father was British and his mother Spanish. He was mostly raised by his mother and maternal grandmother. Unlike many other writers and artists who flocked to Europe in the early part of the century, Williams asked, "Why should I leave the place in which I was born?" He began writing as a medical student at the University of Pennsylvania, where he met the poet Ezra Pound, who influenced Williams's first modernist experiments. After continuing his medical training in Europe, he settled down in a small town in New Jersey, where he wrote and practiced pediatrics and obstetrics. He absorbed artistic culture through frequent journeys across the river to New York City, where he became associated with a group of writers, but more significantly, painters. This association helped nurture Williams's interest in objects in nature and how form serves to illuminate the play of the mind.

Williams considered his first book of poems to be insignificant. His second book, The Tempers *(1913), showed some evidence of his break with the past, but it was with the publication of* Al Que Quiere! *(1917) that Williams began to realize the possibilities of a poetry inflected with the intonations of plain speech. This project continued through the publication of* Kora in Hell *(1920),* Sour Grapes *(1921), and* Spring and All *(1923). These books represented his efforts to explore where the imagination and lived experience converged to create a new idiom. With these poems, Williams sought to "affirm reality," as did the people who first explored the New World. Williams, in fact, was so passionate about these explorers that he wrote about them in a collection of essays titled,* In the American Grain *(1925).*

Williams was a prolific writer, not only of poetry but of fiction, essays, plays, and history—all while sustaining a busy medical practice. Between 1946 and 1958, he published the books of an epic poem titled Paterson, *which appeared in one volume in 1963. In 1953, Williams was awarded the Bollingen Prize acknowledging his significance to the art of poetry. His later poems appeared in* Desert Music *(1954) and* Pictures from Brueghel *(1963), which was awarded the Pulitzer Prize in Poetry shortly after his death. Williams had a profound effect on a generation of poets who came after him, such as Robert Lowell, Robert Creeley, and Allen Ginsberg. As the critic Hugh Kenner once said of him, Williams was a great poet because he, "made a difference to the art of poetry."*

Poem

WILLIAM CARLOS WILLIAMS

As the cat
climbed over
the top of

the jamcloset
first the right
forefoot   5

carefully
then the hind
stepped down
into the pit of   10
the empty
flowerpot

[1934]

Reprinted by permission from *Collected Poems: 1909-1939*. Copyright © 1938 by New Directions Publishing Corp.

Spring and All

WILLIAM CARLOS WILLIAMS

By the road to the contagious hospital
under the surge of the blue
mottled clouds driven from the
northeast—a cold wind. Beyond, the
waste of broad, muddy fields   5
brown with dried weeds, standing and fallen

patches of standing water
the scattering of tall trees

All along the road the reddish
purplish, forked, upstanding, twiggy   10
stuff of bushes and small trees
with dead, brown leaves under them
leafless vines—

Lifeless in appearance, sluggish
dazed spring approaches—   15

They enter the new world naked,
cold, uncertain of all
save that they enter. All about them
the cold, familiar wind—

Now the grass, tomorrow   20
the stiff curl of wildcarrot leaf
One by one objects are defined—
It quickens: clarity, outline of leaf

Reprinted by permission from *Collected Poems: 1909-1939*. Copyright © 1938 by New Directions Publishing Corp.

But now the stark dignity of
entrance—Still, the profound change   25
has come upon them: rooted, they
grip down and begin to awaken

[1923]

The Red Wheelbarrow

WILLIAM CARLOS WILLIAMS

so much depends
upon

a red wheel
barrow

glazed with rain   5
water

beside the white
chickens.

[1923]

Reprinted by permission from *Collected Poems: 1909-1939*. Copyright © 1938 by New Directions Publishing Corp.

ASPHODEL, THAT GREENY FLOWER

Of asphodel, that greeny flower,
    like a buttercup
        upon its branching stem—
save that it's green and wooden—
    I come, my sweet,
        to sing to you.
We lived long together
    a life filled,
        if you will,
with flowers. So that
    I was cheered
        when I came first to know
that there were flowers also
    in hell.
        Today
I'm filled with the fading memory of those flowers
    that we both loved,
        even to this poor
colorless thing—
    I saw it
        when I was a child—
little prized among the living
    but the dead see,
        asking among themselves:
What do I remember
    that was shaped
        as this thing is shaped?

9

Reprinted from *Asphodel, That Greeny Flower and Other Love Poems*
(1994), New Directions Publishing Corp.

while our eyes fill
        with tears.
                Of love, abiding love
it will be telling
        though too weak a wash of crimson
            colors it
to make it wholly credible.
        There is something
            something urgent
I have to say to you
        and you alone
            but it must wait
while I drink in
        the joy of your approach,
            perhaps for the last time.
And so
        with fear in my heart
            I drag it out
and keep on talking
        for I dare not stop.
            Listen while I talk on
against time.
        It will not be
            for long.
I have forgot
        and yet I see clearly enough
            something
central to the sky
        which ranges round it.
            An odor
springs from it!
        A sweetest odor!

10

Honeysuckle! And now
there comes the buzzing of a bee!
and a whole flood
of sister memories!
Only give me time,
time to recall them
before I shall speak out.
Give me time,
time.
When I was a boy
I kept a book
to which, from time
to time,
I added pressed flowers
until, after a time,
I had a good collection.
The asphodel,
forebodingly,
among them.
I bring you,
reawakened,
a memory of those flowers.
They were sweet
when I pressed them
and retained
something of their sweetness
a long time.
It is a curious odor,
a moral odor,
that brings me
near to you.
The color

11

was the first to go.
There had come to me
a challenge,
your dear self,
mortal as I was,
the lily's throat
to the hummingbird!
Endless wealth,
I thought,
held out its arms to me.
A thousand tropics
in an apple blossom.
The generous earth itself
gave us lief.
The whole world
became my garden!
But the sea
which no one tends
is also a garden
when the sun strikes it
and the waves
are wakened.
I have seen it
and so have you
when it puts all flowers
to shame.
Too, there are the starfish
stiffened by the sun
and other sea wrack
and weeds. We knew that
along with the rest of it

12

for we were born by the sea,
            knew its rose hedges
                        to the very water's brink.
There the pink mallow grows
            and in their season
                        strawberries
and there, later,
            we went to gather
                        the wild plum.
I cannot say
            that I have gone to hell
                        for your love
but often
            found myself there
                        in your pursuit.
I do not like it
            and wanted to be
                        in heaven. Hear me out.
Do not turn away.
I have learned much in my life
            from books
                        and out of them
about love.
            Death
                        is not the end of it.
There is a hierarchy
            which can be attained,
                        I think,
in its service.
            Its guerdon
                        is a fairy flower;
a cat of twenty lives.

13

If no one came to try it
the world
would be the loser.
It has been
for you and me
as one who watches a storm
come in over the water.
We have stood
from year to year
before the spectacle of our lives
with joined hands.
The storm unfolds.
Lightning
plays about the edges of the clouds.
The sky to the north
is placid,
blue in the afterglow
as the storm piles up.
It is a flower
that will soon reach
the apex of its bloom.
We danced,
in our minds,
and read a book together.
You remember?
It was a serious book.
And so books
entered our lives.
The sea! The sea!
Always
when I think of the sea
there comes to mind

14

the *Iliad*
            and Helen's public fault
that bred it.
        Were it not for that
            there would have been
no poem but the world
        if we had remembered,
            those crimson petals
spilled among the stones,
        would have called it simply
            murder.
'The sexual orchid that bloomed then
        sending so many
            disinterested
men to their graves
        has left its memory
            to a race of fools
or heroes
        if silence is a virtue.
            The sea alone
with its multiplicity
        holds any hope.
            The storm
has proven abortive
        but we remain
            after the thoughts it roused
to
        re-cement our lives.
            It is the mind
the mind
        that must be cured
            short of death's

15

intervention,
                    and the will becomes again
                                a garden. The poem
is complex and the place made
                in our lives
                                for the poem.
Silence can be complex too,
                but you do not get far
                                with silence.
Begin again.
                It is like Homer's
                                catalogue of ships:
it fills up the time.
                I speak in figures,
                                well enough, the dresses
you wear are figures also,
                we could not meet
                                otherwise. When I speak
of flowers
                it is to recall
                                that at one time
we were young.
                All women are not Helen,
                                I know that,
but have Helen in their hearts.
                My sweet,
                                you have it also, therefore
I love you
                and could not love you otherwise.
                                Imagine you saw
a field made up of women

16

all silver-white.
What should you do
but love them?
The storm bursts
or fades! it is not
the end of the world.
Love is something else,
or so I thought it,
a garden which expands,
though I knew you as a woman
and never thought otherwise,
until the whole sea
has been taken up
and all its gardens.
It was the love of love,
the love that swallows up all else,
a grateful love,
a love of nature, of people,
animals,
a love engendering
gentleness and goodness
that moved me
and *that* I saw in you.
I should have known,
though I did not,
that the lily-of-the-valley
is a flower makes many ill
who whiff it.
We had our children,
rivals in the general onslaught.
I put them aside
though I cared for them

17

as well as any man
                could care for his children
                                according to my lights.
You understand
                I had to meet you
                                after the event
and have still to meet you.
                Love
                                to which you too shall bow
along with me—
                a flower
                                a weakest flower
shall be our trust
                and not because
                                we are too feeble
to do otherwise
                but because
                                at the height of my power
I risked what I had to do,
                therefore to prove
                                that we love each other
while my very bones sweated
                that I could not cry to you
                                in the act..
Of asphodel, that greeny flower,
                I come, my sweet,
                                to sing to you!
My heart rouses
                thinking to bring you news
                                of something
that concerns you
                and concerns many men. Look at

18

what passes for the new.
You will not find it there but in
despised poems.
It is difficult
to get the news from poems
yet men die miserably every day
for lack
of what is found there.
Hear me out
for I too am concerned
and every man
who wants to die at peace in his bed
besides.

BOOK II

Approaching death,
as we think, the death of love,
no distinction
any more suffices to differentiate
the particulars
of place and condition
with which we have been long
familiar.
All appears
as if seen
wavering through water.
We start awake with a cry
of recognition
but soon the outlines
become again vague.
If we are to understand our time,

19

we must find the key to it,
                    not in the eighteenth
and nineteenth centuries,
          but in earlier, wilder
                    and darker epochs
So to know, what I have to know
          about my own death,
                    if it be real,
I have to take it apart.
          What does your generation think
                    of Cézanne?
I asked a young artist.
          The abstractions of Hindu painting,
                    he replied,
is all at the moment which interests me.
          He liked my poem
                    about the parts
of a broken bottle,
          lying green in the cinders
                    of a hospital courtyard.
There was also, to his mind,
          the one on gay wallpaper
                    which he had heard about
but not read.
          I was grateful to him
                    for his interest.
Do you remember
          how at Interlaken
                    we were waiting, four days,
to see the Jungfrau
          but rain had fallen steadily.
                    Then

20

just before train time
                    on a tip from one of the waitresses
                              we rushed
to the Gipfel Platz
                    and there it was!
                              in the distance
covered with new-fallen snow.
                    When I was at Granada,
                              I remember,
in the overpowering heat
                    climbing a treeless hill
                              overlooking the Alhambra.
At my appearance at the summit
                    two small boys
                              who had been playing
there
                    made themselves scarce.
                              Starting to come down
by a new path
                    I at once found myself surrounded
                              by gypsy women
who came up to me,
                    I could speak little Spanish,
                              and directed me,
guided by a young girl,
                    on my way.
                              These were the pinnacles.
The deaths I suffered
                    began in the heads
                              about me, my eyes
were too keen

21

not to see through
                        the world's niggardliness.
I accepted it
                as my fate.
                        The wealthy
I defied
        or not so much they,
                        for they have their uses,
as they who take their cues from them.
                I lived
                        to breathe above the stench
not knowing how I in my own person
                would be overcome
                        finally. I was lost
failing the poem.
                But if I have come from the sea
                        it is not to be
wholly
        fascinated by the glint of waves.
                The free interchange
of light over their surface
                which I have compared
                        to a garden
should not deceive us
                or prove
                        too difficult a figure.
The poem
                if it reflects the sea
                        reflects only
its dance
                upon that profound depth
                        where

it seems to triumph.
                    The bomb puts an end
                              to all that.
I am reminded
          that the bomb
                    also
is a flower
          dedicated
                    howbeit
to our destruction.
          The mere picture
                    of the exploding bomb
fascinates us
          so that we cannot wait
                    to prostrate ourselves
before it. We do not believe
          that love
                    can so wreck our lives.
The end
          will come
                    in its time.
Meanwhile
          we are sick to death
                    of the bomb
and its childlike
          insistence.
                    Death is no answer,
no answer—
          to a blind old man
                    whose bones
have the movement
          of the sea.

23

                    a sexless old man
for whom it is a sea
            of which his verses
                        are made up.
There is no power
            so great as love
                        which is a sea,
which is a garden—
            as enduring
                        as the verses
of that blind old man
            destined
                        to live forever.
Few men believe that
            nor in the games of children.
                        They believe rather
in the bomb
            and shall die by
                        the bomb.
Compare Darwin's voyage of the *Beagle*,
            a voyage of discovery if there ever was one,
                        to the death
incommunicado
            in the electric chair
                        of the Rosenbergs.
It is the mark of the times
            that though we condemn
                        what they stood for
we admire their fortitude.
            But Darwin
                        opened our eyes
to the gardens of the world,

                    24

as *they* closed them.
Or take that other voyage
which promised so much
but due to the world's avarice
breeding hatred
through fear,
ended so disastrously;
a voyage
with which I myself am so deeply concerned,
that of the *Pinta,*
the *Niña*
and the *Santa María.*
How the world opened its eyes!
It was a flower
upon which April
had descended from the skies!
How bitter
a disappointment!
In all,
this led mainly
to the deaths I have suffered.
For there had been kindled
more minds
than that of the discoverers
and set dancing
to a measure,
a new measure!
Soon lost.
The measure itself
has been lost
and we suffer for it.
We come to our deaths

25

in silence.
                    The bomb speaks.
                              All suppressions,
from the witchcraft trials at Salem
                    to the latest
                              book burnings
are confessions
                    that the bomb
                              has entered our lives
to destroy us.
                    Every drill
                              driven into the earth
for oil enters my side
                    also.
                              Waste, waste!
dominates the world.
                    It is the bomb's work.
                              What else was the fire
at the Jockey Club in Buenos Aires
                    (*malos aires*, we should say)
                              when with Perón's connivance
the hoodlums destroyed,
                    along with the books
                              the priceless Goyas
that hung there?
                    You know how we treasured
                              the few paintings
we still cling to
                    especially the one
                              by the dead
Charlie Demuth.
                    With your smiles

26

and other trivia of the sort
my secret life
has been made up,
some baby's life
which had been lost
had I not intervened.
But the words
made solely of air
or less,
that came to me
out of the air
and insisted
on being written down,
I regret most—
that there has come an end
to them.
For in spite of it all,
all that I have brought on myself,
grew that single image
that I adore
equally with you
and so
it brought us together.

BOOK III

What power has love but forgiveness?
In other words
by its intervention
what has been done
can be undone.

27

705

What good is it otherwise?
Because of this
    I have invoked the flower
        in that
frail as it is
    after winter's harshness
        it comes again
to delect us.
    Asphodel, the ancients believed,
        in hell's despite
was such a flower.
    With daisies pied
        and violets blue,
we say, the spring of the year
    comes in!
        So may it be
with the spring of love's year
    also
        if we can but find
the secret word
    to transform it.
        It is ridiculous
what airs we put on
    to seem profound
        while our hearts
gasp dying
    for want of love.
        Having your love
I was rich.
    Thinking to have lost it
        I am tortured
and cannot rest.

28

I do not come to you
                    abjectly
with confessions of my faults,
        I have confessed,
                    all of them.
In the name of love
            I come proudly
                    as to an equal
to be forgiven.
            Let me, for I know
                    you take it hard,
with good reason,
            give the steps
                    if it may be
by which you shall mount,
            again to think well
                    of me.
The statue
        of Colleoni's horse
                    with the thickset little man
on top
            in armor
                    presenting a naked sword
comes persistently
            to my mind.
                    And with him
the horse rampant
            roused by the mare in
                    the Venus and Adonis.
These are pictures
            of crude force.
                    Once at night

29

waiting at a station
        with a friend
               a fast freight
thundered through
        kicking up the dust.
             My friend,
a distinguished artist,
        turned with me
             to protect his eyes:
That's what we'd all like to be, Bill,
        he said. I smiled
             knowing how deeply
he meant it. I saw another man
        yesterday
             in the subway.
I was on my way uptown
        to a meeting.
             He kept looking at me
and I at him:
        He had a worn knobbed stick
             between his knees
suitable
        to keep off dogs,
             a man of perhaps forty.
He wore a beard
        parted in the middle,
             a black beard,
and a hat,
        a brown felt hat
             lighter than
his skin. His eyes,
        which were intelligent,

30

were wide open
but evasive, mild.
            I was frankly curious
                        and looked at him
closely. He was slight of build
            but robust enough
                        had on
a double-breasted black coat
            and a vest
                        which showed at the neck
the edge of a heavy and very dirty
            undershirt.
                        His trousers
were striped
            and a lively
                        reddish brown. His shoes
which were good
            if somewhat worn
                        had been recently polished.
His brown socks
            were about his ankles.
                        In his breast pocket
he carried
            a gold fountain pen
                        and a mechanical
pencil. For some reason
            which I could not fathom
                        I was unable
to keep my eyes off him.
            A worn leather zipper case
                        bulging with its contents
lay between his ankles

31

on the floor.
                    Then I remembered:
When my father was a young man—
                    it came to me
                              from an old photograph—
he wore such a beard.
                    This man
                              reminds me of my father.

I am looking
                    into my father's
                              face! Some surface
of some advertising sign
                    is acting
                              as a reflector. It is
my own.
                    But at once
                              the car grinds to a halt.

Speak to him,
                    I cried. He
                              will know the secret.

He was gone
                    and I did nothing about it.
                              With him
went all men
                    and all women too
                              were in his loins.

Fanciful or not
                    it seemed to me
                              a flower
whose savor had been lost.
                    It was a flower
                              some exotic orchid

32

that Herman Melville had admired
in the
Hawaiian jungle.
Or the lilacs
of men who left their marks,
by torchlight,
rituals of the hunt,
on the walls
of prehistoric
caves in the Pyrenees—
what draftsmen they were—
bison and deer.
Their women
had big buttocks.
But what
draftsmen they were!
By my father's beard,
what draftsmen.
And so, by chance,
how should it be otherwise?
from what came to me
in a subway train
I build a picture
of all men.
It is winter
and there
waiting for you to care for them
are your plants.
Poor things! you say
as you compassionately
pour at their roots
the reviving water.

33

                    Lean-cheeked
I say to myself
            kindness moves her
                        shall she not be kind
also to me? At this
            courage possessed me finally
                        to go on.
Sweet, creep into my arms!
            I spoke hurriedly
                        in the spell
of some wry impulse
            when I boasted
                        that there was
any pride left in me.
            Do not believe it.
                        Unless
in a special way,
            a way I shrink to speak of
                        I am proud. After that manner
I call on you
            as I do on myself the same
                        to forgive all women
who have offended you.
            It is the artist's failing
                        to seek and to yield
such forgiveness.
            It will cure us both.
                        Let us
keep it to ourselves but trust it.
            These heads
                        that stick up all around me

                    34

are, I take it,
            also proud.
                        But the flowers
know at least this much,
            that it is not spring
                        and will be proud only
in the proper season.
            A trance holds men.
                        They are dazed
and their faces in the public print
            show it. We follow them
                        as children followed
the Pied Piper
            of Hamelin—but he
                        was primarily
interested only in rats.
            I say to you
                        privately
that the heads of most men I see
            at meetings
                        or when I come up against them
elsewhere
            are full of cupidity.
                        Let us breed
from those others.
            They are the flowers of the race.
                        The asphodel
poor as it is
            is among them.
                        But in their pride
there come to my mind
            the daisy,

35

                    not the shy flower
of England but the brilliance
            that mantled
                    with white
the fields
            which we knew
                    as children.
Do you remember
            their spicy-sweet
                    odor? What abundance!
There are many other flowers
            I could recall
                    for your pleasure:
the small yellow sweet-scented violet
            that grew
                    in marshy places!
You were like those
            though I quickly
                    correct myself
for you were a woman
            and no flower
                    and had to face
the problems which confront a woman.
            But you were for all that
                    flowerlike
and I say this to you now
            and it is the thing
                    which compounded
my torment
            that I never
                    forgot it.
You have forgiven me

                    36

making me new again.
                    So that here
        in the place
                    dedicated in the imagination
                                to memory
        of the dead
                    I bring you
                                a last flower. Don't think
        that because I say this
                    in a poem
                                it can be treated lightly
        or that the facts will not uphold it.
                    Are facts not flowers
                                and flowers facts
        or poems flowers
                    or all works of the imagination,
                                interchangeable?
        Which proves
                    that love
                                rules them all, for then
        you will be my queen,
                    my queen of love
                                forever more.

                    C O D A

Inseparable from the fire
                    its light
                                takes precedence over it.
        Then follows
                    what we have dreaded—

                    37

but it can never
overcome what has gone before.
In the huge gap
between the flash
and the thunderstroke
spring has come in
or a deep snow fallen.
Call it old age.
In that stretch
we have lived to see
a colt kick up his heels.
Do not hasten
laugh and play
in an eternity
the heat will not overtake the light.
That's sure.
That gelds the bomb,
permitting
that the mind contain it.
This is that interval,
that sweetest interval,
when love will blossom,
come early, come late
and give itself to the lover.
Only the imagination is real!
I have declared it
time without end.
If a man die
it is because death
has first
possessed his imagination.

38

But if he refuse death—
              no greater evil
can befall him
            unless it be the death of love
               meet him
in full career.
            Then indeed
               for him
the light has gone out.
But love and the imagination
            are of a piece,
               swift as the light
to avoid destruction.
            So we come to watch time's flight
               as we might watch
summer lightning
            or fireflies, secure,
               by grace of the imagination,
safe in its care.
            For if
               the light itself
has escaped,
            the whole edifice opposed to it
               goes down.
Light, the imagination
            and love,
               in our age,
by natural law,
            which we worship,
               maintain
all of a piece
            their dominance.

39

So let us love
                    confident as is the light
                              in its struggle with darkness
that there is as much to say
                    and more
                              for the one side
and that not the darker
                    which John Donne
                              for instance
among many men
                    presents to us.
                              In the controversy
touching the younger
                    and the older Tolstoy,
                              Villon, St. Anthony, Kung,
Rimbaud, Buddha
                    and Abraham Lincoln
                              the palm goes
always to the light;
                    who most shall advance the light—
                              call it what you may!
The light
                    for all time shall outspeed
                              the thunder crack.
Medieval pageantry
                    is human and we enjoy
                              the rumor of it
as in our world we enjoy
                    the reading of Chaucer,
                              likewise
a priest's raiment

40

(or that of a savage chieftain).
                    It is all
a celebration of the light.
            All the pomp and ceremony
                    of weddings,
    "Sweet Thames, run softly
            till I end
                    my song,"—
are of an equal sort.
For our wedding, too,
            the light was wakened
                    and shone. The light!
the light stood before us
            waiting!
                    I thought the world
stood still.
            At the altar
                    so intent was I
before my vows,
            so moved by your presence
                    a girl so pale
and ready to faint
            that I pitied
                    and wanted to protect you.
As I think of it now,
            after a lifetime,
                    it is as if
a sweet-scented flower
            were poised
                    and for me did open.
Asphodel

41

has no odor
                save to the imagination
but it too
        celebrates the light.
                It is late
but an odor
        as from our wedding
                has revived for me
and begun again to penetrate
        into all crevices
                of my world.

42

This Is Just to Say

WILLIAM CARLOS WILLIAMS

I have eaten
the plums
that were in
the icebox
and which 5
you were probably
saving
for breakfast

Forgive me
they were delicious 10
so sweet
and so cold

[1934]

Reprinted by permission from *Collected Poems: 1909-1939*. Copyright © 1938 by New Directions Publishing Corp.

William Wordsworth
[1770–1850]

Born in Cockermouth, Cumberland, a country village, WILLIAM WORDSWORTH *was the child of an attorney who was well educated and wealthy. He sent his son to Cambridge in 1787 at the age of seventeen. Wordsworth excelled at school but took time off to travel to Switzerland and northern Italy and then on to France. In France he became excited about the French Revolution and met the philosopher Jean-Jacques Rousseau, whose ideas about nature and humanity greatly influenced the young poet. He lived in France during the turbulent year of 1792, fathering a child, Caroline, with Annette Vallon. He wrote romantically about the affair in later years but seems to have decided after a second visit in 1802 to end the relationship. He married his sister Dorothy's friend Mary Hutchinson shortly thereafter and settled in Grasmere in the Lake Country. In the meantime, around 1795, he met and became extremely close to Samuel Taylor Coleridge. From 1795 to 1798, in quiet Somersetshire, the two men created what was to become the touchstone work for the Romantic movement, the* Lyrical Ballads, *followed by its famous* Preface *in 1800. This work contains the most famous of Wordsworth's and Coleridge's poems as well as Wordsworth's clear statement of their literary values and beliefs. At first light this work was not well received because it was both revolutionary (not a good thing to be so closely after the American Revolution) in that it supported the rights of the common person and was religiously challenging. Wordsworth propounded a love of nature so strong that it could be said to look almost pagan. Needless to say, opinion changed over the centuries, and the work is now considered one of literary history's most important milestones. Some literary historians set the date of 1798 as the great change in the direction of British literature.*

After a trip to Germany with Coleridge and Coleridge's wife, Wordsworth settled at Rydal Mount near Lake Windermere, where he spent the rest of his life in peace and serenity. As the years passed, he became more and more conservative, rejecting the French Revolution with the advent of Napoleon and returning to the church of England. In 1813 he became distributor of stamps, a conservative governmental office, having completely joined the conservatives and turned away from Romantic ideals. During his last years, in 1843 he became Poet Laureate and held the post until his death. His most famous works include the Lucy poems, Tintern Abbey, *and the* Ode on Intimations of Immortality, *all written in his youth. He is also known for his two autobiographical poems,* The Prelude *and* The Excursion, *both of which were included in a longer unfinished work,* The Recluse.

The World Is Too Much with Us

WILLIAM WORDSWORTH

The world is too much with us; late and soon,
Getting and spending, we lay waste our powers;
Little we see in Nature that is ours;
We have given our hearts away, a sordid boon!
This Sea that bares her bosom to the moon;   5
The winds that will be howling at all hours,
And are up-gathered now like sleeping flowers;
For this, for everything, we are out of tune;
It moves us not. Great God! I'd rather be
A Pagan suckled in a creed outworn;   10
So might I, standing on this pleasant lea,
Have glimpses that would make me less forlorn;
Have sight of Proteus rising from the sea;
Or hear old Triton blow his wreathèd horn.

[1807]

Composed in 1804. First published in *Poems in Two Volumes* in 1807.

William Butler Yeats
[1865–1939]

Like many of the upper class in Ireland, WILLIAM BUTLER YEATS *came from an Anglo-Irish background. His father was a noted artist, a portrait painter, and member of the Royal Hibernian Academy. Yeats was born near Dublin, attended school in both London and Dublin, and university at Dublin University. There he began to publish poems and articles in the* Dublin University Review. *By 1888 he moved to London and was initiated into the Rhymers' Club. In 1889 his first volume of verse appeared,* The Wanderings of Oisin and Other Poems. *His early work owes much to the pre-Raphaelites, to the Romantic poets Percy Bysshe Shelley and William Blake, and even to his father's painting. In these early years he helped organize Irish literary societies in both London and Dublin, as well as the Irish Literary Theater, later the Abbey Theater. In his youth he fell in love with a political activist and writer, Maude Gonne, with whom he worked but never married. Many of his most poignant poems are written to and about her. In 1895* Poems *appeared, the first of his lyric volumes, and a collection of prose legends and tales (*The Secret Rose) *followed in 1897. In 1899 another lyric volume,* The Wind among the Reeds *appeared. These lyric poems express much of the Celtic psyche and has a certain elfin charm, always with a touch of melancholy for the age of magic that has passed. At the same time, he was making his mark on the theater with* The Countess Cathleen *(1892) and* The Land of Heart's Desire *(1894). Many more volumes of poetry followed including* The Green Helmet and Other Poems *(1910),* Michael Robartes and the Dancer, *and* Reveries over Childhood and Youth *(1915), but in the 1920s he burst forth into greater public awareness. He became a senator in the new Irish Free State in 1922; in 1923 he received the Noble Prize for Literature, followed by his autobiographical* A Vision *and his greatest poetic work,* The Tower *(1928).*

Yeats's poetry and drama reflect his interest in Irish history and Irish politics, as well as his love for the beauty of the Irish landscape. He was also concerned with the tumult of the early twentieth century, often speaking as a prophet about the war that was to come in the middle of the century, though he did not live to see it. In 1918 he wrote a piece called Per Amica Silentia Lunae *(Friend of the Silent Moon), a volume of philosophical essays that suggested the later interests of his life. He was always a kind of mystic, and in later life he became more and more interested in magic, astrology, and a complex philosophy called Theosophy. The* Silentia Lunae *categorizes humanity according to the phases of the moon, an interest that was a part of the thinking of Jungians and other psychological and philosophical thinkers of the time. Whatever the influences on his thinking, he continued to express the plaintive feelings that are distinctly Irish. Yeats was buried first at Roquebrune but his body was later moved to County Sligo.*

The Second Coming

WILLIAM BUTLER YEATS

Turning and turning in the widening gyre   1
The falcon cannot hear the falconer;
Things fall apart; the center cannot hold;
Mere anarchy is loosed upon the world,
The blood-dimmed tide is loosed, and everywhere   5
The ceremony of innocence is drowned;
The best lack all conviction, while the worst
Are full of passionate intensity.
Surely some revelation is at hand;
Surely the Second Coming is at hand.   10
The Second Coming! Hardly are those words out
When a vast image out of *Spiritus Mundi*
Troubles my sight: somewhere in sands of the desert
A shape with lion body and the head of a man,
A gaze blank and pitiless as the sun,   15
Is moving its slow thighs, while all about it
Reel shadows of the indignant desert birds.
The darkness drops again; but now I know
That twenty centuries of stony sleep
Were vexed to nightmare by a rocking cradle,   20
And what rough beast, its hour come round at last,
Slouches toward Bethlehem to be born?

[1921]

Composed in 1921.

Additional Credit Lines

Jean Anouilh, "Antigone"
Reprinted from *Five Plays* Vol. 1 (1969), Farrar, Straus & Giroux.

i carry your heart with me, "ee cummings"
Reprinted from *Complete Poems 1904-1962*, edited by George Firmage (1991), by permission of Liveright Publishing Corporation.

being to timelessness as it's to time, "ee cummings"
Reprinted from *Complete Poems 1904-1962*, edited by George Firmage (1991), by permission of Liveright Publishing Corporation.